Know Your State

Haryana

Highly Useful for HPSC, HSSC & Other Exams of State

Compiled By
Sohan Singh Khattar
Uttam Singh

arihant
SUCCESS AND NOTHING LESS

About The Book

General Knowledge of Haryana is essential for the competitive examinations of the State. For the same purpose, this book (Know Your State Haryana) is designed to serve as a reference book for the students who appear in Haryana Public Service Commission (HPSC) and other state level competitive examinations.

The book provides comprehensive information about Haryana to familiarize the readers about the state. It has the following features :

- *This book provides detailed study of History, Geography, Polity, Art and Culture and State Government Welfare Schemes and Current Affairs of Haryana.*
- *Important Maps are given in the chapters for better understaing of topics life soils, rivers, Minerals, etc. Box, Tables, Map, Figures are also used to make the presentation more clear.*
- *Multiple Choice Questions (MCQs) at the end of each chapter are given to test the candidates understanding of the subject from the examination point of view.*
- *The book provides the most relevant, authentic and up to date information on various aspects of Haryana.*

We invite and welcome any feedback or suggestion for the further improvement of this book in subsequent editions.

Authors
Sohan Singh Khattar
Uttam Singh

arihant
SUCCESS AND NOTHING LESS

ARIHANT PUBLICATIONS (INDIA) LIMITED

Administrative & Production Offices

Regd. Office
'Ramchhaya' 4577/15, Agarwal Road,
Darya Ganj, New Delhi -110002
Tele: 011- 47630600, 43518550

Head Office
Kalindi, TP Nagar, Meerut (UP) - 250002
Tel: 0121-7156203, 7156204

Sales & Support Offices
Agra, Ahmedabad, Bengaluru, Bareilly, Chennai, Delhi, Guwahati, Hyderabad, Jaipur, Jhansi, Kolkata, Lucknow, Nagpur & Pune.

Price ₹375.00

PO No. : TXT-59-T069270-2-26

Published by Arihant Publications (India) Ltd.

For further information about the books published by Arihant, log on to www.arihantbooks.com or e-mail at info@arihantbooks.com

Follow us on

Inside The Book

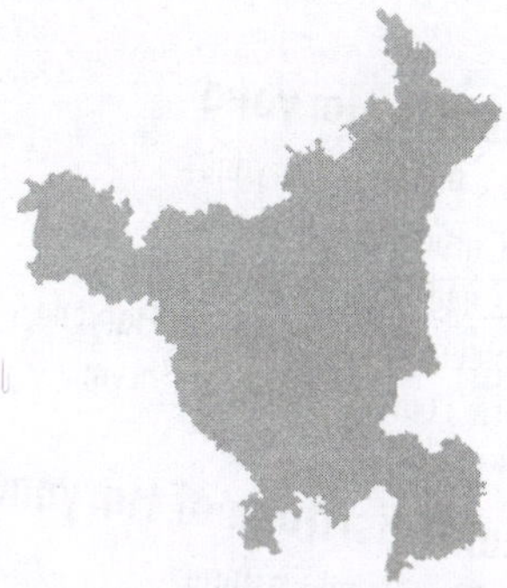

Haryana : Miscellaneous

Features of The Book

Chapter Study

Detailed and accurate information is given about the state in each chapter in easy to understand language with respect to State History, Geography, Political Administration, Economy, Art and Culture and Miscellaneous topics.

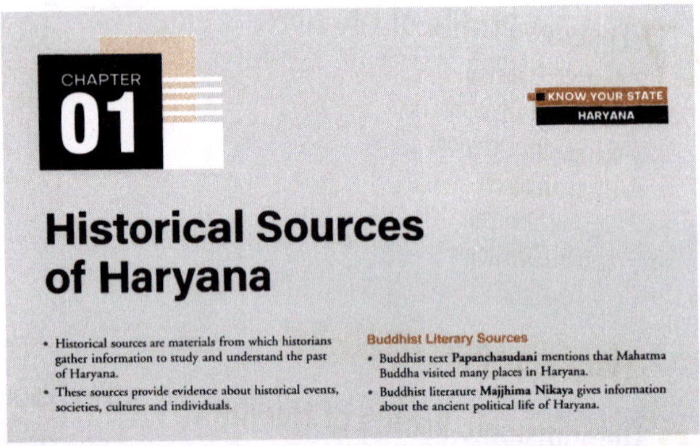

CHAPTER 01

KNOW YOUR STATE HARYANA

Historical Sources of Haryana

- Historical sources are materials from which historians gather information to study and understand the past of Haryana.
- These sources provide evidence about historical events, societies, cultures and individuals.

Buddhist Literary Sources

- Buddhist text **Papanchasudani** mentions that Mahatma Buddha visited many places in Haryana.
- Buddhist literature **Majjhima Nikaya** gives information about the ancient political life of Haryana.

Flow Charts

Flow charts are given in the book for better understanding of topics.

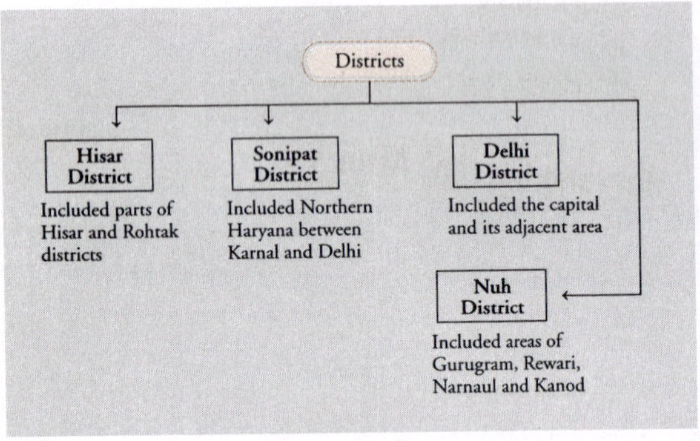

Important Boxes

In each chapter, important boxes are given to cover specific details about important topics.

Important Features of Indus Valley Civilisation

- It was the first Urban Civilisation. Both peasant and commercial groups were represented during this time.
- The primary grain grown here was **barley**, while other crops including **wheat** and **rice** were also grown.
- This civilisation uses a pictograph as its script, which has not yet been deciphered.
- This civilisation was the birthplace of many different kinds of religious beliefs. There were numerous animal species, including peepal trees, also revered.

Haryana

Basic Information

Haryana
At a Glance

Geographical Landscape of Haryana

Location	North-West part of India
Latitudinal Extent	27° 39' N to 30°55' N
Longitudinal Extent	74° 27'E to 77°36' E
Area	44,212 sq km (1.34% of total geographical area of India)
State Boundaries	Himachal Pradesh (North-East), Rajasthan (South-West), Uttar Pradesh, Delhi and Uttarakhand (East) and Punjab, Chandigarh (North-West)
Northernmost District	Panchkula
Southernmost District	Mewat
Important Rivers	Yamuna, Ghaggar, Saraswati, Sahibi, Indori and Markanda

Administrative Structure of Haryana

Established on	1st November, 1966
Meaning of the State's Name	Abode of God (Hari)
Capital	Chandigarh
Divisions	6
Districts	23
Lok Sabha Constituencies	10
Rajya Sabha Constituencies	5
Vidhan Sabha Constituencies	90+1
High Court	Punjab and Haryana High Court (Chandigarh)

Minimum/Smallest of Haryana

District of Haryana with Least Forest Area (As per ISFR-2023)	Palwal
District with Minimum Area of Haryana	Faridabad
District with Minimum Population	Panchkula
District with Minimum Population Density	Sirsa
District with Minimum Literacy Rate	Mewat
District with Minimum Road Length	Faridabad
District with Least Cities	Faridabad

Demography (Census 2011)

Total Population	2,53,51,462
– Male Population	1,34,94,734
– Female Population	1,18,56,728
Population Density	573 person/sq. km
Sex Ratio	879
Decadal Growth Rate of Population	17.64%
Total Literacy Rate	75.55%
– Male Literacy	84.06%
– Female Literacy	65.94%

Largest, Highest and Biggest of Haryana

Highest Peak	Karoh Peak (1,514 m)
Place with Highest Rainfall	Chhachhrauli (Yamunanagar)
Longest River	Yamuna (1,376 km)
District with Largest Area	Sirsa (4,277 sq. km)
District with Maximum Road Length	Hisar (2,108 km)
Most Populous District	Faridabad (18,09,733 persons)
Densely Populated District	Faridabad (2,442 persons/per sq.km)
Largest Rice Producing District	Karnal
Largest Wheat Producing District	Sirsa
District having Maximum Number of Animals	Hisar
Largest Animal Farm in India and Asia	Hisar
Most Literate District	Gurugram (84.70%)
Largest Railway Station	Rewari Junction
District with Highest Sex-Ratio	Mewat (907 : 1000)
Hottest District	Sirsa

First Facts Related to Haryana

Novelist of the First Novel (*Jhadufiri*)	Raja Ram Shastri
First Haryanvi Comic Poet	Mir Jafar Jatthali
First Newspaper	Hariyana (published from Jhajjar)
First Research Magazine	Haryana Shodh Patrika
First Film Producer	Devishankar Prabhakar
First Film Director	Anand Kumar
First Branch of Arya Samaj	Rewari (1880 AD)
First Branch of Sanatan Dharm (Hindu)	Jhajjar (1886 AD)
First Governor	Dharm Vir
First Chief Minister	Bhagwat Dayal Sharma
First Lokayukta	Pritam Pal Singh
First Chief Justice	Ramlal
First Woman Forest Officer	Amrinder Kaur
First Captain of Indian Cricket Team	Nawab Mansoor Ali Khan
First Cancer Institute	Badhsa (Jhajjar)
First University	Kurukshetra University
First College	Pandit Neki Ram Sharma College
First Movie	Dharti (1968)
First Successful Movie in Haryanvi	Bahurani (1983)
First Successful Saang	Sheela Sethani
Most Popular Movie	Chandrawal (1984)

First Saang Artist	Kishanlal Bhatt (Meerut)
First Doordarshan Kendra	Hisar
First Female Judge of Punjab/Haryana High Court	Justice Harmohinder Kaur Sandhu
First Female MP	Chandravati
First Railway Station	Rewari (1873)
First and Sole Nuclear Plant	Gorakhpur (Fatehabad)
First Cashless University	Kurukshetra University
First Cashless Jail	Jind
First Man to Win Rajiv Gandhi Khel Ratna Award	Vijender Singh (2009)
First Woman to Win Khel Ratna Award	Sakshi Malik (2016)
First Woman's Law University	Dr. Bhimrao Ambedkar Law University (Sonipat)
First National Daily Newspaper	Hari Bhoomi (1996)
First Hindi Newspaper	Jain Prakash (1885) (Editor-Jiyalal jain)
First Women Police Training Centre	Hisar

Uday Bhanu Hans *(First State Poet of Haryana)*

Rao Birender Singh *(First Male Speaker of Haryana Vidhan Sabha)*

Santosh Yadav *(First Female Mountaineer of Haryana)*

Shanno Devi *(First Woman Speaker of Haryana Vidhan Sabha)*

Kapil Dev *(Indian Captain who won First Cricket World Cup)*

Naming of Some Famous Districts of Haryana

District	Derived Name From
Fatehabad	Named after son of Firoz Shah Tughlaq, Fateh Khan
Rewari	Named after the daughter of King Rewat named Rewati
Charkhi-Dadri	Named after the Dadar lake
Mahendragarh	Named after the king of Patiala named Raja Mahendra Singh
Gurugram	Named after Guru Dronacharya
Jind	Named after Temple of Jainti Devi
Karnal	Named after Karna, the major character of Hindu Epic Mahabharata
Kurukshetra	Named after King Kuru, ancestor of Kauravas
Yamunanagar	Due to having location on the banks of Yamuna river
Sirsa	Named after Shashwat saint, Shirishvana
Kaithal	Named after the birth place of Hanumanji
Mewat	Due to having abundance of Meo caste
Jhajjar	Named after Chhajju farmer
Hisar	Named after 'Hisar-e-Firoza' a city founded by Firoz Shah Tughlaq

District	Derived Name From
Bhiwani	Named after Rani Bhani
Panchkula	Due to having five wells
Ambala	Named after Goddess Bhawani Ambalika
Palwal	Named after Palawasur, a demon
Faridabad	Named after Sheikh Farid
Rohtak	Named after the son of Queen Taravati named Rohitas
Sonipat	Named after Shravan Kumar
Panipat	Named after Panini Rishi

Nicknames of Geographical Areas of Haryana

Geographical Areas	Nickname
Kurukshetra	City of Parks, Dharamnagari
Rewari	Bronze city, Vir Bhumi
Jind	Heart of Haryana, Milk city
Narnaul	City of Ponds
Karnal	Paris of Haryana, Shoes city
Gurugram	Cyber city, City of Entertainment
Yamunanagar	Paper city
Palwal and Rohtak	Sugar city
Panipat	Textile city, City of Weavers
Fatehabad	Pink city
Hisar	Magnet city, Steel city
Jhajjar	The City of Martyrs
Panchkula-Chandigarh-Mohali	Tri-city
Ambala	Science city, Twin city, City of Equipments
Bhiwani	Kashi of Haryana, City of Temples, Mini Cuba
Palwal	Cotton city
Hathnikund (Yamunanagar)	Heaven of Fishermen

Various Organisations of Haryana

Organisation	Establishment	Headquarters
Haryana Finance Corporation	1st April, 1967	Chandigarh
Haryana Khadi and Gramodyog Board	February, 1969	Panchkula
Haryana Housing Board	1971	Panchkula
Haryana Ware Housing Corporation	1st November, 1967	Faridabad
Haryana Urdu Academy	22nd December, 1985	Panchkula
Horticulture Department of Haryana	1990-91	Panchkula

Organisation	Establishment	Headquarters
Haryana Power Generation Corporation Limited	1997	Panchkula
Haryana Vidyut Prasaran Nigam Limited	19th August, 1997	Panchkula
Haryana State Commission for Women	20th December, 1999	Panchkula

Facts related to Villages and Gram Panchayats of Haryana

Description	Village/ Panchayat	District
First Model Village	Balsamand	Hisar
First Self-inspired Model Village	Sui	Bhiwani
First (CFL) Village	Binola	Gurugram
First Lal Dora Free Village	Sirsi	Karnal
First Child Marriage Free Panchayat	Gandhinagar	Hisar
Country's First Wi-Fi enabled Village	Gumthala Garhu	Kurukshetra
First Village with Free Wi-Fi	Bupania	Jhajjar
First Digital Village	Gurawra	Rewari
First Wi-Fi enabled District	-	Faridabad
Country's First Digital Panchayat	Bibipur	Jind
First Swachh Gram Panchayat	Sultanpuria	Sirsa
First Panchayat to work as per Cabinet	Talwara	Fatehabad
First e-Gram Sabha	Khurdban	Yamunanagar
First Cashless Village	Nillanwali	Sirsa
First Ultra Modern Gram Secretariat	Haibatpur	Jind
First Digital Panchayat	Gumthala Garhu	Kurukshetra
First Modern e-Library	Kachhwa	Karnal
First Digital and Plastic Free Village	Arjaheri	Karnal
First Ultra Modern Anganwadi Centre (Nandghar)	Hasanpur	Sonipat
First Capable (Saksham) Block	Sampla	Rohtak
First Village to Play National Anthem Everyday	Bhanakpur	Faridabad
First Biogas Based Power Plant	Morkhi	Jind
First Block to make All Gram Panchayats Online	Rania	Sirsa
First Village to receive National Pride Award	Dabri	Karnal
First Village to put a Girl's Name Plate outside their Houses	Kiruri	Nuh
First Panchayat to Implement Mandatory Condition of having a Toilet in House for Marriage for Daughters	Godeka	Sirsa
Gram Panchayat Awarded with Nanaji Deshmukh Rashtriya Gaurav Gramsabha Award 2021	Badhana	Jind
Gram Panchayat Awarded with Gram Panchayat Vikas Yojana Award 2020	Mirzapur	Gurugram
Child Friendly Gram Panchayat Award	Kahnaur	Rohtak

Description	Village/ Panchayat	District
Campaign against Veil (Gunaghat) Started	Chusala	Kaithal
A Documentary on Village prepared by a French TV Channel, Published in about 160 Countries	Godeka	Sirsa
Har Ghar Fibre Yojana Started	Aleva Block	Jind

Famous Personalities of Haryana and their Pen-Name

Personality	Pen-Name
Harshavardhana	Shiladitya, Sahityakar Samrat
Mool Chand Jain	Gandhi of Haryana
Chaudhary Chhoturam	Massiha of Farmers
Raja Suraj Mal	Plato of Jats
Chaudhary Bhajan Lal	Chanakya of Haryana
Shah Muhammad	Hadi-e-Haryana
Mansoor Ali Khan Pataudi	Tiger Pataudi
Manohar Lal	Fourth Lal of Haryana
Surendra Sharma	Poet of four lines (Char lines)
Kavita Dalal	Lady Khali
Pandit Neki Ram	Haryana Kesari
Sajjan Singh	Rustam-e-Hind
Om Prakash Jindal	Steel King of Haryana
Pandit Mangeram	Kavi Shiromani
Pandit Jasraj	Swar Samrat
Alhad Bikaneri	Hasya Ratna of Haryana
Khushiram	Michael Jordan of India
Lala Murlidhar	Kesar-e-Hind
Chaudhary Bansi Lal	Architect of Modern Haryana, Iron-Man of Haryana

Mamta Kharab
(Golden Girl)

Kalpna Chavla
(Queen of Space)

Ch. Devi Lal
(Sher-e-Haryana)

Important Museums in Haryana

Museum	Location
Panipat Museum	Panipat
Thanesar Museum	Thanesar
Archaeological Museum	Jhajjar
Jayanti Devi Museum	Jind
Gulzari Lal Nanda Museum	Kurukshetra

Ancient Names of Famous Cities of Haryana

Present Name	Ancient Name
Sirsa	Sairishaka, Saraswati Nagar
Rania (Sirsa)	Rajabpur
Ellenabad (Sirsa)	Kharial
Kaithal	Kapisthal
Hansi (Hisar)	Asika
Agroha (Hisar)	Agrodaka
Bhiwani	Bhani or Bhiyani
Loharu (Bhiwani)	Lohroop
Jhajjar	Chhaju Nagar
Palwal	Apelava
Gurugram	Gurgaon
Nuh (Mewat)	Satyamevpuram
Bilaspur	Kehlur
Rohtak	Rohtasgarh
Balramgarh (Faridabad)	Ballabhgarh

Haryana's First Achievements in the Country

First state in the country

- to manufacture the maximum number of tractors
- to waive off agricultural loans
- to launch Health at You Doorstep Scheme
- to launch Beti Bachao, Beti Padhao Scheme
- to introduce old age pension
- to provide free education to girls till graduation
- to implement crop insurance scheme
- to establish a modern Anganwadi Centre (Hasanpur, Sonipat)
- to provide electricity to all villages
- to form the most educated panchayat
- to pass Cow Protection Law
- to establish Sainik ITI
- to launch Mobile Number Portability (MNP)
- The state which gives the highest reward (₹ 6 Crore) to players under the New Sports Policy, 2015
- The state which runs India's first private metro (14th November, 2003)

HARYANA

History

and Heritage

This section contains all the important topics of Haryana History like Ancient, Medieval and Modern History of Haryana.

CHAPTER 01

Historical Sources of Haryana

- Historical sources are materials from which historians gather information to study and understand the past of Haryana.
- These sources provide evidence about historical events, societies, cultures and individuals.

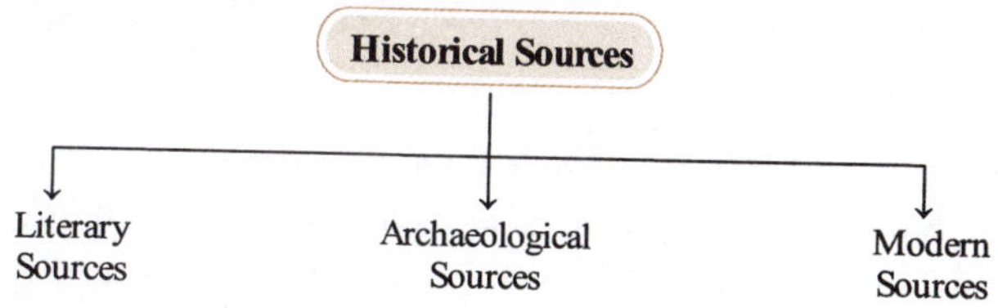

Literary Sources

These sources include **Vedic literature, Buddhist** and **Jain literary sources, Mahabharata** and **later Sanskrit literature** and **Foreign accounts.**

Vedic Literature

- Important literatures like **Vedas, Brahmins, Upanishads, Aranyakas** were composed in Haryana.
- Major ancient rivers of Haryana like Saraswati, Drishadvati, etc. and other geographical facts are mentioned in vedic literature. Saraswati and Drishadvati have been described as holy rivers in vedic literatures.
- In the **Shatapatha Brahmana** and **Aranyakas**, the language of the ancient citizens of Haryana has been described as supreme and the conduct of the people as exemplary and courteous.
- The ancient general life of Haryana has been described in **Jaiminiya Brahamana** and the socio-economic life in **Chandogya Upanishad.**

Buddhist Literary Sources

- Buddhist text **Papanchasudani** mentions that Mahatma Buddha visited many places in Haryana.
- Buddhist literature **Majjhima Nikaya** gives information about the ancient political life of Haryana.
- Mahanidana Sutta and Satipathan Sutta of Buddhist Literature **Digha Nikaya** and Magandiya Sutta and Anjasappaya Sutta of **Majjhima Nikaya** were widely publicised in Haryana.

> **Divyavdan** provides information about the propagation of Buddhism in Haryana. It describes two major Buddhist centres of Haryana namely, **Rohtak** and **Agroha**. At that time, Agroha was a famous cultural centre.

Jain Literary Sources

- The major Jain texts like **Parishishtaparvan, Bhadrabahu Charitra, Kathakosh**, etc. provide information about the social, religious and cultural life of Haryana from the first to third century.
- Jaina literature mentions that **Agroha** was a major centre of Jainism, where the great **Jain Scholar Lohacharya** lived in the first century. **Maharaja Agrasen** also belonged to the city of Agroha.
- Apart from Agroha, Rohtak is also mentioned frequently in Jain texts.

> Jain poet **Pushpadanta** mentioned the state and called Haryana as 'land of warriors' in **Mahapurana** and **Sridhar** in **Pasnahachariu** also mentioned about Haryana in his texts.

Mahabharata and Later Sanskrit Literature

- Great epic Mahabharata, written by sage **Ved Vyas**, also gives detailed description of Haryana state.
- **Srimad Bhagvada Gita** is the main section of epic Mahabharata. The Bhagvada Gita is said to have been delivered to prince Arjuna by Lord Krishna at Kurukshetra before the war.
- Many important sites of Haryana have been mentioned in the **Aranyaka Parva** of Mahabharata.

> The Mahabharata mentions Haryana as **Bahudhanyaka** (the land of plentiful grains) and **Bahudhana** (the land of immense riches).

- **Nakul Digvijayam** of Mahabharata gives information of the ancient, political, economic, geographical conditions in Haryana. Rohtak has been mentioned in its title.
- Puranas also give information about the ancient history of Haryana in which **Vamana Purana** is prominent.
- Vamana Purana mentions **nine rivers flowing in Haryana,** which are Saraswati, Vaitarani, Aapaga, Mandakini, Madhushrava, Anshumati, Kaushiki, Darshanti and Hiranyavati. Thus, the description of the rivers flowing in Thanesar and Kurukshetra of Haryana is found in the Vamana Purana.

Seven Major Forests of Haryana according to Vamana Purana

Forest	Description
Kamyaka Forests (Near Kurukshetra and Kaithal)	Associated with the Pandavas' exile in the Mahabharata; known for its spiritual significance and dense vegetation.
Aditi Forests (Likely in central Haryana regions)	Named after Aditi, the mother of gods in Hindu mythology; possibly associated with nurturing and divine protection.
Vyasa Forests (Near the Saraswati river, Kurukshetra)	Named after sage Vyasa, who is said to have meditated here and composed parts of the Mahabharata.
Falakivan (Speculated near Hisar or Rohtak)	It derives its name from 'Falaka', suggesting connection to the celestial or heavenly. It could symbolise a pristine natural environment.
Suryavan (Near Sonipat or Panipat)	Dedicated to the Sun God (Surya); likely known for rituals and spiritual practices related to solar worship.
Madhu Van (Possibly near the Aravalli ranges)	Known for its sweetness, possibly associated with abundant flora, fruits or honey-producing bees.
Cold Forests (Near the foothills of the Aravallis)	Named for its cooler microclimate, possibly due to its dense tree cover or proximity to water bodies.

Foreign Accounts

- The travelogues of foreign travellers also provide detailed account about the Haryana.
- The prominent among them are Greek historian **Arrian** and Chinese travellers **Fa-Hien** and **Xuanzang** (Hiuen-Tsang).

Other Literary Sources

Other literary texts which give information about the Haryana are

- Ashtadhyayi of Panini
- Mahabhashya of Patanjali
- Harshacharita of Banbhatta (Court poet of Harsha Vardhana King)
- Rajatarangini of Kashmiri historian Kalhana

Archaeological Sources

- **Sir Alexander Cunningham**, also called the **Father of Indian Archaeology**, visited Haryana in 1862 AD. Rogers carried on Cunningham's work in 1888-89 AD.
- The **first archaeological exacavation** in Haryana was done by **D.B. Spooner** of Archaeological Survey of India (ASI) in 1921-23, at **Raja Karna Ka Qila**, Thanesar, Kurukshetra.
- It was first surveyed by Alexander Cunningham and later excavated by D.B. Spooner.
- In the year 1933-34, **Theh Polar** (Southern region of the Saraswati river) was excavated under the leadership of **H.L. Srivastava.** Many copper coins were found in this excavation, including the coins of Kushana ruler **Vasudev** and the coins of **Yaudheyas.**
- Many important archaeological materials were found from the sites of Amin, Pehowa, Thanesar (Kurukshetra) under the leadership of **Prof. B.B. Lal.**
- Under the direction of the Punjab University, **Sugh** (1964-65), **Mitathal** (1968) and **Siswal** (1970) were excavated.
- Under the direction of Kurukshetra University, archaeological excavations took place in Daulatpur (1968-70 and 1976-78), Raja Karna Fort (1970-71 and 1975-76), Mirzapur (1972-73 and 1975-76) and Balu Jind (1978-80).
- The excavations were also done under the direction of Maharishi Dayanand University at Hatt in Jind and Khokhrakot in Rohtak.
- In the year 1974-75, the Haryana Archaeological Survey Department excavated **Banawali, Agroha** and **Kunal** sites.

Similarly, Archaeological excavations at **Bhagwanpur** and **Kaithal** were done in the year 1975-76 in which sources like coins, ornaments, pottery, etc. were found.

- Archaeological sources can be divided into five parts to facilitate their study. These are as follows

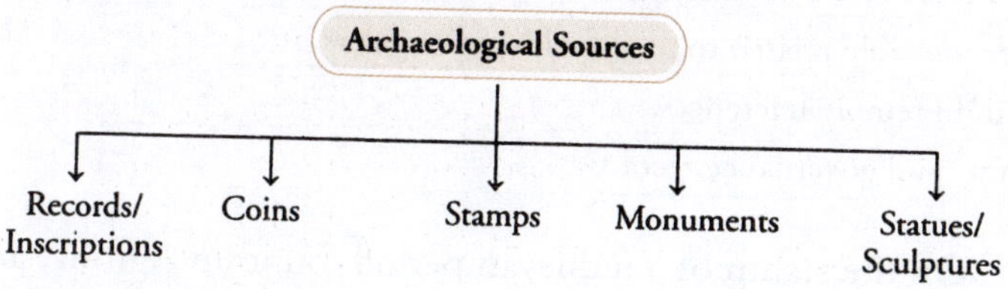

Records /Inscriptions

- A total of 37 record inscriptions of all the categories have been found in Haryana, of which the **Topra inscription** is the oldest record.
- An inscription written in **Kharosthi script** has been found in Karnal which is related to the construction of a pond.

Topra Inscription

- It belongs to Mauryan ruler, Ashoka. Seven inscriptions have been recorded on the Topra pillar, which is located presently at Yamunanagar.
- Three inscriptions of Chauhan ruler **Vigraharaja IV** (11th century) are also recorded on the Topra pillar, which give information about the victory of Vigraharaja over Mlechchhas.
- Topra inscription was transferred by **Firoz Shah Tughlaq** to Delhi. The script of these inscriptions is **Brahmi** and the language is **Sanskrit**.

- An incomplete inscription has been also found in **Kapal Mochan** area of Haryana.
- Raja Devanka wrote about the glory of Kurukshetra in an inscription found from South-East Asian country **Laos**. It belongs to 5th century.
- Two inscriptions of the 3rd-4th century have been found from **Tosham.**
- An inscription has been found from **Sirsa** which mentions about the Pashupati community of this place.
- An inscription has been found in **Agroha** which mentions about all the seven notes of music.
- A commemorative inscription found from **Hansi,** which is associated with Prithviraj-II. According to an inscription which has been found in **Ladnu** (Rajasthan), Delhi was the capital of Haryana.
- Eight inscriptions have been found from a pillar, which is located in **Gujari Mahal** in Hisar. It mentions about Gods which came from eight different places.
- A rock inscription of Pratihara king, **Mahendra Pala,** has been found at **Pehowa,** which mentions about construction of temples.
- Bhojdeva's inscription is also found from Pehowa, which belongs to the 9th century. As per the inscription, Pehowa was famous for horse trading at that period.
- A religious inscription written in Barakhadi has been found from **Sugh** place of Jagadhri.
- Some of the 10th century inscriptions are found from **Mohanbadi** (Rohtak) and **Guravada** (Rewari), which are related to the construction of Vaishnava temples.

Other 10th Century Inscriptions

Name	**Location** (District)	**Significance**
Kurukshetra Inscriptions	Kurukshetra	Vedic and Mahabharata-era references, mentions of pilgrimage sites.
Chanet Inscriptions	Yamunanagar	Possible Buddhist or early medieval Hindu inscriptions.
Sirsa Inscription	Sirsa	Records related to rulers and temple construction.
Fatehabad Inscriptions	Fatehabad	Associated with the early medieval period, possibly referencing trade and administration.
Agroha Inscription	Hisar (Agroha)	Linked to the Agarwal community, mentions temple constructions.
Tirawari Inscriptions	Karnal	Possibly related to religious structures.
Asandh Inscription	Karnal (Asandh)	Possible Kuru-period inscription, linked to Mahabharata times.
Mahmudpur Inscriptions	Rohtak	Likely medieval inscriptions.
Sanghi Inscription	Rohtak	Details about land grants and temple endowments.
Sonipat (Kokarakot) Inscription	Sonipat	Mentions about the ancient city of Kakarakot, possibly related to Mahabharata-era settlements.

Name	Location (District)	Significance
Ashoka Pillar Inscriptions	Delhi	Edicts of Emperor Ashoka, spreading messages of Dharma.
Monastery and Stupa Inscriptions	Delhi	Found in old Buddhist monastery sites, confirming Delhi's Buddhist past.
Palwal Inscription	Palwal	Mentions ancient trade and Buddhist influence.
Mewat Inscriptions	Mewat	Historical records, possibly related to medieval Muslim rulers.
Aherwan Inscription	Hathin (Palwal)	Buddhist and Hindu temple references.
Bhadas Inscription	Mewat	Ancient land grants and governance records.

Coins

- The coins have an important place in the study of the ancient history of Haryana as an archaeological source. In fact, the history of Haryana from 200 to 300 AD is dependent on the basis of coins.
- **Aahat** or **punch-marked coins** have been found from places like Sugh, Agroha, Naurangabad. These coins dated back to the 2nd century BC. Aahat coins were made by stamping a special symbol on a piece of metal.
- Coins of Indo-Greek rulers of 3rd century have been found from **Khokhrakot** of Rohtak.
- Gold and Copper coins obtained from the **Mitathal** of Bhiwani belong to Kushana rulers.

> Coin minting dyes (which belong to the period of Kushana rulers, Huvishka and Kanishka) have been found from **Aurangabad** and **Khokhrakot**. Yaudheyas mint is located in Rohtak.

- **Coins of Agar people** have been found from Agroha, Barwala and Aurangabad and coins of Kuninda rulers from **Karnal**, **Jagadhri**, **Sugh** and **Budiya**.
- **Coins of Gupta ruler Samudragupta** have been found from **Mitathal** of **Bhiwani** and an Indo-Sasanian silver coin is found from Kapal Mochan.
- **Copper currency of Harsha** period has been found from **Sonipat**, which gives information about ancestry Pushyabhuti king Harshavardhana.
- The coins of rulers of **Pratihara**, **Tomar**, **Chauhan**, etc. of the early medieval period have been found from Khokhrakot, Sugh and Budiya.

Stamps

- The stamps also help in studying the history of Haryana. In Haryana, many stamps have been found from Sugh, Daulatpur, Fort of king Karna, Agroha, Naurangabad, Achhej Paharipur, Rakhigarhi, Karnal, Khokhrakot, etc.
- These stamps were used to **mint coins**. Most of these are preserved in the museum of **Jhajjar** district.
- On the stamp of Yaudheyan period found in Agroha, an inscription is minted which reveals the administrative system of Yaudheyan period.

Monuments

- The Fort of king Karna and the remains of fort of emperor Harshavardhana are located in Thanesar of Kurukshetra.
- The fort of ancient Hansi has now been converted into ruins. Some of the 8th and 12th century ruins are found at ancient temples at Rohtak, Pinjore, Kalayat etc.
- Mauryan period stupa is found at **Chaneti** in Jagadhri tehsil and **Ashoka ki Laat** is found in Topra, Hisar and Fatehabad.

▲ Chaneti Buddhist Stupa

Statues/Sculptures

- Most of the sculptures found from Haryana are related to Vaishnavism, Buddhism and Jainism. Some religious sculptures are made of terracotta.
- The sculptures found in Haryana are dated from 2nd century BC to the 10th-11th century.
- In Haryana, the main centre of the sculptures of Shunga period was **Sugh** and of Kushana period was the **area around Rohtak**.
- The medieval sculptures obtained from Haryana mostly belong to **Pratihara** and **Tomar** period.

Modern Sources

- The modern sources are basically concerned with literary texts. These sources include books written in modern times.
- In the context of modern sources, 'The History of Gurugram (Gurgaon), Rohtak and Hisar Districts', **Tarikhe-e-Jhajjar** and **Aabhir Kuldipika (History of Rewari region)** written down in Urdu language through the then Punjab Government are very important.
- Shri Ram Sharma Acharya has written a book called **History of Haryana** which gives a lot of information about the history of Haryana.

CHECK CHAPTER KNOWLEDGE

1 The ancient and sacred river(s) of Haryana is/are *HSSC 2019*

(a) Saraswati (b) Drishadvati
(c) Ganga (d) Both (a) and (b)

2 Agroha (Hisar) is mentioned in which texts? *HSSC 2024*

(a) Divyavdan
(b) Kathakosh
(c) Bhadrabahu Charita
(d) All of the above

3 Which of the following texts has mention about Agroha (Hisar)? *HSSC 2021*

(a) Rajatarangini
(b) Abhigyan Shakuntalam
(c) Maltimadhav
(d) Divyavdan

4 Which of the following Jaina texts provides information from the social, religious cultural life of Haryana from first to third century?

(a) Parishishtaparvan
(b) Bhadrabahu Charitra
(c) Kathakosh
(d) All of the above

5 Maharaja Agrasen was associated with which place? *HSSC 2017, Patwari 2016*

(a) Sirsa (b) Rohtak
(c) Pehowa (d) Agroha

6 Rohtak district got its mention in which historical text? *PGT 2016*

(a) Divyavdan
(b) Majjhima Nikaya
(c) Nakula-Digvijayam
(d) Kathakosh

7 Information about the ancient history of Haryana is found in which Purana?

(a) Narad Purana
(b) Matasya Purana
(c) Vishnu Purana
(d) Vamana Purana

8 The Vamana Purana mentions how many forests of Haryana?

(a) 4 (b) 7
(c) 11 (d) 12

9 Which of the following rivers of Haryana is not mentioned in Vamana Purana?

(a) Indravati
(b) Saraswati
(c) Aapaga
(d) Anshumati

10 Which text has mentioned the description of the rivers flowing in Thanesar and Kurukshetra of Haryana?

(a) Vamana Purana
(b) Prithvi Purana
(c) Purana Katha
(d) Katha Sahitya

11 Harshacharita was written by *HSSC 2019*

(a) Banabhatta
(b) Rajyavardhana
(c) Adityavardhana
(d) Prabhakarvardhana

12 Banabhatta was the friend and court poet of which of the following rulers? *Haryana Patwari 2015*

(a) Prithviraj Chauhan
(b) Harshavardhana
(c) Anangpala
(d) Hemchandra

13 The first archaeological excavation in Haryana was done by which archaeologist? *HSSC 2024*

(a) Cunningham
(b) B.B. Lal
(c) H.L. Srivastava
(d) D.B. Spooner

14 The oldest inscription of Haryana is

(a) Topra inscription
(b) Ropar inscription
(c) Pehowa inscription
(d) Banawali inscription

15 Who established Topra inscription of Ashoka period in Yamunanagar district of Haryana to Firoz Shah Kotla in Delhi? *Haryana Accountant 2018*

(a) Firoz Shah Tughlaq
(b) Sultan Nasiruddin
(c) Ibrahim Lodi
(d) None of the above

16 All the seven notes of music have been mentioned in the inscription which has been found at which place of Haryana? *HSSC 2023*

(a) Sudh (b) Rohtak
(c) Agroha (d) Mitathal

17 Which inscription provides information that Pehowa was famous for horse trading in the ancient period?

(a) Topra inscription (b) Ropar inscription
(c) Bhojdeva inscription (d) Banawali inscription

18 Coins of Indo-Greek rulers have been found from which place of Haryana?

(a) Karnal
(b) Khokhrakot (Rohtak)
(c) Mewat
(d) Hansi

19 From which place of Haryana coins of Gupta ruler Samudragupta have been obtained?

(a) Mitathal (b) Banawali
(c) Rakhigarhi (d) Kapal Mochan

20 Copper currency of Harsha period has been found from which place of Haryana?

(a) Sonipat (b) Panipat
(c) Jhajjar (d) Mewat

21 Most of the Sculptures found in Haryana are related to which religion?

(a) Vaishnavism (b) Buddhism
(c) Jainism (d) All of these

22 In Haryana which of the following is the main centre of Kushana period sculptures?

(a) Rohtak (b) Sirsa
(c) Panipat (d) Kurukshetra

CORRECT ANSWERS

1. (d) **2.** (a) **3.** (d) **4.** (d) **5.** (d) **6.** (a) **7.** (d) **8.** (b) **9.** (a) **10.** (a)
11. (a) **12.** (b) **13.** (d) **14.** (a) **15.** (a) **16.** (b) **17.** (c) **18.** (b) **19.** (a) **20.** (a)
21. (d) **22.** (a)

CHAPTER 02

Ancient History of Haryana

- The ancient history of Haryana can be traced from various sources like archaeological, mythological and monetary sources.
- **Banawali, Daulatpur, Bhagwanpura**, etc sites belonging to the Indus Valley Civilisation flourished well in the state. Haryana also remained a place of many dynasties during ancient period.
- As per **Manusmriti**, the state got its origin by many deities, thus, it was earlier known as **Brahmavrata.** It is also known as **Brahmrishi Pradesh** and **Uttarvedi of Brahma.**
- The state of Haryana existed in ancient times and was also home to humans. British palaeontologist **Guy Ellcock Pilgrim** found a skull from **Pinjore** which proved that about 15 million years ago, there were primitive humans' being in Haryana.

Ancient History of Haryana

- Pre-historic period
- Proto-historic period
- Historical period

Pre-Historic Period

The period which has no written evidence is known as 'pre-historic period'. This period is divided into three different periods, i.e. Palaeolithic age, Mesolithic age and Neolithic age.

Palaeolithic Age

- Archaeologists like **Dilip Chakraborty, S.R. Phogat, Nayanjot Lahiri, M.K. Kumar** and **G.C. Mahapatra**, have found stone tools from various sites in Haryana which were made from palaeolithic milky brown quartzite.

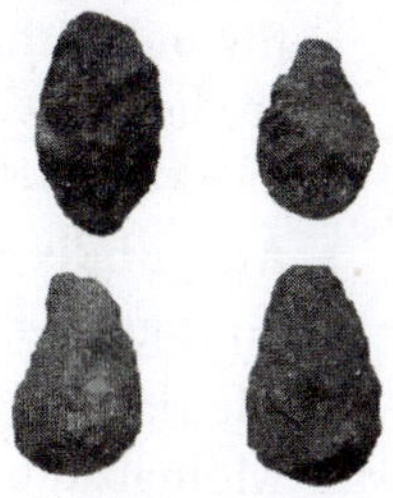

▲ Palaeolithic Tools

- Palaeolithic tools have been procured from the **Dhamli, Kotla, Suketri, Pinjore, Papalina, Jhirka** and other areas of Haryana state. These stone tools are round, small and flat in shape. Probably, they may be used for hunting in early times.
- The Palaeolithic age in Haryana is a significant pre-historic period marked by the earliest stone tools used by humans.
- Palaeolithic tools obtained from Haryana are mainly of two types i.e. **core** and **flake.**
- Core tools were made by breaking and shaping large stones.
- Flake tools were made from smaller pieces of rock and used as a smaller chopper.

Palaeolithic period has been further divided into three periods

Period	Timeframe	Characteristics of Tools	Evidence/Key Sites
Lower Palaeolithic	5,00,000 to 1,25,000 years ago	Core tools such as crood, axe, scraper; made from the inner part of stones.	**Archaeological Sites** Damla, Suketri, Chandi Mandir, Mansa Devi, Dera Kharuni, Mehranwala, Khandi-Khanda, Chandi Kotla, Nayagaon, Pinjore (Pinjore-Kalka region). Evidence also found in the Shivalik hills near **Pinjore-Kalka** and Northern Aravalli range in **Gurugram** and **Faridabad**.
Middle Palaeolithic	1,25,000 to 40,000 years ago	Smaller stone tools like scrapers and borers.	Evidence found in **Kalka region** of Panchkula. Humans started living in caves and near river valleys in **Middle Palaeolithic Period**.
Upper Palaeolithic	40,000 to 10,000 years ago	Smaller, lighter tools made primarily by blades; tools included pestle, mortar and sharp-edged scythes.	Evidence found in **Siswal** (Hisar), **Rakhigarhi** (Hansi), **Mitathal** (Bhiwani), **Banawali** (Fatehabad)

Mesolithic Age

- In this period, the size of tools was reduced which is called **microlith**. The main tools in this period were scraper, borer, chisel, etc.
- Under the supervision of **Dr Dilip Chakraborty** and **Nayanjot Lahiri**, many mesolithic stone tools have been discovered from different sites of Haryana such as
  - **Ankar hills** of Gurugram-Faridabad
  - Mewla hills, Noda, Koh, Mohtabad hills
  - Paliyangaon hills
  - Sirohi, Gothda, Dhauj, Nimaur
  - Tethur, Khori, Jamalpur
  - Nimriwali hills, Chhatarpur, Harchandpur
  - Sikandarpur, Bandhwa Ghati
  - Nangri Ki Thani
  - Dhulawat, Bhutla and Manesar

▲ Mesolithic Tools

Neolithic Age

- Humans started the practice of agriculture in this period. Evidence of agriculture has been found from **Siswal**.
- Besides this, other evidences of this period include beads, earthen bangles, red clay pots made on wheels, grey coloured pottery and so on.
- Neolithic evidence has been found at several places in the **Pinjore-Kalka** region in the lower ranges of Shivalik.

Proto-historic Period

It was the age before the historical period, when the script and letters were known to the people but they could not read it. It includes **Siswal Culture**, **Hakra Culture** and **Indus Valley Civilisation**.

Siswal Culture in Haryana

- The **first excavation** of this culture in **Haryana** was done at **Siswal of Hisar district** in 1970 due to which it has been named as Siswal Culture.
- The ahaeologists believe that around **2500 BC**, some farmers from Rajasthan settled in **Drishadvati river valley** and started doing agricultural work there, due to which Siswal culture emerged in Haryana.

> Siswal culture basically represents the development of the farming community; thus, it is also known as **Farming Culture**. Siswal settlements have also been discovered in **Mahendragarh**.

- There are a total of 29 places under this culture in Haryana which are divided into three levels i.e. **pre-Siswal settlements**, **middle Siswal settlements** and **later Siswal settlements**.

Phase	Total Settlements	Drishadvati River Valley	Saraswati River Valley	Yamuna River Valley	Ghaggar River Valley	Sahabi River Valley
Pre-Siswal	13	9	2	2	–	–
Middle Siswal	20	12	1	5	2	–
Later Siswal	28 (Maximum)	10	1	6	–	11

Important Sites of Siswal Culture

Siswal

- Location — On the banks of Chautang River (West of Hisar)
- Superficial investigation — 1968
- Full-fledged excavation — By **Dr. Suraj Bhan** under direction of Kurukshetra University.
- The items found from the mound of Siswal are **hand-made pottery**, painted bangles of clay, beads, copper handle sickle, stone tools, etc.
- The vessels/pottery found from Siswal have **white** and **black paint** on them. Some pottery is also **grey** in colour.

Mitathal

- Location — Bhiwani
- Noteworthy — Gupta coins found in 1915-16
- Excavator — Suraj Bhan (1968) of Kurukshetra University
- Mitathal's mound is divided into two parts, which are around 4-5 m in height.
- Houses of **sun-dried raw bricks** have been found from Mitathal. The roof of these houses was thatch. The size of the raw bricks found from Mitathal is 30×20×10 cm.
- Pots have been discovered from this site which were made on potter's **wheel and fire-baked.**
- Clay bangles, green bangles of faience, stone balls, stone puddle, copper bangles and elephant tooth pins have been found.
- Some dishes of grey colour have also been found from this site.

Banawali

- Location — On dry bed of Saraswati river, Fatehabad
- Antiquity first discovered — 1965
- Excavator — RS Bisht of Department of Archaeology, Government of Haryana (1974)
- The houses of this site were made of mud bricks, although some baked bricks of **1: 2: 3 ratios** have also been found.
- The Siswalites of this place used copper and bronze. Gold was also prevalent here.
- Other items found from Banawali are a round shaped stove and a furnace, pottery, rare stone jewellery, kitchen utensils, 'S' shaped jar, terracotta plough model and children's toys etc.

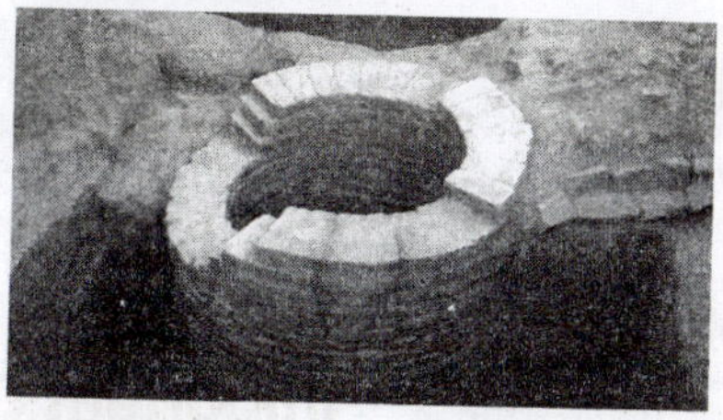

Rakhigarhi

- Also known as — Rakhi Shahpur
- Location — On the bank of Saraswati river, Hansi tehsil, Hisar
- Antiquity first discovered — 1964
- Excavator — Amarendra Nath (Archeological Survey of India)
- Archaeological excavations in this region have yielded important artifacts like **painted bangles**, earthenware and various valuable stones, which provide insight into the Siswal people's civilisation. There are some **grey-coloured** ceramics here.

Balu

- Location — Kaithal district
- Discovered by — Suraj Bhan and Jim Shaffer (1977)
- Excavator — Kurukshetra University (1978-79)
- The items found from here are the remains of raw brick houses, pottery made of red and grey colours on wheels, clay beads, bangles, balls and rare stone beads, etc.
- Apart from this, **clay figurines**, bangles, toys, carts, balls, bone needles, grinding stones, faience bangles, copper tools, etc have also been found.

Farmana

- Location — Small village in Rohtak
- Excavators — Vasant Shinde, Toshiki Osada and Manmohan Kumar
- Associated with — First phase of Siswal Culture
- Some pits of 2-3 have been found from here and clay stoves (chulas) were made in these pits, i.e. these pits were used as kitchens.
- **Pottery made of red colour** and painted with black colour has been found from this site.

Kunal

- Location — On dry bed of Saraswati river, Ratia Tehsil, Fatehabad
- Excavators — J.S. Khatri and M. Acharya
- **Royal crowns** have also been obtained from this place. Gold and silver jewellery have also been found.

Giravad

- Location — Maham tehsil, Rohtak
- Excavators — Vasant Shinde (Deccan College), Toshiki Osada (Kyoto, Japan) and Manmohan Kumar (MDU, Rohtak) (2006-07)
- Findings — 13 pits, 2 kilns and few potteries

Bhirdana

- Location — Fatehabad district
- Excavator — LS Rao of Archaeological Survey of India
- Height of the mound — 4.20 m
- Four cultures — Hakra Wares Culture, Early, Early Mature and Mature Harappan
- Findings — Pits similar to those found at Farmana and Giravad; red and grey pottery

Important Features of Siswal Culture

- This agrarian society was far **more developed**, compared to later societies.
- This was the appropriate moment to begin animal husbandry. The primary **domestic animals** were cows, bulls, goats, dogs, pigs and so forth.
- The dairying also begun at this time and the locals developed their skills in producing cotton fabric, wool and skins, among other items.
- During this time, families, groups and several other social structures became very common.
- Marriage, religious practice and idolatry most likely began during this time.
- This culture was linked to the **Indus Civilisation** at the time its members were transitioning to Urban Civilisation and approximately 2300 BCE, Urban Civilisation spread throughout this culture as well.

Important Places related to Siswal Culture

District	Settlements
• Hisar	Siswal, Salimgarh, Shahpur, Patan, Satrod Khurd, Alipur, Kharar, Sisai, Data, Pali, Rakhigarhi, Sendhwa
• Sirsa/Fatehabad	Bani, Talwada, Rat Tibba, Chimu, Rania
• Bhiwani	Dadri, Manhedu, Chang, Tigdana
• Rewari	Badli, Lohar, Badsha
• Gurugram	Alduka, Sultanpur, Mukkola, Gokalpur, Mundehra, Papra, Mamlika
• Kaithal	Moh, Cheha, Ritauli, Kalayat, Jatheri, Pundri
• Jind	Narwana, Barsana, Khokhri

Hakra Culture in Haryana

- The period of Hakra culture in Haryana is considered before the period of Harappan Civilisation.
- This basically represents the development of the farming community; thus this is also known as **Early Farming Culture.**
- Evidence of this culture has been found in the drainage area of the **Hakra** (Ghaggar) **river** thus, it is also known as Hakra Culture.
- **Kunal is the first excavation site** from where the evidence of Hakra Culture has been excavated.

Indus Valley Civilisation in Haryana

- Indus Valley Civilisation is included in the proto-historic era as its pictographic script has not been deciphered till the date.
- The evidences of Indus Valley Civilisation has also been found in Haryana state.
- Indus Valley Civilisation flourished between approximately 2600 to 1900 BCE.
- The remains of the people of the Indus Valley Civilisation coming first in Haryana have been discovered from two places i.e. as the **Saraswati river valley** and **Drishadvati river valley.**
- This civilisation is also called **Bronze Civilisation.**

> The archaeologists have divided the Indus Valley Civilisation into three phases in Haryana i.e. early, mature and late phases, in which 241 settlements of the initial phase, 145 settlements of the second phase and 842 settlements of the third phase have been found.

Important Centres

The important centres of Indus Valley Civilisation are discussed below

Banawali

• Discovered by	Dr. R.S. Bisht, Archaeological Survey of India (1973-74)
• Town planning	Chess Board Pattern
• Western part	Included people of higher status
• Eastern part	Included common people and evidence of road also found

- A striking animal posture has been found in this place which has the body of lion and horns of bulls.
- Besides, other evidences of this period have been found in this place like a **clay toy** (plough), **signs of wheels of bullockcart**, evidences of **barley** and **grains, first mother goddess terracotta figurine** of independent India and evidences of fire altars.
- Gold and silver pieces have been found here, which shows that people at that time had knowledge of metals as well.
- **Stamps** have also been found here on which there are pictures of wild goats, horses and many other animals.
- **Bones** of many animals have also found in many houses which suggest that people of this period used to eat meat.

- Evidences of beads, bangles, jewellery, weighing tools, built from rare stones, have also been found here.
- In Banawali, there was **lack of drainage system**, which is the major characteristic of the Indus Valley Civilisation.

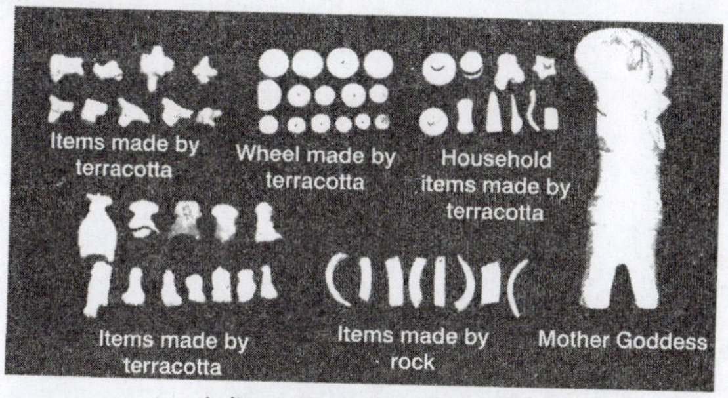

▲ Items found from Banawali

Rakhigarhi

- Size — Largest Indus Valley Civilisation site (350 hectares)
- Excavator — Dr. Amrendra Nath (1997-2000)
- Cultural phases — Pre-Harappan, Mature Harappan and Siswal Culture

- Artifacts include houses, pottery, ornaments of precious stones and a bronze pot decorated with gold and silver.
- Women's skeletons with shell bangles, gold armour and precious stones were discovered.
- Evidences from the Early Harappan (3200 to 2700 BCE) and Mature Harappan (2700 to 1800 BCE) periods were also found.
- The city was divided into two parts and had signs of a Parkota (fortification) for security.

> According to C-14 radio-dating done by ASI (Archaeological Survey of India), the oldest Harappan site is located at **Bhirrana** in Fatehabad district of Haryana. It has been dated to 7570-6200 BCE, far older than the site at Mehrgarh, Pakistan (6400-7000 BCE).

Mitathal

- Excavator — Dr. Suraj Bhan under Kurukshetra University
- Cultural phases — Early, Mature and Late Harappan Cultures

- **Gupta and Kushana coins** were discovered in 1915-16.
- Artifacts include pottery, ornaments, children's toys, clay and **copper tools**, **weighing stones** and steatite, clay beads and faience.
- Other findings include tusk pins, copper bangles, faience bangles and copper spears (harpoons).

Madina

- Location — Rohtak district
- Excavator — Dr. Manmohan Kumar and Vasant Shinde (2007-08)
- Findings — Late Harappan pottery and Painted Grey Ware (PGW) cultures

Bhagwanpura

- Location — On Southern bank of Saraswati river, Kurukshetra
- Excavator — J.P. Joshi and A.K. Sharma Archaeological Survey of India (1975-76)

- The main relics found here are glass and copper bangles of white, black and blue colour.

Farmana Khas

- It is the **second largest archaeological site** of Harappan Civilisation in Haryana. It is also known as **Daksha-Khera.**
- During excavation, four Harappan seals made of talc and remains of the cemetery have been found.
- **Cotton** and **woollen clothes** have also been found here.

Daulatpur

- Location — On the banks of Drishadvati river near Thanesar, Kurukshetra
- Excavator — Department of Antiquities, Kurukshetra University (1968-69, 1969-70, 1976-77 and 1977-78)

- The relics obtained from **Daulatpur** belong to the third phase of the Indus Valley Civilisation, i.e. the Late Harappan period.
- **Daulatpur** was also based on a chess board pattern and pottery, beads, bangles, toys, etc have been found from this site.

Kunal

- Excavators — J.S. Khatri and M. Acharya (1985-86 and 1991-95), B.R. Mani (2016-19)

- During excavation, remains of Hakra Culture, early Harappan Culture and Harappan Civilisation have been found from there.

▲ Remains found from Kunal

Giravad

- Discovered by: Vivek Dangi, Department of History, MDU, Rohtak (2006)
- Excavators: Dr. Vasant Shinde (Deccan College, Pune), Prof. Manmohan Kumar (MDU, Rohtak) and Prof. Toshiki Osada (Kyoto, Japan) in 2007
- The remnants of Hakra culture only have been found in excavations at this site. 13 trough residences and two pottery cooking kilns have also been found here.

Balu

- Location: Kaithal
- Discovered by: Dr. Suraj Bhan and Jim Shaffer (1977)
- Excavators: Suraj Bhan and UV Singh, Kurukshetra University (1978-79)
- The remnants of Early Harappan Culture, Mature Harappan Civilisation and Late Harappan Culture were obtained from this site.

Siswal

- Large quantities of handmade earthen utensils were found, indicating the Siswal people likely did not use a **potter's wheel**.
- The utensils resemble those from **Kalibanga** (Rajasthan) and include painted mud bangles and beads.
- The evidence of copper usage includes a copper-handled gilded object, likely due to the proximity of Khetri copper mines (Rajasthan).
- The excavations were conducted by **Suraj Bhan** under Kurukshetra University (1970).

Important Features of Indus Valley Civilisation

- It was the first Urban Civilisation. Both peasant and commercial groups were represented during this time.
- The primary grain grown here was **barley**, while other crops including **wheat** and **rice** were also grown.
- This civilisation uses a pictograph as its script, which has not yet been deciphered.
- This civilisation was the birthplace of many different kinds of religious beliefs. There were numerous animal species, including peepal trees, also revered.

Important Sites of Indus Valley Civilisation in Haryana

District	Tehsil	Sites
Kurukshetra	Thanesar	Chimarhedi, Fort of King Karna, Bakana, Malari, Boli, Devidaspur, Gadi Rodan, Garhi Sardaran, Gulabgarh, Kalwa, Kanauli, Pipli, Thanesar, Palwal
Ambala	Ambala	Ratankhedi, Mohanpur, Mulana, Samalkhedi, Bodha
Ambala	Naraingarh	Badoli, Tandwal, Andheri
Yamunanagar	Jagadhari	Koharkhana, Santh, Bhadehari, Chaubala
Fatehabad	Fatehabad	Banawali, Burj
Fatehabad	Tohana	Ghaswa
Hisar	Hisar	Sindhuwa, Talu, Alipur, Kharar, Chunar
Hisar	Hansi	Rakhi Shahpur (or Rakhigarhi)
Jind	Narwana	Kalayat
Jind	Jind	Khokhdi, Jiwan Kheda, Malar Kheda, Beri Kheda
Karnal	Karnal	Nisang, Maudi, Sambhi, Bahol, Pujam
Panipat	Panipat	Udhlana Kalan
Sonipat	Gohana	Chhapra, Garhwal, Madina Nuravkheda, Rithala
Bhiwani	Bhiwani	Gagrina, Kachhwa, Nidana, Shamgarh, Jhanjhari Ramba, Kheri Mansingh, Tigdana, Mitathal, Chang
Charkhi-Dadri	Dadri	Mishri, Jhijhad
Rohtak	Rohtak	Mana, Silana, Sisana, Kansala, Kasraunti
Gurugram	Gurugram	Kherki Majra
Gurugram	Ferozpur-Jhirka	Basai Kheda, Papad, Bhadas, Kheda Mundeta
Kaithal	Guhla	Chika, Kasor, Ratakheda, Budanpur, Khambaheda, Rakhi, Malikpur, Banehad
Kaithal	Kaithal	Barsana, Kheri Raiwali, Rithauli, Aarot, Mund, Miyoli, Jatheri, Pundri, Uplana, Sawatkheri, Jogani Kheda, Dudha Kheda, Dhurala, Daulatpur

Historical Period

Historical period refers to that time period whose all recorded history can be read. It includes the following periods

Vedic Period

- The Vedic Civilisation developed after the Indus Valley Civilisation in India.
- Information about this period is mainly received from the **Vedas**, in which the **Rigveda** is the oldest Veda.
- The word Haryana was used in the book Rigveda in the form of **Raj Haryane**. In Rigveda, Haryana is also described as **'Harna'**.

> Haryana was a major part of the Aryavart in the Vedic period. This part was irrigated by the water of **Saraswati** and **Drishadvati** rivers.

- The name of Haryana is **Hariyali** in Skanda Purana. Rohtak is mentioned in **Nakul Digvijayam**.
- During the Vedic period, the ancient name of Panipat district was **Panprastha**.
- Kurukshetra is mentioned as **Harishetra** in Skanda Purana.

Settlements of Aryan People

- On the basis of Vedic evidence of the Aryans, it can be said that Aryans were astonished by seeing the fertile land of Haryana.
- They developed Haryana as their first habitat. This is the reason that the famous historian **Dr. HR Gupta** and other historians consider that the word 'Haryana' is derived from the word 'Aryana'.
- **Aryans** established their settlements in Haryana, as well as many states were established and Vedic culture flourished.
- Archaeologist **B.B. Lal** related Aryans with the **Painted Grey Ware Culture**. There are approximately 300 sites of Painted Grey Ware Culture in Haryana, among which the famous ones are **Daulatpur, Sugh** and **Fort of King Karna**.
- Most scholars have the opinion that the first centre of Aryan Civilisation was Haryana in India. Aryan people called Haryana as **Devbhoomi**.
- According to the Vedic period, Haryana is historically significant as the land of the **Bharat Dynasty**.

> **Struggle of Aryan and Non-Aryan People**
>
> - The first major conflict of Aryans was with **Pani**, which was a local tribal group. The area of the Pani tribal group was called **Panprastha**, which is the current Panipat.
> - This tribal group considered themselves as high and did not consider the **Principle of Krinvanto Vishwamaryam** of Aryans.

Rigvedic Period

- During the Rigvedic period, (1500-1000 BCE), is believed that the first king of Aryans was **Mainu Vaivasvata.** Among the four sons of Manu (Ikshvaku, Parashu, Sudhuman and Sharyati) **Sudhuman** and **Sharyati** were related to Haryana.
- The area between the **Saraswati** and **Sutlej** rivers was under the control of **Sudhuman** (including present-day Ambala and Kurukshetra).
- The area which was situated from the border of Rajasthan to the Mewat region was under the control of **Sharyati**. Their capital was around **Narnaul.**
- Sharyati performed **Ashvamedha Yajna** which was conducted by **Bhargava Rishi Chawyan.** He belonged to Dausi, near Narnaul.
- After the death of Sharyati, the successor of the Sudhuman, **Pururva** took the authority over Sutlej to the Sahibi rivers, because there was no descendant of Sharyati.
- After Pururva, his son **Ayu** became the king. After Ayu, his son **Nahush** became the king and after Nahush, **Yayati** became the king who was quite famous.

> There were five sons of king Yayati- **Yadu**, **Turvas**, **Druha**, **Anu** and **Puru**. Yayati was dissatisfied with his elder son due to which he handed over the ancestral state of Haryana to Puru, who was very brave.

- The dynasty had been named as **Paurav dynasty**, after the name of Puru.
- Another ruler of this dynasty was **Bharata** who was very brave and expanded the kingdom to Ganga. India got its name 'Bharat' after the ruler Bharata and the Paurav dynasty came to be known as the **Bharata dynasty.**

Major Vedic Period Areas of Haryana

District	Areas
Hisar	Kaulgarh, Rattatibba, Uklana Burj, Hansi, Pali, Singhwa
Sirsa	Karivali, Humayunkheda, Bani, Nakora, Rania
Jind	Tohana-Ghaseva, Rupanwali, Kalayat, Ritauli Kalan, Rajound, Beri Khera
Kurukshetra	Rasulpur, Kariala, Chaba, Ratta Khera, Ramthali, Shergarh, Mundakheda, New Village, Arnai, Ladwa, Bhagwanpur, Morthali, Daulatpur
Karnal	Nisang, Asandh, Sambh, Poojam, Bhola
Panipat	Panipat
Sonipat	Saman, Gumad
Rohtak	Baliana, Bahadurgarh, Kharkara, Hulsana, Kansana, Nakoli
Ambala	Basantpur, Kakrunikheda, Harnaula, Mehboob Nagar, Mustafabad, Kamash, Pathreda
Faridabad	Bamnikheda, Badhaula, Balai, Sawarkheda, Sondh, Palwal, Ballabhgarh Tilpat, Sihi, Kheda, Dhanpura, Lohia
Gurugram	Harnaul Kheda, Bhadasa, Chhanpur Kheda, Guhana, Gohana, Gangoli, Ujina, Mandkola, Jaisinghpur, Dhankot

Later Vedic Period

- During the Later Vedic period (1000-600 BCE), Haryana was ruled by the **Kuru dynasty**.
- According to the scholars, **Kurushravana** described in Rigveda is Kuru who is regarded as the descendant of **Trasadasyu**.
- After defeating the Panchals, King Kuru captured the Saraswati region also known as **Kurujangala**. Presently, Kurujangala is known as **Kurukshetra**.
- The name of Kurukshetra had been named after **King Kuru**.
- The successor of the Kuru was **Parikshit** and Parikshit's successor was his second son **Juhu** and Juhu's successor was **Surath**.
- **Shantanu** was a majestic king of Kuru dynasty whose two queens were Ganga and Satyavati.
  He had three sons, **Devavrata** from Ganga and two sons named **Chitrang** and **Vichitravirya** from Satyavati.
- Gandhar attacked the Kuru dynasty during the reign of Shantanu. The war of Kurukshetra was between the Gandhar and Kauravas, which has been called **the first war of Kurukshetra**.

Mahabharata War

- The war of Mahabharata (Kurukshetra war) (900 BCE) was fought between Kauravas and Pandavas in Kurukshetra of Haryana for the throne of **Hastinapur**. Kauravas and Pandavas were both descendants of the **Kuru** lineage. In this war, Pandavas got victory.
- In this glory, Arjun was given an important preaching on the land of **Kurukshetra** by Lord Krishna, which is known as the **Teachings of Srimad Bhagavad Gita**.
- This war is also called **Dharam Yudh**. This war continued in Kurukshetra (Dharam Kshetra) for a total of 18 days.
- The battleground of Mahabharata is believed to be of 48 kos (around 240 km of the perimeter).
- This war had 18 **Akshohini** armies, in which there were 11 Akshohini armies of Kauravas and 7 Akshohini armies of Pandavas.
- Krishna gave the sermon of Bhagavad Gita to Arjun at the **Jyotisar shrine** of Kurukshetra.

Mahabharata Epic

- Mahabharata is the world's largest epic, whose author was **Maharishi Vedvyasa**. Mahabharata is also known as **Jaya Samhita** and **Satasehastri Samhita**. The Mahabharata was written in Kurukshetra. Therefore, Kurukshetra district of Haryana is considered old and sacred. Kurukshetra has been described as the Dharam Kshetra Kurukshetra in the first verse of the Gita.
- The original name of Mahabharata is **Panchali Katha**. In Mahabharata, Haryana has been named as **Bahudhanyaka**.
- **Karnal city** was established by King Karna during Mahabharata period.

Buddhism and Jainism in the Later Vedic Period

- After the Mahabharata period, the life of people became complicated, which was simple and easy in the **Vedic** period.
- The business of rituals increased more in the society. As a result, Buddhism and Jainism emerged against religious complexities.

Buddhism

- Buddhist literature suggests that Mahatma Buddha himself came to Haryana.
- Among the most important places sanctified by Buddha is the place called **Kammasadamma**, where Mahatma Buddha gave many discourses.
- The modern name of Kammasadhamma is **Kaithal**.
- Fa-hein (399 AD) and Hiuen-Tsang (639 AD) documented Buddhism in Haryana in their travelogues.
- Buddhism began to decline in Haryana by the time of Hiuen-Tsang's visit.
- Buddhism revived in the 7th century during **Harsha's reign**, with Harshavardhana's third Buddhist association. Rajyavardhana and Harshavardhana, from the Pushyabhuti dynasty, were noted for their Buddhist righteousness.

Centres of Buddhism in Haryana

Centre	Description
Thanesar (Dulkoti)	• Second important city (present Thanesar) of the state. • Mahatma Buddha preached here and the ruler Ruttpal became his disciple. • According to the Chinese traveller Hiuen-Tsang, Thanesar had three museums. • A 300 feet high stupa was built by Ashoka in its North-West part, in which a metal statue of Mahatma Buddha was placed.
Topra (Yamunanagar)	• A village known for Emperor Ashoka's stone pillar which is 42 feet high and 2.5 feet wide with seven edicts. • The language in scripts are Brahmi and Prakrit. • A Buddhist Vihara, built by Ashoka, is also found here.
Sugh (Yamunanagar)	• According to Hiuen-Tsang, Buddha preached here. • These were five Buddhist Viharas, in which about one thousand Buddhist monks lived. • Ashoka built a stupa on the Yamuna's banks, containing Buddha's nails and hair, with 12 stupas surrounding it. • Nails and hair of Mahatma Sariputra and Acharya Maudgalyan were kept in Buddhist Stupa at the West gate of Sugh. • This city was an education centre in ancient times. It is mentioned in Panini's **Ashtadhyayi**. • Statues of Buddha and two thousand years old remnants of Vanar Sena also found near Sugh.
Agroha	• It was also a prominent Buddhist centre, with remains of stupas and viharas. • It is mentioned in Panini's Ashtadhyayi.
Rohtak and Kalanaur	• Buddha visited these places, delivering sermons. • Disciples like Ratnapala, Nandutara and Mittakali spread his teachings later.
Dharsul, Kunal and Sirsa	• Emperor Ashoka built Buddhist Viharas.

Jainism

- After Buddhism, Jainism continued to have its influence in Haryana, in which Jain Saint **Lohacharya** had a prominent position in the spread of Jainism. He also expanded Jainism in **Agroha and Rohtak**.
- After the sixth-seventh century, when Buddhism began to weaken, Jainism spread in a big way in Haryana with the efforts of **Jain Acharya Jinvallabh Suri, Haribhadra Suri, Abhayadev** and so on.
- Jainism in the state spread to the common people with a **five-colour flag**, in which five colours were considered to be symbols of **Gods** and in five colours, the concept of five **Mahavratas** was also contained.

- Among these colours, **Dhaval colour** was considered as an emblem of **Ahimsa**, **Arunabha** of **truth**, **Pitabha** of **Acharya**, **Haritabh** of **Brahmacharya** and **Neelabha** is the symbol of **renunciation**.
- **Rohtak**, **Sirsa** etc, became the main centres of Jainism in the state, but by the middle ages, the spread of Jainism started to decline and became limited to a few areas.

Centres of Jainism in Haryana

Centre	Description
Thanesar (Kurukshetra)	• A major centre for Jain sages in Haryana, with ancient Jain idols found here. • A book by Sundar Muni, related to Ayurveda, is preserved in the Bikaner Government Museum, dated 1645 AD.
Rohtak	• It became a major Jainism hub by the 7th century. • The Jain idols, including a mother with a child and Jain Saraswati, were discovered in Khokhrakot area of Rohtak. • The Idols of Tirthankaras Parshwanath and Mahavir Swami were also found. • Some idols and remains are kept at the Kali Mata temple situated here.
Jind	• The metal statue of Jain Tirthankar Adinath has been found here.
Pinjore (Panchkula)	• Several Jain idols have been discovered, including prominent statues of Chandraprabha, Parshwanath and Mahavir Swami.
Sirsa	• Jainism's influence in the region is evident from the 10th century. • Fragmented remains of Jain idols have been found in and around Sirsa. • A prominent statue placed on a throne was found, featuring a chakra on the front and lion embellishments on the sides.
Hansi	• A significant number of Jain arhats were present in the medieval period, despite a lack of state patronage for Jainism. • Metal sculptures related to Jainism have been found, including statues of Jain Tirthankara Adinath, Parshwanath, Dharanendra, Kubera and Yaksha-Yakshaniyas. • Other findings include metal idols of Jain Saraswati, Padmavati, birds, Buddha-Jain stupas and statues of Buddha and Brahma.
Asthal Bohar (Rohtak)	• A major historical centre of the Nath sect. • Jain-related artifacts found here include statues of Balram, Jain Tirthankara, Parshwanath, Shantinath and Chakreshwari.

Mahajanpada Period

- In the later Vedic period, tribal states were replaced by territorial states and they were developed in the 6th century BCE. Thus, many big states came into existence.
- The Buddha text **Anguttara Nikaya** has mention of **16 Mahajanapadas** and one of these is **Kuru** which had some areas of Haryana.
- Meerut, Delhi and Thanesar were a part of Kuru Mahajanapada and its capital was **Hastinapur** during Mahabharata period.

Mauryan Period

- Founder — Chandragupta Maurya, defeated Dhanananda of Nanda dynasty of Magadha (324 BCE)
- Haryana under Mauryas — 324 to 232 BCE
- Evidence — Artifacts from Kurukshetra
- Successors — Bindusara (son), Ashoka (grandson)
- The 7 inscriptions of the reign of Mauryan ruler Ashoka are inscribed at a place called **Topra** in Ambala district. Ashoka also built a Buddhist Stupa at Thanesar.
- Thanesar is also called the **ancestral kingdom of Ashoka**.
- Ashoka's successors proven unfit, due to which the Mauryan Empire began to decline and the people of Haryana gradually re-established the republican system.
- The evidence of the governance of the Mauryan dynasty is found from the Northern black Polished Ware from Sugh near Jagadhri, the stupas of Thanesar, the pillars from Hisar and Topra, etc.

The Origin of the Name HARYANA

1 **Sanskrit Derivation**
Hari (God) + Ayan (Home or abode) = The Abode of God

2 **Hariyali (Greenery) Theory**
As per Dr. Yadunath Sarkar (Historian), 'Haryana' comes from Hariyala due to lush vegetation post-rainfall.

3 **Ahirana Theory**
Some scholars associate it with Ahirana, linked to the area's historical grazing grounds.

4 **Bahudhanyakya** (Mahabharata)
Haryana was referred to as Bahudhanyakya, meaning 'land with plenty of grains'.

5 **Dasharana or Haridhanyak Theory**
Some theories purpose Dasharana (ten kilograms) or Haridhanyak, later evolving into Haryana.

6 **Bandits Theory**
Some believe, it is derived from Harna, relating to bandits looting travellers.

7 **Kurukshetra Reference**
Kurukshetra is described as 'Harikhetra' (in Skanda Purana), South of Kurukshetra called as 'Khandavprastha' and South-Eastern region was called as 'Bahudhanyak'.

8 **Inscription Reference**
An inscription (1328 AD) in National Museum, Delhi highlights region named as Haryana. Inscription in Bijavlia (Rajasthan) calls Haryana as 'Haritanak' while Haryana has been called 'Haryanak' in the article of Palam Bawli.

9 **Historical Names in Literature/By Persons**
Hariyala (Skanda Purana), Haryanaye (Pasnaha Chariu), Shrikrinth Janapada (Banabhatta), Haridhanakya (Rahul Sankrityayan), Abhiryana (Budh Prakash), Aryana (S.R. Gupta), Haram (King Krishna), Haribanka (Akhand Prakash book by Dharnidhar)

10 **Present Name**
After 14th century, the state started to be addressed by the present name Haryana.

Emergence of Republican System

After the fall of Mauryan empire, many republics emerged in Haryana state. These republics were Yaudheya, Agar Arjunayana and Kunind. Among these republics, **Yaudheya** was the largest.

Yaudheya Republic

• Established by	Yaudheyas (as per Drona Parva)
• Etymology	Around 5th century BCE, 'Yaudheya' mentioned in Mahabharata, Purana, Mahabhashya, etc.
• Areas included in the Republic	Haryana and some parts of Uttar Pradesh, Rajasthan and Punjab
• Name of Haryana during this period	Bahudhanyaka
• Capital	Naurangabad, Bhiwani (Ancient name Praknitanak)
• Divisions of Haryana in the Republic	Haryana was divided in two parts (Rohtak and Sirsa)
• Main God	Kartikeya
• Symbol	Mayura

- The coins of Yaudheya Republic have been found in Haryana firstly by **Cunningham** in the 19th century.
- The coins have also been found from Sonipat, Hisar, Sirsa, Rohtak, Gurugram, Karnal, etc. of which the coin found from Rohtak district in 1916 is prominent.
- **Sir Rogers** has found the coins of the Yaudheya clan from **Hansi and Kharkhoda**. Similarly, in the year 1938-39, a large pile of Yaudheya coins was found from a place called **Jaijaivati** of Jind.
- Yaudheya coins have been kept safe at the **Haryana Archaeological Museum, Jhajjar.**
- **Yaudheyana Bahudhanyak** belongs to the period of decline of Mauryan Empire and the Mauryan script is inscribed on them.
- In 1936, fossil scientist **Birbal Sahni** got a similar stamp from the mint of **Khokhrakot** of Rohtak, from which coins of Yaudheya Republic were minted.

> Birbal Sahni has written in the book **Technique of Casting Coins in Ancient India (1945)** that "Out of all the ancient materials of minting coins in the world, the material obtained from Rohtak is the best, most valuable and important."

- Mints have also been found from **Aurangabad** in Bhiwani, from where the coins and molds of the Yaudheyan clan have been found.
- The coins of the Kushana rulers Vima Kadphises, Kanishka, Huvishka and Vasudeva, have also been found in the Yaudheya Republic, which means that Kushana rule existed in the region.

Struggle with Kushanas

- The struggle of the Yaudheyas and the Kushanas took place during the reign of **Vima Kadphises.**
- The Yaudheyas made themselves independent at the time of the Kushana ruler **Vasudeva.**
- According to the famous scholar **Dr. Anant Sadashiva Altekar**, the Yaudheyas defeated the Kushanas by forming a union of the republics of **Kunind, Arjunayan**, etc.
- To make this victory permanent, Yaudheyas issued special coins on which **Yaudheya Ganasya Jai** (i.e., Yaudheyas conquered the enemy) was written.
- This is also confirmed by the coin with **Yaudheyanam Jayamantra Dharamanam.**
- According to **Dr. Anant Sadashiva**, Rohtak was the capital of Yaudheya republic.
- The coinage of the last Kushana rulers not found in this area proves that the Yaudheyas had liberalised themselves from the Kushana rulers.

Khokhrakot

- It was the **famous city** of the Yaudheyan Republic. It is also considered the capital of the Republic of Yaudheyas. Presently, it is situated in the form of a huge mound near **Rohtak** district.
- The excavation work of this archaeological site was conducted by the Department of Archaeology and Museums with the help of Maharishi Dayananda University, Rohtak between 1988 and 1990.
- The evidences of the earliest Painted Grey Pottery Culture have been found from this site. After this, the region may have been under the Yaudheyas, Kushana and Gupta rulers. Terracotta coins, stamps, etc. have also been found from this site.

Agar Republic

• Ancient Name	Agraodaka
• Capital	Agroha or Agroda
• Coins found from	Agroha, Barwala
• Greeks called Agar Republic	Agalassoi

- After the Kushana war, Agar was merged into the **Yaudheyas Republic.** After the invasion of Alexander, the Agar Republic came under the Mauryan Empire and then **became independent** after the fall of the Mauryans.
- The Agar Republic was also included in the union formed by the Yaudheyas, who defeated the Kushana ruler Vasudeva.
- The **second major republic** of Haryana was the Agar Republic.
- The **first 10 coins** related to Agar have been found in the state, of which **9 coins** were found in Barwala by **Rogers**, which is in the British Museum, while **1 coin** is in the Indian Museum.
- In the year **1938-39**, HL Srivastava found **51 coins** from Agroha of Hisar. On the basis of coins, it can be said that in ancient times the main centre of the Agar clan was Agroha (Hisar).
- Pictures of tree, bull, lim and goddess have been inscribed on the coins found from Agroha.
- In the year **1979**, during the archaeological excavation many historical materials were obtained from Agroha.

The ancient Agroha city was founded by **Maharaja Agrasen**, the primitive man of Agarwal community (Agar). This is the reason why presently the entire Agarwal community (Vaishya caste) of India considers Agroha as their place of origin.

Kunind Republic

• Most powerful ruler	Amoghabhuti
• Capital	Ambala
• Areas included in Kunind Republic	Ambala and Yamunanagar

- It was an important republic of ancient India.
- The Kunindas and Yaudheyas together fought a war against the Kushanas. This is confirmed by renowned scholar **Dr. Altekar** on the basis of the word **Dhwi** inscribed on the coins of the Yaudheyan clan.

Arjunayana Republic

- According to famous scholar Dr. Jaiswal, Arjunayana Republic was emerged around 200 AD.
- This Republic was located in Rajasthan, covering some areas of Southern Haryana (some part of Mahendragarh).
- Panini's **Ashtadhyayi** is the main source of information about the Arjunayana Republic.

Gupta Period

- According to **Prayag Prashasti**, great Gupta ruler **Samudragupta** had merged the Yaudheya Republic into the Gupta Empire.
- In the 5th century, after the death of Gupta ruler **Skandagupta**, Haryana (Neelkanth district) was captured by **Pushyabhuti dynasty.**

- The name of the Neelkanth Janapada (a large part of Haryana) was probably named after the ruler Srikanth of Naga dynasty.

Pushyabhuti Dynasty

- The founder of Pushyabhuti dynasty or Vardhan dynasty was **Pushyabhuti**, whose capital was Thaneshwar (Thanesar), Kurukshetra.
- Pushyabhuti constructed the **Sthaneshwar** (Thaneshwar) temple and it was renovated by **Maratha Sadashiv Rai.** Thaneshwar is also known as the **Island of the Mughals.**
- Pushyabhuti was conferred with the title **Parammaheshwar.**

Main Rulers of Pushyabhuti Dynasty

***Naravardhana** (505–525 AD)*

- Established power in Thanesar during Gupta downfall.
- At that time, area was part of Shrikanth Janapada.
- Called **Maharaj** in inscriptions.

***Adityavardhana** (550–580 AD)*

- Title Maharaja, also called '**Paramdivya Bhakta.**'
- Married Mahasen Gupta, daughter of Gupta ruler Damodar Gupta, in 565 AD.

***Prabhakarvardhana** (580–605 AD)*

- Took titles Maharajadhiraj Param Bhattarak, Pratapashil.
- Expanded the kingdom from Punjab to Haryana.
- Defeated Huna rulers and conquered Lat, Malav, Sindh and Gandhar.
- Ensured independence of the Vardhana dynasty.
- Died in 605 AD.

***Rajyavardhana II** (605–606 AD)*

- Eldest son of Prabhakarvardhana and Yashomati.
- Married sister Rajyashree to Maukhari ruler Grihavarma.
- Killed by Devgupta and Shashank in 606 AD.

***Harshavardhana** (606–647 AD)*

- Coronation in 612 AD.
- Made **Kannauj the second capital** in 636 AD.
- Defeated Devgupta and Shashank.
- **Court poet** Banabhatta (author of Harshacharita).
- Chinese traveller Hiuen-Tsang visited during his reign (629–644 AD).
- Died in 647 AD, leading to the rise of the Gurjara- Pratihara dynasty.

Haryana and Gurjara-Pratihara Period

- From an inscription obtained from a place called Jodhaka in Sirsa district of Haryana, it is known that the **Pratiharas** had occupied Haryana.
- Pratihara ruler Vatsaraja had made Tomar Sardar named **Galla** as the special administrator here, but Vatsaraja did not remain in power for long.
- After the expulsion of **Vatsaraja**, the Tomar rulers had an opportunity to increase their power, but Tomar could not succeed in establishing his power for long as the Pala Dynasty ruler **Dharmapala** defeated and subjugated him.
- After some time, Haryana and Kannauj were restored under the son of Vatsaraja, Nagabhatta. After the death of Nagabhatta in 833 AD, his son **Rambhadra** became the ruler.
- **Rambhadra** proved to be an incapable ruler. During his short tenure (833-36 AD), a state of chaos arose, but Rambhadra's son Mihirbhoja proved to be a worthy ruler.

> **Mihirbhoja** established a strong Pratihara empire by his ability and intelligence. During the reign of Mihirbhoja, the Pratihara empire started on the path of progress and **Pehowa** was established as a trading centre. **Mihirbhoja** made **Kannauj** his capital.

- Mihirbhoja ruled from 836 to 885 AD. In 885 AD, after his death Mihirbhoja's son **Mahendrapala** became the ruler.
- It is known from the records obtained from **Pehowa** that during Mahendrapala's rule, a vast area of Haryana had come out of his suzerainty and a Tomar chieftain named **Jaul** had increased his power.
- Jaul's eldest son **Vajrat** was also a heroic and mighty chieftain like his father. Under Vajrat's leadership, the peace system continued in Haryana. Vajrat's son Jajjuk was also a worthy chieftain.
- In 910 AD, an atmosphere of political instability arose after the death of Mahendrapala. Taking advantage of this situation, the three sons of Jajuk, (**Goga, Purnaraj** and **Devaraja**) established their dominance in the adjoining areas of Haryana and laid the foundation of Tomar rule independently.

Haryana and Tomar Dynasty

- There are different opinions among different historians in terms of origin of the Tomar dynasty. According to Mughal historian **Khadgaram**, the ruler of the Tomar dynasty was **Somvanshi Kshatriya**.
- In the inscription of **1631 AD**, Tomar is considered a descendant of Somvanshi Kshatriya and Pandavas.
- The **Pehowa inscription** reveals that the Tomar dynasty in Haryana was founded by Jaul.
- A chieftain from the fifth generation of the Tomar ruler **Anangpala**, who established the Tomar kingdom with its capital at Dhillika (Delhi). Jaul, a subordinate of the Pratiharas, popularised his currency.
- He was succeeded by **Aprichhdev** (Gogg), followed by **Pipalraj Dev**, who issued independent currency.
- The dynasty's later rulers included **Raghupala**, **Vilhanpala** and **Gopala**.

Conflicts between Chauhan and Tomar Rulers

- **Harshanath's inscriptions** (973 AD) give information that there was a struggle between Chauhan and Tomar rulers.
- With this inscription, the evidence of the struggles between Shakambari's Chauhan rulers and Pipalraj Dev and Vilhanpal has been found, in which Tomar rulers were defeated.
- Tomar ruler Pipalraj was defeated by his contemporary Chauhan ruler Chandan.
- The successors of **Pipalraj**, Raghupala and Vilhanpala were also defeated by Chauhan rulers.
- **Gopala**, son of Vilhanpala, fought a battle with Chauhan ruler Singhpala to get independence, but he was defeated.
- Gopala was succeeded by **Sulakshanpala** (997-1005 AD). Sulakshanpala had issued new currency in his reign.
- After Sulakshanpala, **Jaipala** became his successor. At this time, Turks started to attack India. It is probably believed that Chauhan and Tomar rulers had been aligned to defeat the Turks.

Ancient Cities in Haryana

Ancient City	River Associated	Excavated by	Year of Excavation
Rakhigarhi	Saraswati-Drishadvati	Amarendra Nath	1960–present
Banawali	Saraswati-Drishadvati	R.S. Bisht	1973
Mitathal	Saraswati-Yamuna Basin	Suraj Bhan	1968
Bhirrana	Ghaggar-Hakra	L.S. Rao	2003
Kunal	Saraswati-Drishadvati	J.S. Khatri and M. Acharya	1986

Ancient Names of Some Districts

Present Name	Ancient Name	Present Name	Ancient Name
Sirsa	Sairishaka	Rohtak	Rohitas/Rohtasgarh
Fatehabad	Ikdar/Dhanagarh	Sonipat	Swarnprastha/ Sonprastha
Hisar	Hisar-e-Firoza	Panipat	Panprastha/ Panduprastha
Mahendragarh	Kanoud	Karnal	Karntal/Karnalaya
Rewari	Rewa wadi	Yamunanagar	Abdulahpur
Mewat	Satyevpuram	Kurukshetra	Sthaneswar (Thanesar)
Palwal	Upbala, Apelava	Kaithal	Kapisthal
Gurugram	Gurugram	Jind	Jaintapuri

Ancient and Present Names of Some Towns

Ancient Name	Present Name	Ancient Name	Present Name
Kharial	Ellenabad (Sirsa)	Sharafabad	Bahadurgarh (Jhajjar)
Agradaka	Agroha (Hisar)	Mahestha	Maham (Rohtak)
Nar Rashtra	Narnaul (Mahendragarh)	Prithudaka	Pehowa (Kurukshetra)
Prakritnak	Aurangabad (Palwal)	Yugandhari	Jagadhri (Yamunanagar)
Balramgarh	Ballabhgarh (Faridabad) (renamed as Balramgarh (2017))	Kalakula	Kalka (Panchkula)

Relevant Places of Ancient Remains of Haryana

Remains	Location (From where received)	Remains	Location (From where received)
Mauryan stupa and relics	Hisar and Fatehabad	Tablet of Shunga Period	Sugh
Ornaments and relics of Pre-Harappan civilisation	Kunal (Fatehabad)	Copper Currency of Harsha Period	Sonipat
Relics of Harappan civilisation	Bhiwani	Stamps of Yaudheyan Period	Naurangabad (Bhiwani)
Gold and copper coins of Kushana period	Mitathal (Bhiwani)	Statues of Jain Period	Hansi and Ranila
Indo-Greek coins	Khokhrakot (Rohtak)	Dwara Pillar of Kushana Style	Rohtak
Gold and copper coins	Mitathal (Bhiwani)	Sculptures of Yaksha	Palwal
Coins mint	Khokhrakot, Aurangabad	Tablet with Ramayan Verses	Nacharkheda (Bhiwani)
Mints of Yaudheyan period	Khokhrakot (Rohtak)	Clay Stamps	Daulatpur
Mints	Agroha, Barwala, Aurangabad	Coins of Agreya Janapada	Agroha (Hisar)
Coins of Kuninda period	Karnal, Jagadhari, Budiya	Statue of Baliram	Asthal Bohar (Rohtak)
Coins of Samudragupta period	Mitathal	Inscriptions of Gurjara-Pratihara Period	Pehowa
Currencies of Gupta period	Rohtak		

CHECK CHAPTER KNOWLEDGE

1 In ancient times, Haryana was known as *Haryana Fire Station Officer 2018*
(a) Brahmavrata (b) Gujarat
(c) Kurukshetra (d) Delhi

2 By what name was the state of Haryana known in ancient times? *HSSC 2015*
(a) Brahmavrata Pradesh
(b) Brahmashri Pradesh
(c) Brahma ki Uttarvedi
(d) All of the above

3 Stone tools of palaeolithic age are found at which place of Haryana?
(a) Dhamli (b) Pinjore
(c) Firozpur (d) Both (a) and (b)

4 From which place of Haryana evidences of lower palaeolithic period have been found?
(a) Pinjore-Kalka region
(b) Mewat region
(c) Malwa region
(d) Jhajjar-Nuh region

5 Evidences of agriculture of Neolithic period have been found from which place of Haryana?
(a) Sirsa (b) Hisar
(c) Siswal (d) Kurukshetra

6 The first evidences of Siswal culture have been found from which district of Haryana?
(a) Hisar (b) Rohtak
(c) Kurukshetra (d) Sirsa

7 At first, Siswal people were settled near which river valley in Haryana?
(a) Yamuna River Valley
(b) Sahibi River Valley
(c) Saraswati River Valley
(d) Drishadvati River Valley

8 Black-shiny decorated pottery have been found in Haryana, it depicts culture of which period?
(a) Vedic Period
(b) Indus Valley Civilisation
(c) Siswal Civilisation
(d) None of the above

9 The excavation of Mitathal village, located in Bhiwani district of Haryana, was conducted by *HSSC 2020*
(a) Dr. Manmohan Kumar
(b) Dr. Suraj Bhan
(c) R.S. Bisht
(d) Dr. Amrendra Nath

10 Banawali is located in which district of Haryana?
(a) Fatehabad (b) Rohtak
(c) Sirsa (d) Hisar

11 Rakhigarhi, a famous site of Siswal culture is located in which district of Haryana?
(a) Hisar
(b) Sonipat
(c) Kurukshetra
(d) Sirsa

12 Painted pottery of Siswal culture has been found from which place of Haryana?
(a) Kunal (b) Farmana
(c) Giravad (d) Balu

13 Royal crown has been found from which place of Haryana? *Haryana Police Constable 2018*
(a) Banawali (b) Rakhigarhi
(c) Kunal (d) All of these

14 Which is the first excavated site of 'Hakra Culture'? *HSSC CET 2024*
(a) Kunal
(b) Mitathal
(c) Bhirrana
(d) None of the above

15 Around 5000 years old Indus Valley Civilisation has been found in the .... district of Haryana. *HSSC 2018*
(a) Ranchi (b) Hisar
(c) Kurukshetra (d) Angirus

16 Which Harappan site is located in Fatehabad district of Haryana? *PGT 2016*
(a) Banawali (b) Lothal
(c) Dholavira (d) Kalibangas

17 At which place, two terracotta sculptures of Matradevi have been found in Haryana?
(a) Banawali (b) Rakhigarhi
(c) Mitathal (d) Bhirrana

18 The largest number of barley and grains evidences have been discovered at which Harappan site of Haryana?
(a) Mitathal (b) Banawali
(c) Siswal (d) Bhirrana

19 Rakhigarhi, a Harappan civilisation place is located in which of the following district of Haryana? *PGT 2016*
(a) Hisar (b) Kurukshetra
(c) Fatehabad (d) Sirsa

20 In the excavation of which of the following sites of Haryana, the remains of 4500 years old civilisation found? *HSSC 2019*
(a) Rakhigarhi (b) Siswal
(c) Rohtak (d) Karnal

21 Which of the following is the oldest Harappan historical site in Haryana? *HSSC 2020*
(a) Bhadana (b) Rakhigarhi
(c) Banawali (d) Kunal

22 The historical site Mitathal is located in which district of Haryana? *HSSC 2017*
(a) Rohtak (b) Sirsa
(c) Bhiwani (d) Bahadurgarh

23 Which of the following archaeological site of Indus Valley Civilisation in Haryana is correctly matched? *Haryana Tehsil Welfare Officer 2018*
(a) Mitathal-Bhiwani
(b) Rakhigarhi-Fatehabad
(c) Banawali-Yamunanagar
(d) Siswal-Kurukshetra

24 Which of the following is not a Harappan site? *HSSC 2017*
(a) Rakhigarhi (b) Faridabad
(c) Banawali (d) Daulatpur

25 What is the name of Haryana in Rigveda? *Haryana Agriculture Inspector 2017*
(a) Raj Haryana (b) Harivi
(c) Haryali (d) Harna

26 In which Purana, Haryana is named as 'Hariyali'? *HSSC 2017*
(a) Vamana Purana (b) Prithvi Purana
(c) Purana Katha (d) Skanda Purana

27 'Panprastha' is the oldest name of which district of Haryana? *Haryana Group D 2018*
(a) Sonipat (b) Kurukshetra
(c) Panipat (d) Kaithal

28 In which text Kurukshetra is known as 'Harishetra'?
(a) Vayu Purana (b) Garuda Purana
(c) Shiva Purana (d) Skanda Purana

29 The oldest epic of Haryana is *Haryana Police Sub-inspector 2018*
(a) Rigveda (b) Bhagavad Gita
(c) Chaturveda (d) Ausho

30 .... said that the word 'Haryana' came from Aryan. *HSSC 2017*
(a) Dr. HR Gupta
(b) Pt. Rahul Sankrityayan
(c) Satish Dwiwedi
(d) Chahmana

31 Aryan people called Haryana as
(a) Devlok (b) Devprayag
(c) Devbhoomi (d) Devsangam

32 Which of the following mighty kings are associated with history of Haryana?
(a) Puru Clan (b) Bharat Clan
(c) Kuru Clan (d) All of these

33 Haryana state was the home of which dynasty?
(a) Bharata dynasty
(b) Maurya dynasty
(c) Lodhi dynasty
(d) Gupta dynasty

34 The war of Mahabharata took place in .... BCE. *HSSC 2017*
(a) 900 (b) 800
(c) 700 (d) 600

35 The famous Kurukshetra War (Mahabharat) was fought for the throne of *HSSC Filed Cadre 2020*
(a) Indraprashta (b) Hastinapur
(c) Gandhar (d) Yadu

36 The holy district of Haryana is *HSSC 2017*
(a) Panchkula (b) Kurukshetra
(c) Ambala (d) Hisar

37 Ved Vyasa wrote Mahabharata at which place? *Haryana Group D 2018*
(a) Sonipat (b) Kurukshetra
(c) Hisar (d) Panipat

38 The name of Mahabharata is *HSSC 2017*
(a) Dharam Bharata (b) Panchali Katha
(c) Jaya Samhita (d) Jay Bharata

39 The famous religious book/text of 'Mahabharata' was written in which district of Haryana? *PGT 2016*
(a) Hisar (b) Sonipat
(c) Karnal (d) Kurukshetra

40 .... battleground is known as 'Dharam Shetra'. *Haryana Group D 2018*

(a) Panipat (b) Kurukshetra
(c) Mewat (d) Kargil

41 Which city of Haryana is associated with Karna of Mahabharata? *HSSC 2024*

(a) Karnal (b) Kurukshetra
(c) Kunjpura (d) Kunal

42 In which epic Haryana is known as 'Bahudhanyak'? *HSSC 2017*

(a) Mahabharata (b) Vishnu Purana
(c) Ramayana (d) Ashtadhyayi

43 In which region of Haryana, did the battle of Mahabharata took place? *HSSC 2024*

(a) Kurukshetra (b) Panipat
(c) Hisar (d) Jhajjar

44 Kurukshetra has been described as the Dharmakshetra Kurukshetra in the first verse of the *HSSC Field Cadre 2020*

(a) Puranas (b) Ramayana
(c) Mahabharatha (d) Gita

45 Haryana has been illustrated in which epic? *HSSC 2017*

(a) Ramayana (b) Gitanjali
(c) Mahabharata (d) Shakuntala

46 During the times of Mahabharata, Haryana was referred with which of the following names? *HSSC 2023-22*

(a) Hitapradesh (b) Vindyapradesh
(c) Ditarashtra (d) Bahudhanyaka

47 Lord Krishna gave teachings of Gita to Arjun at which holy place of Haryana? *Haryana Accountant 2018*

(a) Markandey Teertha (b) Jyotisar
(c) Brahma Kund (d) Kaleshwar Teertha

48 The book written by the Chinese traveller depicts power and glory of which place of Haryana? *PGT 2018, HSSC 2017*

(a) Thanesar (b) Patiala
(c) Mahendragarh (d) Kurukshetra

49 Who is the author of the epic 'Mahabharata'? *Haryana CET 2023*

(a) Magh (b) Kalidas
(c) Maharishi Valmiki (d) Maharishi Ved Vyasa

50 Statue of Baliram has been found from which place of Haryana?

(a) Asthal Bohar (Rohtak)
(b) Sonipat
(c) Naurangabad (Bhiwani)
(d) Barwala

51 The famous traveller Hiuen-Tsang who had come to Haryana in the 17th century to learn Buddhism was from *HSSC Field Cadre 2020*

(a) Israel (b) Sri Lanka
(c) Indonesia (d) China

52 Which one of the following is the correct meaning of Haryana? *HSSC Head Office Cadre 2020*

(a) The Adobe of God (b) The God of Crop
(c) The God of Money (d) The Adobe of Grains

53 Who called the region of Haryana as Hariyala?

(a) Dr. Budh Prakash (b) Yadunath Sarkar
(c) Dr. H.R. Gupta (d) Vibhu Shridhar

54 .... called the region of Haryana as Haridhanakya. *HSSC Filed Cadre 2020*

(a) Dr. H.R. Gupta (b) Dr. Budh Prakash
(c) Rahul Sankrityayan (d) Yadunath Sarkar

55 What was the capital of Kuru Clan, which was among the 16 Mahajanapadas, during Mahabharata period ? *PGT 2016*

(a) Hastinapur (b) Indraprastha
(c) Kurukshetra (d) None of these

56 Haryana region was under the reign of which Mauryan king? *Haryana Panchayat Officer 2017*

(a) Bindusara
(b) Ashoka
(c) Chandragupta Maurya
(d) All of the above

57 The coins of Yaudheya clan have been discovered at which place of Haryana?

(a) Hisar (b) Sonipat
(c) Bhiwani (d) Both (a) and (b)

58 Haryana was known by which name during Yaudheya Period? *HSSC 2024*

(a) Haritdesha (b) Harit Pradesh
(c) Bahudhanyak (d) Haritdhanyaka

59 The period of Yaudheya Republic is considered after

(a) Post Harappan period
(b) Post Mauryan period
(c) Post Gupta period
(d) Medieval period

60 The capital of Agar Republic was *PGT 2016*

(a) Agroha (b) Hisar
(c) Rewari (d) Hansi

61 Who was the founder of Vardhana dynasty?

(a) Pushyabhuti (b) Aditya Vardhana
(c) Naravardhana (d) Rajyavardhana

62 Vardhana dynasty was founded at which place of Haryana ? *HSSC 2015*

(a) Thanesar (b) Rohtak
(c) Panipat (d) Kurukshetra

63 Where did King Harshavardhana establish his capital in Kurukshetra in 700 AD? *HSSC 2021, HSSC Field Cadre 2020*

(a) Pehowa (b) Kannauj
(c) Ladwa (d) Jhansa

64 .... was near the Thanesar which was ruled by Harshavardhana. *Haryana Sub-Inspector 2018*

(a) Kurukshetra (b) Ambala
(c) Bhiwani (d) Panchkula

65 Chinese traveller Hiuen-Tsang visited Haryana during the reign of which ruler? *Haryana Clerk 2016*

(a) Harshavardhana
(b) Rajyavardhana
(c) Prabhakarvardhana
(d) Madhavardhana

66 Copper currency of Harshavardhana period has been found from which place of Haryana?

(a) Sonipat (b) Pehowa
(c) Agroha (d) Panipat

67 The inscriptions of Gurjara-Pratihara period have been found from

(a) Pehowa (b) Sonipat
(c) Mitathal (d) Agroha

68 Mauryan Stupas and relics have been found from which place of Haryana?

(a) Bhiwani (b) Hisar
(c) Agroha (d) Mitathal

69 The old name of Kurukshetra was *HSSC 2017*

(a) Narashtra (b) Thanesar
(c) Yugandhar (d) Rohitasgarh

70 Sthaneshvara was the ancient name of

(a) Sirsa (b) Sonipat
(c) Kurukshetra (d) Karnal

71 Thanesar was the capital of which famous ruler? *Haryana Police Constable 2018, PGT 2016*

(a) Harshavardhana
(b) Ashoka
(c) Chandragupta Vikramaditya
(d) Kanishka

72 Match the following

Ancient Remains	Location
A. Tablet of Shunga period	1. Agroha
B. Sculptures of Yaksha	2. Khokhrakot
C. Mints of Yaudheyan period	3. Palwal
D. Coins of Agreya Janapada	4. Sugh

Codes

	A	B	C	D		A	B	C	D
(a)	4	3	2	1	(b)	4	2	1	3
(c)	1	2	3	4	(d)	3	2	1	4

73 Match the following.

Ancient Name	Present Name
A. Sairishaka	1. Sirsa
B. Kanaud	2. Kaithal
C. Kapisthal	3. Panipat
D. Panprastha	4. Mahendragarh

Codes

	A	B	C	D		A	B	C	D
(a)	4	1	2	3	(b)	1	4	2	3
(c)	3	1	2	4	(d)	3	2	4	1

CORRECT ANSWERS

1. (a)	2. (d)	3. (d)	4. (a)	5. (c)	6. (a)	7. (d)	8. (a)	9. (b)	10. (a)
11. (a)	12. (b)	13. (c)	14. (a)	15. (b)	16. (a)	17. (a)	18. (b)	19. (a)	20. (a)
21. (b)	22. (c)	23. (a)	24. (b)	25. (d)	26. (d)	27. (c)	28. (d)	29. (b)	30. (a)
31. (c)	32. (d)	33. (a)	34. (a)	35. (b)	36. (b)	37. (b)	38. (c)	39. (d)	40. (b)
41. (a)	42. (a)	43. (a)	44. (d)	45. (c)	46. (d)	47. (b)	48. (a)	49. (d)	50. (a)
51. (d)	52. (a)	53. (b)	54. (c)	55. (a)	56. (d)	57. (b)	58. (c)	59. (b)	60. (a)
61. (a)	62. (a)	63. (b)	64. (a)	65. (a)	66. (a)	67. (a)	68. (b)	69. (b)	70. (c)
71. (a)	72. (a)	73. (b)							

CHAPTER 03

Medieval History of Haryana

- The beginning of medieval period of Haryana is considered with the invasion of Muslims in India.
- Haryana being in the Northern part of India was more affected by these invasions.
- **Mahmud of Ghazni** was prominent among the Muslim invaders, who used the territory of Haryana to pass during his invasion.

Turk Invasion and Haryana

- Jaipala was the famous king of Tomar dynasty. When he became the ruler of Tomar dynasty, Turk (Ottoman) invasions started from the North-Western part of India.
- After the decline of the power of the Caliph of Baghdad in the last phase of the 10th century, **Sabuktigin** established an independent kingdom in Ghazni.
- In 986 AD after defeating Jaipala, Sabuktigin established his suzerainty (domain) over Peshawar.
- In 997 AD after the death of Sabuktigin, Mahmud of Ghazni became ruler.

Invasion of Mahmud of Ghazni and Tomar Ruler Jaipala

- Mahmud of Ghazni invaded India for 17 times from 1000 to 1026 AD.
- Mahmud of Ghazni attacked **Thanesar** in 1009 AD. This was Mahmud of Ghazni's **sixth invasion of India** and the **first attack on Haryana** region.
- At that time, the ruler of Haryana region (Delhi and Hansi) was Tomar King Jaipala. Mahmud of Ghazni returned without any war.
- In 1014 AD, Mahmud of Ghazni attacked again on Thanesar.
- There was a war between the armies of King Jaipala and Mahmud of Ghazni on the banks of **Markanda river** near Shahabad, in which King Jaipala was defeated.
- Mahmud of Ghazni looted Thanesar. He destroyed the sculpture of **Chakra Swami** made of bronze and also damaged the Vishnu temple.
- During the invasion of Mahmud of Ghazni, his court poet, **Al-Biruni** was also with him.
- Al-Biruni in his book **Kitab-ul-Hind**, mentioned that Thanesar was an important centre for Hindus.

> Jaipala ruled Haryana region till 1021 AD even after Thanesar was conquered by Mahmud of Ghazni.

Invasion of Masud and Mawdud

- In 1030 AD, after Mahmud of Ghazni's death, his son Masud ascended the throne.
- In 1037 AD, Masud invaded **Hansi**, **defeated Tomar ruler Kumarapala Dev** and captured Hansi and nearby areas.
- In 1043 AD, Mawdud (son of Masud) invaded Haryana but was defeated by **Kumarapala Dev** with help from other rulers (Chauhan and Parmar), liberated Haryana from the Ghaznavid Empire.
- In 1051 AD, **Anangpala II** succeeded Kumarapala Dev and ruled until 1081 AD. He built **Surajkund** near Faridabad and **Mehrauli's iron pillar** was installed in Delhi.
- In 1081 AD, Ghazni's ruler Ibrahim invaded Haryana. **Tejpala**, Anangpala II's successor, accepted Ibrahim's subjection without a fight.

Rise of Chauhans in Haryana

- As the Tomar dynasty declined in Haryana, Shakambhari Chauhans (Chahamanas) from Rajasthan began moving towards Haryana and Delhi; some historians consider them **Agnikul Rajputs.**
- Around 1139 AD, Chauhan ruler Arnoraj of Ajmer with the title **Maharajadhiraj Parameshwara Shri** led an army to Haryana.
- He didn't fully abolish the Tomar kingdom but established suzerainty and converted it into **Karad State.**
- Chauhan ruler **Vigraharaj IV** defeated the Tomars, took control of Delhi and Hansi forts and became the real ruler of the region, though he granted feudal rights to the Tomars.

Rise of Bhadanakas and Haryana

- Bhadanakas were ancient people of Haryana, also known as **Bhadras** and their state included Gurugram, Mahendragarh (Haryana) and Alwar (Rajasthan).
- Bhadanakas were contemporaries of the Tomar and Chauhan rulers and spoke the **Apbhramsha** language. Historian Dashratha Sharma related Bhadras with **Ahir** caste.
- After defeating the Tomars, Chauhan ruler Arnoraj attacked Bhadanaka, but an inscription shows the Bhadanakas accepted his subjection without war.
- After Arnoraj's death and the ensuing power struggle, the Bhadanakas regained independent control.
- In the Mahabharata, Bhadanakas are mentioned alongside Rohtak, Agroha and Malwa (people settled between Ghaggar and Satluj) river and the region is now known as **Bhadra** (including presently Rewari and Bhiwani, Haryana).
- The Bhadra region, from the Mahabharata to the Middle Ages, was known at Bhadanaka.

Conflict between Bhadanakas and Chauhans

- After the death of Chauhan ruler Arnoraj, anarchy spread in the region. Bhadanakas became feudal lords by accepting Arnoraj's subjugation. However, by taking advantage of the chaos caused by the civil war for the throne, the Bhadanakas established independent rule.
- In 1151 AD, Chauhan ruler Vigraharaja-IV, after becoming the ruler, attacked the Bhadanakas and defeated them and forced them to accept his subjugation.
- However, under the reign of Amar Gangay, Prithviraj-II and Someshwar, Bhadanakas again became powerful and independent rulers.
- After the death of Someshwar, Prithviraj-III became the ruler of Chauhans. In 1182 AD, Prithviraj-III attacked Bhadanakas. Bhadanakas were defeated in this war. After this defeat, the rule of Bhadanakas ended.

Invasion of Muhammad Ghori and Haryana

- Muhammad Ghori, the ruler of Ghor, (a small state of Afghanistan) attacked India many times from 1175 to 1186 AD and established the possession on Punjab.
- Prithviraj-III was the ruler of Haryana and Delhi at the time of the invasion of Ghori.

Battles of Tarain

↓

First Battle

- In 1191 CE, Muhammad Ghori attacked Haryana. Prithviraj-III resisted this attack.
- In this battle, Muhammad Ghori was defeated by Prithviraj-III. This battle was fought in Taraori (Karnal) place of Haryana. It is known as the First Battle of Tarain (Taraori) in Indian history.
- The ruler of Delhi, Govindraj and many territories of North India were with Prithviraj III in First Battle of Tarain. After the Third Battle of Tarain, Prithviraj-III took over the fort of Tabarhind (Sirhind).

↓

Second Battle

- In 1192 CE, the Second Battle of Tarain was fought again between Prithviraj-III and Muhammad Ghori at Taraori. In this battle, Prithviraj-III was defeated.
- After this battle, Qutb-ud-din Aibak ruled over the region as a representative of Muhammad Ghori till 1206 AD and Agroha became a part of Muslim rule.
- After the death of Muhammad Ghori in 1206 AD, Aibak founded the Slave dynasty at Delhi.

Haryana after the Second Battle of Tarain

- In 1192 AD, after the Second Battle of Tarain, the people of Haryana fought against Muhammad Ghori under the leadership of **Rajput Sardar Vir Jatwan** in the region of Hansi-Hisar. In this battle Vir Jatwan died.
- The Governor of Rewari **Tejpala** fought against Muhammad Ghori in Ahirwal region, in which Afghan Commander Ibrahim died. Thereafter, Rewari was attacked by Ghori's Commander Qutb-ud-din Aibak, in which Tejpala died.

Haryana in Sultanate Period

During the Sultanate period, many dynasties ruled over Haryana. Some of these are

Sultanate Period

Slave dynasty	Khilji dynasty	Tughlaq dynasty	Sayyid dynasty	Lodi dynasty
(1206-1290 AD)	(1290-1320 AD)	(1320-1414 AD)	(1414-1451 AD)	(1451-1526 AD)

The Slave Dynasty

- The Slave dynasty (also known as Mamluk dynasty) was founded in 1206 AD by **Qutb-ud-din Aibak**, a slave of Muhammad Ghori. His capital was Lahore. Aibak acquired his authority in Haryana during his rule (1206-10 AD).
- After the death of Qutb-ud-din Aibak in 1210 AD, the Ahirs, Rajputs and Jats created obstacles against the central authority.

The major rulers of the Slave dynasty are described as follows

Iltutmish

• Successor of	Qutb-ud-din-Aibak
• Rule	Sultan of Delhi (1210-1236 AD)

- During his reign, Kubacha (ruler of Punjab) and Yaldoj (ruler of Ghazni) invaded the Haryana region.
- In 1227 AD, Kubacha declared suzerainty over **Sirsa**, but the ruler of Ghazni Yaldoj invaded this region and defeated Kubacha and annexed the conquered territory into the Ghazni kingdom.
- During the reign of Iltutmish, seven iqtas are mentioned in contemporary texts. These were (i) Delhi (ii) Rewari (iii) Hansi (iv) Narnaul (v) Sirsa (vi) Palwal (vii) Pipli.
- **Delhi, Hansi** and **Sirsa** were very large and important iqtas. Hansi's iqta was considered as the most important from military and economic point of view.

Ruknuddin and Razia Sultan

- Razia Sultan was the successor of Iltutmish after his death.
- Ruknuddin was an incompetent ruler due to which Razia Sultan, daughter of Iltutmish declared herself Nawab.
- Ruknuddin was the Sultan of Delhi for less than seven months in 1236 AD.
- The Jats and Rajputs of Northern Haryana opposed Razia's step of becoming Nawab.
- **Razia** abandoned the **Purdah System** and wore Choga (Kaba) and Kulah (Cap) like men.
- On 14th October, 1240 AD, Razia and her husband Altunia were captured and killed near Kaithal in Haryana.

> The tomb of Razia Sultan and Altunia is located in Kaithal. The tomb of Razia Sultan is the **first female monument in South Asia**.

Bahram Shah and Masood

• Successor of	Razia Sultan (after her death)
• Relation of Bahram Shah	Son of Iltutmish and brother of Razia
• Relation of Masood	Grandson of Iltutmish

- They both (Bahram Shah and Masood) were incompetent rulers. Their reign was very short. Nearly all the iqtas of Haryana were completely independent during their reign.

Nasiruddin Mahmud

• Successor of	Masood Shah
• Son of	Iltutmish

- He sent an army to subdue the powerful Mufti under Ulugh Khan (Balban) of **Hansi** but had to negotiate due to a revolt by the people of **Mewat**. Ulugh Khan was made **Aamir-e-Hajib**.
- Balban himself also wanted to establish control over Mewat, but was not successful. During 1248-49 AD, in order to punish the people of Mewat, Ulugh Khan reached Mewat with a huge army, but Ulugh Khan had to retreat during a fierce struggle.
- In 1257 AD, Mewati chieftain Malkha attacked Sultan Nasiruddin Mahmud's caravan near Hansi, coinciding with a Mongol invasion of Sindh and Lahore.
- In 1260 AD, Balban was sent again to suppress the Mewatis, but they couldn't be fully subdued during Nasiruddin's reign.

Ulugh Khan (Balban)

• Original name	Bahauddin
• Former slave of	Iltutmish
• Reign	1266-1287 AD as Ghiyas-ud-din Balban

- He protected Delhi from Mongol invasions and worked to improve the disorganised state of Haryana.
- He was given the title **Ulugh Khan** by Nasiruddin Mahmud.
- Balban destroyed **Mewat forests** to prevent Mewati rebels from hiding, eventually defeated them with a large army.
- He built a fort in Gopalgir to establish peace in Mewat.
- Military posts were established at Narnaul, Kanod, Sonipat, Thanesar, Hansi, Barwala and Dhatrat, including Afghan posts.

- New iqta areas, like **Sonipat**, **Kaithal** and **Shivalik** were created to strengthen civil administration.
- **Shamsuddin Kayumars** was the last Sultan of the Slave dynasty.

Khilji Dynasty

- In 1290 AD, Jalaluddin Firoz Khilji, who was the iqtedar of Kaithal became the Sultan of Delhi Sultanate.
- He made **Kilokhari** his capital.

The major rulers of the Khilji dynasty were as follows

Alauddin Khilji

- In 1296 AD, Jalaluddin's nephew and son-in-law, Alauddin Khilji (1296-1316 AD), became the Sultan of Delhi after killing Jalaluddin.
- In 1305 AD, Mongols invaded Haryana during the reign of Alauddin Khilji. Nanak, the Hindu General of Alauddin Khilji, stopped the Mongol army between Hansi and Sirsa.
- During the reign of Alauddin, **Hakim Ghazi Malik** of Dipalpur revolted and reached Sirsa, but was stopped by Khusro Shah's army.

> According to Amir Khusro, after capturing **Sirsa** and **Hansi**, Ghazi Malik went to **Lahrawat** *via* the route of Madina, Rohtak, Mandoni and Palam. After conquering Lahrawat, he made Haryana under his jurisdiction.

Qutbuddin Mubarak Shah

- Qutbuddin Mubarak Shah (1316-1320 AD) became the ruler after the death of Alauddin. He fell victim to a conspiracy, after which Nasiruddin Khusro Khan became the Sultan of Delhi on 15th April, 1320.
- During the reign of Mubarak Shah, all the iqtedars became independent one by one and their power started increasing.

Tughlaq Dynasty

- After defeating Nasiruddin Khusro Khan's army, Ghazi Malik took control of Delhi Sultanate in 1320 AD.
- Ghazi Malik became the **first Tughlaq Sultan of Delhi**, bearing the name of **Ghiyasuddin Tughlaq**.

The major rulers of the Tughlaq dynasty were as follows

Muhammad-bin-Tughlaq II

- Successor of — Ghiyasuddin Tughlaq
- Rule — 1325-1351 AD
- During his reign, the iqtas of Delhi, Hansi and Sirsa were very prominent. Muhammad Shah adopted a policy like Alauddin Khilji for administrative control.
- People of many areas of Haryana like Kaithal, Samana, Sunam, Gahram, etc. stopped giving revenues to him.

Firoz Shah Tughlaq

- Successor of — Muhammad-bin-Tughlaq
- Reign — 1351-1388 AD
- Son of — Hindu Princess of Dipalpur
- In his book **Futuhat-i-Firozshahi**, he had given a detailed description of destroying Gohana's Shiva temple, burnt religious books of Hindus and spread religious violence. He also forced many Hindus to become Muslims along with the Mewatis of Haryana.
- During the reign of Firuz Shah Tughlaq, there were many revolts in **Hisar** and **Safidon**, over which the Sultan got control through his army.
- He re-stablished Hisar as **Hisar-e-Firoza**, established **Fatehabad city** a few kilometre from Hisar, after the name of his son **Fateh Khan**.
- He established a third city, **Ferozabad Harni Kheda**, 12 miles from Sirsa.
- He also established a fort **Firoz Shah Palace** in Hisar. The fort had four gates – Delhi Gate, Nagauri Gate, Mauri Gate and Talaki Gate.
- He had built the **Gujari Mahal** in Hisar for his beloved Gujri Rani.

▲ A View of Gujari Mahal built by Firoz Shah Tughlaq

- According to historian Afiq, Firoz Shah Tughlaq replaced **Hisar-e-Firoza** as iqta in place of Hansi and included the area up to Hansi, Agroha, Fatehabad and Saloda of Sarasuti (Sirsa) in it.
- Firoz Shah Tughlaq directly took possession of the area between Hisar and Fatehabad, such as Jind, Tughlakpur, Dhatrat.
- Several Iktadars of Firoz Shah Tughlaq were mentioned in **Tarikh-i-Muhammadi**.

- **Yalkhan of Safidon, Tajuddin Turk of Rewari** and **Bahadur Nahar Mewati of Mewat** were prominent among them.

Nasiruddin Mahmud

- Grandson of — Firoz Shah Tughlaq
- Reign — 1394 -1412 AD (Last ruler of Tughlaq dynasty)
- His rule was left only up to Delhi.
- He was an unfit ruler. He made **Indri** and **Karnal** a joint iqta and handed it over to Amir Khabas Khan.

Timur Lang

- Invasion — Invaded India in 1398 AD
- Entered Haryana *via* — Ghaggar river after destroying Bhatner (present Hanumangarh)
- According to Timur's autobiography **Malfuzat-i-Timuri**, Timur had reached Delhi during the invasion of India *via* Sirsa, Fatehabad, Tohana, Munak, Kaithal, Asangha and Panipat.
- After his invasion, the foundation of the Tughlaq Empire became weaker. Anarchy spread everywhere and areas were becoming independent.
- Jalal and Hasan Khan emerged as the two most powerful kings of South-Western Haryana among the independent princely states.

SAYYID DYNASTY RULERS

Khizr Khan

Timur made his commander Khizr Khan as the Governor of Lahore, Multan and Dipalpur. In 1414 AD, Khizr Khan defeated Daulat Khan and captured Delhi and founded a new dynasty which is known as Sayyid dynasty. He died on 20th May, 1421 AD.

Mubarak Khan

- After the death of Khizr Khan, his son Mubarak Khan assumed the title of Shah. He also established the city of Mubarakabad on the banks of the Yamuna.
- **Jasrath Khokhar** invaded the present Haryana region during the time of Mubarak Shah, in which Mubarak Shah's empire suffered extensive damage.

Muhammad Shah

In 1433 AD, after the death of Mubarak Shah, his successor Muhammad Shah ascended the throne.

Alauddin Alamshah

- He was the last Sultan of the Sayyid dynasty.
- The Sayyid dynasty ruled for about 37 years.

Lodi Dynasty

The major rulers of the Lodi dynasty were as follows

Bahlul Lodi

- After the fall of Sayyid dynasty, he established the Lodi dynasty. He dominated Haryana during his reign (1451-89 AD).
- During his region, the revolt of Tatar Khan Yusuf, Mukti of Hisar and Lahore was considered more important among the rebellious muktas.

> During the Lodi period, Muktas were provincial chief or officials responsible for law and order and collection of taxes in their iqtas.

- There was a war between **Tatar Khan Yusuf** and **Prince Nizam Khan** near Ambala. Nizam Khan was a worthy prince of the Royal Army. Tatar Khan Yusuf was defeated in this war.
- After the defeat of Yusuf, Nizam Khan was appointed as Mukti of Hisar. Narnaul was under Ibrahim Sur and Omar Khan was the Mukti of Shahabad and Payal. Matthi Khan Sur was the head of a small estate near Hansi-Hisar region.

Sikander Lodi

- In 1489 AD, Nizam Khan (Sikander Lodi), ascended the throne of Delhi with the title of Sultan Sikander Shah. His pen-name was **Gulrukhi.**
- During his region, different Pargana/Region were ruled by different Ruler/Shikdar. Some of them are as follows

Region/Pargana	Shikdar/Ruler
Shamshabad, Thanesar, Shahabad Pargana	Mian Emad
Jalesar and Indri Pargana	Suleiman
Mahavan Pargana	Ali Khan
Jhajjar	Usman
Hansi region	Sheikh Syed
Panipat	Dariya Khan
Mewat	Hassan Khan

Ibrahim Lodi

- In 1517 AD, Ibrahim Lodi ascended the throne. He was the **last Sultan of Delhi Sultanate.**
- He misbehaved with the Muktis of Indri and Karnal, due to which they turned against him.

- Ibrahim Lodi was defeated by Babur in the **First Battle of Panipat** in April, 1526 AD. The tomb of Ibrahim Lodi is located in **Panipat**.
- Ibrahim Lodi was likely the first medieval ruler to be killed in battle.

Mughal Empire and Haryana

- The Mughal dynasty was founded by Babur. He was a resident of **Fargana** in Central Asia.
- In 1526 AD, Babur invaded India. At the time of this invasion, Hamid Khan, the Shikdar of Hisar-e-Firoza, also faced Babur's forces, but he was unsuccessful.
- At the time of Babur's arrival, Jalal Khan was the ruler of Tawadu (present day Rewari).

Babur and First Battle of Panipat

- The First Battle of Panipat (21st April, 1526) was fought between **Ibrahim Lodi** (last ruler of the Lodi dynasty) and **Babur** (ruler of Kabul), in which Babur defeated Ibrahim Lodi.
- After the battle, Babur established Mughal rule not only in Haryana but across India.
- Babur introduced Tulughma Warfare and Artillery for the first time in the Battle of Panipat.

Babur and Haryana Region

- In November, 1526 AD, Babur appointed Timur Sultan (Chagatai), Ahmed Parwanchi, Abul Fatah Turkman, and Mujahid Khan of Multan to suppress the rebellion of Afghan leader, Hamid Khan Sarangwani, near Hisar-e-Firoza.
- **Hassan Khan Mewati** was a rebel leader against Babur in Mewat. Babur faced Mewati warriors on 17th March, 1527 AD.
- Hassan Khan Mewati led these Mewati warriors.
- Mewatis were defeated in this war. Hassan Khan Mewati and his warriors were killed in the battlefield.
- After the Battle of Khanwa, Babur possessed the **title of Ghazi**. He also possessed the **title of Kalandar** for his generosity.

> Babur divided the conquered territories of Haryana into 4 governments (districts) i.e., Delhi Government, Mewat Government, Hisar Government and Sirhind Government.

- Babur handed over Narnaul to Timur and Shamshabad to Bugra Sultan.
- Many revolts took place during the last days of Babur's rule and the most terrible revolt took place in 1530 AD in **Kaithal**.
- In 1530 AD, Mandhar Rajputs of Kaithal, rebelled under the leadership of **Mohan Singh Mandhar** (the ruler of Mandhar region).
- Babur sent Sirhind's Governor Alikuli Hamdan to suppress the rebellion of Mandhar Rajputs, but he was defeated.
- Babur again sent an army under the leadership of Taram Beg and Naurang Beg, which defeated Mandhar Rajputs.

Humayun

- After the death of Babur on 26th December, 1530 AD, Humayun ascended the throne and he gave the Government of Mewat to his brother **Hindal Mirza** and Hisar and Sirhind to **Kamran Mirza**.
- Sher Shah Suri defeated Humayun in Battle of Chausa and established Afghan rule on Delhi in 1540 AD.
- He allowed the entire Haryana region to be in four governments (Delhi, Mewat, Hisar and Sirhind).
- After the death of Sher Shah, his son Islam Shah became the ruler of Delhi. His successors failed to rule over Delhi, due to which Humayun re-established his power in Haryana and Delhi in 1555 AD.
- Humayun died on 26th January, 1556 AD.
- The two most important monuments of Haryana, Lat and Humayun's Mosque are located in Fatehabad.

Sher Shah Suri

• Full Name	Farid Khan (Sher Shah Suri)
• Born	1486 CE, Sasaram, Bihar
• Reign	1540–1545 AD
• Dynasty	Suri Dynasty
• Legacy	Admired for military genius and reforms, influencing later rulers like Akbar
• Autobiography	Tuzuk-i-Sher Shahi
• Death	1545 AD, due to injuries from a gunpowder explosion

- Major Achievements
  - Defeated Humayun at Battle of Kannauj (1540)
  - Reformed administration and military system
  - Introduced Rupiya (silver coin) and land revenue reforms
  - Built Grand Trunk Road and Fort Rohtas

Akbar

- Born in October, 1542 AD
- Place Palace of Rana Virsal in Amarkot
- After the death of Humayun, Akbar became the Emperor of Mughal Empire in 1556 AD.
- Akbar divided his territory into 15 provinces to govern the state in a well-organised manner. At that period, there were 70 Parganas and 5 Governments i.e.,
  (i) Sarkar-e-Dilli (ii) Sarkar-e-Rewari
  (iii) Sarkare-Hisar-e-Firoza (iv) Sarkar-e-Mewati
  (v) Sarkar-e-Hind
- During Akbar's reign, a large part of Haryana came under the Delhi Province.
- **Rewari, Hisar, Sirhind** in Haryana and **Saharanpur** in modern day Uttar Pradesh came under the Delhi Province, while **Tijara, Narnaul** and **Sahar** came under Agra Province.
- Akbar introduced the new land system named as **Confiscation System**, which was implemented in only 8 provinces, including Delhi Province.

The **Second Battle of Panipat** took place between **Hemu** and **Akbar** on 5th November, 1556 in which Hemu was defeated and killed by Mughal army.

Jahangir

- Jahangir became the ruler of the Mughal Empire after Akbar's death in 1605 AD.
- He maintained the administrative system implemented by Akbar in Haryana.
- He developed mass facilities in Haryana. Several inns were built to provide facilities to the passengers.
- All the travellers who came to Haryana during the reign of Jahangir described it as a prosperous and well-governed state.
- He planted a large number of trees in Haryana in the first year of his rule.
- A war took place between Jahangir and his son, Khusro, at **Bherawal**.

Shah Jahan

- Shah Jahan became the ruler of the Mughal Empire after Jahangir's death in 1627 AD.
- He created a new unit of administration **Chakla**. It was made by mixing some parganas together. Mentions about **Hisar Chakla** is found from the reign of Shah Jahan. Kriparam was appointed as the ruler of Hisar Chakla.
- He separated the governments of Tijara and Narnaul from Agra Province and included them in Delhi Province.
- Shah Jahan and his eldest son, Dara Shikoh had special affection with Thanesar because their religious leader **Sheikh Chilli** resided here.

Hemchandra (Hemu)

- Hemchandra (Hemu) was a brave warrior and a resident of **Rewari**.
- He served as the Prime Minister of Adil Shah and took control of all powers due to Adil Shah's disqualification and inability.
- On 7th October, 1556 AD, Hemu captured Delhi's throne, adopted the title Maharaja **Vikramaditya** and became the Hindu Emperor of Delhi.
- Hemu was the last Hindu ruler to ascend the throne of Delhi.

Aurangzeb

- Shah Jahan's son Aurangzeb became Emperor of Delhi in 1658 AD. He was religiously staunch (orthodox).
- Aurangzeb imposed many taxes and committed religious atrocities towards the people of Haryana.
- In Haryana, Aurangzeb had to face the army of Meo under the leadership of Savlia Meo (resident of Sanhola). Savlia Meo used guerrilla technique against Aurangzeb's army.
- Aurangzeb appointed **Hathi Singh Badgurjar** as the administrative officer of Rewari region.

Dara Shikoh

- Dara Shikoh had a special attachment with the state of Haryana. He used to spend most of his time in Palwal near Faridabad. Siphar Shikoh, his eldest son was also born in Palwal.
- **Firoz Khan Mewati**, the famous Chieftain of Mewat served Dara Shikoh.
- Dara Shikoh also considered **Sheikh Chilli** as his mentor. After the death of Sheikh Chilli, Dara Shikoh built the Tomb of Sheikh Chilli in Thanesar, also known as the **Taj Mahal of Haryana**.

Jats Revolt in Mughal Period

- The rise of the Jats in Southern-Eastern Haryana during the Mughal rule was a significant event.
- Veer Gokula unified the Jats during Aurangzeb's reign, leading a revolt in 1669 AD. Rajaram succeeded Gokula in 1670 AD, continuing the fight against the Mughals.
- In 1688 AD, Rajaram's Jat soldiers attacked and destroyed Akbar's Tomb but Rajaram was killed by the Mughals.

- Rajaram's nephew, Chudaman, became his successor. After Aurangzeb's death, Mughal ruler Bahadur Shah recognised the Jats' political existence and the state of Bharatpur.

Mughals and the Revolt of Satnamis

- Satnamis revolt took place in Narnaul, between Tahir Khan and Satnamis in 1672 AD. In this revolt, Tahir Khan was defeated and Narnaul was possessed by the Satnamis.
- The Satnamis completely ended the Mughal rule in Narnaul.
- On 15th March, 1672 AD, a large army led by military chieftain Prince Mohammad Akbar, Hamad Khan and Yahia Khan Kamaluddin was sent to Narnaul , as a result the Satnamis were defeated.

- In 1721, **Badan Singh** consolidated Bharatpur and Surajmal elevated it to prominence, earning the title **Plato of Jats**. He expanded the Bharatpur kingdom into Mewat, Rohtak and Jhajjar.
- Surajmal, with his son Jawahar Singh, took over Farrukhnagar Fort on 12th December, 1763 but was killed in battle with Mughal commander **Najib-ad-Daulah**.
- **Jawahar Singh** succeeded Surajmal, but the empire saw the loss of Mewat, Farrukhnagar, Jhajjar and Bharatpur during his reign.
- Nawal Singh took over after Jawahar Singh's death, but the Bharatpur Empire was in decline.

Later Mughal Period and Haryana

Revolt of Banda Bairagi

- After Aurangzeb's death on 3rd March, 1707 AD, several revolts erupted in Haryana. Banda Bairagi (Banda Bahadur) took advantage and rebelled in 1709-10 AD, using **Sihrikhanda** near Sonipat as his headquarters.
- Following Guru Gobind Singh's Ji guidance, he renounced himself and took up arms, establishing a new headquarters at **Sadhaura** in Yamunanagar.
- He conquered **Sonipat**, **Kaithal**, **Thanesar**, **Sirhind**, **Shahabad** and **Kunjpura**.
- Banda Bairagi killed Vazir Khan, the Faujadar of Sirhind and took over Sirhind on 22nd May, 1707 AD. He made Sirhind as the headquarter of the new state won in the war.
- He was defeated in the **Battle of Karnal** and Indri on 26th October, 1710 AD and later in the Battle of Taraori by Firoz Khan Mewati.
- After Farrukhsiyar's attack, Banda Bahadur retreated to **Lohagarh Fort**, where he was killed by the Mughal Emperor on 9th June, 1715.

Ahir Rulers of Rewari

- Ahir rule in Rewari was established by **Nandram**, an Ahir from Garhi-Belna village, during Aurangzeb's reign.
- **Balakishan** succeeded Nandram as the Ahir ruler and Mughal Emperor Muhammad Shah granted him the title of **Shamsher Bahadur** for his bravery.
- After Balakishan's death, **Gujaramal** became the ruler of Rewari and was appointed Faujdar by Muhammad Shah, incorporating Hisar, Hansi, Narnaul, Jhajjar and Dadri into his kingdom, with **Gokulgarh** as his capital.
- Gujaramal was assassinated by Bahadur Singh and his son **Bhavani Singh** took over. However, his empire was reduced to just 23 villages after Jhajjar, Jaipur and Farrukhnagar rulers took control of his territories.

Invasion of Nader Shah

- The **Battle of Karnal** took place on 24th February, 1739, between Nader Shah (Iranian ruler) and Mughal emperor **Muhammad Shah**, resulted in a decisive Mughal defeat.
- Rewari ruler Rao Balakishan also supported the Mughal forces but killed in the battle.
- After the defeat, Muhammad Shah gave the **Koh-i-Noor** diamond to Nader Shah, who then left Delhi.
- After Nadir Shah's invasion, entire North India was in chaos and different rulers were trying to capture land under this advantage.
- Here are rulers who captured territory after his invasion

Territory Captured	Ruler/Clan
Faridabad	Surajmal (Jat ruler of Bharatpur)
Narnaul, Kanod (Mahendragarh)	Raja Madho Singh
Tawadu	Asadullah Khan
Bahadurgarh	Bahadur Khan
Jhajjar	Hasan Ali
Fatehabad, Rania and Sirsa	Mohd. Amir and Hasan Khan
Parts of Kurukshetra and Karnal (about 150 villages Indri, Pipli, Azimabad, Shahbad Parganas)	Najawat Khan
Panipat, Sirhind	Qutub Shah

Ballabhgarh Principality

- During Farrukhsiyar's reign, the Jats of Ballabhgarh led by **Chaudhary Gopal Singh**, controlled the Delhi-Agra route. His son, **Charan Das**, resisted Mughal subjugation.
- Charan Das' son **Ballabh Singh**, consolidated his rule from Faridabad to Delhi, building Ballabhgarh Fort as his headquarters.
- Ballabh Singh was killed by Akibat Khan on 29th Novermber, 1753, during the battle with Ahmad Shah Abdali and the Marathas. Thereafter, Akibat Khan captured Ballabhgarh Fort and renamed it as **Nizamgarh.**
- Few years later, Ballabh Singh's successor regained Ballabhgarh with the help of Surajmal.

Emergence of Maratha and Sikh Powers

- The emergence of Maratha power took place in South India in the 18th century. Emperor Alamgir gifted **Kurukshetra to the Marathas** on 15th October, 1754, to avoid a situation of war between the Mughals and the Marathas.
- The Marathas invaded the Mughals in the late 18th century. At the time of the Maratha invasion, the rulers of Rohtak and Hisar and the Ahir rulers of Rewari were defeated.
- The Marathas occupied the whole of Haryana in 1756-57 AD.
- Ahmad Shah Abdali's army entered India in 1756 AD. Abdali defeated Adina Begh and took the whole of Northern Haryana under the authority of the Sirhind Government.
- He invaded Faridabad on 1st February, 1757 AD. Ahmad Shah Abdali left India in April, 1757.

Authority over Haryana by Najib ad-Daulah

- Ahmad Shah Abdali appointed Najib ad-Daulah as ruler of Delhi and after Abdali's return, Najib ad-Daulah captured all of Haryana beyond Panipat.
- In January 1764 AD, the Sikhs defeated Durrani Governor Zain Khan and took control of **Ambala, Kurukshetra, Jind, Karnal** and **Panipat**. Maharaja Surajmal captured Mewat, Rohtak and Jhajjar.
- After Surajmal's death in 1764 AD, Najib ad-Daulah took over Sonipat, Mewat and Farrukhnagar.
- Jabit Khan, son of Najib ad-Daulah, ascended the throne but failed to maintain control.

Third Battle of Panipat

- Maratha forces besieged Panipat on 1st November, 1760 AD and Maratha chieftain **Sadashiv Rao Bhau** and **Vishwas Rao** also came there with their forces.
- The third Battle of Panipat took place between the Afghan invader **Ahmad Shah Abdali** and the Maratha forces on 14th January, 1761.
- In this war, the Commander of the Marathas was Sadashiv Rao Bhau. Maratha soldiers were defeated in this battle. After this battle, the decline of the Maratha Empire started.
- Before returning to Afghanistan, Abdali handed over the area of Jind, Ambala, Kurukshetra and Karnal to Zain Khan, who was the then Governor of Sirhind.
- The remaining other areas were occupied by Mughal Commander Najib.
- **Kala Amb** site of Haryana is associated with the Third Battle of Panipat.

Najaf Khan and Haryana

- After Maratha left Delhi, Najaf Khan ascended the throne of Delhi.
- He seized different territories from different rulers which are as follows

Territory	Area
Jat Territories	Rewari, Jhajjar, Gurugram
Rajput Territories	Kanod, Narnaul
Bhattin Territories	Hisar, Sirsa
Sikh Territories	Karnal, Ambala
Bilauch Territories	Sonipat, Rohtak, Bhiwani

- After the death of Najaf Khan, **Najaf Quli Khan** became an independent ruler and started governing from Gokulgarh.
- This created an atmosphere of chaos in Delhi. The Mughal ruler Shah Alam had to take help from the Scindia ruler of Gwalior, Mahadji Scindia, to deal with this situation.

Mahadji Scindia and Haryana

- Mahadji Scindia, ruler of the Maratha Empire, was expelled from Delhi in 1787 AD by a coalition of rulers.
- In 1789 AD, Mahadji Scindia attacked Delhi, imprisoned and killed Ghulam Qadir.
- After accepting Shah Alam's proposal, Mahadji Scindia established suzerainty over Haryana by defeating the Sikhs, Bhattis, Najaf Quli Khan and other regional rulers.

- Mahadji Scindia divided the state into four districts to properly administer his conquered territory. These districts were

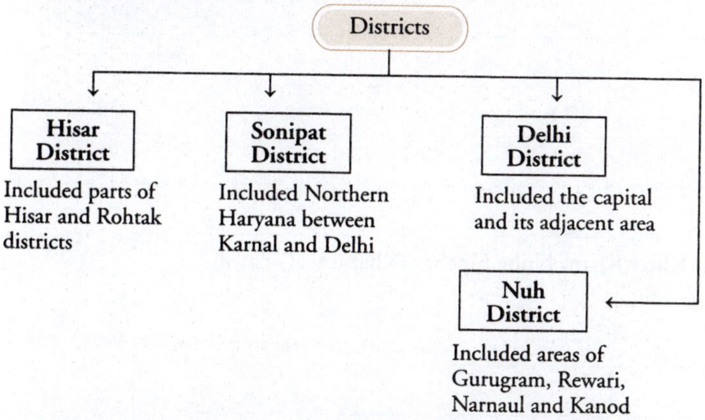

- After Mahadji Scindia's death in 1794, his successor, **Daulat Rao Scindia**, was ineffective and defeated in the Second Anglo-Maratha War.
- Daulat Rao Scindia signed the Treaty of **Surji-Arjungaon** on 30th December, 1803. The treaty was a settlement with the British East India Company.

George Thomas and Haryana

- George Thomas, born in 1756 AD in Ireland, arrived in Madras as a sailor in 1782 AD. He became an artillerist under the Nizam and was known as **Jahazi Sahib** in Haryana.
- In 1787 AD, he joined the military of **Begum Samru** of Sardhana (Meerut), married her daughter and was given the Tappal estate.

The Rise and Region of George Thomas

- In 1793 AD, George Thomas worked for Maratha Chieftain **Apa Khande Rao** under Mahadji Scindia of Gwalior State.
- Initially responsible for Mewat, he was later made the administrator of Jhajjar-Pataudi.
- After receiving Jagirs in **Panipat, Sonipat** and **Karnal**, George Thomas aimed to establish an independent state.
- In 1794 AD, he plundered **Bahadurgarh** and **Jhajjar** but was forced to leave Jind after a combined attack by Patiala, Nabha, Thanesar and Ladwa forces at the call of Sahib Kaur.
- His growing influence alarmed the Marathas, Paro and Sikhs, who trapped him near Jhajjar, but he escaped.
- George Thomas made Hansi fort his capital in 1797 AD and occupied large areas of **Gurugram, Rohtak, Sonipat, Hisar** and **Bhiwani.**
- George Thomas' state initially included 14 Parganas and 253 villages, with an additional 5 Parganas (151 villages) from the Marathas.
- George Thomas had 800 villages by the time of 1798 AD.
- Later, he controlled 1200 villages, including Hansi, Hisar, Bhiwani, Fatehabad and Georgegarh.
- He established a mint at Hansi, issuing coins called **Sikka-e-Sahib.**

Struggles and End of George Thomas

- In 1798 AD, George Thomas attempted to establish an **independent kingdom** by attacking Sikh ruler Maharaja Bhag Singh of Jind. The Sikh Ruler made him retreated but later he came and captured Jind successfully.
- The **Battle of Narnaund** took place in March, 1799 AD between the Sikhs and Hansi ruler George Thomas in the village of Narnaund, situated between Hansi and Jind.
- George Thomas surrendered to French General Bougain in January, 1801 AD, who took control of his kingdom and allowed him to enter British India. Thomas died near Baharampur in 1802 AD.

Books and Authors during Medieval Period

Author	Books
Chand Bardai	Prithviraj Raso
Ziauddin Barani	Tarikh-i-Firozshahi, Fatwa-e-Jahandari
Babur	Tuzuk-i-Babri, Diwan, Risal-i-Usaj
Gulbadan Begum	Humayunnama
Jahangir	Tuzuki-i-Jahangiri
Amir Khusrau	Kiranusain, Mifataulfatuh, Devalrani Khizr Khan, Nuhe Sipehar, Khazain-ul- Fatuh, Tughlaqnama
Al-Biruni	Tehqeedq-i-Hind
Ibn Battuta	Rehla
Firoz Shah Tughlaq	Futuhat-i-Firoz Shahi
Isami	Futuh-us-Salatin
Taimur	Malfuzat-e-Taimuri
Dara Shikoh	Majma-ul-Bahrain, Bhagavad Gita, Sirr-e-Akbar, Yogavasistha, Safinat-al-Auliya, Shakinat-al-Auliya
Abul Fazl	Bahar-e-Damish, Kalila and Dimna, Razmanama, Akbar Nama
Krishnadevaraya	Amuktamalyada, Jambati Kalyanam
Tulsidas	Vinaya Patrika, Ramcharitmanas, Barvai Ramayana, Parvati Mangal, Ramlala Nahchu
Kabir	Sakhi, Bijak, Rekhta, Gyan Sagar
Malik Muhammad Jayasi	Akhravat, Akhiri Kalam, Padmavat

CHECK CHAPTER KNOWLEDGE

1 Haryana was under the rule of which dynasty when the Ghaznavis attacked the North-West of India? *HSSC 2024*

(a) Tughlaq (b) Gupta
(c) Pushyabhuti (d) Tomar

2 In which year, Mahmud of Ghazni invaded Thanesar?

(a) 1004 AD (b) 1006 AD
(c) 1009 AD (d) 1012 AD

3 Which of the following places was said to be the important centre of Hindus in the book of Al-Biruni? *PGT 2016*

(a) Thanesar
(b) Hathnikund
(c) Karnal
(d) Surajkund

4 Masud of Ghazni defeated which Tomar ruler in 1037 AD? *HSSC 2023*

(a) Tejpala (b) Kumarapala Dev
(c) Vigrahapala (d) Anangpala

5 Who built Surajkund near Faridabad?

(a) Anangpala-II (b) Tejpal
(c) Kumarapala (d) Vigrahapala

6 Who assumed the title 'Maharajadhiraj Parameshwara Shri'?

(a) Arnoraj (b) Tejpal
(c) Kumarapala (d) Vigrahapala

7 Which Chauhan ruler captured Delhi and Hansi?

(a) Vigraharaj-IV (c) Arnoraj
(b) Ajayraj (d) Vigrahapala

8 Which of the following parts was related to Bhadanaka people? *HSSC 2021*

(a) Gurugram
(b) Mahendragarh
(c) Alwar
(d) All of the above

9 Which of the following regions is known as 'Bhadra region'?

(a) Kurukshetra-Hisar region
(b) Rohtak-Hisar region
(c) Rewari-Bhiwani region
(d) None of the above

10 Who led the resistance against Muhammad Ghori in theAhirwal region?

(a) Qutb-ud-din Aibak
(b) Iltutmish
(c) Tejpala, the Governor of Rewari
(d) Balban

11 At which place battles were fought between Muhammad of Ghor and Prithviraj Chauhan in 1191 and 1192 AD? *Haryana Clerk 2016*

(a) Gharaunda (b) Panipat
(c) Taraori (d) Kurukshetra

12 Who won the first Battle of Tarain? *Patwari Tax Inspector 2016*

(a) Balban
(b) Hemchandra
(c) Prithviraj Chauhan
(d) Qutb-ud-din Aibak

13 Taraori, where the first Battle of Tarain, took place, is located in which place of Haryana?

(a) Kurukshetra (b) Karnal
(c) Hansi (d) Hisar

14 After whose defeat, Agroha region became a part of a Muslim ruler in the Second Battle of Tarain? *TGT 2015*

(a) Prithviraj-I (b) Prithviraj-II
(c) Prithviraj-III (d) Prithviraj-IV

15 Who became the representative of Muhammad of Ghor after the Second Battle of Tarain?

(a) Razia Sultan (b) Iltutmish
(c) Qutb-ud-din Aibak (d) None of these

16 Who founded 'Slave dynasty' in 1206 AD?

(a) Iltutmish (b) Qutb-ud-din Aibak
(c) Ruknuddin (d) Razia Sultan

17 Which of the following was the capital of Qutb-ud-din Aibak, the founder of Slave dynasty?

(a) Lahore (b) Delhi (c) Agra (d) Lucknow

18 During the rule of which ruler of Slave dynasty, Kubacha, the ruler of Punjab and Yaldoz, the ruler of Ghazni, invaded Haryana region?

(a) Razia Sultan
(b) Qutb-ud-din Aibak
(c) Iltutmish
(d) Ruknuddin

19 Which of the following were prominent Iqtas during the reign of Iltutmish? *HSSC 2023*
(a) Delhi, Narnaul (b) Rewari, Sirsa
(c) Hansi, Palwal (d) All of these

20 In which place of Haryana, Razia Sultan and her husband, Altunia were captured and killed?
(a) Rewari (b) Sirsa
(c) Kaithal (d) Hansi

21 Who constructed the Gopalgir Fort on the border of Delhi-Gurugram?
(a) Razia Sultana (c) Qutb-ud-din Aibak
(b) Iltutmish (d) Balban

22 Jalauddin Firoz Khilji, the founder of Khilji dynasty, made which place his capital?
(a) Sonipat (b) Gopalgiri
(c) Kilokhari (d) Hansi

23 Which General of Alauddin Khilji stopped the Mongol army between Hansi and Sirsa? *HSSC 2023*
(a) Angad (b) Nanak
(c) Lakshman (d) Ranjit

24 Due to whose unsatisfactory policies, farmers of many places of Haryana stopped giving revenue to that ruler?
(a) Muhammad-bin-Tughlaq
(b) Balban
(c) Ghazi Malik
(d) Razia Sultana

25 Fatehabad was founded after whose name? *Panchayat Officer 2016*
(a) Fateh Khan (b) Firoz Shah
(c) Shah Jahan (d) Pushyabhuti

26 Firoz Shah Tughlaq founded which city of Haryana? *Haryana Patwari 2015*
(a) Mewat (b) Hisar
(c) Mahendragarh (d) Jhajjar

27 Fatehabad district derives its name from its headquarters town, which was established by in 14th century, after his son Fateh Khan. *Haryana Tehsil Welfare Officer 2018*
(a) Ghiyasuddin Tughlaq
(b) Alauddin Khilji
(c) Firoz Shah Tughlaq
(d) None of the above

28 Against which ruler a revolt took place in the village of Gohana? *TGT 2016*
(a) Balban
(b) Firoz Shah Tughlaq
(c) Babur
(d) Alauddin Khilji

29 Timur Lang's invasion took place in which place of Haryana? *Bus Conductor 2017*
(a) Tohana (b) Sirsa
(c) Fatehabad (d) All of these

30 Tomb of Ibrahim Lodi is located at *HSSC 2024*
(a) Pinjore (b) Rewari
(c) Gurugram (d) Panipat

31 The first Battle of Panipat was fought in 1526 AD between *HSSC 2017*
(a) Akbar and Ibrahim Lodi
(b) Babur and Ibrahim Lodi
(c) Humayun and Ibrahim Lodi
(d) Akbar and Hemu

32 Where are the two most important monuments of the state 'Lat and Humayun's Mosque' located? *HSSC 2023*
(a) Kurukshetra (b) Naurangabad
(c) Fatehabad (d) Mahendragarh

33 Who ascended the throne after the death of Babur?
(a) Akbar (b) Islam Shah
(c) Humayan (d) Ibrahim Lodi

34 Which of the following ruler of Haryana was famous by the name 'Hemu'? *Haryana Clerk 2016*
(a) Hemchandra Vikramaditya
(b) Muhammad of Ghor
(c) Harshavardhana
(d) Akbar

35 The second Battle of Panipat took place in which year between the Mughal forces of Akbar and Hemu? *HSSC 2017*
(a) 1526 AD (b) 556 AD
(c) 1192 AD (d) 1911 AD

36 The second Battle of Panipat was fought between *HSSC 2017*
(a) Babur and Ibrahim Lodi
(b) Abdali and Maratha
(c) Hemu and Akbar
(d) Maharana Pratap and Akbar

37 Mughal emperor Akbar divided his territory into how many subahs provinces?
(a) 10 (b) 12
(c) 15 (d) 20

38 During Akbar's reign Tijara and Narnaul came under which province?
(a) Delhi Province
(b) Agra Province
(c) Awadh Province
(d) Jaipur Province

39 Who built several inns for passengers in Haryana during Mughal period?
(a) Jahangir (b) Humayun
(c) Sher Shah (d) Babur

40 Which Mughal ruler created a new unit of administration 'Chakla'? *HSSC 2023*
(a) Jahangir (b) Humayun
(c) Akbar (d) Shah Jahan

41 The tomb of Sheikh Chilli, also known as 'Taj Mahal of Haryana', was made by
(a) Shah Jahan (b) Dara Shikoh
(c) Firoz Shah (d) Ahmad Shah

42 Who became Mughal ruler after Shah Jahan?
(a) Akbar (b) Sher Shah
(c) Band Bairagi (d) Aurangzeb

43 Who was known as 'Plato of Jats'?
(a) Rajaram (b) Veer Gokula
(c) Chudaman (d) Surajmal

44 Satnamis revolt took place in which year?
(a) 1526 AD (b) 1556 AD
(c) 1600 AD (d) 1672 AD

45 Banda Bairagi renounced his retirement and took the path of war at the behest of which Guru? *HSSC 2019*
(a) Guru Teg Bahadur
(b) Guru Arjan Dev
(c) Guru Gobind Singh
(d) Guru Nanak Dev

46 Ahir rule was established at which place of Haryana during the period of Aurangzeb?
(a) Hisar (b) Ballabhgarh
(c) Rewari (d) Kurukshetra

47 The Battle of Karnal took place in which year? *HSSC 2015*
(a) 1723 AD (b) 1756 AD
(c) 1789 AD (d) 1739 AD

48 The Battle of Karnal was fought between *HSSC 2018*
(a) Nader Shah and Shah Alam
(b) Nader Shah and Muhammad Shah
(c) Shah Alam and Muhammad Shah
(d) Nader Shah and Aurangzeb

49 The third Battle of Panipat took place in which year? *HSSC 2020*
(a) 1526 AD (b) 1556 AD
(c) 1761 AD (d) 1739 AD

50 Which place is related to the third Battle of Panipat? *HSSC 2017*
(a) Salarganj Gate (b) Kabuli Bag
(c) Kos Minar (d) Kala Amb

51 The third Battle of Panipat was fought between whom? *Haryana CET 2023*
(a) Shah Alam and Mohammad Shah
(b) Guru Gobind Singh and Aurangzeb
(c) Nadir Shah and Aurangzeb
(d) Ahmad Shah Abdali and Maratha

52 During 1789-94 AD, Delhi and Haryana were under the rule of
(a) Mahadji Scindia (b) Madhav Rao Scindia
(c) Rajaji Scindia (d) Raja Umed Singh

53 Who among the following is popularly known as 'Jahazi Sahib' in Haryana?
(a) Mahadji Scindia (b) Apa Khande Rao
(c) George Thomas (d) Hemchandra

54 What was the primary reason for Aurangzeb's failure to capture the Deccan region?
(a) Inferior Mughal military technology
(b) Lack of adequate resources
(c) Relentless Maratha resistance and guerrilla warfare
(d) Internal rebellions within the Mughal court

55 Which of the following poets wrote the book 'Akbar Nama'? *HSSC CTET 2024*
(a) Noor Jahan (b) Jahangir
(c) Abul Fazl (d) Mehrunnisa

CORRECT ANSWERS

1. (d)	2. (c)	3. (a)	4. (b)	5. (a)	6. (a)	7. (a)	8. (d)	9. (c)	10. (c)
11. (c)	12. (c)	13. (b)	14. (c)	15. (c)	16. (b)	17. (a)	18. (c)	19. (d)	20. (c)
21. (d)	22. (c)	23. (b)	24. (a)	25. (b)	26. (b)	27. (c)	28. (b)	29. (d)	30. (d)
31. (b)	32. (c)	33. (c)	34. (a)	35. (b)	36. (c)	37. (c)	38. (a)	39. (a)	40. (d)
41. (b)	42. (d)	43. (d)	44. (d)	45. (c)	46. (c)	47. (d)	48. (b)	49. (c)	50. (d)
51. (d)	52. (a)	53. (c)	54. (c)	55. (c)					

Modern History of Haryana

- After **George Thomas**' death in 1802, the East India Company moved forward to the Haryana region.
- The British East India Company exploited political instability in India to gain political power.
- Haryana had been ceded to the British East India Company by Daulat Rao Scindia under the Treaty of Surji-Arjungaon.

British East India Company Rule in Haryana

- The British East India Company included Haryana under the Bengal Presidency in 1805 and divided it into two parts for administrative and political reasons.
- The smaller part called **Assigned Territories** remained directly under the company's control.
- The larger part was redistributed to loyal local rulers in the following manner

Region/Area	Recipient
Ballabhgarh	Raja Hira Singh
Farrukhnagar	Nawab Ahmed Ali Khan
Pataudi Pargana	Faiz Khan
Loharu and Firozpur-Jhirka	Ahmad Baksh Khan
Pargana of Hodal	Murtaza Khan
Pargana of Palwal	Muhammad Ali
Rewari Pargana (87 villages of Istamrari Jagir)	Rao Tej Singh

- Rohtak, Meham, Beri, Hisar, Hansi, Agroha, Barwala, Jamalpur and Tosham Parganas were initially given to **Bambu Khan** but he faced a public uprising. Thus, these Parganas were transferred to **Ahmad Baksh**, who also left due to the same uprising.
- **Abdul Samad Khan** was later appointed as administrator, but the uprising persisted. Ultimately, the responsibility was handed over to **Nawab Muhammad Ali Khan**.

Istamrari Estates were small feudal states in 17th and 18th century Rajputana.

Revolts against British Rule in Haryana by Sikh Confederacy

- **Guru Dutt Singh** (ruler of Ladwa) and **Bhanga Singh** (ruler of Thanesar) formed a Union of Sikh rulers to revolt against the British.
- A fierce battle occurred between British Commander Colonel Burn and the Sikh confederates in which **Sher Singh**, the ruler of Budiya, was killed.
- The Sikh Confederacy's power ended after Guru Dutt Singh was defeated by Colonel Burn on 20th April, 1805 in Karnal.

Resistance Faced by British in Southern Haryana

- The revolts persisted in Southern Haryana, with people refused to pay taxes and used guerrilla warfare, which delayed British suppression.
- The British took 7 years to establish control over the Mewat region, eventually consolidated their administration in Southern Haryana.

- The Bhatti rulers of Sirsa and Fatehabad in Western Haryana resisted British subjugation.
- In 1809 AD, **Colonel Adams** defeated the two rulers. After the battle, Sirsa and Rania were returned to Jabita Khan but the Princely State Fatehabad was taken from Bahadur Khan.

Administrative Changes in Haryana by the British

- In 1819 AD, the British East India Company introduced administrative reforms. A Commissioner, under the name **Resident**, was appointed and granted political powers.
- The British also divided the ceded part into **three sub-divisions**

Northern Area: It consisted of area Rohtak, Hisar, Panipat and Sonipat.

Central Area: It consisted of Delhi region.

Southern Area: It consisted of Rewari, Gurugram, Hodal, Palwal and Mewat.

- British rule made Haryana, a part of the North-Western province in1833-34 AD and **Agra** was made as its centre.

Mahalwari Settlement

- The Mahalwari System was a **land revenue system** introduced by Holt Mackenzie.
- It was implemented in 1822 AD as a part of the British efforts to standardise land revenue systems in North-Western regions, including parts of Haryana.
- It relied on collective responsibility for a group of villages (mahal), with the village headman accountable for revenue payment.
- Land revenue was assessed for each mahal and its inhabitants, with assessments typically fixed every 30 years.
- Mahalwari system was a modified version of the zamindari system, focused on village-level autonomy.

Major Revolts against the East India Company

Revolt of Chhachhrauli

- The Princely State of Chhachhrauli, located in Ambala region, spanned an area of 63 sq km. It was ruled by **Baghel Singh** of the **Karora Singhia Misl**.
- Its ruler passed away in 1809 AD, after which **Jodh Singh**, the King of Kalsia and the eldest chief of Karora Singhia Misl, ascended the throne.
- Baghel Singh's widow, **Rani Ramkaur**, sought British help to remove Jodh Singh.
- David Ochterlony (English resident of Delhi) ordered the British Army to attack on Chhachhrauli and Jodh Singh was retreated. The state was given to Rani Ramkaur.

Rani Ramkaur's ineffective rule led to Jodh Singh's return in 1818 AD. Later, **Brigadier General Arnold** led the British army to attack Chhachhrauli.

Jodh Singh's revolt against the British was defeated and Chhachhrauli was merged into the British kingdom.

Revolt of Rania

- **Jabit Khan**, ruler of the Princely State of Rania in Hisar, accepted British subjugation in 1810 AD.
- The British returned Rania and Sirsa to Jabit Khan, but he defied the company's orders.
- The British defeated Jabit Khan during the War of Rania in 1818 AD. The Princely State of Hisar was then brought under British control.

The Peasant Uprisings in Rohtak, Gurugram and Hisar

- In 1824 AD, following the British defeat in the First Burma War (1824-26), widespread dissatisfaction arose among Haryana's farmers due to harsh recovery methods.
- Peasants revolted by looting government treasuries and banks, while the people of Bhiwani attacked army vehicles.
- **Maharaja Suraj Mal** rallied the rebels and led the battle, but they were ultimately defeated by British army. Following their defeat, the British forces subjected the peasants to brutal torture.

Revolt of Jind

- In 1813 AD, due to Bhagat Singh's paralysis, his son Pratap Singh was appointed executive ruler of Jind, but the British made **Rani Saudrahi** the administrator.
- On 23rd June, 1814, **Pratap Singh** killed her to establish his power. After the British army arrived, Pratap Singh retreated to the Banawali Fort, under Ranjit Singh's region.
- After Bhagat Singh's death in 1819 AD, **Fateh Singh** became king of Jind, succeeded by his son **Sangat Singh** in 1822 AD.
- Sangat Singh was succeeded by his cousin **Sarup Singh**, who aligned with the British, allowing the company to establish firm control over Jind.

Banawali Revolt

- After Sangat Singh's death, the British took over his territories in 1835 AD.
- The people of Banawali revolted under the leadership of **Gulab Singh Gill**, the brother-in-law of Pratap Singh.
- British officers attacked and killed Gulab Singh Gill in March, 1835 AD. His widow, Maisul Rani and their son Dal Singh, were subsequently arrested.

Kaithal Revolt

- Kaithal, located in Northern Haryana, was founded in 1763 AD by **Gurbaksh Singh**.
- **Desa Singh**, his successor, freed Kaithal from Afghan invaders, but his son **Lal Singh** accepted British subordination.
- **Pratap Singh** (son of Lal Singh) ascended the throne in 1818 AD, followed by his brother **Uday Singh** in 1823 AD.
- After Uday Singh's death in 1843 AD, Gulab Singh, the ruler of Princely State Arnoli asserted his authority over Kaithal, but the British rejected it.
- **Rani Surajkaur** (widow of Uday Singh) and **Sahiba Kaur**, (Uday Singh's mother) fought to protect the state.
- The British ordered Kaithal's handover to the East India Company on 23rd March, 1843.

> British forces, led by **Officer Clarke**, surrounded **Kaithal** on 10th April, 1843. Despite resistance from **Rani Sahiba Kaur**, Surajkaur and the people, Kaithal was annexed on 16th April, 1843 with help from the rulers of Jind, Patiala and Nabha.

Ladwa Revolt

- **Sardar Singh** founded the state of Ladwa in Haryana in 1763 AD.
- **Gurudutt Singh** became the ruler of Ladwa in 1803 AD and opposed British policies. He was succeeded by his son **Ajit Singh**.
- Ajit Singh was tough opponent of the British. Thus, he was declared a rebel without any basis and imprisoned in Saharanpur jail in 1845 AD.
- Ajit Singh escaped prison in 1845-46 AD, fought several battles and arrested British General Henry Smith.
- During this period, Ajit Singh died and his Princely State faced a shift in control.

Principalities Annexed by the British East India Company

Principality	Annexation	Reason for Annexation
Chhachhrauli	1818	Incapability of Rani Ramkaur, interference of Jodh Singh
Rania	1818	Revolt by Nawab Jabit Khan
Ambala	1824	Death of Daya Kaur, widow of Raja Gurbaksh Singh
Radaur	1828	Death of Indra Kaur, widow of Raja Dayal Singh
Dialgarh	1829	Death of Mai Daya Kaur, widow of Raja Bhagwan Singh
Thanesar (2/5th Part of Bhagal Singh)	1832	Death of Raja Jamiyat Singh without successor
Bufaul	1838	Death of Raja Harnam Singh without successor
Kaithal	1843	Death of Raja Uday Singh without successor
Chalaudi	1844	Death of Ramkaur, widow of Raja Baghel Singh
Ladwa	1845	Revolt by Raja Ajit Singh
Thanesar (3/5th Part of Bhagal Singh)	1850	Death of Chand Kaur, widow of Raja Fateh Singh
Halahar	1850	Death of Raja Fateh Singh without successor
Dayalgarh (Part of Mai Sukhan)	1851	Death of Mai Sukhan, widow of Raja Bhagwan Singh

Revolt of 1857 and Haryana

The revolts which took place in Haryana during 1857 are discussed below

Revolt in Gurugram

- On 13th May, 1857, 300 soldiers marched from Delhi towards Gurugram and looted the government treasury. **William Ford**, the English Collector, failed to stop them.
- **Rao Tularam** and his brother **Gopal Dev** organised the Ahirs and fought against the British at **Nasirpur**.
- Ahmad Ali of Farrukhnagar and Nahar Singh of **Ballabhgarh** joined the revolt but were accused of having British ties.
- In June, 1857, **Major Aden**, the English Resident of Jaipur, tried to suppress the Mewati rebellions with a large force and artillery.
- Revolts occurred in Sohna and Tawadu and **Major Aden** eventually had to retreat.

Revolt in Rohtak

- The 1857 revolt in Rohtak began at the end of May, led by courageous **Ranghars.** British control over Rohtak nearly ended.
- The British sent an army from Ambala, but their army also rebelled.
- In August, 1857, a contingent led by **Hudson** fought against Subedar Birasat near Rohtak at Kharkhoda, where Birasat was defeated.
- The ruler of Jind assisted Hudson in capturing Rohtak, which was merged with Jind.
- However, Hudson had to return to Delhi due to the weakening position of the British.

Revolt in Hisar and Sirsa

- The 1857 revolt began in Hisar in May, led by military troops of **Haryana Light Infantry** in Hisar, Sirsa and Hansi.
- The British army, led by **General Warne Courtland**, faced the revolutionaries from Ferozepur.
- In June, 1857, a battle took place between the British and revolutionaries led by **Noor Mohammad Khan**, Nawab of Udha village, in which the British defeated the revolutionaries.
- Following the battle, the British tortured the people of **Chatravan** village, where an English officer, **Hillard**, was killed by the villagers.
- The British also tortured people in **Khirka village** and set it on fire.
- **Hukamchand** and **Munir Beg** led the revolt in Hansi. When the British failed to suppress it, General Courtland took charge and forced the revolutionaries to retreat.
- The revolt ceased after the British took over Delhi.

Revolt in Ambala

- In Haryana, the Revolt of 1857 was **first started in Ambala.** The sepoy mutiny of Meerut which started on 10th May, 1857, reached Ambala Cantt in Haryana on 13th May, 1857.
- The soldiers of Ambala Cantonment planned to loot the armoury and march towards Delhi, but a soldier named **Sham Singh** informed the British authorities about this plan.
- This agitated the British and they beset the Indian soldiers and forced them to surrender.

Revolt in Thanesar

- The 1857 revolt also took place in Thanesar, near Panipat and Kurukshetra, with **Imam Ali Kalandar** leading the revolt in Panipat. The people in Panipat nearly eliminated British control.
- The main GT Road, connecting Punjab and Northern India to Delhi, passed through Patiala, Kunjpura, Jind and Karnal.
- The British attacked Karnal but were defeated and forced to retreat. **General Ansen**, a British officer, died during a battle near Panipat. By the end of May, 1857, all of Haryana, except Ambala, was liberated from British influence.
- The local rulers and people pledged allegiance to Mughal Emperor **Bahadur Shah Zafar** and followed his orders.

Role of Principalities in the Revolt of 1857

- There are a number of factors for the failure of the 1857 revolt such as non-cooperation of Princely States, insufficient arms along with lack of leadership, etc.
- At the time of the revolt, there were mainly three types of Princely States in Haryana and they were as follows

Princely States in Haryana (At Revolt Time)

1. Pro-Revolutionary Princely States
2. Pro-British Princely States
3. Neighbouring Princely States

1. Pro-Revolutionary Princely States

Jhajjar

• Area	1,230 sq miles; the largest Princely State
• Ruler during 1857 revolt	Abdurrahman Khan (Since 1845)
• Ruler hanged on	23rd December, 1857 at Red Fort, Delhi

- The regions of Bawal, Kanti and Kanina in Southern Jhajjar were given to Raja of Nabha.
- The area of Narnaul was handed over to the Raja of Patiala.

Ballabhgarh

• Area	190 sq miles (in 1857)
• Borders	Yamuna river on one side; Mewat region to the South; rest annexed by the British
• Ruler during 1857 revolt	Nahar Singh

- After the revolt, Nahar Singh was arrested on 6th December, 1857, taken to the Red Fort in Delhi and tried.
- He was sentenced to death and hanged at Chandni Chowk in Delhi on 9th January, 1858.

Farrukhnagar

• Area	22 sq miles (in 1857)
• Ruler during 1857 revolt	Ahmad Ali Ghulam Khan

- After the revolt, Ahmad Ali Ghulam was arrested on 22nd October, 1857 and tried at the Red Fort, Delhi.
- He was sentenced to death by Brigadier **General Shawarz.**
- Ahmad Ali Ghulam was hanged on 23rd January, 1858 at Chandni Chowk, Delhi.

Bahadurgarh

• Area	48 sq miles. Smallest Princely State in Haryana
• Former name	Sarrafabad (including Dadri and Bahadurgarh regions)
• Ruler during 1857 revolt	Nawab Bahadur Jung

- After the revolt, he was deported to Lahore and received an annual pension of ₹ 1,000.

Mewat, Rewari and Hansi

• Mewat	Taken over by the British during the 1857 revolt
• Ruler of Mewat	Nawab Sadruddin Mewati
• Rewari revolt leaders	Rao Tularam, Rao Krishna Gopal and Rao Gopal Dev
• Hansi revolt leader	Lala Hukamchand (hanged in front of his house after the revolt)

Leaders of the Revolt of 1857 in Haryana

Region	Place	Leader
Gurugram	Gurugram	*No leader*
	Mewat	Sadruddin (Farmer)
	Ahirwal	Tularam (Main Feudal Lord)
	Palwal	Gafur Ali (Trader), Harsukh Rai (Farmer)
	Faridabad	Dhanu Singh (Farmer)
	Ballabhnagar	Nahar Singh (Main Feudal Lord)
	Farrukhnagar	Ahmad Ali (Main Feudal Lord, Ghulam Muhammad (Government Employee)
	Pataudi	Akbar Ali (Main Feudal Lord)
Panipat	Panipat	Imam Ali Kalandar (Maulvi)
	Karnal	*No Leader*
	Jalmana	*No Leader*
Rohtak	Kharkhoda	Bisarat Ali (Farmer, Risaldar)
	Sampla	Sabar Khan (Farmer)
	Dujana	Hasan Ali (Main Feudal Lord)
	Dadri	Bahadur Jang (Feudal Lord)
	Jhajjar	Abdul Ahmed (General of Nawab of Jhajjar), Abdul Rahman (Main Feudal Lord)
Hisar	Bhattu	Muhammad Azam (Government Employee)
	Hansi	Hukumchand (Government Employee)
	Rania	Noor Muhammad Khan (Main Feudal Lord)
	Loharu	Aminuddin (Main Feudal Lord)
Thanesar	Thanesar	*No Leader*
	Ladwa	*No Leader*
Delhi	Delhi Khas	Bahadur Shah (Main Feudal Lord)
	Sonipat	*No Leader*
Other Places	Ambala	*No Leader*
	Jagadhari	*No Leader*
	Ropar	Mohan Singh

2. Pro-British Princely States

Jind

• Founded in	1763 AD
• Founded by	Gajpat Singh, grandson of Phool Singh
• Area	376 sq miles (covering both Haryana and Punjab)

- **Gajpat Singh** built a huge fort in Jind and Maharaja Ranjit Singh was his nephew.
- **Bhag Singh** ruled after Gajpat Singh and Ranjit Singh; assisted the British during the Second Anglo-Maratha War (1803-05).
- **Pratap Singh**, who succeeded Bhag Singh, opposed the British and revolted in 1814 AD. British arrested him with Ranjit Singh's help. He died in imprisonment in 1816 AD.
- **Sarup Singh** became ruler in 1834 AD, who supported the British and ruled during the 1857 revolt.
- After the revolt, **Dadri** was given to Sarup Singh as a reward and **Sangrur** and **Kurlana** were included in Jind state.

Loharu

• Established	In 1827 AD in Hisar district
• Location	Between Bikaner and Jaipur Princely States
• Area	225 sq miles

- **Samsuddin Khan**, eldest son of British military chief Ahmad Baksh Khan, became the ruler.
- In 1835 AD, Samsuddin Khan was charged with killing William Fraser, a resident of Delhi.
- The British sentenced Samsuddin to death and took over Ferozepur-Jhirka region.
- After Samsuddin Khan, his brother **Aminuddin Ahmad Khan** became the ruler of Loharu Princely State.
- Alauddin Ahmad Khan, first conferred with the title of Nawab, was the ruler during the Revolt of 1857.
- Initially, Alauddin Ahmad Khan communicated with the British at the beginning of the revolt.

Chhachhrauli (Kalsia)

• Location	Near the Yamuna river in present-day Northern Haryana
• Ruler during 1857 revolt	Shobha Singh

- **Shobha Singh** took a loan from Jagadhri's moneylender and gave it to the British.
- **Lahna Singh**, Shobha Singh's son, conducted several campaigns with the British.

Pataudi

• Established in	1805 AD by Faiz Talab Khan
• Area	75 sq miles
• Location	Between Rohtak and Gurugram districts

- After the Second Anglo-Maratha War in 1803 AD, the East India Company gave 40 villages and Pataudi town to **Faiz Talab Khan** as a reward for his assistance.
- Pataudi was a Pargana under the Rewari Government during Mughal rule.
- Faiz Talab Khan assumed the title of **Nawab** in 1805 AD.
- At the time of the 1857 revolt, **Akbar Ali** was the Nawab and he was given additional villages, Jatauli and Sherpur.

Dujana

• Founded in	1806 AD
• Founded by	Abdul Samad Khan (A Yusufzai Pathan)

- The ruler assisted the British, leading to the establishment of the Princely State between 1803-05 AD.
- Abdul Samad Khan had served as **Risaldar** under Maratha Peshwa Baji Rao II and aided the **British** during the Scindia-English struggle, earning 24 villages which he organised into a Princely State.
- Abdul Samad Khan became the first ruler in 1806 AD of his state. After his death in 1825 AD, **Muhammad Dunde Khan** succeeded him.
- During the Revolt of 1857, **Dunde Khan** ruled the state and was rewarded with the villages of Berli and Chowki in Rewari.

Karnal

- In 1847 AD, the British rescheduled the tax of Karnal.
- During the Revolt of 1857, the ruler of Karnal, **Ahmad Ali Khan**, surrendered all rights to the British.
- Karnal was a crucial location for the British defense purposes.

> The British appointed Ahmad Ali Khan as the **Assistant Commissioner** to manage the administration of Karnal district. His family members were granted a pension by the British.

Sampala-Asanda

• Location	Between Rohtak and Bahadurgarh
• Ruler	Mirza Ilahibaksh

- He played a key role in thwarting the Revolt of 1857 and informed the British about the revolutionaries' actions.
- He reported the hiding place of **Bahadur Shah Zafar** in the Tomb of Humayun.

Kunjpura

- The Princely State of Kunjpura located East of Karnal towards the Yamuna river.
- During the Revolt of 1857, the Nawab of Kunjpura fully supported the British. The British granted the Nawab Thanesar and surrounding areas.
- The Nawab was also given the responsibility of the Thanesar-Pehowa road.

3. Neighbouring Princely States

- Besides these Princely States, there were also some neighbouring Princely States, which played an important role in the region of Haryana.
- With the help of these Princely States, the British re-established their authority in Haryana.

Neighbouring Princely States

State	Description
Patiala	• It was more widespread in Northern Haryana and had close ties with Jind. This State was also supported by **Kaithal** and **Arnoli**. • The British were highly pleased with the military activities of this Princely State. • During the Revolt of 1857, the rulers of Patiala provided extensive assistance to the British Government. In return for this assistance, the **Narnaul region of Mahendragarh district** was given to the ruler of Patiala as a reward.
Nabha	• It was located near Patiala. The British were assisted by the **Sikh rulers** of Nabha during the Revolt of 1857 AD. • In return, the British gave the Bawal area of Rewari district and the Kanina and Atteli areas of Mahendragarh district to the Sikh rulers as rewards.
Bikaner	• It was mainly located in Western Haryana. The revolt began in this region in the last week of May. • It had an important role in the suppression of the revolution of Western Haryana.
Jaipur	• It had an important role in Southern Haryana. At the beginning of the Revolt of 1857 during the incidents Gurugram, Mewat and Ahirwal, the British went to the Princely State of Jaipur for their protection.

Suppression of the Revolt of 1857 by British in Haryana

- After suppressing the 1857 revolt in Delhi, the British moved towards Haryana.
- **Brigadier General Shavers** attacked Mewat, in which **Jhajjar** Nawab Abdur Rahman Khan surrendered to the Shavers at Chhuchnakwas.
- After the invasion of Jhajjar, Shavers attacked **Farrukhnagar.** Nawab Ahmad Ali of Farrukhnagar surrendered without fighting.
- **Colonel Gerrard** faced a joint rebellion in **Narnaul** by Prince Muhammad Azim Beg of Hisar, General Samad of Jhajjar and Rao Tularam. The English army emerged victorious in this war.
- The main reasons behind the failure of 1857 revolt in Haryana were lack of leadership, insufficient weapons, etc and lack of internal cooperation of ruling principality.

Suppression of the 1857 Revolt

Area/Place	British Official
Suppression of revolution in Tosham	General Van Cortland
Suppression near Hansi	Cortland
Suppression near Hisar and Rohtak	Captain Pearson
Suppression in Thanesar region	Deputy Commissioner McNeill
Suppression from Delhi to Sohna region	Assistant Commissioner Kilford
Suppression in Mewat	Colonel Gerrard

Administrative and Political Effects of 1857

- The 1857 revolt significantly impacted Haryana's administrative and political systems.
- The Charter Act of 1858 incorporated North-West Haryana under the jurisdiction of Punjab Province.

- From administrative point of view, Haryana region was divided into Delhi and Hisar divisions

Delhi Division	Hisar Division
• **Headquarter** Delhi • The administration of district was under Deputy Commissioner.	• **Headquarter** Hisar • The administration of district was under Deputy Commissioner.
• It included Delhi, Gurugram and Panipat.	• It included Hisar, Sirsa and Rohtak.

- The rulers of Bahadurgarh did not join the revolt, but their Princely States were confiscated.
- The Princely States of Dujana, Pataudi and Loharu were granted concessions. The rulers of Jind, Nabha and Patiala supported the British and were rewarded.
- **Sarup Singh**, the ruler of Jind, received the entire Dadri State and parts of Kanod (Mahendragarh) as a reward.
- The Nabha ruler was granted Kanti and Bawal Parganas. The Patiala ruler received a large tract of land near Narnaul as a reward.

Native Principalities of Haryana after the Revolt of 1857

Loharu Principality

- Strong protests erupted against Nawab Aminuddin Ahmad's misrule in Loharu Princely State in 1935.
- Nawab Aminuddin fired on a peaceful demonstration in **Simhani** village, killing many people on 8th August, 1935.
- Following the incident, **Praja Mandal** was formed to challenge the Nawab's rule, led by Subedar Dilsukh, Chaudhary Mohar Singh, Pandit Satyavrat, Chaudhary Chandgiram, Thakur Bhagwant Singh and Shri Nathuram.
- The continued protests resulted in a compromise between the Nawab and the agitators.

> Loharu Princely State was merged into Hisar district after independence in 1947.

Jind Principality

- In 1864, Sarup Singh, ruler of Jind principality, passed away and was succeeded by **Raghuvir Singh**.
- In 1911, **Ranvir Singh** was granted the **title of Maharaja**, but his policies were unpopular with the public.
- The **Jind State Praja Mandal** was established in Narwana as part of the broader Praja Mandal Movement, opposing Maharaja Ranvir Singh's policies in 1927.

Pataudi Principality

- **Nawab Iftikhar Ali Khan** was the **last ruler** of Pataudi Princely State; excelled in cricket, hockey and billiards. He was known as 'Tiger' in the sports world.
- His successor, **Nawab Mansoor Ali Khan Pataudi**, was an international level cricket player.
- In 1942 during **Quit India Movement**, people of Pataudi revolted against Nawab Iftikhar Ali Khan, forming a Praja Mandal led by Gauri Shankar Vaidya, Pt Babudayal Sharma, Thakur Ram Singh and Nand Kishore.
- The Nawab tried to suppress demands, imprisoning Gauri Shankar Vaidya, which fueled public resentment. He released prisoners to ease tensions with the Praja Mandal.
- After independence, **Pataudi Princely State was merged into Gurugram district.**

Dujana Principality

- Praja Mandal in Dujana was formed to oppose British and Nawab's rule.

> The centre of Dujana Praja Mandal was Nahar near Kosli, led by **Rao Devkaran Singh** (Head) and **Sardar Singh** (Secretary). The other leaders were Pt. Hariram, Rao Nekiram, Pt. Tara Chandra, Mahashya Ramjilal, Hakeem Mangaturam. They launched **Kar Na Do Movement**.

- Nawab Muhammad Iqtadar Ali Khan couldn't suppress the movement and had to bow down before the public and release all detained leaders.
- Dujana merged into Rohtak district in March, 1948.

Narnaul Region of Patiala Principality

- The rulers of Patiala Princely State focused on a luxurious lifestyle, causing public discontent in Narnaul.
- Praja Mandal was formed in Narnaul in **1945** to address public grievances, with leaders like Rao Madho Singh, Ram Kishore, Ayodhya Prasad, Kamala Devi, Ramcharanchand Mittal, Shri Ram Kaushik and Matadin.
- Despite the Patiala ruler's efforts to suppress the movement, it was unsuccessful.

- After independence, the **Princely State of Patiala,** along with Narnaul, was merged into the Union of India.

Bawal, Kanina and Atteli Regions of Nabha Principality

- **Pratap Singh,** the last Maharaja of Nabha, imposed heavy taxes and led a luxurious life, causing public anger.
- Praja Mandal was formed in 1946 to protest against his rule.
- The movement, led by Praja Mandal, used the slogan **Nabha Wale Chhetro Ko Chhodo** (Leave the Nabha regions).
- Pratap Singh was forced to compromise with the agitators.
- After independence, Nabha **Princely State was merged with the Indian Union** in 1948 and became part of **Patiala.**

Congress and National Movement in Haryana

Congress

- **Rai Bahadur Murlidhar** established a Congress branch in Ambala in 1886 AD.
- Lala Lajpat Rai came to Rohtak in 1884.
- The **first session** of Congress branch in Rohtak was held in October, 1886, chaired by **Turrabaz Khan.** Lala Lajpat Rai was the principal speaker of the gathering.
- In the **Second Congress Session** (1886, Calcutta), three Haryana representatives, **Deen Dayal Sharma, Babu Bal Mukund Gupt** and **Lala Murlidhar** participated.
- In 1887 AD, **Lala Lajpat Rai** began Congress work in Hisar and Rohtak, with Hisar as his center of social and political activities.
- In 1888 AD, **Rai Bahadur Murlidhar** participated for the first time as a representative of Hisar Congress session in Allahabad.
- He attended the 1889 AD, Congress session in Mumbai with Babu Chudamani and Gauri Shankar.
- In May, 1907, Lala Lajpat Rai was exiled to Mandalay prison by the British, but was released on 14th November, 1907 due to mass pressure.

> Lala Lajpat Rai founded the Arya Samaj of Hisar in 1886 AD, with **Lala Chandulal** as its head.

Response of Haryana on Morley Minto Reforms

- **Ambala** became a major centre of resistance against Morley-Minto Reforms, with a bomb thrown on the Deputy Commissioner's bungalow on 27th December, 1909.
- Bal Mukund Gupt, a journalist, opposed the Morley-Minto Reforms through his articles titled **Shivshambhu ka Chittha.**
- In 1909, Morley-Minto Reforms allowed the election of a member to the Punjab Legislative Assembly through votes from District Boards of Rohtak, Gurugram and Hisar.

> The reform included **Ambala** and **Karnal** districts along with Shimla for membership.

Home Rule Movement

- **Pt. Nekiram Sharma** is credited with propagating the Home Rule Movement in Haryana. He was particularly influenced by Bal Gangadhar Tilak's policies.
- The British government prohibited Tilak's arrival in Haryana.
- Pt Nekiram Sharma is known as the '**Kesari of Haryana.**'

Rowlatt Act and Satyagraha

- The Rowlatt Act was a law passed by the British colonial government in India on 18th March, 1919. It was officially called the **Anarchical** and **Revolutionary Crimes Act of 1919.**
- **Mahatma Gandhi** came to Haryana to oppose Rowlatt Act on the recommendation of Swami Shraddhananda.

Events during Rowlatt Act in Haryana

Date	Event
11th February, 1919	A huge rally organised in Ambala against the Rowlatt Act, chaired by Sardar Jhanda Singh.
28th February, 1919	Protests against the Rowlatt Act held in Hisar.
30th March, 1919	Partial strike in Rohtak, Karnal, Ambala and Panipat.
6th April, 1919	A big conference held in Rohtak against the Rowlatt Act.
10th April, 1919	Mahatma Gandhi arrested in Palwal for opposing the Rowlatt Act.
14th April, 1919	Railway workers attacked the Bahadurgarh station in protest.
19th April, 1919	Revolutionaries set fire to the store of the 1/34 **Sikh Pioneer Regiment at Ambala Cantonment.**
28th April, 1919	Chaudhary Piru Singh arrested under the Defence of India Rules.
30th July, 1919	Gandhiji arrested in Hisar district.

Non-Cooperation Movement

- The **first meeting** of the Non-Cooperation Movement was held in October, 1920 in Panipat, under the leadership of Lala Lajpat Rai.
- The **Ambala Divisional Political Conference** was organised on 22nd October, 1920, in Bhiwani under **Lala Murlidhar's** Chairmanship.
- Mahatma Gandhi, Maulana Muhammad Ali, Shaukat Ali and Maulana Azad participated in the conference. Mahatma Gandhi called the British Government to be an evil government for the first time.
- A conference was held in Rohtak from 6-8th November, 1920, chaired by **Pt. Ramraj Dutt**. During this conference, the Congress Party split.
- **Chaudhary Chhoturam** and his supporters left Congress due to disagreements over the opposition to the British Government in the Non-Cooperation Movement resolution.
- During the Non-Cooperation Movement, people of the state returned prizes and medals, including Lala Murlidhar of Ambala returning the **Rai Bahadur** honour.
- Lawyers boycotted government courts and Gram Panchayats were formed. National Courts were established but were not very successful.
- Pt. Nekiram Sharma, a prominent Haryana leader, was arrested, along with many other agitators and satyagrahis, who were sent to Ambala jail.

> Several leaders from Rohtak and Hisar districts, including Pt. Shriram Sharma, Chaudhary Harphool Singh, Daulatram Gupta, Baldev Singh, Pt. Janardan Sharma, Lala Lajpat Rai and others were arrested during the Non-Cooperation Movement.

- Other leaders like Lala Ganpat Rai, Lala Hukamchand, Lala Deshbandhu Gupt in Karnal and Lala Dulichand, Mohammad Shamimullah, Lala Murlidhar and Pt. Aryanand Sharma in Ambala were also arrested.

Mahatma Gandhi during Non-Cooperation Movement in Haryana

- Gandhiji addressed a large gathering in Bhiwani on 15th February, 1921, presided over by Lala Murlidhar.
- In February, 1921, Mahatma Gandhi visited Haryana with Lala Lajpat Rai, Maulana Azad, Kasturba Gandhi, Pyare Lal Sharma and Jamnalal Bajaj to strengthen the Non-Cooperation Movement.
- On 16th February, Gandhiji opened the Jat school in Rohtak and assessed the National Education System. He also addressed a large gathering chaired by Chaudhary Maturam Hooda in Rohtak.

Swaraj Party

- Swaraj Party was popular in Haryana with leaders like **Lala Dulichand** (Ambala), **Lala Ganpat Rai** (Karnal), Nekiram Sharma and Babu Shyamalal Satyagrahi (Hisar), Pt. Rupnarayan (Gurugram) and Shriram Sharma (Rohtak).
- Shriram Sharma launched the newspaper **Haryana Tilak** on 18th March, 1923, to promote the Swaraj Party. Shubh Chopra published the newspaper **Swaraj** from Gurugram.
- After **Chittaranjan Das'** death in 1925, the Swaraj Party began to disintegrate. The influential leaders formed new parties and joined new alliances. Eventually, the Swaraj Party merged with the Congress Party.

Newly Founded Parties

Leader	Party Formed	Alliance
Chaudhary Chhoturam	Unionist Party	Allied with Mian Fazle Hussain
Lala Lajpat Rai and Pt. Nekiram Sharma	Independent Congress Party	Supported by Unionist Party candidates

Protest against Simon Commission

- The Simon Commission faced strong protests in **Rohtak, Jhajjar, Bhiwani** and **Ambala** districts of Haryana.
- Lala Lajpat Rai was injured during the protests in Lahore on 14th November, 1927 and died, which sparked further outrage in Punjab-Haryana.

Civil Disobedience Movement

- Started — 12th March, 1930 (Dandi March by Gandhiji)
- Total Satyagrahis — 78
- Haryana's Representative — Lala Surajbhan from Ambala

- People in Haryana broke the **Salt Law** in Rohtak, Jhajjar, Ambala, Panipat and Bhiwani.
- Salt Laws were also broken in Beri, Sanghi, Gurugram and Sonipat; foreign goods were boycotted.
- Khadag Bahadur, a representative of Gandhiji, propagated the Satyagraha in the region.
- The agitators led by Sarojini Naidu launched a non-violent revolt at the **Dharsana Salt Depot** in which the Haryana agitators also took part.

- Many women participated in this movement in Ambala under the leadership of Lala Dulichand's daughters Vidyavati, Yashoda and Jamna.

> Haryana Satyagrahis tried to break the Salt Law in **Zahidpur** (Jhajjar) on 15th April, 1930, but were suppressed.

- Traders in Ambala, Rohtak and Bhiwani announced not to trade in foreign goods and students from Chandulal Anglo-Vedic School (Hisar) and DAV School (Kurukshetra) participated.
- The British Government formed the peace meetings through its supporters, but government activities did not break the morale of the agitators.
- Over 600 people broke the Salt Law, with 380 arrested in Rohtak alone which was the highest.
- Peasants also launched **Kar Mat Do** movement on the sidelines of Civil Disobedience Movement in Haryana.

Individual Satyagraha

- Launched by — Mahatma Gandhi
- Launched on — 17th October, 1940
- Against — British policies
- Many people were arrested in Rohtak, Ambala, Hisar, Karnal and Gurugram during this movement.
- Several prominent leaders arrested from different districts of Haryana, which were as follows

District	Leaders Arrested
Hisar	Gopichand Bhargava, Pt. Nekiram Sharma, Chaudhary Sahab Ram, Lala Shyamlal
Rohtak	Shriram Sharma, Rao Mangliram
Gurugram	Syed Mulalvi, Mahashya Bhagwan Das
Karnal	Hammed Hussain
Ambala	Dulichand, Prem Prakash Azad

- The second phase of the movement started on 10th January, 1940, with Hisar district at the forefront.
- The third phase began on 10th April, 1941, with Rohtak district leading. Around 73 people were arrested in Rohtak.

Quit India Movement

- The Quit India Movement was announced on 8th August, 1942, leading to demonstrations at railway stations, post offices, telegraph offices and police stations in Haryana.
- After the arrest of key leaders, the people organised the movement.
- Prominent agitators included Mangeram Vats, Sheeshpal Singh, Vaidya Lekhram Singh, Radhakrishna, Laxman Singh and Ramkumar Vichhat.

Indian National Army (INA)

- Indian National Army (INA) or Azad Hind Fauj had 2715 soldiers from Haryana, including 398 officers and 2317 soldiers.
- Rohtak district (Rohtak, Sonipat and Jhajjar regions) had the maximum officers (149) and 724 soldiers.
- **Major Suraj Mal** and **Lieutenant Colonel Rana Singh** headed the first and second brigade battalions of INA, respectively.
- Netaji Subhash Chandra Bose awarded Major Suraj Mal the title of Sarkar-e-Jung.
- 22 officers and 324 soldiers from Haryana were martyred during the fight.

Haryana in the World War

↓

First World War

- Haryana was a major recruitment area during the First World War, with rich people and Mahajans providing financial support to the Imperial Relief Fund.
- Ram Bahadur Sukhlal of Sirsa donated ₹ 10 lakhs; Bhiwani district collected the highest donation of ₹ 25 lakh in the state.
- The government provided separate representation to rural and urban areas based on population for soldiers' participation from the Punjab region.
- This decision was opposed by Raibahadur Chaudhary, Lalchand of Rohtak, leading to political conflicts with Sir Fazle Hussain, Lala Harkishan Lal and Chaudhary Lal Chand.
- Pt. Nekiram Sharma in Haryana opposed the military recruitment drive by the British during the First World War.

↓

Second World War

- On 3rd September, 1939, England declared war on Germany, starting the Second World War and India was included by Lord Linlithgow, the then Viceroy.
- Congress declared the government's move invalid and demanded an assurance from the British Government for a democratic government in Post-War India.
- In 1940, a Company of the Hyderabad Regiment in Singapore, consisting of Ahir soldiers from Haryana, declared rebellion after being influenced by their Muslim officer, Zaheer Khan, who opposed British policies.
- Zaheer Khan was dismissed, leading to a revolt by Ahir soldiers, joined later by a Jat Company of the same regiment.

1946 Elections and Independence

- The **Unionist Party of Punjab** and **Haryana** got weakened before the elections of 1946. Consequently, in the election, Muslim League got 75 seats, Congress got 51 seats, Akali Dal got 22 seats and Unionist Party got 20 seats. Independent candidates won on 7 places.

- Congress formed the government with the support of Unionist Party. **Chaudhary Lahri Singh**; the Congress Leader from Haryana was a part of this government.
- The demand for the creation of a separate Pakistan was increased with the successful representation of the Muslim League in the 1946 elections.
- There were communal riots in Punjab. Thousands of people from both communities (Hindu and Muslim) were killed. The riots in Mewat region were more severe.
- During the 1946 elections, the Western part of Punjab was Muslim dominated area and the Eastern part of Punjab and Haryana were the Hindu dominated areas.
- The leader of Mewatis, **Muhammad Yasin Khan** continued to become MLC and MLA from Gurugram-Hisar region and Unionist Party of Punjab but he lost the 1946 election. Gandhiji visited Sohna (Mewat) on 19th December, 1946 in support of Muhammad Yasin Khan.
- India was divided into two countries on 14th August, 1947 and Pakistan came into existence. India got Independance on 15th August, 1947 and Haryana remained a part of Punjab Province.
- Panipat was a Muslim dominated region. Many Muslims migrated to Pakistan after independence. Due to this dismal, the patriot **Maulana Lakaulla** appealed Gandhiji to visit Panipat. Thus, Gandhiji visited Panipat on 9th December, 1947 and appealed all the Muslims to be united.

> After attaining independence, Gandhiji visited Mewat in December, 1947. While addressing a public meeting at village **Ghasera** in Mewat, he assured complete security.
> As a result, the migration from Mewat stopped. Ghasera village of Mewat is also called **Gandhi Gram**.

- On 30th January, 1948, Gandhiji was assassinated by Nathuram Godse. After the whole legal process, Nathuram Godse was hanged in the Ambala jail.

Important Freedom Fighters from Haryana

Lala Hukamchand Jain

- Born in — 1816
- Place — Hisar district
- Occupation — Government officer
- Role in 1857 revolt — Joined the revolt in Jhansi against the British and supported the Delhi Emperor
- Death — Hanged on 19th January, 1858

Nahar Singh

- Born in — 1823
- Place — Ballabhgarh
- Ruler of — Princely State of Ballabhgarh (since 1829)
- Known as — Lion of Ballabhgarh
- Role in 1857 Revolt — Allied with Bahadur Shah Zafar and joined the revolt in Delhi
- Imprisonment — Imprisoned on 23rd September, 1857 in Ghusdal by British officer Shavers
- Death — Hanged for treason on 9th January, 1858 in Chandni Chowk

Rao Tularam

- Born — 9th December, 1825
- Place — Rewari district
- Role in 1857 revolt — Regarded as a State Hero of Haryana for his contribution to the revolt

- He captured Rewari, Bohra and Shahjahanpur during the revolt.
- After a prolonged struggle, he was defeated by the British and fled to Afghanistan and died on 23rd September, 1863 in Kabul.

Rai Bahadur Lala Murlidhar

- Born in — 1850
- Place — Ambala district
- Titles — *Rai Bahadur* and *Kesar-e-Hind* (awarded by the British Government)
- He was founding member of Congress in the state. He participated in the National Movement in 1886 and went to jail.
- He gave back all his titles in the protest against the Rowlatt Act, 1921. He is also known as **Grand Old Man of Punjab**.

Noor Samand Khan

- He was the ruler of Rania (Sirsa).
- On 17th June, 1857, he fought against the British Army at Odhan village but not succeeded.

Sir Chhotu Ram

- Born — 24th November, 1881
- Place — Garhi Sampla village, Rohtak district
- Education — Studied Law at Agra University

- He published Urdu Weekly **Jaat Gazette** in 1916 from Rohtak.
- He co-founded the **Zamindar League** with Fazle Hussain in 1923 to strengthen the Unionist Party in Haryana.
- He got title **Sir** in 1937 and formed the **Marketing Board** in 1938 to help farmers sell grains.
- He was known as **Rahbare-Azam** and **Messiah of the poor and farmers**.

Pandit Nekiram

- Born 4th September, 1887
- Place Kelanga village, Rohtak district
- He became a member of Swaraj Union of Bal Gangadhar Tilak in 1916 and became the Secretary of Divisional Conference in 1920.
- He remained with Lala Lajpat Rai and Madan Mohan Malaviya from 1925 to 1930.
- He published a weekly paper, Sandesh from Bhiwani.
- He died on 8th June, 1956.
- He is referred as the '**Haryana Kesari**'.

Abdul Gaffar Khan

- Born in 1888
- Place Loha village, Ambala district
- He joined the Indian National Congress in 1919.
- He also led a public meeting on 26th January, 1930 to celebrate Independence Day.
- He elected to the Punjab Legislative Assembly in 1952 and continued as a member of the Haryana Cabinet after 1966.
- He died on 16th June, 1976.

Pandit Shriram Sharma

- Born 1st October, 1899
- Place Jhajjar district

- He participated in all five Satyagraha Movements (1921, 1930, 1932, 1940, 1942) and was imprisoned for seven years.
- He published the weekly **Haryana Tilak** in Hindi and Urdu from Rohtak in 1923 to support the freedom movement.
- He was the author of **Haryana Ka Itihas** and **Haryana ke Navratan**.
- Pandit Shriram Sharma was known as the **Grand Old Man of Haryana**.

Sucheta Kriplani

- Born 25th June, 1908
- Place Ambala district of Haryana

- She was an Indian freedom fighter and Politician.
- She joined the Quit India Movement of 1942 and played a great role along with Ram Manohar Lohia, Jaiprakash Narayan and Aruna Asaf Ali.
- She was India's **first woman Chief Minister of Uttar Pradesh** from 1963 to 1967.
- She died on 1st December, 1974 in Delhi.

Fateh Singh

- Born 5th October, 1912
- Place Khedar village of Hisar district.
- He was an active member of the Indian National Army, which was established by Netaji Subhas Chandra Bose in 1943.
- He was appointed as the Captain of Armed Corps Company of Indian National Army in 1943 by Subhas Chandra Bose.

Ram Singh Jakhar

- Born in 1916
- Place Ladain village of Jhajjar district.
- He was also the President of **Swatantrata Senani Samiti**.

Abdur Rahman Khan

- Also known as Nawab of Jhajjar
- He took part in the Revolt of 1857 against the British rule.
- He was hanged on 23rd October, 1857 in front of Red Fort.

Banarasi Das

- Born 5th November, 1917
- Place Bhiwani district

- He left his home in 1930-31 to take part in the Civil Disobedience Movement and went to Satyarahis camp in Meerut.
- He was arrested in 1941 during Individual Satyagraha and was sentenced for two years.
- He founded **Youth Assembly** in Rewari and was the founder member of Jind State Praja Mandal.
- He died on 29th August, 2007.

Arya Samaj in Haryana

- Arya Samaj played a key role in awakening social and political consciousness in Haryana.
- It was founded by **Swami Dayanand** on 10th April, 1875 in Mumbai.
- Swami Dayanand first visited Haryana on 17th July, 1878 (Ambala) and again on 24th December, 1880 (Rewari) at the invitation of Rao Yudhishthir.
- He campaigned against illiteracy, ignorance and conservatism, establishing an Arya Samaj branch and a cowshed in Rewari.
- **Chaudhary Ram Narayan Bhagan** and **Pandit Shambhu Dutt** founded the Arya Samaj in Sonipat.
- **Swami Shradhanand** founded **Farmana Arya Samaj** in 1905 and **Khatkhad Arya Samaj** in 1907.
- Lala Lajpat Rai helped establish an Arya Samaj branch in Hisar.

Arya Samaj in Haryana

City/Village	Year	Members
Rewari	1880	21
Rohtak	1885	10
Hisar	1889	59
Hansi	1889	12
Hathin (Gurugram)	1890	5
Ambala	1883	14
Bhiwani	1890	36
Jhajjar	1891	13
Sirsa	1892	21
Shahabad (Kurukshetra)	1893	19
Thanesar	1894	15
Ballabhgarh (Faridabad)	1896	10
Kausali (Rohtak)	1897	10
Pundari (Kurukshetra)	1900	20
Kaithal (Kurukshetra)	1900	30

Arya Samaj Movements in Haryana

- The important Arya Samaj missionaries of Haryana were Bhakt Phool Singh, Swami Swatantratanand and Acharya Bhagwan Dev. They promoted Arya Samaj in the state and also led many Arya Samaj movements in Haryana.

Arya Samaj Movements in Haryana

Movement	Year	Events
Samalekha Movement	1916	Started by Arya Samajis against British cow slaughtering centres in Samalekha, led by **Phool Singh**.
Panipat Movement	1930	Against the government ban on Aryan processions; Arya Samajis launched the '**Aryan Raksha Samiti**'.
Lahore Slaughterhouse Movement	1937-38	Protest against the opening of cow slaughtering centres in Lahore during the Second World War.
Hyderabad Movement	1939	Led by **Bhakt Phool Singh** against the Hyderabad principality's ban on Aryan activities.
Loharu Movement	1940	Started against the ban on Arya Samaj activities in Loharu principality.
Moth Movement	1940	Bhakt Phool Singh worked to settle disputes, open schools and release pasture grounds and founded the '**EK Bahu Regiment**'.
Hindi Satyagraha Movement	1957	Initiated during Sardar Pratap Singh Kairon's reign to give Hindi a rightful place in United Punjab.
Kundli Slaughterhouse Movement	1968	Protested against the decision to open a slaughterhouse in Kundli, Rohtak, by the Haryana and Central Governments.

Promotion of Sanatan Dharma

- Influenced by the movement of Arya Samaj, orthodox Hindus of Haryana established **Sanatan Dharma Sabha.**
- **Pt Deendayal Sharma** of Jhajjar was the ideological leader of this movement. He was born in 1863 AD in Jhajjar village of Rohtak district.
- He also formed the **Rifa-e-Aam Society** in Jhajjar, which included people from both Hindu and Muslim communities. He also published an Urdu magazine called **Haryana** from Jhajjar itself.
- On 22th August, 1886, Pt. Deendayal Sharma established the first **Sanatan Dharma Sabha at Jhajjar**, the first Chairman of which was **Ram Nathulal.**
- In 1890, **the Surdham Prakasika Sabha** was formed at Bhiwani which was established in the form of Sanatan Dharm Sabha in 1891. In 1890, **Sudharma Bal Sabha** of youth was also formed in Bhiwani.
- In 1891, **Sanatan Dharma Sabha** was established in Sirsa by Pt. Deendayal Sharma.
- Sanatan Dharma Sabha was established in Karnal and Kurukshetra in 1892 and Safido, Rewari, Palwal, Rohtak, Gurugram, Kaithal, Panipat and Beri in 1895.

Timeline of Haryana : Important Events

324-232 BC	Mauryan's authority over Haryana
580 AD	Pushyabhuti Naresh Prabhakarvardhan became King
605 AD	Harshavardhana became King
634-635 AD	War between Harsha and Chalukya King Pulakeshin
805 AD	Pratihara Ruler Nagabhatta-II occupied Haryana
1009 AD	Mahmud of Ghazni invaded India for the first time
1191 AD	Prithviraj Chauhan defeated invader Mohammad Ghori in Taraori
1192 AD	For the second time in Taraori, Chauhan's defeat at the hands of Ghori
1194 AD	Mohammad Ghori invaded Rohtak and targeted the temples here
1206 AD	Qutubuddin Aibak suzerainty over Haryana
1240 AD	Razia Begum killed in Kaithal
1266 AD	Suzerainty of Balban over Haryana
1290 AD	Establishment of Khilji dynasty
1398 AD	Timur invaded Haryana
1526 AD	First Battle of Panipat
1530 AD	Mohan Singh Mandar's rebellion against Babar
1556 AD	Second Battle of Panipat
1672 AD	Satnami's rebellion against Narnaul
1739 AD	Battle of Karnal
1761 AD	Third Battle of Panipat between Marathas and Ahmad Shah Abdali
1789 AD	Mahadev Scindia's authority over Delhi and Haryana
1803 AD	British authority over Haryana
1809 AD	Chhachhrauli rebellion
1818 AD	Rebellion of Rania
1834 AD	Haryana became a part of North-Western Province
1843 AD	Rebellion in Kaithal
1845 AD	Rebellion of Ajit Singh Ladwa
1858 AD	Haryana merged with Punjab
1886 AD	Babu Murlidhar became the first satyagrahi of Congress Movement, first Sanatan Dharma formed in Jhajjar.
1892 AD	Lala Lajpat Rai went to Lahore from Hisar
1928 AD	Elections of Punjab Legislative Council
1937 AD	Election in Punjab Assembly
1947 AD	The country became independent and Haryana became a part of East Punjab
1966 AD	Identify Haryana as a separate state

CHECK CHAPTER KNOWLEDGE

1 By which of the following treaties, Haryana was acquired by the East India Company from Marathas? *HSSC 2016*
(a) Treaty of Surji-Arjungaon
(b) Rain Treaty
(c) Ambala Treaty
(d) None of the above

2 The Treaty of Surji-Arjungaon took place in which year? *HSSC 2023*
(a) 1799 AD (b) 1800 AD
(c) 1803 AD (d) 1903 AD

3 Who among the following got Firozpur Jhirka by the British Government?
(a) Faiz Talab Khan (b) Ahmad Baksh Khan
(c) Raja Ummed Singh (d) None of these

4 Who was the ruler of Thanesar, who revolted against the British along with the Guru Dutt Singh, the ruler of Ladwa?
(a) Nabha Singh (b) Bhanga Singh
(c) Ganga Singh (d) None of these

5 Who was the ruler of Fatehabad whose Princely State was taken over by the British?
(a) Jabita Khan (b) Baunba Khan
(c) Bahadur Khan (d) Abdul Samad Khan

6 The British divided the ceded part of Haryana into how many sub-divisions?
(a) 1 (b) 3 (c) 7 (d) 11

7 Northern area of the ceded part of Haryana was consisted of which of the following regions?
(a) Hisar (b) Rohtak
(c) Panipat (d) All of these

8 Who was the leader of 'Chhachhrauli Revolt'?
(a) Pratap Singh (b) Jodh Singh
(c) Jabit Singh (d) Gulab Singh

9 Which ruler of Chhachharauli was defeated and whose reign was annexed by the British?
(a) Baghel Singh (b) Fateh Singh
(c) Jodh Singh (d) Bhagwan Singh

10 The British East India Company annexed the Rania principality due to the reason of
(a) revolt by Nawab Jabit Khan
(b) incapability of Rani Ramkaur and Interference of Jodh Singh
(c) death of Maya Daya Kau
(d) death of Bhai Uday Singh without his successor

11 In which year the 'Peasant Uprising' took place in Rohtak, Gurugram and Hisar against the British?
(a) 1820 AD (b) 1822 AD
(c) 1824 AD (d) 1830 AD

12 Which ruler of Jind principality revolted against the British?
(a) Jodh Singh (b) Pratap Singh
(c) Jat Surajmal (d) Ajeet Singh

13 Who was the leader of Banawali revolt? *HSSC 2024*
(a) Gulab Singh (b) Jat Surajmal
(c) Ajeet Singh (d) Pratap Singh

14 Who laid the foundation stone of Kaithal principality in 1763 AD?
(a) Uday Singh (b) Gurbaksh Singh
(c) Gurudatt Singh (d) Sardar Singh

15 In which year Kaithal Principality was annexed by the British East India Company?
(a) 1818 AD (b) 1824 AD
(c) 1843 AD (d) 1850 AD

16 Ladwa Princely State was founded by which of the following rulers? *HSSC 2016*
(a) Jodh Singh (b) Ajeet Singh
(c) Sardar Singh (d) Gurbaksh Singh

17 Ladwa revolt took place in which year?
(a) 1814 AD (b) 1818 AD
(c) 1824 AD (d) 1845 AD

18 Who was the leader of Ladwa revolt which took place in the year 1845 AD? *Haryana Police IRB Constable 2018*
(a) Jodh Singh (b) Ajeet Singh
(c) Jabit Singh (d) Pratap Singh

19 The British East India Company annexed the Ambala principality due to the reason of
(a) death of Sardarni Indra Kaur
(b) revolt of Nawab Jabit Khan
(c) death of Mai Sukhan
(d) None of the above

20 The '1857 Revolt' was started at which place of Haryana? *HSSC 2021, 2016*
(a) Farrukhnagar (b) Ambala Cantt
(c) Narnaul (d) Hisar

21 During the 1857 revolt, William Ford was the Collector of which place of Haryana?
(a) Gurugram (b) Ambala
(c) Rohtak (d) Hisar

22 Name the last ruler of Ballabhgarh, who martyred in the '1857 Revolt'. *HSSC 2021*
(a) Nahar Singh (b) Vijay Singh
(c) Pratap Singh (d) Mehar Singh

23 Light Infantry Troop of which place revolted against the British in the '1857 Revolt'?
(a) Hisar (b) Hansi (c) Sirsa (d) All of these

24 Who led the revolt of 1857 in Hansi?
(a) Hukamchand
(b) Munir Beg
(c) Both (a) and (b)
(d) Noor Mohammad Khan

25 Which of the following districts of Haryana had greatly contributed in the '1857 Revolt'? *Mandi Supervisor 2017, HSSC 2017*
(a) Rohtak (b) Hisar
(c) Gurugram (d) All of these

26 Who led the revolt of 1857 in Thanesar?
(a) Rao Tularam (b) Rao Sukh Ram
(c) Imam Ali (d) None of these

27 Who was the leader of 1857 Revolt in Pataudi?
(a) Sadrauddin (b) Tularam
(c) Ahmad Ali (d) Akbar Ali

28 What was the reason behind the failure of 1857 Revolt in Haryana? *Haryana Clerk 2019, Mandi Supervisor 2017*
(a) No support from other principalities
(b) Lack of weapons
(c) Lack of leadership
(d) All of the above

29 Who was known as the Nawab of Jhajjar? *HSSC Field Cadre 2020*
(a) Abdur Rahman Khan
(b) Banarasi Das
(c) Hukamchand Jain
(d) Chaudhary Devi Lal

30 The Nawab of Farrukhnagar, who revolted against the British Army in the '1857 Revolt' was *Grid Sub-Station Operator 2016*
(a) Sirajuddaula
(b) Firoz Khan
(c) Rahman Khan
(d) Nawab Ahmad Ali Khan

31 'Sarrafabad' was the old name of which Princely State?
(a) Ballabhgarh (b) Bahadurgarh
(c) Mewat (d) Hansi

32 In the Freedom Struggle of 1857, Rao Tularam revolted against the British from which place? *Haryana Patwari 2016,15*
(a) Hisar, Sirsa (b) Kaithal, Kurukshetra
(c) Rohtak, Jind (d) Narnaul, Rewari

33 Which ruler of Rewari Princely State was amongst the prominent leaders of 1857 Revolt? *Haryana Tabla Virtuoso 2018*
(a) Rao Sukhram (b) Rao Tularam
(c) Rao Gujrimal Singh (d) Rao Ruda Singh

34 Who was the founder of Jind Princely State?
(a) Tularam (b) Gajpat Singh
(c) Phool Singh (d) None of these

35 Which Princely State was the most prominent state in Haryana during the 1857 Revolt?
(a) Sirsa (b) Jind (c) Mewat (d) Rewari

36 Which Loharu ruler was sentenced to death by the British under the charge of killing William Fraser, a resident of Delhi in 1835 AD?
(a) Samsuddin Khan (b) Ahmad Baksh Khan
(c) Shobha Singh (d) Faiz Talab Khan

37 Who was the last ruler of Princely State of Pataudi?
(a) Nawab Muhammad Ibrahim Ali Khan
(b) Nawab Iftikhar Ali Khan
(c) Nawab Muhammad Hussain Ali Khan
(d) Nawab Muhammad Ali Khan

38 Who among the following started 'Kar Na Do' Movement in Dujana Principality?
(a) Pt. Hariram (b) Rao Nekiram
(c) Pt. Tara Chandra (d) All of these

39 In which year Praja Mandal was formed in Narnaul? *HSSC 2024*
(a) 1844 (b) 1898 (c) 1905 (d) 1945

40 Who established a branch of Congress in Ambala?
(a) Deen Dayal Sharma
(b) Lala Murlidhar
(c) Lala Lajpat Rai
(d) None of the above

41 In 1888, in the Allahabad Session of Congress, who became the representative of Hisar Congress?
(a) Lala Sultan Singh (b) Baldev Singh
(c) Lala Lajpat Rai (d) Beni Singh

42 Which among the following places was the main centre of social and political activities of the freedom fighter, Lala Lajpat Rai? *HSSC Group D 2018*
(a) Ambala (b) Jhajjar
(c) Jind (d) Hisar

43 Who was the head of the Hisar Arya Samaj?
(a) Lala Lajpat Rai (b) Lala Chandulal
(c) Babu Chudamani (d) Gauri Shankar

44 Which Journalist from Haryana oppossed the Morley-Minto Reforms through his articles 'Shivshambhu ke Chitte'?
(a) Deshbandho Gupta (b) Balmukund Gupt
(c) Bal Gangadhar Tilak (d) Fateh Singh

45 In 1919, the first protest against the Rowlatt Act was held at which place of Haryana?
Mandi Supervisor 2017, HSSC 2017
(a) Hisar (b) Sonipat
(c) Ambala (d) Panipat

46 On 6th April, 1919, at which place a big conference was held against the Rowlatt Act?
Haryana Police 2016
(a) Rohtak (b) Ambala
(c) Sonipat (d) Panipat

47 Gandhiji was arrested from which place of Haryana during the protest against Rowlatt Act?
(a) Palwal (b) Hisar
(c) Sirsa (d) Kurukshetra

48 In which year, the Non-Cooperation Movement was started in Haryana?
Haryana Agriculture Inspector 2017
(a) 1925 (b) 1930 (c) 1920 (d) 1918

49 The first meeting during the Non-Cooperation Movement was held in October, 1920 in Panipat, under the Leadership of
(a) Lala Lajapat Rai
(b) Shaukat Ali
(c) Gandhiji
(d) Chaudhary Devi Lal

50 Freedom Fighter Rao Tula Ram died in
HSSC 2024
(a) Afghanistan (b) Nepal
(c) Pakistan (d) Burma

51 Who gave back his title of 'Rai Bahadur' during Non-Cooperation Movement?
(a) Lala Murlidhar (b) Gokul Chand
(c) Nazir Begh (d) Ganpat Rai

52 'Haryana Tilak' newspaper was published in which year? *Haryana Accountant 2018*
(a) 1933 (b) 1923
(c) 1942 (d) None of these

53 Who was the editor of 'Haryana Tilak'?
HSSC 2017
(a) Nekiram Sharma (b) Baldev Singh
(c) Shriram Sharma (d) Sir Chhotu Ram

54 Which district of Haryana was at the forefront in the second phase of individual Satyagraha Movement?
(a) Hisar (b) Sirsa
(c) Rohtak (d) Kurukshetra

55 In which year Salt Satyagraha was started?
HSSC 2019
(a) 24th May, 1930 (b) 12th March, 1930
(c) 24th November, 1930 (d) 24th April, 1930

56 At which place of Haryana, women participated in a movement which was started by daughters of Lala Duli Chand, namely, Vidhyawati, Yashoda and Jamuna?
(a) Panipat (b) Ambala
(c) Rewari (d) Hisar

57 Who was awarded the title of 'Sarkar-e-Jung' by Netaji Subhash Chandra Bose?
(a) Major Suraj Mal (b) Rao Tularam
(c) Lala Lajpat Rai (d) Lala Murlidhar

58 In Haryana, who was against the military recruitment drive by the British during the First World War?
(a) Pandit Nekiram (b) Muhammad Azam
(c) Mohan Singh (d) None of these

59 Who was the leader of Mewatis from Gurugram-Hisar region?
(a) Muhammad Yasin Khan
(b) Lala Lajpat Rai
(c) Lala Murlidhar
(d) Suraj Mal

60 Which region of Haryana was the Muslim dominated region?
(a) Hisar (b) Jind (c) Sonipat (d) Panipat

61 When India got freedom in 1947, Haryana was the part of which Indian Province? *PGT 2016*
(a) Delhi (b) Punjab
(c) Uttar Pradesh (d) Rajasthan

62 Who among the following is also known as the 'Lion of Ballabhgarh'?
(a) Nahar Singh (b) Samand Khan
(c) Fateh Singh (d) Chhotu Ram

63 In order to make the Unionist Party important and well-known in all Haryana regions, Sir Chhotu Ram conducted a campaign. It was known by which name in Haryana?
Anganbadi 2016
(a) Zamindar League
(b) Zamindari System
(c) Hindu-Muslim
(d) None of the above

64 Who is known as 'Rahbare Azam' in Haryana?
(a) Sir Chhotu Ram
(b) Rai Bahadur Lala Murlidhar
(c) Mohan Singh
(d) Abdul Rahman

65 Who published a weekly paper, 'Sandesh' from 'Bhiwani'? *HSSC Head Office Cadre 2020*
(a) Lala Lajpat Rai
(b) Nekiram Sharma
(c) Lala Hukamchand Jain
(d) Noor Samad Khan

66 Who among the following persons is referred as the 'Haryana Kesari'? *HSSC 2020, Haryana Junior Engineer 2018*
(a) Bhopal Singh Arya (b) Nekiram Sharma
(c) Kanwal Singh (d) Udami Ram

67 Who was popularly known as the 'Grand old Man' of Haryana? *HSSC Field Cadre 2020*
(a) Sir Chhotu Ram
(b) Rao Tularam
(c) Pandit Nekiram Sharma
(d) Pandit Shriram Sharma

68 Freedom fighter Sucheta Kriplani was born in which district of Haryana?
(a) Hisar (b) Sirsa
(c) Ambala (d) Rohtak

69 Who among the following was an active member of the Indian National Army, established by Netaji Subhash Chandra Bose?
(a) Chhotu Ram (b) Chaudhary Devi Lal
(c) Fateh Singh (d) Lala Hukumchand

70 Who was the President of 'Swatantrata Senani Samiti' of Haryana?
(a) Abdul Rahman (b) Ram Singh Jakhar
(c) Sucheta Kriplani (d) Nahar Singh

71 Who founded 'Youth Assembly' in Rewari?
(a) Nekiram Sharma (b) Sucheta Kriplani
(c) Ram Singh Jhakkar (d) Banarasi Das

72 What did Swami Dayanand Saraswati start when he reached Rewari in Haryana? *Haryana Clerk 2016*
(a) Temple construction
(b) Construction of Dayanand Math
(c) Construction of Dharamshala
(d) Construction of Cowshed

73 Who founded the Arya Samaj in Sonipat district of Haryana?
(a) Chaudhary Ram Narayan Bhagan
(b) Pt. Shambhu Dutt
(c) Both (a) and (b)
(d) None of the above

74 After the Revolt of 1857, Haryana was annexed to *HSSC J.S.E. 2020*
(a) Punjab (b) Delhi
(c) Himachal Pradesh (d) Rajasthan

75 Which brave soldier of Haryana was the 'Nayab Kotwal' of Meerut during the Meerut Revolution? *HSSC Wild Life Gaurd-2017*
(a) Abdus Samad Khan (b) Vikram Singh
(c) Rao Krishna Gopal (d) Rameshwar Dayal

76 Who played an important role in the 1857 revolution in Rohtak? *HSSC Junior Eng. 2018*
(a) Myons (b) Ranghars
(c) Gujjars (d) None of these

77 Naseebpur (Narnaul) is known for what? *HSSC Roadways 2017*
(a) Victory of Marathas
(b) Invasion of Aurangzeb
(c) Revolution of 1857
(d) Atrocities of Timur Lang

78 Who is credited with the first attempt at the Home Rule Movement in Haryana? *HSSC 2022*
(a) Ram Kishore
(b) Thakur Ram Singh
(c) Lala Lajpat Rai
(d) Pandit Nekiram Sharma

CORRECT ANSWERS

1. (a)	2. (c)	3. (b)	4. (b)	5. (c)	6. (d)	7. (b)	8. (b)	9. (c)	10. (a)
11. (c)	12. (b)	13. (a)	14. (b)	15. (c)	16. (c)	17. (d)	18. (b)	19. (a)	20. (b)
21. (a)	22. (a)	23. (d)	24. (c)	25. (d)	26. (c)	27. (d)	28. (d)	29. (a)	30. (d)
31. (b)	32. (d)	33. (c)	34. (b)	35. (b)	36. (a)	37. (b)	38. (d)	39. (d)	40. (b)
41. (c)	42. (d)	43. (b)	44. (c)	45. (c)	46. (c)	47. (a)	48. (c)	49. (a)	50. (a)
51. (a)	52. (b)	53. (c)	54. (a)	55. (b)	56. (b)	57. (a)	58. (a)	59. (a)	60. (d)
61. (b)	62. (a)	63. (a)	64. (a)	65. (b)	66. (b)	67. (d)	68. (c)	69. (c)	70. (b)
71. (d)	72. (d)	73. (c)	74. (a)	75. (c)	76. (b)	77. (c)	78. (d)		

CHAPTER
05

Formation of Haryana as a Separate State

Demand for a Separate State

- After the Revolt of 1857, the British Government included much of Haryana in the Punjab Province in 1858.
- The demand for a separate state of Haryana emerged in 1907, supported by **Lala Lajpat Rai, Aruna Asaf Ali** and other prominent leaders of the Indian National Movement.
- **Haryana Development Committee**, chaired by **Shri Ram Sharma**, was formed to create an autonomous Haryana state, but the effort was not successful.
- The demand for separating Haryana from Punjab and merging it with Delhi was made for the first time by **Pirzada Muhammad Hussain** (Chairman, Swagat Committee) at the All India Muslim League session in Delhi, in 1926.
- In 1928, the Delhi Regional Congress Committee raised this demand again at the All-Party Conference in Delhi.
- In the Second Round Table Conference, **Geoffrey Corbett** proposed separation of the Ambala Division (Haryana) from Punjab, with Gandhiji's support.
- On 9th December, 1932, **Deenbandhu Gupta** demanded a separate state of Haryana from Punjab.
- Dr. Pattabhi Sitaramayya supported Deenbandhu Gupta's demand at the All-India Linguistic Conference in Delhi in 1946.

Demand for Punjab Province

- Haryana was part of **PEPSU** (Patiala and East Punjab States Union) when India attained independence on 15th August, 1947.
- **Master Tara Singh** demanded a Sikh state through his paper **Ajeet** in 1948.
- The Communist Party of PEPSU also demanded the Punjab Province, which was supported by the people.

On 1st October, 1949, the then Punjab Chief Minister Bhimsen Sacchar introduced the **Sacchar Formula** to address the linguistic reorganisation of Punjab.

Hindi and Punjabi Language Area Based on the Sacchar Formula

- According to this formula, the state was sub-divided into two parts i.e. Punjabi area and Hindi area.

State Division

Punjabi Area	Hindi Area
It included the areas that are located in present day Punjab i.e. Hoshiarpur, Ludhiana, Amritsar, Ferozepur, Patiala, Barnala, etc. The official language of Punjabi region was Punjabi (Gurmukhi script).	It included the districts of Rohtak, Hisar, Gurugram, Kangra, Karnal and the tehsils of Jagadhri (Ambala) and Naraingarh. The official language of the Hindi region was Hindi (Devanagari script).

- According to the Sacchar Formula, the medium of education was **Hindi** in the Hindi region and **Punjabi** in the Punjabi region until pre-university exams.
- **Hindi was mandatory** as a second language in schools in the Punjabi region and Punjabi as a second language in schools in the Hindi region.

State Reorganisation Commission

- On 29th December, 1953, the Indian Government set up the **Syed Fazal Ali Commission** to suggest the reorganisation of states on linguistic and cultural basis.
- The commission's report, presented in September 1955, rejected the demand for reorganisation on these grounds.
- In April, 1955, Congress MLAs from the Haryana region met in Rohtak to discuss state boundaries, demanded a separate state of Haryana before the State Reorganisation Commission.

Regional Formula

- In April 1956, the Central Government introduced the Regional Formula.
- According to this formula, the provision of the Sacchar Formula was further extended with the provision of creating a single Legislative Assembly and Governor for both the regions (Haryana and Punjab).
- After the 7th Amendment to the Indian Constitution in 1956, Regional Formula came into force from 24th July, 1956.

Provisions of the Regional Formula

- → Punjab would be a bilingual state with Hindi and Punjabi as official languages.
- → The region was divided into two parts i.e. Hindi and Punjabi.
- → Each region's district got its own languages.
- → The minorities from each region got full security.
- → The Central Government pledged full support to develop Hindi and Punjabi languages.

Hindi and Punjabi Regions Based on the Regional Formula

Region	Districts\Divisions
Hindi	Rohtak, Gurgaon (Gurugram), Karnal, Hisar, Ambala, Jagadhri and Naraingarh tehsils, Mahendragarh, Shimla, Kangra, Kohistan (present Patiala) and Jind and Narwana tehsils of Sangrur.
Punjabi	Ludhiana, Amritsar, Hoshiarpur, Jalandhar, Gurdaspur, Ferozepur, Ropar and Kharar tehsils of Ambala, Bhatinda, Kapurthala, Patiala, Barnala (present Sangrur), Sangrur and Sunam tehsils and Fatehabad Sahib (present Patiala).

- According to the Regional Formula, the following places of Kharar tehsil have been instructed to include in the Hindi region
  - The area of Kalka Police Station
  - Jail of Chandi temple
  - 17 villages located in Naraingarh Constituency

Failure of Regional Formula and Sant Fateh Singh

- In 1956, Punjab Chief Minister Pratap Singh Kairon failed to effectively implement the Regional Formula. He restricted the powers of regional committees, hindering their autonomy and resulting in its partial failure.

> In 1965, **Akali Dal** leader **Sant Fateh Singh** announced a 15-days hunger strike for a Punjabi Province, sparked demands for a separate Haryana Province in the Haryana region.

- Sant Fateh Singh postponed his fast due to the Pakistan war but resumed a 25-days fast on 10th August, 1965.
- The government of India on 23rd September, 1965, formed a Parliamentary Committee, led by Lok Sabha Speaker Hukum Singh, to consider Punjab's partition.
- In October, 1965, three resolutions were passed in a meeting organised by the MLAs of Haryana in Rohtak, which were as follows
  - A new Hindi speaking state should be created in which in addition to Hindi speaking area of Punjab, some parts of Delhi, Uttar Pradesh and Rajasthan should be included.
  - If Delhi, Uttar Pradesh and Rajasthan do not agree on this plan, then form a separate Haryana state by joining Hindi speaking areas of Punjab.
  - In Punjab, it will not be allowed to reduce the already designated Hindi area.
- On 3rd March, 1966, the **Haryana Sangharsh Samiti** met Sant Fateh Singh under the leadership of Chaudhary Devi Lal.
- Finally, the **Hukum Singh Committee** accepted the reorganisation of Punjab and recommended the formation of the **Shah Commission** (Punjab Boundary Commission).

Shah Commission

- On 23rd April, 1966, the Government of India formed the Shah Commission, chaired by **Supreme Court Judge J.C. Shah**, with members **S. Dutt** and **M.M. Philip**

- The **Punjab Border Commission's** report on 31st May, 1966, recommended including Kharar (with Chandigarh), Naraingarh and Jagadhri tehsils in Haryana.
- However, S. Dutt opposed Kharar and Chandigarh.

Formation of Haryana as a New State

- The Government of India approved the Punjab Reorganisation Bill on 18th September, 1966, based on JC Shah's proposal. Home Minister **Gulzarilal Nanda** introduced the bill in the Lok Sabha.
- It was also decided as per Article 231, that the two states of Haryana and Punjab would have a common High Court called the **Punjab** and **Haryana High Court**.

Salient Features of the Punjab Reorganisation Bill

(i) Formation of a new state within a stipulated time which will be called as Haryana. This state of Haryana will include the following places of Punjab

(a) Hisar, Rohtak, Gurugram, Karnal and Mahendragarh

(b) Narwana and Jind tehsils of Sangrur

(c) Ambala, Jagadhri and Naraingarh tehsils of Ambala

(d) Pinjore Kanungo Circle of Kharar tehsil of Ambala district

(e) The scheduled area included in first section of Manimajra Kanungo Circle of Kharar tehsil.

(ii) The area mentioned in sub-clause (b) shall become a separate district in the state of Haryana under the name Jind.

(iii) The territories referred to in clauses (c), (d) and (e) of sub-section (i) shall form separate district to be known as Ambala district in the state of Haryana.

In Ambala district

- The territories referred to in clauses (d) and (e) of sub-section (i) shall be a part of the Naraingarh tehsil.
- The territories referred to in clause (e) of sub-section (i) shall be a part of Pinjore Kanungo Circle in the Naraingarh tehsil.

Key Facts about Newly Carved Out State

- **Haryana** was formed as the 17th State of India on **1st November, 1966** under the 18th Amendment Act (1966) of the Indian Constitution.
- At the time of formation, Haryana had seven districts. These seven districts were Hisar, Karnal, Gurugram, Rohtak, Ambala, Mahendragarh and Jind.
- At the time of formation of Haryana, the largest district was **Hisar** (13891 sq km) and the smallest district was **Jind** (2712 sq km).

Dharamveer was appointed as the **First Governor of Haryana** and **Pandit Bhagwat Dayal Sharma** was made the first Chief Minister of Haryana.

Haryana's first newspaper was **Haryana Jhajjar**, with **Deen Dayal Sharma** as its Editor.

CHECK **CHAPTER KNOWLEDGE**

1 During the British Colonial period, Haryana was administered as a part of which province? *HSSC 2020*
(a) Punjab (b) Bengal
(c) Bombay (d) Madras

2 In which year Haryana region was merged with Punjab state? *Haryana Group D 2018*
(a) 1858 (b) 1958
(c) 1757 (d) None of these

3 In which year the demand for a separate state of Haryana was raised?
(a) 1905 (b) 1907
(c) 1909 (d) 1912

4 Who was the Chairman of the Haryana Development Committee?
(a) Hasrat Mohani (b) BB Dutt
(c) Shri Ram Sharma (d) None of these

5 Which organisation proposed the separation of Haryana for the first time in 1926? *PGT 2016*
(a) Arya Samaj
(b) Indian National Congress
(c) All India Muslim League
(d) Hindu Mahasabha

6 The demand for separation of Haryana region from Punjab Province and merging with Delhi was made for the first time in which session of the All India Muslim League?
(a) Lahore Session
(b) Amritsar Session
(c) Allahabad Session
(d) Delhi Session

7 In which Round Table Conference, Geoffrey Corbett talks about separating the Ambala Division (Haryana) from Punjab?
(a) First (b) Second
(c) Third (d) None of these

8 After India's Independence in 1947, Haryana was part of which Indian state? *PGT 2016*
(a) Punjab (b) Himachal Pradesh
(c) Rajasthan (d) Uttar Pradesh

9 Who first raised the demand for a separate state in 1948 called 'Punjab Province'?
(a) Tara Singh (b) Pandit Neki Ram
(c) Sant Fateh Singh (d) Pratap Singh Kairo

10 During which year, Sacchar Formula was introduced? *HSSC 2019, PGT 2016*
(a) 1947 (b) 1948 (c) 1949 (d) 1946

11 According to Sacchar Formula, Haryana state was subdivided into how many parts? *HSSC Field Cadre 2020*
(a) 1 (b) 2 (c) 3 (d) 4

12 According to the Sacchar Formula, which among the following districts came under 'Hindi Area'?
(a) Rohtak (b) Hisar
(c) Gurugram (d) All of these

13 Which of the following was not included under the Hindi region?
(a) Rohtak (b) Kangra
(c) Jagadhri (d) Sangrur

14 In which year Fazal Ali Commission was formed?
(a) 1951 (b) 1966 (c) 1953 (d) 1959

15 On 29th December, 1953, the Indian Government set-up a commission under the Chairmanship of Syed Fazal Ali for suggesting the reorganisation of states according to
(a) language (b) culture
(c) Both (a) and (b) (d) None of these

16 In which year, the Fazal Ali Commission submitted its report? *HSSC 2016*
(a) 1953 (b) 1954
(c) 1955 (d) 1956

17 Under which formula, an internal reorganisation of Punjab was done in July 1956?
(a) Regional Formula (b) Bifurcation Formula
(c) Shah Formula (d) Punjab Formula

18 After which amendment to the Indian Constitution in the year 1956, the Punjab Government implemented the Regional Formula?
(a) 2nd (b) 4th (c) 5th (d) 7th

19 Under the Regional Formula, the Punjabi region included
(a) Ludhiana (b) Amritsar
(c) Jalandhar (d) All of these

20 According to the Regional Formula, which area was not included in the Hindi region?
(a) Karnal (b) Hisar
(c) Gurugram (d) Ferozepur

21 Who announced a 15-day Hungar Strike in the year 1965, for the Punjabi state but postponed his fast due to the war with Pakistan?
(a) Master Tara Singh (b) Sant Fateh Singh
(c) Devi Lal (d) Pratap Singh Kairo

22 At which place in October 1965, three resolutions were passed in a meeting organised by the MLAs of Haryana?
(a) Gurugram (b) Hisar
(c) Rohtak (d) Ambala

23 Haryana state was formed on the recommendation of which among the following committees? *HSSC 2021*
(a) Indira Gandhi
(b) Sir Chhotu Ram
(c) Sardar Hukum Singh
(d) Lal Bahadur Shastri

24 Who was the member of Shah Commission?
(a) J.C. Shah (b) S. Dutt
(c) M.M. Philip (d) All of these

25 In which year, the Punjab Border Commission submitted its report?
(a) 1950 (b) 1955 (c) 1960 (d) 1966

26 The Punjab Reorganisation Bill was approved in which year?
(a) September, 1966 (b) October, 1968
(c) November, 1970 (d) December, 1972

27 On which date, Haryana emerged as a separate state? *HSSC 2023, 21, 20*
(a) 14th November, 1966
(b) 1st November, 1966
(c) 25th October, 1970
(d) 25th November, 1977

28 Under which amendment Haryana was formed as the 17th state of India?
(a) 7th (b) 11th (c) 15th (d) 18th

29 The first Governor of Haryana was *HSSC Group D 2018*
(a) BN Chakraborti
(b) Dharamveer
(c) RS Narula
(d) Bhagwat Dayal Sharma

30 Who was the first Chief Minister of Haryana?
(a) B.N. Chakraborti
(b) R.S. Narula
(c) Bhagwat Dayal Sharma
(d) G.D. Tapsi

31 In which year, the British Government politically divided Haryana into two parts? *HSSC CET 2023*
(a) 1805 (b) 1810
(c) 1815 (d) 1800

32 .... was the Editor of Haryana's first newspaper 'Haryana Jhajjar'. *HSSC CET 2023*
(a) Rajaram Shastri
(b) Bhagwat Dayal Sharma
(c) Deen Dayal Sharma
(d) Ramacharan Shastri

33 During the First World War of Ambala district in Haryana was one of the architects of the Ghadar party in San Francisco *HSSC CET 2023*
(a) Deen Dayal Sharma (b) Teeku Ram
(c) Neki Ram (d) Kanshi Ram

34 Consider the following statements.
(i) Haryana state was formed on the recommendations of Sardar Hukum Singh Parliamentary Committee.
(ii) Shah Commission was set up under the Chairmanship of Justice J.C. Shah to divide and set up the boundaries of Punjab and Haryana state.
(iii) On 1st November, 1966. Haryana as the 17th State of India came into existence

Which of the above statements is/are correct about Haryana? *HCS Prelims 2021*
(a) (i) and (ii) (b) (ii) and (iii)
(c) (i) and (iii) (d) All of these

CORRECT ANSWERS

1. (a)	2. (a)	3. (b)	4. (c)	5. (c)	6. (d)	7. (b)	8. (a)	9. (a)	10. (c)
11. (b)	12. (d)	13. (d)	14. (c)	15. (c)	16. (c)	17. (d)	18. (d)	19. (d)	20. (d)
21. (b)	22. (c)	23. (c)	24. (d)	25. (d)	26. (a)	27. (b)	28. (d)	29. (b)	30. (c)
31. (a)	32. (c)	33. (c)	34. (d)						

HARYANA

Art, Culture

and Tourism

This section contains all the important topics of Haryana Art, Culture and Tourism like Fairs, Festivals, Art, Architecture, Culture, Music and Dance, Famous tourist places,etc.

CHAPTER

06

Architecture, Art and Crafts in Haryana

The state of Haryana has been known for its architecture, sculpture and painting since ancient times. The Arts and Crafts of Haryana depict its rich cultural heritage. The town planning of Rohtak city mentioned in Buddhist scripture i.e. **Divyavadana**, is an example of an artistic features of the state of Haryana.

Architecture in Haryana

The architecture of Haryana has been divided into ancient, medieval and British period.

Ancient Architecture

- There is a mention of magnificent buildings and cities in Vedic literature. According to Buddhist scripture Divyavadana, Rohtak city was 12 Yojan long and 7 Yojan wide. For its protection, strong walls were built around it, which had 62 doors.
- **Mahabhasaya** (written by Patanjali) mentioned about a multi-storeyed building in Sugh of Yamunanagar district.
- The towns of Tosham, Sirsa, Kaithal (Thul Kot), Hisar and Sonipat were well-organised settlements.
- It is evident from archaelogical excavations that **Agroha in Hisar** was an important site and well planned city located between ancient trade routes of Taxila and Mathura.
- **Nar-Narayana cave** in Yamunanagar, is the best example of the ancient period architecture in Haryana.

Ancient Fort Architecture

- The forts in Haryana were built on raised platforms or hills and surrounded by moat that was filled with water.
- In ancient scriptures, description of 10 forts of Haryana has been found of which three forts in Sirsa, Meham and Rohtak are mentioned in **Nakul Digvijayam**.

- **Karna's Fort** in Thanesar and **Sohna Fort** in Karnal are the examples of ancient architecture. Banabhatta gave complete description about the Fort of Thanesar.
- **Hansi Fort** (Asigarh fort) was considered as the best fort of India in pre-medieval period. The **Barsi Gate** of this fort is still in good condition.
- This fort was built by **Prithviraj Chauhan** and was repaired by Alauddin Khilji in 1304 AD.

Religious Buildings of Ancient Period

Building	Explanation
Chaneti Stupa	• According to Hieun Tsang, The **Chaneti Stupa** was built by Mauryan king Ashoka, located in Chaneti village, near sugh in Yamunanagar district, Haryana. This stupa dates back to the 3rd century BCE and is an important site for Buddhism.
Thanesar Stupa	• In Thanesar a stupa was also built by Ashoka. • Its height is 80m. It contains the relics of Buddha. • The information about this stupa is found in the account of Chinese pilgrim Hiuen-Tsang. 
Monasteries in Thanesar and Sugh	Hiuen-Tsang had mentioned about 3 monasteries in Thanesar and 5 monasteries in Sugh in which many Buddhist monks used to live.
Temples in Thanesar	Banabhatta had given information about many temples of Thanesar such as Lord Shiv temple, Goddess Durga temple and Lord Vishwakarma temple.
Vishnu Temple in Tosham	It in Tosham is considered the most ancient Hindu temple in Haryana. It holds great historical and cultural significance.
Vishnu Temple during the Gupta Period	Evidence of Vishnu temple from the Gupta period has been found in Agroha and Nachar Khera, highlighting the prominence of Vaishnavism in Haryana during that era.

Medieval Architecture

- The oldest mansion (Haveli) of the state was the **palace of Feroz Shah Tughlaq**, located in **Fatehabad** district. It is an example of Turkish architectural style.
- **Gujri Mahal** in Hisar was built by **Feroz Shah Tughlaq** for his beloved Gujri Rani. Its construction was started in 1354 AD and it was completed in two years. The palace was constructed from **black stone** and **Lat ki Masjid** is also situated in this palace.
- **Jal Mahal** in Narnaul (Mahendragarh district) is another example of Medieval architecture. It was built by **Shah Quli Khan** in 1591 AD, who was the Mughal Governor of Narnaul during the reign of Akbar. The palace is made of **red** and **yellow sandstone** and is situated in the middle of a pond.
- Jal Mahal is built in Akbari style and the roof inside the palace is decorated like Rajput palaces. Five canopies are built on this palace.
- **Rang Mahal** at Buria in Yamunanagar district was built by a chief courtier of Shah Jahan in 1630 AD.
- The entire work of Rang Mahal has been done with stones and no wood has been used in making this palace. It is a three-storeyed palace and it had beautiful paintings on its inside walls.

Shish Mahal

- Shish Mahal in Farrukhnagar of Gurugram district is an example of the architecture of post-Mughal period. It was built in 1711 AD by **Faujdar Khan.** This palace was made of stone, slate and lime.
- During this period, two beautiful palaces were also built in Ballabhgarh and Rewari respectively. These palaces are made of black stone, slate and lime.
- The tomb and dome of Razia Sultana, the first woman ruler of India located in Kaithal, are other examples of medieval architecture.

Examples of Medieval Architecture in Haryana

Gujri Mahal

Jal Mahal

Rang Mahal

Shish Mahal

Some Other Famous Forts of Haryana

Fort Name	Location	Period/Building	Features
Gopal Giri Fort	Delhi-Gurugram Road	Built by Balban in the 13th century	Represents medieval architecture
Mewat Fort	Sohna, Kotla, Umrawat, Indore	Built by Mewat rulers	Located on hillocks; depict Turk-Afghan style of architecture
Kanod Fort	Mahendragarh District	Built by Maratha rulers in 1775 AD	A significant fort of the post-Mughal period; built for protection

Religious Buildings of Medieval Period

- Hindu temples in Haryana were mostly build during early medieval period from 8th to 11th century AD.
- Some of these temples are **temple of Gurbuda**, built in 9th century and **temple of Rohtak** built in 11th century. These temples are made of red stone and depict **Nagara style** of architecture.
- Rock inscriptions found in Sirsa describes about **Shiva temple** built by Pushp Dutt.
- Description of many **Vishnu temples** is found in Pehowa inscription (882 AD) of Bhoja Dev.
- Many Shiv temples had been built in **Kalayat**, in which all except two temples were destroyed by the invaders.
- These two temples were built in Nagara style in 9th century. The top parts of these temples is similar to **Odia temples** and the remaining parts resembles the Surya temple of Rajasthan.

Islamic Buildings of Medieval Period

Building Name	Location	Period/Builder	Features
Lat Masjid	Hisar	Built in the 14th century AD by Feroz Shah Tughlaq	• Features an **L shaped** lake beside the mosque and a lat (pillar). • The leaning walls of the mosque are inspired by the Seljuk style, Hindu style and the pillars of Ashoka.
Chahar Qutub	Hansi	Medieval period	• Houses the tombs of Sufi saints Jamal-ud-din, Qutub-ud-din, Bahar-ud-din and Nur-ud-din. • The tomb of Qutub's disciple, Mir Tajara, is regarded as the most magnificent piece of art in North India.
Dargarh of Sheikh Bu Ali Shah Qalandar	Panipat	Medieval period	• An example of Islamic architectural style.
Mausoleum of Ibrahim Suri	Narnaul	Built in 1540 CE by Sher Shah Suri	• Known for its intricate and unique architectural design.
Mausoleum of Khijr Khan	Sonipat	Built in the Pathan style by Ibrahim Lodi	• An octagonal mausoleum located in the Northern part of Sonipat, showcases the Pathan style of architecture.
Kabulibagh Mosque and its Tower 	Panipat	Built in 1527 AD by Babur	• Constructed after Babur's victory over Ibrahim Lodhi in the **First Battle of Panipat** in 1526 AD. • Named after Babur's first wife, Kabuli Begam. • The architectural style resembles royal mosques in Samarkand. • The mosque features octagonal towers and a large central dome supported by 26 smaller domes. • The gate and walls are made of bricks and red sandstone.
Tomb of Shah Quli	Narnaul	Built in 1574 AD	• An octagonal tomb with a narrow passage along the base, exemplifying Islamic architecture.

Other Architectural Examples of Medieval Period

Sheikh Chilli's Tomb

- It is located in Thanesar (Kurukshetra) and built in 1650 AD by Dara Shukoh.
- Constructed using **marble, red sandstone, bricks,** limestone and coloured tiles.
- The tomb is built on a raised plinth and the roof inside the tomb is adorned with paintings.
- It is popularly known as the **Taj Mahal of Haryana** and was declared a **national heritage** site under the Archaeological Land Remains Act, 1958.

Kos Minar

- It is located in Ambala, built in 1540 AD
- Sher Shah Suri erected Kos Minars at every Kos (unit for measuring distance) in the state.

Meham Chaubisi ka Chabutra

- It is located in Meham (Rohtak), built in 1656 AD.

- It was built by Suddo Kalal, representative of Shah Jahan.
- It is also known as 'Swarg ka Jharna' and 'Meham ki Shaan'.

Sheikh Tayyab's Tomb

- It is located in Kaithal, built in 17th Century AD.
- It was built by Hazrat Shah Sikander.
- It has a hemispherical dome in the centre and is built in Pathan style.

Birbal ka Chhatta

- It is located in Narnaul, built in 17th Century AD.
- It was built by **Rai Mukundas.**
- It is also known as **Palace of Mukundas.**

Fort of Nahar Singh

- It is located in Ballabhgarh (Faridabad), built in 1739 AD.
- It was built by ancestors of **Nahar Singh.** It is also known as **Nahar Singh Palace.**
- It is made of sandstone.
- It is a heritage site of the State Government of Haryana.

Other Examples of Ancient and Medieval Architecture

- **Baoli** were also constructed in medieval period in many parts of Haryana. They were built by stones, rocks and bricks and depict Hamams (man made ponds).
- The most ancient Baoli of the state was **Pinangwan** (in Mewat region), built with bricks and limestones.
- **Bridges** were also constructed in Mughal period in Haryana. They were built in bricks and limestone.
- **Saray or rest houses** were built in many places of Haryana. Shah Jahan had built rest houses in Samalkha, Narnaul, Tarawadi, Gharaunda. Aaram-e-Kausar is a rest house built by Shah Quli Khan in Narnaul.
- The **Badshahi** or **Mughal Bridge** in Karnal is one of the best example of architecture of Mughal period.

British and Modern Architecture

- Many towns and buildings have been built in this period on the basis of modern technique.
- **Karnal** is the first in Haryana which is formed on a pre-planned and modern technique or architecture.
- In 1806 AD, the British set up many military camps and barracks in Karnal in Haryana which are examples of modern architecture.

> **Octor Loni House** and **Adams House** in the state represent an example of the Indo-European architectural style of modern period.

- **Chandigarh is the first planned city of India.** It was designed by French architect, Le Corbusier who also designed the state High Court in Chandigarh.
- **Open Hand Monument** was also constructed by Le Corbusier.
- **Birla Temple** situated in Kurukshetra is a modern building built in 1952 by Jugal Kishore Birla. The temple is built in white marble. Its walls are decorated with verses from Bhagavad Gita. Therefore it is also known as **Gita Mandir.**
- **Gauri Shankar Temple** in Bhiwani is also famous for its architecture. It was constructed by Seth Kirori Mal therefore it is also called Kirori Mal temple.

- Some Mosques had been built in modern period in which the two mosques in **Rohtak district and Jama Masjid of Gurugram** are very famous.
- Jama Masjid was built by Aurangzeb. There was an ancient Mahavir temple inside the Jama Masjid.
- This temple was converted into a mosque during Alauddin's reign. It was again converted into temple after 1947.
- **Saint Paul Church in Ambala** is built in Gothic style and is one of the oldest church in the state. It was built during the British era in India. It was damaged by Pakistani attack in 1971.

Sculpture in Haryana

Many statues of Yakshas and Yakshinis have been found in archaeological excavations from various places of Haryana. Sculpture developed during the reign of the following rulers in the state

Sculpture in Haryana
- Sculpture during Shunga and Kushana Period
- Sculpture during Gupta Period
- Sculpture during Post-Gupta Period
- Sculpture of Medieval and Modern Period

Sculpture during Shung and Kushana Period

- Statues dating back to 2nd century CE that belong to Kushan period were discovered. These statues are of a **mythical character** Yakshas and Yakshinis. They are made up of red sandstone.
- **Surya Stamba** founded at Amin in Thanesar is a work of art that has resembles art of Bharhut Sanchi Stupa.
- Several statues of Yakshas and Yakshinis are also found from Palwal, Bhadas, Hathin and Faridabad which are not in proper form.
- The statues of Gods and Goddesses have been found of Shung and Kushana period.

> Statues found from **Sanghel** (Gurugram), **Saundh** (Faridabad) and **Khekrakot** (Rohtak) are made in red sandstone and had an influence of Mathura School of Art.

- Statues depicting Buddha are found from Gurugram, Mohanbadi, Jhaswa (Rohtak), etc.
- Two statues of Buddha are found in Rohtak and Bhiwani which are influenced by Mathura School of Art.
- Ancient Buddhist texts refer to Buddha's long journey from Hastinapur to Gaundhara *via* Rohitaka, Mahangara and Srughra. Of these, **Rohitaka** as **Rohtak** and **Srughra** as **Sugh** are correctly identified.
- Several non-religious statues are also discovered from these places such as dancing girl, trees, etc.
- A statue of lion is found in Rohtak on which Yaksh had been seated.

Sculpture during Gupta Period

- The Gupta period was marked by huge developments in art and culture. The statues of this period were magnificent and attractive and resembles the nature.
- **Buddha statues** are discovered from Thanesar and **Sandhi** and **Shiva statue** (made of red stone) is discovered from Harnaul in Gurugram.
- The statues of Gupta period represent reality which is evident from statue of Sun God from Agroha (Hisar) and statues of Vishnu from Sonipat and Mohanbari (Rohtak).

> Over period of time, the influence of the Gupta art has been reduced which is evident from statues of Shiva found from **Barwala** (Hisar) and **Naurangabad** (Bhiwani).

Sculpture during Post-Gupta Period

- In 10th century AD, kings patronised the sculptors due to which they started creating excellent work of art.
- The statues of this period are attractive, realistic and artistic. Several sculptures made during this period are found throughout in Haryana.
- Some of the sculptures in 10th century are related to Jainism and sculptures of Chauhan period were also found.

Sculpture of Medieval and Modern Period

Sculpture did not develop in the state during medieval as well as modern period.

Prominent Sculptures in Haryana

Sculpture	Location
Yaksha-Yakshini	Palwal, Bhadas, Hathin, Faridabad
Statue made on Sun pillar	Amin, Thanesar
Statue of Buddha	Bahmanwas (Rohtak), Naurangabad (Bhiwani)
Statue of Sun God	Agroha
Statue of Lord Shiva	Barwala (Hisar), Aurangabad
Statue of Lord Vishnu	Mohanbadi (Rohtak)
Statue of Vishnu lying on Sheshnag	Fazilpur (Sonipat)
Statue of Balram	Rohtak
Sculptures of Jain	Hansi and Rania (Sirsa)

Art in Haryana

- The art of painting in Haryana flourished during the ancient period.
- The ancient cities of **Banawali** (Fatehabad) and **Mitathal** (Bhiwani) were the main centre of paintings.
- Though no cave paintings have been found in pre-historic period, but some paintings of Siswal culture have been found in the state.
- The earthenware of this period had been found which was painted with black and white colours and displayed the art of contemporary period.

In Haryana, paintings depicting different time periods are discussed below

Painting in Different Time Periods

- Paintings of Indus Valley Civilisation
- Paintings of Vedic Period
- Paintings of Harsha Period
- Paintings of Medieval Period
- Paintings of Modern Period

Paintings of Indus Valley Civilisation

- The paintings of this period are the best examples of different emotions and feelings.
- Many paintings with criss-crossed lines have been found on **earthenwares** at **Mitathal** and **Banawali.**
- These earthenwares have been decorated with pictures of flower-petals.

Paintings of Vedic Period

- The paintings of this period were emotionless and done in an unskilled way.
- The development in painting was started during later Vedic period.

Paintings of Harsha Period

- During 7th century AD, Harshavardhana was a skilled painter, who also had good painters in his court.
- Harsha's court writer **Banabhatta described about the mural paintings in the chamber of Harsha which had the paintings of Rati and Priti (Wives of Kamadeva)** on opposite sides.
- After Harsha's death, painting flourished for a while under the Rajputs, but the establishment of the Delhi Sultanate put an end to this art.
- During the Mughal period, art of painting evolved again.

Paintings of Medieval Period

- Medieval paintings in Haryana include the paintings on the walls, ceilings of buildings and inside the palaces.
- Three major styles of paintings are found in Haryana. They are Rajput style, Mural style and Mughal style paintings.

Paintings of Medieval Period

Style of Painting	Description Points
Rajput Style of Paintings 	• The style was developed during the Rajput reign in Haryana. These paintings depict the great epic of Ramayana. • **Maharaja Tej Singh palace** in Mirpur (Gurugram) and **Matru Mad ki Piao** (famous in Gurugram) are examples of Rajput style of painting. • The paintings like **Asthal Bohar** are in the Rajput style. • The influence of this style of paintings can be seen in the temples of Lord Shiva at Panchkula and also at the Pinjore, Pabnama and Kaithal temples, at Kaul temple of Venumadhava, at Sirsa temple of Sarsainth and at Kapil Muni temple in Kalayat.
Mural Style of Paintings 	• This style is made on the walls or ceilings. This style is famous in Haryana. • Queen **Rani Chand Kaur's Haveli, the Lord Ram Radha's temple, Baba Nath's** temple at Pehowa and Bhadra Kali temple in Kurukshetra, have the presence of mural paintings. • Similar mural paintings can be seen in other temples and at religious Hindu locations in the whole of Haryana state.

Paintings of Medieval Period

Style of Painting	Description Points
Mughal Style of Paintings 	• This style evolved from the **Persian school of miniature painting** with Hindu, Buddhist and Jain influences. • These paintings evolved during the rule of various Mughal Emperors in India. • This style is also famous in Haryana. Its influence can be seen in temples of **Rohtak** and **Kaithal**. • These paintings are dominated by use of green, red, pink, blue and orange colours, decorated by pictures of flowers and birds. • The paintings found in the Rohtak temples are now kept in Kurukshetra University. • **Samadhis** of **Lala Balak Ram** and **Lala Jamuna Das** in Jagadhri in Ambala have paintings on the walls in Mughal style.

Paintings of the Modern Period

Paintings in Rewari

- During the first half of the 18th century, painting flourished in Haryana under the **Rao of Rewari**. The art developed in Rewari was a branch of Rajasthani art.
- Paintings of Rewari were associated with **Lord Krishna**. These paintings primarily depicted various scenes from Krishna's life.

Paintings in Manuscripts

- In the modern period, paintings were also done on book covers and their inner pages.
- Two manuscripts of Bhagavat Purana, containing handmade paintings, are preserved in Kurukshetra University.
- One manuscript used black and white colours in its paintings, while the other features vivid colours.

Wall Paintings

- Wall paintings were very popular in Haryana. The walls of many temples, rest houses and public places in rural Haryana are adorned with paintings.
- These paintings are especially found in regions such as Sonipat, Panipat, Hisar, Kaithal, Beri, Meham and Dadri.

Calligraphy in Mosques

- The Persian script is written in calligraphic style in many mosques.
- The side panels of doors and walls feature written verses of the Quran in flowing styles. This calligraphic style is especially common in mosques located in Rohtak and Kalayat.

Folk Art of Haryana : Sanjhi

- On the first day of Ashwin- Shukla Pratipada, the young girls and village women adore the walls of their houses with images of Goddess Sanjhi.
- The image is made on walls using clay and cowdung. It is decorated with using different colours and ornaments.
- Earthen lamps are lightened and songs are sung during the night in praise of Sanjhi.
- This beautiful rural art form is mainly found in Jat villages of Haryana.

Crafts of Haryana

The crafts of Haryana are very famous and also exported all over the world. Craft is one of the major modes of income for the rural people of the state.

Leather Craft

- Leather based footwear, known as **Juttis** are famous in Haryana.
- These are usually designed intricately with copper, silver and silk threads.
- Juttis are famous for both formal as well as informal occasions in Haryana.
- Rewari, Jhajjar, Karnal and Hisar are famous for **Zari Juttis**, whereas Rohtak is famous for **leather work**.

▲ Zari Jutis

Metal Work

- In metal work, brass sheets are used to make kitchen utensils. These utensils are a part of bride's wedding gifts.

Metal work is mainly done in **Gurugram** and **Rewari** districts of Haryana.

Ornament Work

- Jewellery of silver and lac, crafted with filigree and decorative work is very famous in Haryana.
- The jewellery is made in traditional and folk designs and is very popular among urban and rural folks.
- Silver waist belts made with stiff broad bands, which are flattened and twisted, are very famous in the state.
- **Gurugram** and **Sirsa** are important places of jewellery making in Haryana.
- **Mahendragarh** is famous for lac bangles.

Filgree work is a delicate and intricate form of metal work where fine, pliable metal wires (typically gold, silver) are twisted, braided or coiled to create intricate designs.

Pidi or Footstool Craft

- Haryana is famous for the craft of low stool or 'Pidi' which is made with strands of thread twined to form different kinds of coloured patterns.
- The thickness of the thread varies according to the size of the article, for example, thick twine is needed for making a bed or charpai.
- Famous patterns like 'Pacchisi' (design of the game of dice), 'Giani Chor ka Chatta' (maze consisting of a secret passage made by the thief Giani), etc are woven intricately.
- The reverse side of the Pidi has a different design. Haryana is famous for two types of woven furniture, Mudhas (round stools) and chairs made of sarkandas (a reed) from Farrukhnagar and Pidis from Sonipat.

Embroidery and Textile Works

Embroidery and Textile Works	Description
Phulkari Work 	• The meaning of Phulkari is work of flower and this craft is very much demanded and famous in Haryana. • The Phulkari shawl is similar to Kashmiri shawls. • It is woven by women in rural Haryana, especially in Jind, Kaithal, Fatehabad and Ambala districts. • Birds, animals, flowers, trees and human figures are beautifully embroidered into the shawls by rural women. • Silk threads of different colours are used to create simple yet elegant designs.
Bagh Work 	• A unique form of shawl popular in Haryana is known as Bagh. The Bagh shawl is totally designed by using the intricate embroidery work. • The designs used on the Bagh shawls are always inspired by the **pattern of geometry.** • **Green colour clothes** are generally used in the Baghs. • The designs that are made commonly include elements like elephants, houses, crops, sun, moon, kites, garden scenes, etc.
Chope Work	• Another style of shawl manufactured by Haryana artisans is Chope. It is more simple as compared to Phulkari and Bagh shawls. • This fabric is gifted to a newly married bride by her maternal grandmother.
Darshan Dwar Work 	• The religious shawl is known as **Darshan Dwar.** It is usually gifted by the devotees to the temple. • Human figures are usually depicted in these shawl designs. • Darshan Dwar means gateway to the divine and the two ends of this shawl are decorated with bands of wheat design. • There is a thick border patterned with alternating diagonal bands of five colours i.e. yellow, green, white, orange and pink.
Lungis	• Lungi is the long piece of fabric, which is worn by men. It is mainly a rural dress. • Karnal is very famous for the bright colour lungis.

Embroidery and Textile Works	Description
Durry 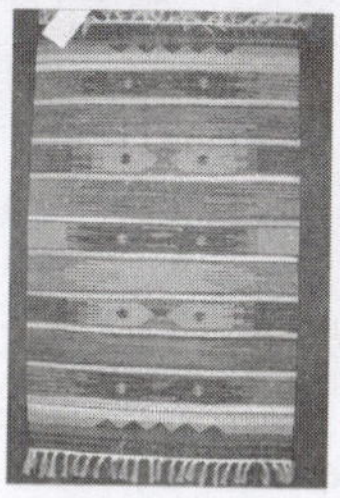	• The durries are very common in the state, but these contain very dynamic designs which give a grace to the whole rug. • The **Jat community** of Haryana state is well-known for **manufacturing of durries.** • They use designs like white colour triangles, opposite to the background of blue colour. • **Panipat** is the hub of durries manufacturing in Haryana. Its adjacent areas also manufacture durries. It is also known as **City of Weavers.** • The most famous durries are **Punja durries** that are common in every household.

Pottery

- Pottery is a famous rural craft in Haryana. The kick-operated type of potter's wheel is commonly used for making this craft which is operated by foot instead of hand.
- **Rewari, Jhajjar, Pinjore** and **Bahadurgarh** are famous for pottery.
- Jhajjar is famous for **Surahi,** a slim-necked pitcher. Cups, plates, water vessels, pipe bowls, etc are made in Rohtak. **Terracotta items** are produced in Gurugram, Jhajjar, Faridabad and Kurukshetra districts of Haryana.

▲ Terracotta Potteries

- Other important pottery items are household utensils, toys, animal figures such as cow, horse, decorative items like vases, lamp shades, pitchers, flower vases, etc.

Wood Craft

- Women artisans of Haryana make beautiful hand fans, also known as **Kundaladar Pakkhi**.
- Bamboo sheets are used as curtains in summer season which reduce the intensity of sunlight.
- **Changeri craft** (basket with lids) is mainly done by women folk, who use wheat grass to made beautiful baskets, dressing table, mats and other items.
- Bhiwani, Mahendragarh, Rohtak and Panchkula are important centres of wood and bamboo crafts.

Toy Making Craft

- Traditional toy making is a major craft in Haryana. Doll making is also practised in the state.
- Bright coloured wooden dolls are very famous in the state.
- Babushka dolls, lacquer dolls, string puppets, clay Indian toys and leather stuffs are also very popular.
- **Gurugram** and **Faridabad** are important centres of toy making. Haryana Arts Council has been making efforts for keeping this art alive.

Craft Cluster Division of Haryana

District	Craft Cluster	Craft
Gurugram	Firozpur-Jhirka, Pataudi, Farrukhnagar	Terracotta, Metal Jewellery, Mudha Making
Rewari	Kaisthwada, Rampura, Qutabpur	Brass Metal, Zari Jutti
Jhajjar	Bahadurgarh, Jhajjar	Sandalwood Carving, Terracotta
Faridabad	Badkhal, Palwal, Hodal	Terracotta, Basketry, Bone Carving
Sonipat	Farmana	Zari Jutti, Peedha Making
Panipat	Panipat	Punja Durries
Karnal	–	Zari Jutti
Ambala	Barara, Akbarpur, Racheri	Crochet, Embroidery, Punja Durries
Bhiwani	Dinod, Biran, Halawas, Nandha	Wooden beads, Mudha Making
Chandigarh	–	Embroidery, Pot Painting
Kurukshetra	Thanesar	Terracotta, Peedha Making
Hisar	Shanti Nagar Bigher	Zari Jutti, Punja Durries
Sirsa	–	Jewellery, Pot Painting
Mahendragarh	Narnaul, Talot	Lac bangles, Woodcraft
Yamunanagar	Jagadhri	Hand embroidery
Rohtak	–	Leather and Woodwork
Jind		Sanghi Craft
Kaithal	–	Sanghi Craft
Panchkula	–	Embroidery, Woodwork

***Source** *Haryana tourism.gov.in*

CHECK CHAPTER KNOWLEDGE

1 Which ancient fort in Haryana was repaired by Alauddin Khilji in 1304 AD?

(a) Karna's Fort (b) Hansi Fort
(c) Asigarh Fort (d) Kanod Fort

2 The Chaneti Stupa, constructed during the Mauryan period, is located in which district of Haryana? *HSSC 2023*

(a) Hisar
(b) Karnal
(c) Yamunanagar
(d) Kurukshetra

3 Who built the Gujri Mahal in Hisar?

(a) Feroz Shah Tughlaq (b) Shah Quli Khan
(c) Akbar (d) Alauddin Khilji

4 Which structure in Haryana is known as the "Hansi Fort"? *HSSC 2023*

(a) Asigarh Fort
(b) Gopal Giri Fort
(c) Kanod Fort
(d) Sohna Fort

5 Which Vishnu temple in Haryana is considered the most ancient Hindu temple?

(a) Nachar Khera Temple
(b) Agroha Vishnu Temple
(c) Tosham Vishnu Temple
(d) Thanesar Temple

6 Consider the following statements about the Jal Mahal in Narnaul

1. It was built by Shah Quli Khan in 1591 AD.
2. The palace is made of red and yellow sandstone and located in the middle of a pond.

Which of the statements given above is/are correct?

(a) Only 1 (b) Only 2
(c) 1 and 2 (d) All of these

7 Consider the following statements about Chaneti Stupa

1. It is constructed with baked bricks in a spherical structure.
2. Its construction is attributed to the reign of Ashoka.
3. It has a height of 80 meters.

Which of the statements given above is/are correct?

(a) 1 and 2 (b) 1 and 3
(c) 2 and 3 (d) All of these

8 Consider the following statements about the architecture of Haryana

1. Hansi Fort was considered the best fort in India during the pre-medieval period.
2. The Rang Mahal at Buria was built in 1630 AD without using wood.
3. The tomb of Razia Sultana is located in Rohtak.
4. Vishnu temples from the Gupta Period were found in Agroha and Nachar Khera.

Which of the statements given above is/are correct?

(a) 1 and 2 (b) 2 and 4
(c) 1, 3 and 4 (d) 1, 2 and 4

9 Sheikh Chilli's Tomb, popularly known as the 'Taj Mahal of Haryana,' is located in which city?

(a) Sonipat
(b) Thanesar (Kurukshetra)
(c) Karnal
(d) Panipat

10 Which architectural style is depicted in the temples of Kalayat built during the 9th century?

(a) Dravidian (b) Nagara
(c) Gothic (d) Indo-European

11 What was the Kabulibagh Mosque named after?

(a) The region of Kabul
(b) A local saint
(c) Babur's victory in Panipat
(d) Babur's first wife, Kabuli Begam

12 Which of the following statements about Chahar Qutub in Hansi is correct?

1. It houses the tombs of four Sufi saints.
2. The tomb of Mir Tajara is part of the structure.
3. It was built by Babur after his victory in Panipat.

(a) 1 and 2 (b) 2 and 3
(c) 1 and 2 (d) All of these

13 Which of the following statements is correct about Sheikh Chelli's Tomb?
(a) It was built using marble, bricks and limestone and is located in Sonipat.
(b) It was constructed by Dara Shukoh and declared a national heritage site under the Archaeological Land Remains Act, 1958.
(c) The tomb has paintings on its roof and is popularly known as the Taj Mahal of Haryana.
(d) Both (b) and (c)

14 Which of the following city was the first in Haryana to be built by modern architecture?
(a) Chandigarh (b) Karnal
(c) Narnaul (d) Rohtak

15 Which region is associated with the discovery of the Surya Stamba resembling Bharhut and Sanchi Stupa art?
(a) Mohanbadi (b) Agroha
(c) Amin, Thanesar (d) Palwal

16 In which city of Haryana were two Buddha statues influenced by the Mathura School of Art discovered?
(a) Gurugram (b) Rohtak
(c) Bhiwani (d) Faridabad

17 In the villages of Haryana, the walls of the houses are decorated with the images of Goddess Sanjhi for *HSSC 2017*
(a) the health of the senior citizens
(b) welfare of the girl child
(c) the good crop of farmers
(d) the improvement of the players

18 Which kind of art is very famous in Haryana? *HSSC 2020*
(a) Lehariya (b) Gota
(c) Phulkari (d) Kadhai

19 Which districts of Haryana is known as the 'hub of making durries' in Haryana? *Patwari 2016*
(a) Gurugram (b) Panipat
(c) Bhiwani (c) Hisar

20 Which city of Haryana is known as 'City of Weavers'? *HSSC 2020*
(a) Rewari (b) Rohtak (c) Hisar (d) Panipat

21 Which districts of Haryana is well known for leather work? *HSSC 2016*
(a) Rohtak (b) Jhajjar
(c) Faridabad (d) Kurukshetra

22 Which of the following city was the first in Haryana to be built by modern architecture?
(a) Chandigarh (b) Karnal
(c) Narnaul (d) Rohtak

23 The Birla temple, situated in Kurukshetra was built by
(a) Le Corbusier (b) Jugal Kishore Birla
(c) Kirori Mal (d) Ratan Tata

24 The Yakshas and Yakshinis discovered in Haryana during archaeological excavations are made up of
(a) grey sandstone (b) red sandstone
(c) marble (d) None of these

25 Statues of Buddha have been found at which of the following places in Haryana?
(a) Gurugram (b) Jhaswa
(c) Mohanbadi (d) All of these

26 Paintings of Rewari flourished during the 18th century in Haryana. These paintings depict which of the following?
(a) Mughal Palaces (b) Rajput Customs
(c) Lord Krishna's life (d) None of these

27 Phulkari refers to
(a) big gardens in Haryana villages
(b) art of pottery
(c) flower designing on buildings
(d) art of making shawl

28 Which among the following is an art of making shawl?
(a) Durries (b) Robing
(c) Bagh (d) All of these

29 Which colour is mostly used to prepare Bagh shawl in Haryana?
(a) Red (b) Orange (c) Green (d) Black

30 Which of the following handlooms is gifted to new bride by groom's grandmother?
(a) Phulkari (b) Robe
(c) Bagh (d) Chope

31 Jat community of Haryana is popular for the manufacturing of
(a) phulkari shawl (b) chope
(c) bagh (d) durries

32 Which city of Haryana is known as "City of Weavers"? *HSSC 2020*
(a) Rewari (b) Rohtak (c) Hisar (d) Panipat

33 Which among the following districts of Haryana is famous for lungis?
(a) Hisar (b) Kaithal
(c) Rohtak (d) Karnal

34 Which districts of Haryana is well known for leather work? *HSSC 2016*
(a) Rohtak (b) Jhajjar
(c) Faridabad (d) Kurukshetra

35 Metal work is mainly done in which of the following districts of Haryana?
(a) Gurugram (b) Rewari
(c) Jhajjar (d) Both (a) and (b)

36 Which districts of Haryana are famous for jewellery making?
(a) Gurugram (b) Sirsa
(c) Hisar (d) Both (a) and (b)

37 Which district is famous for lac bangles?
(a) Panipat (b) Bhiwani
(c) Mahendragarh (d) Karnal

38 Which district is famous for 'Surahi', a slim-necked pitcher in Haryana?
(a) Jhajjar (b) Rewari
(c) Gurugram (d) Fatehabad

39 Match List I (Medieval Structures) with List II (Builders/Features). *HSSC 2023*

List I	List II
A. Gujri Mahal	1. Built by Feroz Shah Tughlaq
B. Jal Mahal	2. Built by Shah Quli Khan
C. Shish Mahal	3. Built by Faujdar Khan
D. Kanod Fort	4. Built by Maratha rulers

Codes

	A	B	C	D		A	B	C	D
(a)	3	4	2	1	(b)	1	2	3	4
(c)	4	1	3	2	(d)	2	4	1	3

40 Match List I (Ancient Sites) with List II (Features).

List I	List II
A. Agroha	1. Well-planned town, Gupta period evidence
B. Sugh	2. Mentioned in Mahabhasya
C. Rohtak	3. 12 Yojan long, 62 doors
D. Thanesar Stupa	4. Built by Ashoka, relics of Buddha

Codes

	A	B	C	D		A	B	C	D
(a)	4	1	3	2	(b)	3	2	4	1
(c)	2	4	1	3	(d)	1	2	3	4

41 Match the distinctive aspects given in List I with the correct districts of Haryana given in List II and select the correct answer using the options given below in columns. *HSSC 2019*

List I (Distinctive Aspect)	List II (District of Haryana)
A. This district has the Tomb of Sheikh Chilli	1. Kurukshetra
B. This city is associated with the temple called Panchvati	2. Palwal
C. This district is associated with the temple of Jayanti Devi	3. Jind
D. This district is associated with the ancient town of Khokhrakot	4. Rohtak

Codes

	A	B	C	D		A	B	C	D
(a)	3	4	2	1	(b)	1	2	3	4
(c)	2	3	1	4	(d)	4	1	3	2

42 Match List I with List II and choose the correct option. *HSSC 2023*

List I (Monument)	List II (Location)
A. Gujri Mahal	1. Hisar
B. Sheikh Chilli's tomb	2. Kurukshetra
C. Choron Ki Baoli	3. Rohtak
D. Jal Mahal	4. Mahendragarh

Codes

	A	B	C	D		A	B	C	D
(a)	1	2	3	4	(b)	2	3	4	1
(c)	3	4	1	2	(d)	4	1	2	3

CORRECT ANSWERS

1. (b)	**2.** (c)	**3.** (a)	**4.** (a)	**5.** (c)	**6.** (c)	**7.** (c)	**8.** (d)	**9.** (b)	**10.** (b)
11. (d)	**12.** (c)	**13.** (d)	**14.** (b)	**15.** (c)	**16.** (b)	**17.** (b)	**18.** (c)	**19.** (b)	**20.** (d)
21. (a)	**22.** (b)	**23.** (b)	**24.** (b)	**25.** (d)	**26.** (c)	**27.** (d)	**28.** (c)	**29.** (c)	**30.** (d)
31. (d)	**32.** (d)	**33.** (d)	**34.** (b)	**35.** (d)	**36.** (d)	**37.** (c)	**38.** (a)	**39.** (b)	**40.** (d)
41. (b)	**42.** (a)								

CHAPTER 07

Music and Dance of Haryana

Haryana has a vivid culture enriched with folk music, folk instruments and folk dance. Haryana also plays an important role in Indian culture and civilisation, from where the entire country has been given knowledge of the Indian philosophy and spirituality.

Evolution of Music in Haryana

The first evidence of music of Haryana have been obtained from **Vedic period**. The music in Haryana has further developed during the post Vedic period, Medieval period and the Post-Mughal period.

Music in Vedic Period

- Evidence of music in Haryana has emerged from the Vedic period. Music mainly emerged under the patronage of sages and wise monks during this period.
- Vedic music developed in the monasteries and spiritual hermitages (ashrams) of these monks and sages.

Music Evolved during Vedic Period
(By Spiritual Hermitages of Saints)

↓

The hymns of Rigveda, addressed to the Vedic Gods such as Indra, Agni, Soma, etc. Sung in three tones Uddatta (high tone), Anudatta (low tone), Svarita (middle tone).

↓

Songs of Samveda, which were sung in seven notes. It was also known as Marga sangeet.

↓

Gandharva and indigeneous music were other forms of music during the Vedic period.

Music in Post-Vedic Period

- Professional musicians emerged during post-Vedic period which includes **flute players, drummers, veena players**, etc. Classical music was very popular during the post-vedic period.
- A sculpture had been found at a place called **Sugh** in Ambala, which depicts various singers and musicians travelling on a bullock cart.
- Folk musicians of Rohtak were also famous in Ujjain.
- A **brick** was found from a place called **Agroha** in 9th century AD, which mentions 'Sa Re Ga Ma Pa Dha Ni, on it. This indicates a strong connection with music during that period.

Music in Medieval Period

- **Mahatma Surdas** of Sihi village is most prominent name among the musicians of medieval period. Sant Surdas was born in 1478 AD.
- He was a contemporary of Mughal emperor Akbar and a disciple of **Haridas** and later Vallabhacharya.
- Music forms such as **dhrupad, khayal, thumri, tarana,** etc developed in the medieval period in Haryana and in North India.
- **Haddu Khan** was a famous **Khayal singer** of Gwalior Gharana.

Music in Post-Mughal Period

- **Ustad Kallan Khan** was a famous Khayal singer in the post-Mughal period. He was the resident of Rewari in Haryana and was the disciple of Haddu Khan.
- **Hafiz Khan**, the son of Kallan Khan, was also a famous Khayal singer. He performed in the Royal Court of Mysore and Indore.

Folk Music in Haryana

The folk music is very popular in Haryana. The ragas of music in Haryana have been named after the names of villages, e.g. Sarangpur in Charkhi-Dadri, Brindabana, Todi, Asaveri, Malakoshna, Hindola, Nandyam, etc are the names of the ragas of music in Haryana.

Raga Pilu is used by **Ahirs** in some of their songs, in which a scale of twelve semi-tones is used.

Folk Music of Haryana

- **Country Form**
  It is based on different ragas and includes ceremonial songs, ballads, mythological songs like Puran Bhagat (Raga Maand), etc. It is based on Hindustani ragas like Raga Bhairvi, Kafi,Jaijaivanti, Jhinjhoti and Pahadi.
- **Classical Form**
  This type of music includes songs whose subjects are mostly mythological, e.g. Brahmas, Jaimal Fatta, etc.

Popular Folk Songs of Haryana

- According to Banabhatta, folk songs were sung on the wedding of Harsha's sister, **Rajshree** in Haryana.
- Weddings, births, festivals and harvest period are the auspicious occasions when folk songs are usually sung mainly in the rural parts of Haryana.
- The folk songs sung in the state are based on the seasons and rituals.

Folk Songs in Modern Period

Folk Song Type	Occasion/Detail
Wedding Songs	• Sung during wedding ceremonies, focusing on auspicious themes and relationships like Devar-Bhabhi, Jija-Sali, Nanad-Bhabhi, Saas-Bahu, Devrani-Jethani, Samdhi-Samdhan, etc. • Banda-Bandi, Ghodi songs are sung on boy's marriage. • Suhaag songs are sung on girl's marriage. Example *"Babul Desh Aayio Pardesh Jaayio, Gori Ka Var Tu Dhoondiyo"*
Seethne	• Joyful songs sung during weddings; also known as **Gali songs**.
Jakdi	• Performed after singing folk songs on various occasions.
Birthday Songs	• Sung at birth ceremony of **male** child, conveying blessings for his future. • Include forms like Sohar, Jachcha (Maternal), Pilia, Badhai and Ashish songs. Example *"Pilla odh Hamari Jachcha Mundhala Baithee Geet"*
Sohar	• Sung on the occasion of a child's birth. Some are known as **Mangla Char.**
Pilia	• Associated with the yellow colour (Pila Rang) symbolising fortune and luck. Sung during birth ceremonies.
Holi Songs	• Sung in February/March (Phagun month), characterised by humour and fun.
Sawan Songs	• Express happiness in the Sawan month (July/August). • Includes Badal, Varsha, Jhule, Khet, Teej, Kothali, Sindhara, etc.
Religious Songs	• Sung during Kartik month (October-November) or religious ceremonies. Focus on Hindu Goddess songs, Devuthani songs, Katak Nahane songs, Sanjhi songs and local bhajans.
Panghat Songs	• Sung by women, often depicting *Shringar Rasa* (love, attraction and beauty).
Other Songs	• Include love and quarrel songs and those related to seasons, agriculture, soldiers and lifestyle themes.

Famous Musicians and Singers of Haryana

Zohrabai Ambalewali

- Born in 1918
- Place Ambala District
- Disciple of Ghulam Hussain Khan and Ustad Nasir Hussain Khan (Agra Gharana)
- Debut Film Daku ki Ladki in 1933
- She started her career at the age of 13 years with the All India Radio, singing classical and semi-classical songs.
- She made her debut in film industry by the film 'Daku ki Ladki' in 1933.
- She had sung around 1200 songs in the middle of the year 1941-50.
- She retired in the 1950s from the film industry. She passed away in the year 1990.

Baje Bhagat

- Born on 16th July, 1898
- Place Sisha Village, Sonipat
- Childhood name Bajeram
- Title Swara Samrat
- Famous for Poems, Ragini writings, Saang atrist
- Popular Writings Satyavadi Harishchandra, Nal-Damyanti, Jani Chor, Puranmal, Gopichand, Sarovar-Neer, etc
- Death 26th February, 1939

Pandit Jasraj

- Born on 28th January, 1930
- Place Pili Mandori village, Hisar (now Fatehabad district)
- Disciple of Thakur Saheb (Mewati Gharana)
- Famous for Creating a new form of Jugalbandi, known as 'Jasrangi'
- Awards Sangeet Natak Akademi Award (1987), Padma Bhushan (1990), Padma Vibhushan (2000)
- Title Swara Samrat
- Honoured Haridas Sangeet Ratna and Sangeet Martandeya Award by Haryana Government
- Death 17th August, 2020 in New Jersey, (USA).

Folk Musical Instruments

Musical instruments are popular in Haryana since vedic period. The folk musical instruments in Haryana were broadly divided into three categories

- Dhol, daph, damru, dundubi, etc.
- Veena
- Flute, algoza, etc.

Various popular folk musical instruments of the state include string instruments, wind instruments, membrane instruments and percussion instruments.

String Instruments

Instruments which are played with the help of vibrations created by string pulls are known as string instruments.

Some Famous String Instruments in Haryana

Instrument	Description
Sarangi 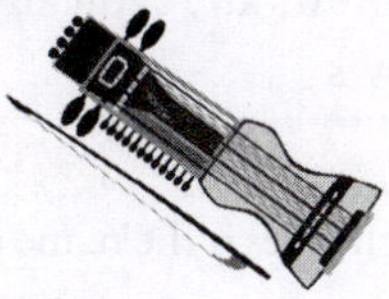	• This instrument is made from **red cedar wood** and its ancient name is **Sarinda.** • Sarangi bow (Gaj) is used to play Sarangi and Gaj is made by tying horse hair on a piece of command. • It has four pegs and four strings are attached to these pegs. • This instrument has been made popular by **Jogis. Maman Khan** was most popular Sarangi player, belonged to Panipat Gharana.
Tumba 	• Also known as **Tumbi**, it is a single-string high-pitched instrument associated with the folk music of Haryana. • It is made from a wooden stick mounted with a gourd shell resonator. • Some famous Tumba players are Lal Chand Yamla Jatt, Kuldeep Manak, Amar Singh Chamkila, Didar Sandhu and Sarbajit Cheema.
Iktara 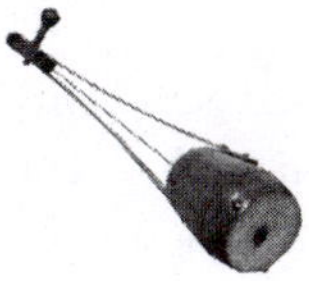	• This instrument is made by attaching a piece of bamboo to a tumba. • A string is stretched across this piece of bamboo, which gives it the name **Iktara.** • It is commonly used in **Bhajan-Kirtan.** • In ancient times, it was used by the **Bhat and Charan communities.**
Datara	• This instrument is similar to the Iktara but has two strings instead of one.
Bulbul Tarang (Indian Banjo)	• It has vocals on the left side like a harmonium. • Thin strings below the vocals produce sound when played with the right hand or with a piece of plastic or blade. • In modern times, this instrument has been transformed into the electric banjo.

Instrument	Description
Sitar	• This instrument is a combination of the veena and the Iranian tambura. • The sitar was invented by **Amir Khusrau.** • It is a popular musical instrument used in both classical and modern music.
Veena 	• This is a classical music instrument **mentioned in** Rigveda, Samaveda and other vedic literature. • It is one of the most ancient musical instruments used in Indian music. • Made from **Jackwood,** it has a large body with a thick and wide neck. • It has 24 metal frets and sound is produced by four metal strings attached to the frets.
Harmonium 	• It is also known as **Peti Baja.** • It produces sound through several keys that are pressed during playing. • It is extensively used to accompany folk, classical, sufi and ghazal compositions for both music and dance.

Wind Instruments

A wind instrument produces sound through the vibration of air, typically by blowing into or across the instrument. Some popular wind instruments in Haryana are as follows

Instrument	Description
Flute (Bansuri) 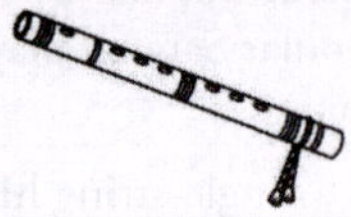	• It is made of **bamboo,** which gives it the name **bansuri.** It is used in Hindustani classical music. • The holes of bansuri are used to produce different tones and the first hole is for blowing air into the instrument.
Shankh	• It is made from a conch shell, primarily used in religious ceremonies in Hinduism. • According to the **Brahma Vaivarta Purana,** the Shankh is considered a form of God, like the Sun and Moon. Varuna resides in its middle part, Brahma its backside and Ganga and Saraswati in its side.
Alghoza 	• It holds a special place in Haryanvi folk music. • It is usually like a flute, made of **wood** or **bamboo.** • It is often used by shepherds while grazing cattle.
Been 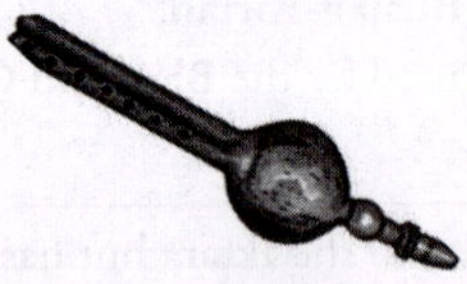	• It is made from a dry, hollowed gourd with two bamboo attachments. • It is a double-reed instrument, with its upper part long and its lower part round. • It is also known as **Pungi** and is mostly played by snake charmers. • Its lower part has two tubes with holes; air is blown through one tube and sound is produced from the other. • One pipe creates a drone-like sound and the other produces melody. Both sounds are played simultaneously using circular breathing, creating a hypnotic effect.

Membrane Based Instruments

Some famous membrane based instruments of the state are

Instrument	Description
Dholak 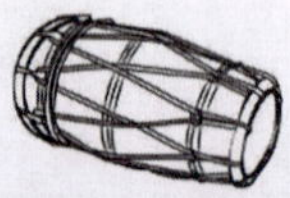	• It is an important musical instrument in Haryanvi folk music and is used in almost all household ceremonies, such as **kirtans** and **wedding ceremonies.** • It is made of **mango, sheesham** and **teak wood,** with both ends covered in animal hide.

Instrument	Description
Nagada 	• It is a type of drum that is circular and can be considered a larger form of tabla. • It is placed on the ground and played. • A nagadi, a small nagada known as '**Jhil**,' is always kept on the left side of the nagada. • The wooden stick used to play nagada is called '**Chob**.' • It is used in Haryanvi folk dance Manjira and is played along with Shehnai.
Daph 	• It is used during **daph** and **dhamal dance** and is a popular instrument in the **Mahendragarh district**. • The daph is made of an open circular frame with one side covered in skin. • It can be played either by hands or with sticks.
Damru 	• It is an ancient instrument associated with **Lord Shiva**. • It is made of wood and metal with leather drum heads at both ends and two short ropes attached in the middle. • Its shape consists of two wooden conical pieces joined at their tips. • Beads attached to the ends of the leather cords strike the drum heads to create melodious sounds. It is used in **Goga dance**.
Deru 	• The shape of deru is similar to the damru but larger. • It is made of mango wood, with both ends mounted with thin leather and a rope tied in the middle to adjust the leather. • It is played with a thin, bent wooden stick. • It is used in worshipping **Goga Ji** by the Dhanak community.
Dafli	• It is a smaller version of the daph and is shaped like a plate. • One side of its circular frame is covered with leather and bells are threaded in the middle of the frame. • The dafli is mostly used by snake charmers.
Ghadwa 	• It is a strong earthen pot with a rubber piece tightened over its mouth. • One hand is used to beat the rubber at the mouth, while the wrist and palm of the other hand are used to strike the pot. • The ghadwa was created by **Kavi Shree Pandit Jagannath Bhardwaj**.
Nobat	• It signifies a group of instruments, including large 'Kettledrums' or 'Nagara'. • It is played at Royal ceremonies in the South-East Asian regions like Malaysia.

Percussion Instruments

These instruments are made up of metal and are played by striking against each other or by a beater. Some popular percussion instruments of the stall are given below

Instrument	Description
Jhanjh (Cymbal)	• A round piece of metal with a diameter of 8 to 16 finger length is known as Jhanjh. • It consists of thin, rounded plates made up of various alloys such as **tin and copper**. • A hole is drilled at the centre for tying straps so it can be held in the hands for playing. • In some regions, it is also known as **khartal**.
Manjira 	• Manjira is a smaller version of Jhanjh, but the middle part is deeper compared to Jhanjh. • It is made up of a combination of **copper**, **brass** and **zinc**. • It consists of two small cup-like structures tied together with a chord. • It is used during bhajans and kirtans along with dholak and harmonium.

Instrument	Description
Tasha	• It is a popular folk instrument made of baked clay, copper or iron. • Its top is covered with the hide of a goat. • A lace is attached to it so it can be worn around the neck and is played with sticks. • It is often used on the **occasion of marriages.**
Khanjari 	• It is made of a circular brass and wooden frame covered with goat hide. • It has a round shape with bells and thin pieces of metal hanging around it to produce a twinkling sound. • It is held in one hand and played with the palm and fingers of the other hand.
Jhalar	• It is a type of musical instrument formed by a single metal plate. • It is beaten with the help of a wooden stick. • It is mainly used during worship and prayers in temples.
Chimta (*Tongs*) 	• It is similar to a kitchen tong but is much bigger in size. • It consists of a long, flat piece of steel or iron pointed at both ends and joined at the other end. • Small bells or ghunghru are attached to it to produce melodious sounds.
Khartal and *Bells* 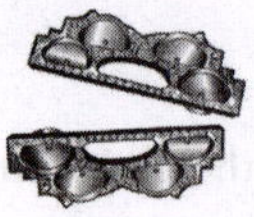	• Khartal is made up of mango wood. • Metallic rings are attached to khartal to produce tinkling sounds. • Bells are played in temples during religious occasions at the time of worship and kirtans.

Folk Dances in Haryana

There is a systematic tradition of folk dances in the state of Haryana. Folk dances are organised at every festival, rituals, ceremonies and celebrations.

Folk Dances of Haryana
- Dances Performed by Men
- Dances Performed by Women
- Combined Dance

Dances Performed by Men

The main dances performed by men in Haryana include Gugga dance, Dhamal dance, Daph dance, Damru dance, Chaupaiyan dance, Saang, etc.

Gugga Dance

- Occasion — Performed in memory of Gugga pir on Gugga Navami
- Performed by — Both Hindus and Muslims
- Music — Devotees sing praises of Gugga Pir
- Also known as — Gugga Rahim Pir, Bagad Wale and Charri dance
- Dance — Perfomed to the beats of **Sarangi** and **Deru**
- The worshippers and followers of Gugga wear yellow coloured dresses and the dance is performed in a procession.
- A week before Gugga Navami, the devotees take out the procession carrying a long and strong bamboo stick known as **Gugga Ki Charri.**
- The Charri is decorated with garlands, flowers, peacock feathers, coloured clothes, etc.

> Gugga dance is very simple but has **spiritual rhythm.** The feet of dancers move according to the rhythm on their songs.

- During the dance, the devotees beat their bodies with iron chains. It is believed that by doing so they do not get hurt because the soul of Gugga dwells in their body.
- It is considered as a religious dance form.

Chaupaiyan Dance

- Performed by — Men of Haryana
- Significance — Symbolise the religious tradition of state
- Popular in — Banchori village of Hodal tehsil of Palwal district

Saang Dance

- Combination of — Music, dance and drama performance
- Performed by — Heroic dance of men
- The raginis are also presented in this dance.

Daph Dance

- Nature — Seasonal dance form
- Performed by — Farmers
- In this dance form, farmers express their feelings because they have got good harvest and spring season is going to start.
- In this dance, the dancers keep the daphs on their shoulders and beat them with their right hands.

Damru Dance

- Performed by — Men
- Performed on — The night of Shivratri
- In this dance, the men play damru with their hands while dancing.

Dhamal Dance

- Practiced — Since great Hindu epic war of Mahabharata
- Mostly popular in — Mahendragarh and Jhajjar districts
- Musical instrument used — Daph, tumbi, khanjari, sarangi, been, dholak, bansuri, etc.
- This is performed on the moonlit nights of Phalgun. Presently, it is performed when the crops are ready for harvesting.
- It is believed that the dance was used to motivate soldiers during war by the kings.

Dances Performed by Women

The main dance forms practised by women in Haryana include ghoomar, jhoomar, loor, teej, khoria, chathi, ghodi, etc.

Ghoomar Dance

- Popular among — Southern part of Haryana
- Performed on — Occasions of Diwali, Holi and Gangor Puja
- It is performed in circular movements by the performers.
- The dancers first make one circle and then start moving while singing and clapping.
- The circle formed by the dress (Lehenga) in this dance is known as **Ghoom.** It is also considered to be the origin of the name Ghoomar.

Jhumar Dance

- Also known as — Haryanvi Gidda and performers wear very colourful attires to perform dance
- Performed on — Beats of dholak and plates
- The name of this dance form is similar with the ornament called **jhumar**, which married women wear to decorate their forehead.
- In this dance, women wear daman, kurta, odhani and other traditional clothes and ornaments.

Teej Dance

- Performed on — The occasion of teej
- Performed in — Month of monsoon (Sawan)
- Women wear beautiful dresses in this dance such as ghaghara, odhani and kurti along with traditional ornaments.
- Women sing songs and dance to celebrate teej. On this day in Haryana, sweets are made by **jaggery.**

Loor Dance

- Performed by Young girls
- Performed in Month of Phalgun (February-March)
- Also known as Tunmuniya
- This dance is performed by the girls of Bangar area in Haryana before two weeks of Holi.
- In this region, 'Loor' means a girl, due to which the dance has been named as Loor dance.
- This dance form is a signal, which signifies that spring season is coming and rabi crops are ready to be sown by the farmers.
- During this dance, girls wear their **traditional dress**, e.g. ghaghara, kurti, chanda and chunri.
- The girls stand in **two groups facing each other** in a **semi-circle.**

Khoria Dance

- Popular in Central region of Haryana
- Performed on Occasion of marriage
- Performed by Women in bridegroom's family
- It is performed at bridegroom's house till the time the bride arrives at the house after the marriage.
- Bokda is spoken before Khoria dance which is related to humorous act between sister-in-laws.

Ghodi Dance

- It is mainly performed on marriage ceremony.
- In this dance, mask of horse made of colourful papers and cardboard is used.

Chathi Dance

- It is performed at the sixth day of the birth of child during the night.
- During this dance ceremony, boiled grains and salted peas are distributed. These are known as 'Bakli'.

Combined Dances

These dances are performed by both the men and women. These include Been-Bansuri, Holi, Phag, Manjira, Ratwai, Gangor dance, etc.

Been-Bansuri Dance

- It is mainly performed in the Bangar region of Haryana.
- It is performed on the tunes of been, bansuri and ghadwa.

Phag Dance

- Performed in Lunar month of Phalgun
- Occasion To celebrate the festival of Holi

- The women wear traditional clothes whereas the men wear colourful turbans on their heads.
- The men and women dance together on the beats of daph, manjira, etc.

Raas Dance

- Associated with Raaslila of Lord Krishna
- It is the traditional dance of **Brij region** of Uttar Pradesh, but it has culturally spread to the Palwal, Hodal, Faridabad, Gurugram and Ballabhgarh regions of Haryana.
- In this dance, the Gopis dance around Lord Krishna by forming a circle.
- Instruments such as jhanjh, thali, dholak etc, are used in this dance.
- Raas dance is mainly practised in two forms
  - **Tandav Dance** (performed by males)
  - **Lasya Dance** (performed by females)

Ratwai Dance

- Popular in Mewat region, Gurugram and Firozpur-Jhirka town of Nuh district
- Performed by During the rainy season

Manjira Dance

- Popular in Mewat region of Haryana
- Musical instruments used Nagada, daph and manjira

Gangor Dance

- Occasion: Gangor festival in Hisar, Bhiwani and Sirsa regions of Haryana
- Dedicated to: Lord Shiva and Goddess Parvati
- It is also popular in Fatehabad.

Swang : Folk Theatre of Haryana

- Swang or Saang is a popular folk theatre of Haryana. The **first description** of Haryana's theatre is found in Ladwa town of Kurukshetra in the book **Saang Raja Ratan Sen Ka**.
- According to famous writer, **Dr. Shankar Lal Yadav**, Swang's religious version was adopted by **Vaishnavite saints** in the 16th century.
- **Vallabhacharya** started the tradition of song drama by promoting Krishna act as **Raslila**.
- In 16th century, Raslila and Ramlila started in Haryana. Later, Syed Agha Hasan Amanat composed **'Inder Sabha'** in this tradition.

> The origin of Saang and music can also be found in **Harivansha Purana**. The swang tradition began in Haryana in 1730 AD.

Stage of Swang

- In swang theatre, themes of morality, folk tales, lives of inspiring personalities, stories from Indian Mythology, literacy, health and hygiene, women's empowerment are used.
- Bhairav raga, bhairavi raga, todi raga, kalyan raga, bhupali raga, malkoshna raga, etc are used during swang performances.
- Kaherwa taal, dadra tin taal and rupak taal are also used. Shringar rasa, shant rasa and veer rasa are also visible in swang performances.
- The performance begins with **Gugga dance**. The dancers dance on the beats of dholak and tunes sarangi. The plot of the swang is performed with **chaubola**.
- The play begins with a Chaubola (a poem of four lines).
- Imitation or mimicry is an important part of the play. The person who imitates is known as **Nakali**.
- Folk theatre has a strong base in Haryana but with the emergence of modern forms of entertainment, the popularity of swang is declining.

> - Artists such as Harish Kataria, Bhal Singh, Raghu Malik, Arvind Swami, Devishankar Prabhakar, Pradeep Hudda, Balak Ram, Pandit Shankarlal, etc are still working hard to save this declining theatre form.

Pandit Lakhmi Chand : Swang Samrat

- He is the most celebrated swang artist in Haryana. He is famous as **Swang Samrat** and **Surya Kavi** in Haryana.
- He was born in 1901, in Janti Kalan village of Sonipat district, in the family of a farmer. He considered **Pt. Maan Singh** as his teacher.
- His important swangs include Raja Bhoj, Chandra Kiran, Gyani Chor, Draupadi Cheer, Heer-Ranjha, Nal-Damyanti, Satyavan-Savitri, Kichak-Virat, Parab, Bhagat Puranmal, Mirabai, Shakuntla, Lakadhara,
- Lakhmi Chand also gave Ragini a new form. He is also known as the **Shakespeare of Haryana.**
- Some of the contemporaries of Lakhmi Chand were Ramanand Azad, Ram Singh Nai, Sultan, Hoshiyar Singh, Ramkishan Vyas, Dhanpat Singh, Chandan, Jamujha Mir, etc.
- He died in 1945 at the age of 44.

Popular Swang Personalities of Haryana

Swangi	Contribution and Famous Works
Kishanlal Bhaat (Meerut)	• In modern times, swang was made popular by Kishanlal Bhaat of Meerut in 1730. He is considered as the first Swangi. • The popular swangs performed by him include *Heer-Ranjha, Laila-Majnu, Nautanki, etc.*
Ahmad Baksh	• Ahmad Baksh was another popular swang artist. • *Ramayan* was performed by him in Kauravi dialect.
Banshilal	• Banshilal was a famous artist who is known for swang performances like *Raja Nal, Guru Gugga, Raja Gopichand,* etc. • The book 'Two Legends of Punjab', published in 1884, describes his play as 'Raja Gopichand'.

Swangi	Contribution and Famous Works
Ali Baksh (Ambaram, Rewari)	• Another notable pioneer of swang theatre was Ali Baksh or Ambaram of Rewari. • In the swangs of Ali Baksh, a combination of music and Brij language can be seen. • Ali Baksh stayed his swangs through the medium of *Chambola Jikdi, Bahar Ghazal* and *Bhajan*. He was the disciple of Saint Garibdas. • His famous plays include *Fisana, Padmavat, Krishnalila, Nihaldev, Chandrawal, Gulabkavli,* etc.
Shankar Lal	• Shankar Lal was another popular swangi. • His famous works include *Mordhwaj, Bhagat Prahlad, Bhura Badal, Rani Padmini,* etc.
Balak Ram	• The swangs of Balak Ram also earned appreciation among the people in Haryana. • He composed swangs on the stories of *Puran Bhagat and Raja Gopichand.* • His famous works include *Shilande, Kunjadi* and *Ramayan.*
Netaram	• In the 19th century, *Netaram* was a famous swangi. • His play 'Seela Sethani' is considered as the first successful swang of Haryana.
Pt. Deepchand (Sonipat)	• He is credited with giving a new dimension to this folk art. • Sorath was the first swang created by Pt. Deepchand. • Gyani Chor, Nal-Damyanti, Sarande, Maharaja Harishchandra, Uttanpad, Raja Bhoj, etc., were other popular swangs created by him. • He was given the title of **Rai Sahib** by the British Government.
Swangi Hardev (Rohtak)	• Swangi Hardev was the successor of Deepchand. He belonged to the Gorad village of Rohtak. • He started the use of simple 'Kamiz' instead of *Angiya.* • His famous works include Heer-Ranjha, Gyani Chor, Chandra Kiran, etc.
Pt. Mangeram	• Pt. Mangeram, a popular poet and theatre artist, is known for his works, including Dushyant, Shakuntala, Krishna Janma, Navratan and Dhruv Bhakt, etc.
Dhanpat Singh	• Dhanpat Singh is another popular swangi of Haryana. • His famous works include Puranmal Gyani Chor, Bandevi, Leelo Chaman, etc.
Ramkishan Vyas	• Ramkishan Vyas, a famous swang artist, is known for his works like Gopichand, Hiramal Jamaal, Jaadukhori, Roopkala, etc.
Baje Bhagat	• Baje Bhagat, the disciple of Hardev, is known for using historic and puranic stories in his swangs. • The popular works of Baje Bhagat include *Chandra Kiran, Jamal and Gyani Chor.*
Other Famous Swangi	• Govardhan Saangi (Krishnalila), Jaswant Singh (Mahabharat), Krishna Goswami (Dilbar Bishna), Ahmad Baksh (Kanslila, Jaimal Fatta, Chandra Kiran, Gugga Chauhan, Navalde, etc.

CHECK CHAPTER KNOWLEDGE

1 In which period did music in Haryana first emerge?
(a) Vedic period
(b) Medieval period
(c) Post-Vedic period
(d) Post-Mughal period

2 The hymns of Rigveda were sung in which of the following tones?
(a) Uddatta (b) Anudatta
(c) Svarita (d) All of these

3 The songs and music of which of the following Veda was known as Marga sangeet?
(a) Rigveda (b) Samveda
(c) Atharvaveda (d) None of these

4 Which of the following is not a music form developed during the Vedic period?
(a) Hymns of Rigveda (b) Khayal
(c) Songs of Samveda (d) Gandharva music

5 Who was a famous Khayal singer from the medieval period of Haryana?
(a) Mahatma Surdas
(b) Haddu Khan
(c) Ustad Kallan Khan
(d) Pandit Jasraj

6 The first sculpture depicting musicians on a bullock cart was found in which place?
(a) Hisar (b) Sugh, Ambala
(c) Rewari (d) Ujjain

7 The classical music form of Haryana comprises of which of the following?
(a) Brahmas (b) Puran Bhagat
(c) Bhairavi (d) Jaijaivanti

8 The raga of countryside form of music in Haryana is/are
(a) Jhinjhoti (b) Jaijaivanti
(c) Pahadi (d) All of these

9 According to the records of which of the following, folk songs were sung on the wedding of Harsha's sister Rajshree?
(a) Abul Fazl (b) Banabhatta
(c) Ashoka (d) Fa Hien

10 Banda-Bandi and Ghodi songs are sung on which of the following occasions?
(a) Birthdays (b) Wedding
(c) Holi (d) Teej

11 Sohar, Jachcha, Pilia, Badhai songs are a form of which of the following?
(a) Seethne (b) Wedding songs
(c) Birthday songs (d) All of these

12 Which of the following instruments is commonly used in Haryanvi folk music and is made from red cedar wood?
(a) Tumba (b) Sarangi (c) Iktara (d) Sitar

13 Shringar Rasa usually depicts
(a) Pilia (b) Sawan songs
(c) Panghat songs (d) Sohar

14 Which among the following invented a unique form of Jugalbandi?
(a) Baje Bhagat (b) Lakhmichand
(c) Pt Jasraj (d) Hussain Khan

15 ………….. was a popular Sarangi player.
(a) Kuldeep Manak (b) Amar Singh
(c) Maman Khan (d) All of these

16 Which instrument, made from a hollow gourd and bamboo, is commonly used by snake charmers?
(a) Been (b) Shankh
(c) Dholak (d) Veena

17 Which of the following instruments is a combination of Veena and Tamboora?
(a) Guitar (b) Iktara
(c) Banzo (d) Sitar

18 The musical instrument used to worship Goga ji is
(a) Dafli (b) Damru
(c) Deru (d) Daph

19 Ghadwa was invented by whom ?
(a) Amir Khusrao
(b) Shahjahan
(c) Jagannath Bhardwaj
(d) None of the above

20 Which of the following is/are a percussion instrument?
(a) Manjira (b) Jhanjh
(c) Khartal (d) All of these

21 Which of these instruments is used by Jogis during their worship?
(a) Cymbals (b) Chimta
(c) Khartal (d) Manjira

22 Which of these instrument is beaten and played with the help of a wooden stick?
(a) Khartal (b) Jhalar
(c) Chimta (d) None of these

23 Which of these instruments are used in Gugga dance?
(a) Deru (b) Manjira
(c) Chimta (d) All of these

24 The Alghoza, a special instrument in Haryanvi folk music, is most similar to which of the following?
(a) Flute (b) Shankh
(c) Been (d) Dholak

25 Which of the following instruments is a round piece of metal with a diameter of 8 to 16 finger lengths and is known as Jhanjh?
(a) Manjira (b) Jhanjh (Cymbal)
(c) Khartal (d) Chimta (Tongs)

26 Which of the following dances is performed to celebrate the festival of Holi in the lunar month of Phalgun?
(a) Ghoomar dance (b) Loor dance
(c) Phag dance (d) Teej dance

27 Which among these is a dance form of Haryana whose origin goes back to the days of the Mahabharata? *HSSC 2020*
(a) Daph (b) Ghoomar
(c) Chhathi (d) Dhamal

28 Which of the following dances of Haryana marks the arrival of the Rabi crop? *HSSC CET 2024*
(a) Ghoomar (b) Jhumar
(c) Lohri (d) Loor

29 Which folk song of Haryana is sung to celebrate the arrival of the rainy season? *HSSC JE 2024*
(a) Phag (b) Khoria
(c) Loor (d) None of these

30 The dance form of Haryana which is symbolic of the ornament worn by the young married women on their forehead is called as .... *HSSC 2020*
(a) Ghoomar (b) Jhumar
(c) Loor (d) Gugga dance

31 Gangor dance is dedicated to
(a) Lakshmi and Ganesha
(b) Shiva and Parvati
(c) Ram and Seeta
(d) All of the above

32 In 'Loor dance' style, the word loor means *HSSC CET 2023*
(a) jewellery (b) music (c) crop (d) girl

33 What is the main purpose of the Gugga dance?
(a) To celebrate the arrival of monsoon
(b) To worship Gugga Pir
(c) To mark the harvest season
(d) To honour Lord Krishna

34 Which of the following is not a dance form of Haryana? *Haryana CET 2023*
(a) Loor (b) Khona (c) Talgadi (d) Phag

35 Which of the following dance styles of Haryana is associated with the Mewat tribe? *Haryana CET 2023*
(a) Dhamal (b) Ratwai
(c) Phag (d) Gugga

36 Match List I with List II.

List I (Dance Forms)		List II (Occasions)	
A.	Ghoomar	1.	To motivate soldiers
B.	Dhamal Dance	2.	Diwali
C.	Loor Dance	3.	Tunmunija
D.	Khoria Dance	4.	Marriage

Codes

	A	B	C	D		A	B	C	D
(a)	2	1	3	4	(b)	1	2	3	4
(c)	2	3	4	1	(d)	3	1	4	2

37 Which of the following is not true about the Teej dance?
(a) It is performed in the month of Sawan.
(b) Women wear ghaghara, odhani and kurti during the dance.
(c) It is celebrated by men and women together.
(d) Sweets made of sugar are prepared for the occasion.

38 Who is considered as the first Swangi in modern times?
(a) Banshilal
(b) Kishanlal Bhaat (Meerut)
(c) Ahmad Baksh
(d) Shankar Lal

39 Which of the following is/are theme/s in swang?
(a) Nal-Damyanti (b) Heer-Ranjha
(c) Leelo Chaman (d) All of these

40 The performance in swang begins with which of these dances?
(a) Gugga dance (b) Ghodi dance
(c) Daph dance (d) None of these

41 The first swang created by Pt. Deepchand was
(a) Gopi Chand (b) Sorath
(c) Krishnalila (d) Seela Sethani

42 Which among the following swangs were created by Pt Lakhmichand?

I. Nal-Damyanti II. Shakuntala
III. Lakadhara IV. Seth Tarachand

Codes

(a) I and II (b) I, II and II
(c) I, II, III and V (d) II, III and V

43 Which of the following is a famous work of Pandit Lakhmi Chand?

(a) Gyani Chor (b) Raja Nal
(c) Chandra Kiran (d) Heer-Ranjha

44 Choose the correct statements about Swang.

1. Swang theatre performances often include themes related to Indian mythology.
2. The plays are mostly performed in closed indoor venues.
3. Shringar rasa, shant rasa and veer rasa are commonly visible in performances.

(a) Only 1 (b) 1 and 3
(c) 2 and 3 (d) All of these

45 Match List I with List II.

List I	List II
A. Kishanlal Bhaat	1. Raja Nal, Guru Gugga
B. Pandit Lakhmi Chand	2. Heer-Ranjha, Laila-Majnu
C. Ali Baksh	3. Gyani Chor, Nal-Damyanti
D. Banshilal	4. Krishnalila, Raja Gopichand

Codes

	A	B	C	D
(a)	2	3	4	1
(b)	2	1	4	3
(c)	3	2	1	4
(d)	1	4	2	3

CORRECT ANSWERS

1. (c)	**2.** (d)	**3.** (b)	**4.** (b)	**5.** (b)	**6.** (b)	**7.** (a)	**8.** (d)	**9.** (b)	**10.** (b)
11. (c)	**12.** (b)	**13.** (c)	**14.** (c)	**15.** (c)	**16.** (a)	**17.** (d)	**18.** (c)	**19.** (c)	**20.** (d)
21. (d)	**22.** (b)	**23.** (d)	**24.** (a)	**25.** (b)	**26.** (c)	**27.** (d)	**28.** (d)	**29.** (d)	**30.** (b)
31. (b)	**32.** (d)	**33.** (b)	**34.** (c)	**35.** (b)	**36.** (a)	**37.** (d)	**38.** (b)	**39.** (d)	**40.** (a)
41. (a)	**42.** (a)	**43.** (a)	**44.** (b)	**45.** (b)					

CHAPTER 08

Fairs and Festivals of Haryana

The state of Haryana celebrates the rich, glorious culture of India in its various fairs and festivals that are celebrated with great zeal by its people.

There are several fairs and festivals in Haryana that attracts a large number of visitors to the state at different times of the year.

Important Festivals of Haryana

The important festivals in Haryana are celebrated according to the **Vikram Samvat**. The important festivals of Haryana are as follows

Nav Samvatsar Festival

- Month/Occasion 1st day of Shukla Paksha in Chaitra (March-April)
- It marked the **beginning of Hindu New Year.**
- This festival has been observed by the people of Haryana since ancient times, making it a part of their cultural heritage.
- It is traditionally associated with the **origin of the Universe**, symbolising creation and new beginnings.

Sili Sate or Sili Satam

- Month/Occasion Chaitra (March-April)
- It is celebrated six days after Nav Samvatsar Utsav on Krishna Paksha Saptami.
- Women worship Goddess Sheetala Mata during this festival.
- It is also known as **Basoda** due to the tradition of eating stale food (usually sweet rice).
- During this festival, prayers are offered to **Budho Mata** on Wednesday.

Matridevi Poojan

- Month/Occasion Chaitra (March-April)
- Place Villages like Beri, Bas and Banbhori in Haryana
- It begins on the 1st day of Krishna Paksha and 2nd day of Shukla Paksha in Chaitra.
- It often starts from **Sili Satam** (Sheetala Saptami).
- Several goddesses like Randhani, Mandhani, Sheetala and Pahadan are worshipped.
- Women prepare sweet rice, porridge and poode as offerings to goddess.

Durga Ashtami

- Month/Occasion Chaitra (March-April)
- Place Naneola region of Ambala, Haryana
- Worshipped Goddess Durga with special significance in the region.

Ram Navami

- Month/Occasion Chaitra (March-April)
- Place Bhaindoli village, Faridabad
- It is celebrated on the 9th day of Shukla Paksha.
- According to Hindu scriptures, Lord Rama was born on this day.

Gangaur Festival

- Month/Occasion: Chaitra (March-April)
- Place: Mainly celebrated in Rajasthan but also widely celebrated in Hisar, Haryana
- Begins on the 3rd day of Shukla Paksha in Chaitra month (March-April).
- Married women fast for their husbands and unmarried women fast to seek a good husband.
- **Images of Gangaur** are made with cow dung or clay and covered with a red cloth.
- Sweets made from wheat flour and Ghewar are distributed during the festival.

Jethudi

- Month/Occasion: Jyestha (May-June, intense summer)
- People distribute water (to drink) at various places during this festival.

Bhadliya Navami

- Month/Occasion: Ashad (June-July)
- It is celebrated at the beginning of the monsoon season in Ashad.
- On this day, any auspicious work including marriage can be done without looking at Panchang.

Teej

- Month/Occasion: Shravana (Jul-Aug)
- Place: Haryana, Punjab and Rajasthan
- Also known as: Swarna Gauri Vrat, Madhushrava Teej

- It is celebrated on the 3rd day after the New Moon in Shravana during Shukla Paksha.It symbolises the dedication of Goddess Parvati to Lord Shiva.
- Women observe a **Nirjala Vrat** (fast without drinking water) for their husband's well-being and long life.
- Swings are hung from trees and women sing songs while enjoying the swings.
- Wrestling events are also organised in some places.

Salono (Raksha Bandhan)

- Month/Occasion: Shravana Shukla Paksha
- Popularly known as: Raksha Bandhan
- The day of the full moon in the month of Shravana is known as **Shravani.**
- **Baba Kheda fair** is also organised on this day in Bhiwani district.

> After three days of Raksha Bandhan, **Budhi Teej** is celebrated across India. The festival is celebrated with splendour in Panchvati (Palwal), Aurangabad and Khambi. Processions of Gods and Goddesses are also taken out.

Shiv Mandir Festival

- Month/Occasion: Shravana (July-August) and Phalgun (February-March)
- Place: Burayan, Jind district
- The festival has been celebrated at a place named **Burayan** in the Jind district.

Goga Navami

- Month/Occasion: Bhadrapad month (August-September)
- Place: Kanina, Hudina and Narnaul areas of Mahendragarh district
- It is celebrated on the 9th day of Krishna Paksha.
- On this festival, the people worship Goga Ji, a folk deity. The place of worship of Goga Ji is **Goga ki Medi**, situated in Haryana. On Goga Navami, fairs are also, organised.
- The worshippers and followers take out a procession with a stick in their hands known as 'Guga ki Chari'. It is decorated with flowers, Peacock's feathers, etc.

> It is believed that there are **four incarnations** of Goga Ji. The Muslims consider him a 'Guga Pir' whereas the Hindus call him 'Guru Gugga'. Other than these, he is believed to take the form of 'Zahar Pir' and 'Bagad Wala Pir' (born in Bagad region).

- As per the legends, Goga was a Rajput prince who had supernatural powers to control venomous snakes.
- Goga Ji is called by the name **Snake God** in many parts of Haryana. In modern times, he was named as **Gugga Ji.**

Dussehra

- Month/Occasion: Ashwin (September-October)
- Also known as: Vijayadashmi
- It is commonly celebrated on the 10th day of Shukla Paksha. It signifies the victory of good over evil.

- It is mainly celebrated in the **Rohtak** district of Haryana with great zeal and fervour. Here, people celebrate it by singing folk songs and dancing.

> Prior to Dussehra festival, women decorate their walls with **Saanjhi** (image of Goddess Durga). On the 10th day (the day of Dashami), it is immersed in water.

Dev Uthani Gyaras/Ekadashi

- Month/Occasion — 11th day of Shukla Paksha in the month of Kartik
- Worship — Lord Vishnu
- Also known as — **Prabodhini Ekadashi** and **Devothan ki Ekadashi** in the Puranas
- Evening rituals involve preparing floor designs using geru and rice paste, depicting images of Lakshmi and Vishnu.
- **Tulsi Vivah**, the marriage ritual of Lord Vishnu and Tulsi (incarnation of **Vrinda**), is performed by devotees.

Deepawali

- Month/Occasion — 15th day of Kartik month (October-November)
- Worship — Goddess Lakshmi and God of Wealth Kuber
- It marks Lord Rama's return to Ayodhya after a 14-year exile.
- Chhoti Diwali (Giridih) is celebrated in Haryana a day before Diwali. On Chhoti Diwali, **Yandiva** or **Moridiva** are also organised.
- **Govardhan Pooja** is observed a day after Diwali, where women create images of Govardhan using **cow dung** and perform rituals.

Kartik Snan

- Month/Occasion — Full Moon Day (Purnima) in Kartik (October-November)
- Event — Sacred bathing
- Ritual involves taking a holy bath in sacred rivers or water bodies at sunrise.
- **Pathwari Pooja** is also organised at several places in the state.

Kartik Purnima

- Month/Occasion — Last day of Kartik (October-November)
- Place — Celebrated across holy places like Ganga, Yamuna, Kurukshetra, Pushkar and others
- Worship — Lord Vishnu and Satyanarayan Katha
- Holy bathing in rivers like Ganga and Yamuna is considered auspicious. Devotees observe fast and read Satyanarayan Katha.
- It marks **Guru Nanak Dev Ji's birth anniversary** making it significant for Sikhs.

Basant Panchami

- Month/Occasion — 5th day of Magh (January-February)
- Worship — Goddess Saraswati, Kamdeva and Rati
- Marks the harvest season and nature's beauty, with fields full of yellow mustard flowers. People wear yellow clothes, eat yellow dishes and decorate homes with yellow flowers.
- **Kite flying** is a popular activity organised in Haryana on this day.

Makar Sankranti

- Month/Occasion — 14th January (sometimes 15th in specific years)
- Also known as — Uttarayan
- Worship — Lord Sun

- **Sun enters Capricorn** (Makar), initiating its **Uttarayan** (Northward) journey.
- People take dips in holy rivers, like Saraswati, Yamuna and others. Newly married women present gifts to in-laws, known as **Tevar**.

> In Haryanvi language, Makar Sankranti is called as 'Sankrant' or 'Sakrat'.

Shivratri

- Month/Occasion — 14th day of Krishna Paksha in Phalgun (March-April)
- Place — Celebrated across India, especially in Durana village, Ambala, Haryana
- Worship — Lord Shiva and Goddess Parvati

Holi and Phag

- Month/Occasion Phalgun (March-April)
- Mythology The story of Prahlad and Holika (Sister of Hiranyakashyap)
- Prior to Holika Dahan, on the day of Basant Panchami, a long stick is dug in the ground around which bushes, wood, etc., are kept for the next 40 days.
- This stick is symbolic of Prahlad. It is also known as **Holi Mangalna** in Haryana.
- The next day, **Dulhendi** (Phag) is celebrated with colours and gulal.
- Traditional dances like **dhamal** and **swangs** are also organised in some parts of Haryana.

Festivals of Sikhs

Festival	Explanation
Baisakhi 	• It is usually celebrated on 13th or 14th April or the 1st day of the month Baisakh. • On this day (13th April, 1699), the 10th Guru, **Guru Gobind Singh** laid the foundation of **Khalsa Panth**. • It is celebrated with joy and fervour in the **Pinjore** region of **Panchkula** district. Fairs are also organised in Panchkula, on the occasion of Baisakhi.
Martyrdom Day of Guru Arjan Dev	• He was appointed as the Sikh Guru in 1581 after the death of his father and martyred in 1606. • Guru Arjan Dev, the 5th Guru of Sikhs, was the first of the two gurus to be martyred in Sikh faith. • Martyrdom day of Guru Arjan Dev is celebrated on the 14th day of Shukla Paksha in the month of Jyestha, as a tribute every year.
Guru Nanak Jayanti (Gurpurab)	• It is celebrated on the birth anniversary of the first Sikh Guru, **Guru Nanak**, the founder of Sikh religion. It is celebrated on the full Moon Day of the month of Kartik (October-November). • The celebrations usually begins with prabhat feris, which are early morning processions. Generally two days before the Gurpurab, reading of **Guru Grantha Sahib** is held in Gurudwaras across the state.
Guru Teg Bahadur's Martyrdom Day 	• It is celebrated in the month of Margashirsha (November-December) on the 5th day of Shukla Paksha. • Guru Teg Bahadur was the 9th Guru of Sikhs. • He was martyred on 24th November, 1675.
Martyrdom of Baba Zorawar Singh and Baba Fateh Singh	• Baba Zorawar Singh and Baba Fateh Singh were the sons of the 10th Guru of Sikhs, **Guru Govind Singh**. • The martyrdom of these two is celebrated on the 1st day of the Krishna Paksha in the month of Pausha (December-January).
Lohri 	• It is a winter folk festival. It is celebrated a day before Makar Sankranti. This day is also called **Sikho ki Sankranti**. • Lohri falls in the month of Pausha mostly on 13th January every year.
Ramdas Jayanti Utsav	• Guru Ramdas was the 4th Guru of Sikhs. The anniversary of 4th Sikh Guru is celebrated on the 9th day of Phalgun month (February-March). • It is celebrated with joy in **Hindol** (Dadri) in Haryana along with Punjab. People visit the Gurudwaras to listen to the hymns that were composed by **Guru Ramdas Ji**.

Important Fasts in Haryana

The most important fasts of Haryana region are as follows

Chamahi Atham Sanjhi

- Occasion — Devi (Shakti) Pooja twice every year
- Timing — Chaitra (March-April) as well as Ashwin (September-October)
- Significance — Known as Chamahi Atham (Once in 6 months)
- Worship — Images of Goddess Sanjhi (Durga) made of mud and molded into various shapes
- This festival starts after **Petri Amavasya**. Goddess Sanjhi (Durga) is worshipped by the girls and women.

Nirjala Gyas/Ekadashi

- Date of observance — 11th day of Krishna Paksha in month of Jyestha (May-June)
- Fasting rituals — Undertaken by women for their husband's longer life.
- Pooja is offered to Lord Vishnu to seek his grace. People believed that offering cold 'Sharbat' is a pious act.

Durga Vrat

- First fast — Month of Shravana (July-August) on 8th day of Shukla Paksha
- Frequency — Ashtami of every month
- Worship — Goddess Durga

Odhdwas-Doobri

- Odhdwas is celebrated in the month of Bhadrapad on 2nd day of Krishna Paksha.
- Doobri is celebrated on the ashtami of Shukla Paksha in the month of Bhadrapad (August-September).
- In Odhdwas, the women fast and worship for the long lives of their children whereas in Doobri, the women fast and worship for long lives of their husbands.

Krishna Janmashtami

- Occassion — Birth anniversary of Lord Krishna
- Date — Ashtami of Krishna Paksha in month of Bhadrapad (August-September)
- Both men and women observe fasting on this day, **Krishna Leelas** are organised in the temples where people pray and worship Lord Krishna in his child form.
- In Haryana, it is also known as **Krishna Jayanti**. On the next day, **Goga Pir** is worshipped by the people.

Ahoi Mata

- Date of observance — 8th day of Shukla Paksha in month of Kartik (October-November)
- Also known as — **Ahoi Aathe** or **Ahoi Ashtami**
- On this day, women draw the symbolic images of Goddess Ahoi with **Shyau mata** or **Sei mata** with her children on the wall. These images are made with **geru** or **ochre**, a natural clay Earth pigment.
- On this festival, brides also offer **Bayna** (clothes, food items, etc) to the elder woman (mother-in-law or married sister-in-law) of the family and receive their blessings.

Gopashtami

- Occasion — Dedicated to Lord Krishna
- Date of observation — 8th day of Shukla Paksha in month of Kartik (October-November)
- It is celebrated as it is believed that Krishna's father Nanda Maharaj gave Krishna the responsibility for taking care of the cows of Vrindavan.

Karwa Chauth

- Celebrated on — 4th day of Krishna Paksha in month of Kartik (October-November)
- On this day, married women fast from sunrise to moonrise for the safety and longevity of their husbands.
- In Haryana, the women eat **Sargi** early in the morning which includes fenia.

Sakat Chauth

- Occasion — 4th day of Krishna Paksha in month of Magh (January-February)
- Also known as — Ganesh Chaturthi
- Sakat Chauth is observed mainly by women who fast for the well-being of their children. This fast is dedicated to **Goddess Sakat**. On this day, Lord Ganesha is also worshipped.

Fairs Associated with Saints in Haryana

Baba Suraj Giri : A fair organised in Khori, near Rewari district is dedicated to Baba Suraj Giri, which held on the 1st day of Krishna Paksha in the month of Chaitra (March-April).

Saint Haridas : A fair is organised in the memory of Saint Haridas on the 4th day of Krishna Paksha in the month of Chaitra (March-April). It is organised in Jharoda near Jhajjar.

Saint Mohandas : A fair is organised every year in Lahrada in Sonipat district. This fair is organised on the New Moon Day (Amavasya) in the month of Chaitra (March-April).

Boodhla Saint : In the memory of Boodhla saint a fair is organised in Tohana and Hisar.This fair is organised on the 1st day of Vikram Samvat.

Baba Sarsai Nath : He is associated with the Nath community. His hermitage is located in South-East part of Sirsanagar. Here, a fair is organised in his memory on the 1st day of Shukla Paksha of Chaitra (March-April).

Saint Jamnadas : A fair is organised in the memory of saint Jamnadas in Bhaloth in Rohtak district. It is organised on the 8th day of Shukla Paksha in the month of Chaitra (March-April).

***Sidh Mahatma** (Pir)* In his memory, a fair is organised in the month of Baisakh (April-May) on the Full Moon Day in Kushek, Palwal district.

Karma Wala Baba : A fair is organised in Baas, Dadri every year in the month of Jyestha (May-June). It is organised on the Full Moon Day in the memory of Karma Wala Baba.

Nikka Pir : In his memory, a fair is organised every year on Poornima in the month of Ashad (June-July) in Madh, located in Fatehabad district.

Bhagat Phulsingh A fair is organised in his memory on the 2nd day of Shukla Paksha in the month of Shravana (July-August). It is organised in Khanpur Kalan, Sonipat district.

Suraj Fair : In his memory, a fair is organised in Lakkarpur in Ballabhgarh in the month of Shravana (July-August). It is organised every year on every Sunday in Shravana month.

Saint Nityanand : He was born in Narnaul, Haryana and died on the 1st day of Shukla Paksha in the month of Bhadrapada (August-September) in 1856. On this day, a fair is organised in Majra, Jhajjar, the place of his death. He is known for his writing **Nityanand Vani**.

Naktadev : A fair is organised every year in Kamaspur, Sonipat in his memory. It is organised on the 6th day of Shukla Paksha in the month of Bhadrapada (August-September).

Swami Dayal : A fair is organised every year in Charkhi-Dadri in his memory. It is organised on the 8th day of Krishna Paksha in the month of Bhadrapada (August-September) each year.

Baba Amarnath : A fair is organised in Banipur, Rewari on the New Moon Day (Amavasya) of Bhadrapad month (August-September) in the memory of Baba Amarnath.

Baba Zinda (*Bhojvas*) : A fair is organised in Bhojvas in Mahendragarh district. It is organised on the 2nd day of Shukla Paksha in the month of Bhadrapad (August- September).

Budha Baba : A fair is organised in Asoda Todram in Jhajjar district in his memory. It is organised on the 3rd day of Bhadrapad (August-September).

Baba Joharnath : Each year, a fair is organised in his memory in Bhandwa in Dadri, Haryana. It is organised on the 12th day of Shukla Paksha in the month of Bhadrapada.

Baba Narayandas : A fair in the memory of Baba Narayandas is organised in Jhansa, near Thanesar. It is organised on the 1st day of the Bhadrapad month (August-September).

Guru Gosai Laldas : A fair is organised in Tohana in Hisar in his memory. It is organised on the 9th day of the Bhadrapad month (August-September).

Baba Ladana Rajpuri : In his memory, a fair is organised near Kaithal in the month of Ashwin (September-October).

Sahab Swami : A fair is organised in his memory in Bujheda, located in Nuh. It is held on Poornima in the month of Kartik (October-November).

Baba Simran Das : A fair is organised in Indri, Karnal district of Haryana. The resting place (Samadhi) of Baba Simran Das is located in Indri. An annual fair is organised here in the month of Kartik (October-November).

Kheegaj Devta : In the memory of Kheegaj devta, a fair is organised every year on the 7th day of Krishna Paksha in Magh month (January-February). It is organised annually in Selang in the Mahendragarh district.

Saint Narasingh Das : A fair is organised in Kanti, Narnaul in his memory. It is organised on the 5th day of Shukla Paksha in the month of Magh (January-February).

Saint Vanakhandeshwar : A fair is organised in his memory on the 2nd day of Shukla Paksha in the month of Magh (January-February). It is organised every year in Palwal. It is also known as Budha Baba Mela.

Saint Ramdev : A fair is organised in the memory of saint Ramdev in village Gangwa in the Hisar district every year. It is organised on the 10th day of Shukla Paksha of Magh (January-February).

Baba Sabaadh : A fair is organised in Sanghi, Rohtak every year in his memory. It is organised on the 3rd day of Shukla Paksha in the Magh month (January-February).

Baba Narayan Nath : A fair is organised in Malenava, Ballabhgarh every year. It is organised on the 3rd day of Krishna Paksha in the month of Phalgun (February- March).

Baba Himmat Nath : A fair is held every year on the 9th day of Krishna Paksha in Phalgun (February-March). It is organised in Nahri located in Sonipat.

Baba Maaldev : A fair is organised on the 13th day of Krishna Paksha in Phalgun month (February-March). It is organised in Jhal, located in Jhajjar.

Nag Devta : A fair is organised in Barsalu located in Karnal. It is organised on the 6th day of Shukla Paksha in the month of Phalgun (February-March).

Baba Balaknath : A fair is organised in Rabhda, Sonipat on the 9th day of Shukla Paksha.
It is organised in the month of Phalgun (February-March).

Baba Bhilai Nath : In Nangalgarh, Mahendragarh a fair is organised in his memory.
It is organised in the month of Phalgun (February-March).

Baba Mastnath (Shambhu)

He was a great sage. He was a Nathpanthis of **Guru Gorakhnath Sect**. In his memory, a fair is organised in the month of Chaitra (March-April) on the 9th day of Shukla Paksha. It is organised in Dheki, located in Sonipat. Other than this, a fair is organised on the 7th day of Shukla Paksha in Asthal Bohar, Rohtak. Another fair is organised on 8th day of Shukla Paksha in the month of Phalgun. It is organised in Khedi Sadh, located in Rohtak.

Fairs Associated with Lord Vishnu

Avatar of Lord Vishnu	Fair Details	Location and Events
Narsingh	Celebrated in the month of Shravana. **Narsingh Jayanti** is observed on the 14th day of Shukla Paksha in the month of Baisakh (April-May) with fairs across the state.	Lord Narsingh is worshipped in Varaha forest in **Jind district**.
Parashuram	**Parashuram Jayanti** is celebrated on the 3rd day of Shukla Paksha in the month of Baisakh (April-May), which coincides with **Akshaya Tritiya**.	Worship of Lord Parashuram's parents is held in **Thanesar**. Sage Jamadagni's hermitage is near Pindara in Jind district. He is known as the father of Parashuram.
Vamana	**Vamana Jayanti** is observed on the 2nd day of Shukla Paksha in the month of Bhadrapad (August-September).	Vamana Kund in **Kurukshetra** is believed to be the birthplace of Lord Vamana. **Vamana Dwadashi Mela** is organised in **Kaithal** and **Ambala**.
Krishna	**Krishna Janmashtami** is celebrated on the 8th day of Bhadrapad (August-September).	The **Jagannatha Temple** in Hansi hosts a fair on the 10th day of Bhadrapad. **Jal Jhulni Fair** is held on the 11th day of Shukla Paksha in Firozpur Jhirka. **Phooldor Fair** is held in Bhiduki, Palwal, on the 1st day of Krishna Paksha.
Varaha	**Varaha Jayanti** is celebrated on the 12th day of Shukla Paksha in the month of Magh (January-February) or on the 3rd day of Shukla Paksha in Bhadrapad (August-September).	Pilgrimage places include Varaha Van and Varaha Kalan village in **Jind** district, associated with Vishnu's legend of lifting the Earth out of the cosmic ocean.

Fairs Associated with Sages

Sage	Explanation
Yayati	• It is believed that Yayati organised a sacred yagya on the banks of river Saraswati. At this place, a fair is organised on the 11th day of Krishna Paksha in the month of Chaitra (March-April).
Parashar	• The pilgrimage site of sage Parashar is situated in Bahlolpur village in Karnal. Fairs are organised every year at this place in the months of Chaitra (March-April) and Baisakh (April-May). Saint Parashar is said to have composed **Parashara Smriti Granth** in Sanskrit language.
Bhishma Pitamah	• In Manesar (Gurugram), a fair is organised annually in the hermitage of Bhishma. This fair is organised in the month of Shravana (July-August). Bhishma Pitamah is worshipped daily during this fair.
Satkumbh (Chakwa Bain)	• It is organised in Khed-Khedika Gujar in Sonipat on the last Sunday in the month of Shravana (July-August). This place has been the capital of **Raja Chakwa Bain**.
Ajat	• Sage Ajat's fair is organised every year at Jui in Bhiwani, Haryana. This is organised on the 6th day of Krishna Paksha in the month of Bhadrapad (August-September). • According to Matsya Purana, sage Ajat was one of the ten sons of Hridik, a King of the **Yadava dynasty**.
Bharthari	• The fair of Bharthari is organised on the 2nd day of Krishna Paksha of Bhadrapad at a place known as **Din Vyal** in Narnaul. Another fair is organised in **Kharak Kalan** village in Kalanaur.
Puranmal	• This fair is organised in the Kasan village on the 13th day of Shukla Paksha of Bhadrapad (August-September) in the memories of Bhakta Puranmal. Another fair is also organised in Baliyana village in Rohtak in his name.
Markandeya	• A fair for Markandeya Rishi is organised on the Full Moon Night (Amavasya) of Ashwin (September-October) in Hariyoyo, district Ambala. The **river Markandeya**, located in Haryana is named on sage Markandeya.
Prahlad Bhagat	• It is organised on the 2nd day of Shukla Paksha of Phalgun (February-March) near Allika in Palwal. Prahlad Bhagat was the son of **Hiranyakashyap**.

Sage	Explanation
Chyavan Rishi	• Sage Chyavan Rishi was the son of Sage Bhrigu. The hermitage of Saint Chyavan Rishi is situated in **Aasan** village of Jind district. • It is situated in the **Dhosi hills** located near Kultajpur village in Narnaul, Mahendragarh. It is also known as **Dhosi Tirth**. This place is also considered as the place of pilgrimage for **Sage Chyavan**. Here, a grand fair is organised annually which is dedicated to Sage Chyavan.
Kartikeya	• Kartikeya is associated with the holy places such as Surajkund or Sarak tirth in Shergarh village of Hisar district. • A temple of Kartikeya is located in **Pehowa** (Kurukshetra) where an annual fair is organised. Here, the women are not allowed to offer worship.
Dadhichi	• Pehowa Tirth Mela (also known as the Pehowa Fair) is associated with sage Dadhichi. • It is held annually in Pehowa, near Kurukshetra on the Chaitra Krishna Paksha Chaturdashi day. • The fair is linked to the belief that a small pond there is where the river Saraswati went underground.

Fairs of Different Sects and Communities in Haryana

Sect/Community	Founder	Fair Location	Date/Month
Parmanandi Sect	Parmanand	Haryana	• 9th day of the Krishna Paksha of Shravana (July-August)
Nityanandi Sect	Saint Nityanand	Majra (Dubaldhan)	• Shukla Paksha Pratipada of Bhadrapad (August-September)
Charandasi Community	Saint Charandas	Haryana	• 7th day of Krishna Paksha in Margashirsha (November-December)
Ravidasi Sect	Saint Ravidas	Sirsa district of Haryana	• Full Moon Day in Margashirsha (November-December)
Kabir Sect	Saint Harde Das	Badli	• 7th day of Shukla Paksha in Phalgun (February-March)
Garibdasi Sect	Saint Garibdas	Chhudani in Jhajjar district of Haryana	• 12th day of Shukla Paksha in Phalgun (February-March)
Sadh Community	Saint Udhadas	Haryana	• From the 13th day of Shukla Paksha to the Full Moon Day in Phalgun (February-March)
Dadu Sect	Dadu Maharaj	Haryana	• The fair is organised on the birthday of Dadu Maharaj
Samta Sect	–	Jagadhri	• 4th February every year
Benami Community	Saint Kakkad	A fair of Haryana's Kakkad community	• Organised in the memory of Saint Kakkad

Fairs of Sikhism in Haryana

Fair	Explanation
Baba Haridas Nath	• In memory of Baba Haridas Nath, a fair called **Dhani** is organised in Dadri. This fair is organised on the 9th day of Shukla Paksha of Phalgun (February-March).
Baba Gulab Gir	• A fair is organised in **Hindol (Dadri)** in the memory of Baba Gulab Gir. This fair is organised on the 9th day of Shukla Paksha of Phalgun month (February-March).
Baba Naga	• In the memory of Baba Naga, a fair is organised every year on the 8th day of Phalgun (February-March). This fair is organised in Dadri at a place called Rajgarh.
Baba Chhillardas	• In his memory, a fair is organised every year during the month of Phalgun (February-March). The fair is organised at a place called Surkhpur Veeran in Jhajjar district of Haryana.
Baba Narsantadas	• He was a disciple of Guru Ramdas. In his memory, a fair is organised every year in Phalgun (February-March) at a place called Murund in Narnaul.
Baba Raghunath	• A fair is organised in Tigra, Narnaul in the memory of Baba Raghunath. This fair is organised every year on the 12th day of Shukla Paksha of Phalgun (February-March).

Fair	Explanation
Baba Sadaram	• In his memory, a fair is organised at a place called Malda in Mahendragarh district. This fair is organised on the Full Moon Day of Phalgun (February-March).
Fair Baba Buta Singh	• In his memory, a fair is organised at Suchan Mandi in Sirsa district. This fair takes place on the day of **Baisakhi**. Buta Singh Ji had an interest in spirituality since childhood and developed a special ability to recite Gurbani (sacred verse from the Adi Granth).
Fair Guru Gobind Singh	• He was the 10th and last Guru of the Sikhs. The birthday of Gobind Singh is celebrated on the 7th day of the Shukla Paksha of Paush (December-January). A fair is also organised on this occasion.

Major Fairs of Various Districts of Haryana

Ambala District

- ***Kali Mai Fair*** It is organised in Chaitra month (March-April). People perform prayer of Kali Mai in this fair.
- ***Sharda Devi Fair*** It is organised at Trilokpur area of Ambala district in the month of Chaitra (March-April).
- ***Gugga Navami Fair*** This fair is organised in the month of Bhadrapada (August-September) in Keseri, Ambala. It is a religious fair.
- ***Teej Fair*** This fair is organised at Panjokhara area of Ambala district. It is organised in the Shravana month on Shukla Paksha Tritiya (August-September). On this occasion, Kothli gift is given to sisters.
- ***Vaman Dwadashi Fair*** It is organised in the month of Bhadrapad on Dashami, Ekadashi and Dwadashi in Ambala district.

Fairs of Bhiwani District

- ***Sati Fair*** This fair is organised at Kharak Kalan village of Bhiwani district (August-September) in the month of Bhadrapada on 5th day of Shukla Paksha . This fair is devoted to **Dadi Jagade Sati.**
- ***Dussehra Fair*** This fair is organised at Bhiwani, Dadri and Loharu region of Haryana on Vijayadashami (at the end of Navratri).
- ***Puranmasi Fair*** This fair is organised at Tosham town of Bhiwani district.

Charkhi-Dadri District

- ***Janmashtami Fair*** This fair is organised in Charkhi-Dadri district to celebrate the birth of Lord Krishna in the month of Bhadrapada (August-September).
- ***Dussehra Fair*** This fair is organised in Charkhi Dadri district on Vijayadashami (at the end of Navratri).

Fairs of Jind District

Fair	Explanation
Sachcha Sauda	This fair is organised in Singhpura village of Jind district in the memory of Guru Tegh Bahadur on his birth anniversary (in Poornima) in the month of April.
Ramraihrid	This fair is organised in Ramraihrid village of Jind district. It is organised in the months of Vaisakha (April-May) and Kartik (October- November) on Poornima.
Hatkeshwar	This fair is organised in Hat village of Jind district on the last Sunday of the month of Shravana Shukla Paksha (July-August).
Bilsar	This fair is organised in Hansdeher village in Jind district on the day of Somvati Amavasya.

Fairs of Faridabad District

Fair	Explanation
Kanha Gaushala	This fair is organised at Bahin Faridabad in the month of Phalgun, Panchmi (February-March). The fair is commemorated in the memory of **Dada Kanha Rawat** of Rawat Jats.
Phooldor	This fair is organised at Attar Chattha village in Faridabad in the month of Chaitra (March-April) on 2nd day of Krishna Paksha . It is commemorated in the memory of **Baba Bakshinath.**
Kalka	This fair is organised at Mohna village in Faridabad in the month of Chaitra (March- April) on 8th day of Shukla Paksha. This fair is organised due to the worship of **Mata Kalka Devi.**
Gugga Pir	This fair is organised at Bahbalpur village in Faridabad in the month of Bhadrapada (August-September) on Shukla Paksha Navami. It is commemorated in the memory of **Gugga Pir.**
Janmashtami	This fair is organised at Dhatir village in Faridabad district. It is organised in the month of Bhadrapad on Krishna Paksha Ashtami (August-September). In this fair, **wrestling** is organised which is an important feature of this fair.

Fair	Explanation
Baldev Chhat	This fair is organised at Balramgarh town in Faridabad. It is organised in the month of Bhadrapad (August-September) on 9 or 10th day of Shukla Paksha. It is organised to celebrate the birth anniversary of **Baldev**.
Kanuwa	This fair is organised in Faridabad in the month of Bhadrapad (August-September) on Krishna Paksha Ekadashi.
Kartik Cultural	This fair is organised at Nahar Singh Mahal in Balramgarh town in Faridabad. It is organised by the Haryana Tourism Department to promote the arts and crafts of the state.
Shiv Chaudas	It is organised at Mitauli in Faridabad for the celebration of Shivratri.

Gurugram District

- ***Mahadev Fair*** This fair is organised in Inchhapuri village in Gurugram district.
- This fair is organised on 4th day of Shukla Paksha and Poornima in Shravana (July-August) and Phalguna (February-March).
- ***Buddho Mata Fair*** This fair is organised in Mubarikpur village in Gurugram district. It is organised at every week in the month of March.
- ***Sheetala Mata Fair*** It is organised on every Monday in the month of Chaitra (March-April) and Asadha (June-July).
- ***Shahchokha Khori Fair*** This fair is organised in Khori village in Gurugram district in the month of April-May. It is organised by Muslim community.
- ***Budhi Teej Fair*** This fair is organised in Aladurka place of Gurugram district in the month of Bhadrapad (August-September) on Shukla Paksha Teej by the Muslim community of the district.

Hisar District

- ***Agrasen Jayanti Fair*** This fair is organised in Agroha town of Hisar district in the month of March-April in the memory of Maharaja Agrasen. This fair is organised for three days.
- ***Navratri Fair*** This fair is organised in Bass and Banbhori villages of Hisar district. It is organised in two months of Hindu Lunar calendar i.e., Chaitra (March-April) and Ashvina (June-July).
- ***Kali Devi Fair*** This fair is organised in Hansi town of Hisar district in the month of May when people celebrate the festival of Kali Devi Puja.
- ***Gugga Navami Fair*** This fair is organised in the month of Bhadrapad (August-September) on 9th day of Shukla Paksha. It is organised in the memory of Gugga Pir.

Karnal District

- ***Parasar Fair*** This fair is organised in the historical place of Taraori in Karnal district. It is organised in the month of February in which people worship Lord Shiva.
- ***Chhadi Fair*** This fair is organised in Amrapur village in Karnal district in the month of September. A 'holy stick' is worshipped in this fair. Sticks are also sold in this fair.
- ***Baba Simrandas Fair*** This fair is organised in Indri city of Karnal district in the month of October on the mausoleum of Baba Simrandas.
- ***Pandu Fair*** This fair is organised in Paphana village of Karnal district every month.

Fairs of Kaithal District

Fair	Explanation
Vaman Dwadashi	• This fair is organised on 12th day of Shukla Paksha in month of Bhadrapad (August-September).
Dehati	• This fair is organised in the month of October in Ludana village. It is organised for seven days.
Pundrak	• This fair is organised in Pundari town of Kaithal district in the month of April.
Phalgu	• This fair is organised in Pharal village of Kaithal district in the month of Ashvina (September-October).

Kurukshetra District

- ***Pehowa Fair*** This fair is organised in Pehowa town of Kurukshetra district in the month of March. **Somwati Amavasya festival** is also organised at this place.
- ***Devi Fair*** This fair is organised in Shahabad town of Kurukshetra district in the month of April. Goddess is worshipped by people in this fair.
- ***Markanda Fair*** This fair is organised in Shahabad town in Kurukshetra district in the month of April. This place is considered the hermitage of Markandey Rishi.

- ***Surya Grahan Fair*** This fair is organised in Kurukshetra district on the day of Solar Eclipse (July). On this day, devotees gather around and take holy bath.
- ***Baisakhi Fair*** This fair is organised every year on 13th April with great enthusiasm and faith.

Mahendragarh District

- ***Hanumanji Fair*** This fair is organised in Shobhasagar, Narnaul and Dochana villages of Mahendragarh district. This fair is organised in the month of Chaitra on Shukla Paksha (Poornima) March-April.
- ***Bhura Bhawani Fair*** This fair is organised on the 9th day of Navami in the month of Baisakh (April-May).
- ***Dhosi Fair*** This is a huge fair which is organised at a pilgrimage site on Dhosi hills near Narnaul city. It is organised every year in the district. This place is considered the dwelling place of **Maharishi Chyavana**.
- ***Teej Fair*** This fair is organised in Shravana month (July-August) on Shukla Paksha Tritiya.

Gopal-Mochan Fair

- Gopal-Mochan fair is organised in Jagadhri tehsil near Bilaspur in Yamunanagar district in the month of Kartik (October-November) on the Gopal Mochan tank.
- According to a legend, Lord Shiva also took bath in Gopal Mochan sacred tank.
- The **Rin Mochan** is another water tank situated close to the Gopal Mochan tank. A gurdwara named **Kapal Mochan** is also establised here in the memory of Guru Gobind Singh ji.

Palwal District

- ***Sati Fair*** This fair is organised near Sati pond in Hodal town of Palwal district. The fair is organised right before Basant Panchmi in January month.
- ***Raksha Bandhan Fair*** This fair is organised in Panchvati area of Palwal district in the month of Shravana Poornima (July-August).
- ***Dauji Fair*** This fair is organised near Dauji temple in Banchari village in Palwal district in the month of August-September. Dauji temple is dedicated to **Lord Balram**, the elder brother of Lord Krishna.

Fairs of Panipat District

Fair	Explanation
Chaitra Mata	• This fair is organised in Tewah, Aadmi and Biholi places of Panipat district. It is organised in the month of Chaitra (March-April). **People worship their** parents and it is also believed that after worshipping of parents, children remain safe from diseases like measles and chicken pox.
Pathri Mata	• This fair is organised in Pathri village of Panipat district. It is organised on every Wednesday in the month of Chaitra (March-April) and Asadha (June-July).
Qalandar Shrine	• This fair is organised after Ramzan month (July-August) on the day of 'Chaand Rat' It is organised in the **Qalandar Shrine**.
Shivratri	• This fair is organised at Bhadar village in the month of Phalguna and Shravana on Krishna Paksha teej.

Rewari District

- ***Basant Panchmi Fair*** This fair is organised in Kathuwas village in Rewari district in the month of Magh (January-February) on 5th day of Shukla Paksha.
- ***Gugga Navami Fair*** This fair is organised in Dharuhera town. It is organised in the month of Chaitra (March-April) on 9th day of Krishna Paksha.
- ***Shivratri Fair*** This fair is organised at Kharagwas, Chimnawas and Kanhori villages in Haryana. It is organised in the month Phalguna (February-March) on 13th day of Krishna Paksha.

Rohtak District

- ***Shivratri Fair*** This fair is organised at Kiloi in the month of Phalgun (February-March) and Shravana (July-August).
- ***Teej Fair*** This fair is organised in the month of Shravana (July-August) on Shukla Paksha.
- ***Janmashtami Fair*** This fair is organised in the month of Bhadrapad (August-September) on 8th day of Krishna Paksha.

Fairs of Sirsa District

Fair	Explanation
Ganga-Gaur or Ganagaur	• This fair is organised in the month of Chaitra (March-April) on Shukla Paksha from 3rd to 5th day. **Ganga-Gaur** is worshipped in this fair.
Ramdevji	• This fair is organised in Girorani and Kaagdana of Sirsa district. This fair is organised at Baba Ramdev temple in Pratapgarh. It is organised in the month of Magha (January-February) on 10th day of Shukla Paksha.
Radhaswami	• This fair is organised in Sikandarpur area of the district in the months of March and September.

Fair	Explanation
Guru Nanak Dev	• This fair is organised in Chaurmar area of the district in the month of Ashvina (Poornima).
Mela Sacha Sauda	• This fair is organised at Sirsa town on the last Sunday and at Shahpur Begu and Jagmalwali on first Sunday of every month. This fair is celebrated in the memory of **Faqir Shah Mastana** who preached thankfulness and fair dealings.
Baisakhi	• It is organised at Sirsa town on the day of Baisakhi (13th April). On this day, a fair known as **Mela Baba Boota Singh** is also organised at Suehan (Mandi) in the memory of the Baba.
Mela Shah-Bu-Shah	• A fair is organised at Panihari on Bhadon month (August-September). It is celebrated in the memory of Muslim Saint **Shah-Bu-Shah**. People worship the samadhi of the saint on this day.

Sonipat District

- ***Dera Nagn Balaknath Fair*** This fair is organised in Rabhra village in Sonipat district in the month of Phalgun (February-March) on 9th day of Shukla Paksha.
- ***Satkumbha Fair*** This fair is organised in Khedi Gujjar village in Sonipat district. It is organised on the last Sunday in the month of Shravana (July-August).
- ***Raksha Bandhan Fair*** This fair is organised in Sonipat district on Poornima in the month of Shravana (July-August). Many traditional games are organised in this fair, e.g. archery, wrestling, music and dance, etc.
- ***Navratri Devi Fair*** This fair is organised in Rabhra village of Gohana tehsil in Sonipat. It is organised on Navaratri in the months of Chaitra (March-April) on 8th day of Shukla Paksha.

Other Important Fairs of Haryana

Fair	Explanation
Pinjore Mango	• This fair is organised at the **Yadavindra Gardens** in Pinjore, Panchkula. The Mango fair in Haryana takes place in the months of June or July. This mango fair has been organised since 1992 by Haryana Tourism Department. • During the Mango fair in Haryana, different varieties of mangoes from all over India are exhibited there. • There is also a competition organised between mango growers from all over the country.
Surya Grahan	• This fair is organised in Kurukshetra district of Haryana. • **Brahma Sarovar** mythological shrine is located in Kurukshetra, believed to have been built by **Lord Brahma** himself. Here, a huge fair is organised on the occasion of Solar Eclipse, Somvati Amavasya and Makar Sankranti.

International Fairs of Haryana

Fair	Explanation
International Gita Festival	• This festival is celebrated in the month of Margashirsha (November-December) on 11th day of Shukla Paksha. Haryana Government organises this festival at the Brahma Sarovar, located in Kurukshetra every year. • The festival is being celebrated globally from 2017. • This festival is organised collectively by Kurukshetra Development Board, Haryana Tourism Department, District Administration, North Regional Cultural Centre Patiala and Information and Public Relations Department. • Around 18000 verses of Gita are recited by saints in this festival. Along with this, many economic, cultural and spiritual programmes are organised here.
Surajkund International Craft	• This fair is organised at a place called Surajkund in Faridabad district. The **fortnight-long** fair takes place every year in the month of February. • For the first time in the year 1987, Surajkund fair was organised to promote Indian handicraft. In the year 2013, this fair was given the status of International fair. • The fair lasts for 15 days, in which various products of handicraft are displayed. • This fair is organised by the **Tourism Department of the Government of Haryana** and **Surajkund Mela Authority** in collaboration with the Union Ministries of Tourism Textiles, Culture and External Affairs.

CHECK CHAPTER KNOWLEDGE

1 When is the Nav Samvatsar festival celebrated?
(a) Chaitra (March-April)
(b) Jyestha (May-June)
(c) Ashad (June-July)
(d) Bhadliya Navami

2 Which goddess is worshipped during the Sili Sate festival?
(a) Goddess Durga (b) Goddess Sheetala
(c) Goddess Gauri (d) Goddess Saraswati

3 What is the significance of the Gangaur festival in Hisar, Haryana?
(a) It marks the harvest season
(b) Women fast for their husbands
(c) It is a celebration of Lord Shiva
(d) It is a spring festival

4 During Matridevi Poojan, which of the following goddesses are worshipped?
(a) Saraswati and Lakshmi
(b) Mandhani, Sheetala and Randhani
(c) Parvati and Kali
(d) Durga and Gauri

5 What is the primary activity during the Ram Navami festival in Bhaindoli village of Faridabad?
(a) Fasting for good health
(b) Distributing sweets
(c) Worshipping Lord Rama
(d) Planting trees

6 Teej festival is celebrated in which month in Haryana? *HSSC 2016*
(a) Kartik (b) Phalguna
(c) Shravana (d) Baisakh

7 The festival which is celebrated on Shukla Paksha in the month of Shravana is known as ………... *Haryana Lab Attendant 2018*
(a) Gugga Navami (b) Sanjhi
(c) Teej (d) Govardhan Puja

8 'Kothli' gift is given in which festival in Haryana? *HSSC Shift Attendant 2016*
(a) Diwali (b) Holi
(c) Teej (d) Makar Sankranti

9 On the occasion of Raksha Bandhan, Baba Kheda fair is organised in which district of Haryana? *HSSC 2019, Haryana Lab Attendant 2018*
(a) Ambala (b) Bhiwani
(c) Kurukshetra (d) Panipat

10 Which of the following animal is worshipped as a part of the celebration of Guga Navami festival? *HSSC 2020*
(a) Cow (b) Snake
(c) Elephant (d) Peacock

11 When is the Teej festival celebrated?
(a) During the month of Magh
(b) In the month of Shravana (July-August)
(c) In the month of Bhadrapada
(d) In the month of Kartik

12 On which day is Raksha Bandhan celebrated?
(a) 10th day of Shukla Paksha in Shravana
(b) Full Moon Day of Shravana month
(c) 5th day of Krishna Paksha in Bhadrapada
(d) 2nd day of Shukla Paksha in Kartik

13 Makar Sankranti is celebrated in which month? *HSSC Shift Attendant 2016*
(a) January (b) December
(c) February (d) March

14 Which festival is known as 'Festival of Changing Season' and 'Festival of Donation' in Haryana? *TGT 2016*
(a) Makar Sankranti (b) Holi
(c) Diwali (d) Baisakhi

15 Which of the following festivals is not celebrated in Haryana? *HSSC 2020*
(a) Lohri (b) Holi
(c) Onam (d) Baisakhi

16 Which festival is dedicated to Lord Krishna and involves the worship of cows?
(a) Karwa Chauth (b) Gopashtami
(c) Ahoi Mata (d) Sakat Chauth

17 A grand fair dedicated to Sage Chyavan is organised in which place in Haryana? *HSSC 2016*
(a) Harthal (b) Morni hills
(c) Dhosi hills (d) Mohali

18 Dhosi pilgrimage is associated with which of the following sages? *Haryana Sub-Inspector 2018*

(a) Vishwamitra (b) Bhrigu
(c) Chyavan (d) None of these

19 Match List I with List II.

List 1	List 2
A. Parashar fair	1. Dedicated to Lord Vishnu
B. Ajat fair	2. Organised in Bahlolpur, Karnal
C. Bharthari fair	3. Sage Ajat's sacred place
D. Prahlad Bhagat fair	4. Held on the 6th day of Krishna Paksha in Bhadrapad

Codes

	A	B	C	D		A	B	C	D
(a)	1	3	4	2	(b)	2	1	3	4
(c)	2	4	1	3	(d)	4	1	2	3

20 Which saint is associated with a fair organised in Khori, near Rewari district in Haryana?

(a) Baba Ramgir (b) Baba Suraj Giri
(c) Saint Haridas (d) Baba Vanadev

21 Where is the fair in memory of Baba Sabaadh held?

(a) In Sanghi, Rohtak (b) In Indri, Karnal
(c) In Narnaul, Haryana (d) In Tohana, Hisar

22 Match the fairs with their respective places.

List I	List II
A. Fair of Baba Naga	1. Rajgarh, Dadri
B. Fair of Baba Gulab Gir	2. Surkhpur Veeran, Jhajjar
C. Fair of Baba Sadaram	3. Malda, Mahendragarh
D. Fair of Baba Raghunath	4. Tigra, Narnaul

Codes

	A	B	C	D		A	B	C	D
(a)	1	2	3	4	(b)	2	1	4	3
(c)	1	3	4	2	(d)	3	2	1	4

23 In which district is the Agrasen Jayanti fair organised to commemorate Maharaja Agrasen?

(a) Jind (b) Hisar (c) Jhajjar (d) Karnal

24 What is the special feature of the Chhadi fair held in Karnal district?

(a) Wrestling competitions
(b) Worship of a holy stick
(c) Sticks being sold and worshipped
(d) Kite flying

25 Sharda Devi fair is held in which district of Haryana? *HSSC 2016*

(a) Palwal (b) Sonipat
(c) Ambala (d) Yamunanagar

26 Kalka fair is held in which of the following districts of Haryana? *PGT 2016*

(a) Faridabad (b) Fatehabad
(c) Gurugram (d) All of these

27 What is the significance of the Surya Grahan fair in Kurukshetra?

(a) It celebrates the birth of Lord Ram
(b) Devotees take a holy bath during the Solar Eclipse
(c) It marks the end of Navratri
(d) Worship of Goddess Kali takes place

28 Consider the following statements about fairs in Haryana.

I. The Basant Panchmi fair in Rewari district is organised in the month of Magh.
II. The Qalandar Shrine fair is organised on the day of 'Chaand Rat' after Ramzan.
III. The Baisakhi fair in Kurukshetra takes place on 13th April every year.

Which of the above statements is/are correct?

(a) I and II (b) II and III
(c) I and III (d) All of these

29 Match the fairs listed in List I with their corresponding locations or significance in List II.

List I	List II
A. Bhura Bhawani fair	1. Ferozpur Jhirka
B. Sati fair	2. Shahabad
C. Ram Navami fair	3. Hodal
D. Devi fair	4. Celebrated during Navami in Baisakh (April-May)

Codes

	A	B	C	D		A	B	C	D
(a)	3	4	2	1	(b)	2	1	3	4
(c)	4	3	1	2	(d)	1	2	4	3

30 Consider the following statements about the Gopal-Mochan fair in Yamunanagar district.

I. It is held in the month of Kartik (October-November).
II. The fair is associated with Lord Shiva, who is believed to have bathed in the Gopal Mochan tank.

III. The Rin Mochan tank, close to Gopal Mochan, is believed to relieve people of their debts.

Which of the above statements is/are correct?

(a) I and II (b) II and III
(c) I and III (d) All of these

31 Surajkund International fair is organised in which district of Haryana? *HSSC 2015*

(a) Gurugram (b) Faridabad
(c) Rewari (d) Sonipat

32 Surajkund International fair is a colourful Indian craft fair, held every year in the month of *Haryana Tehsil Welfare Officer 2018*

(a) January (b) February
(c) March (d) April

33 When was the first time the Surajkund International Crafts Mela was held? *HSSC 2020*

(a) 1957 (b) 1967 (c) 1997 (d) 1987

34 All of the artists and craft men of India participate in which fair of Haryana? *HSSC 2016*

(a) Surajkund Craft fair
(b) Kurukshetra Surya Grahan fair
(c) Balram garh Kartik fair
(d) Kalesar fair

35 Two festivals are celebrated every year to promote the ancient heritage of Pinjore, one festival being the Pinjore Heritage Festival. Which is the other festival? *HSSC CET (Pre) 2023*

(a) Orange Festival (b) Dates Festival
(c) Mango Festival (d) Lemon Festival

36 Where is the International Gita Festival celebrated in Haryana every year? *HSSC CET (Pre) 2023*

(a) Surajkund (b) Pinjore
(c) Sultanpur (d) Kurukshetra

37 In which month of the year is the famous Surajkund fair annually organised in Haryana? *HSSC CET (Pre) 2023*

(a) March (b) December
(c) October (d) February

38 Pehowa Mela is held in which of the following districts of Haryana? *HSSC CET (Mains) 2023*

(a) Kurukshetra (b) Karnal
(c) Panipat (d) Sirsa

39 This famous fair of Haryana is annually organised in September *HSSC CET (Mains) 2023*

(a) Gopal Mochan fair (b) Kisan fair
(c) Gangaur fair (d) Mango fair

CORRECT ANSWERS

1. (a)	**2.** (b)	**3.** (b)	**4.** (b)	**5.** (c)	**6.** (c)	**7.** (c)	**8.** (c)	**9.** (b)	**10.** (b)
11. (b)	**12.** (b)	**13.** (a)	**14.** (a)	**15.** (c)	**16.** (b)	**17.** (c)	**18.** (c)	**19.** (c)	**20.** (b)
21. (a)	**22.** (c)	**23.** (b)	**24.** (c)	**25.** (c)	**26.** (a)	**27.** (b)	**28.** (d)	**29.** (c)	**30.** (d)
31. (b)	**32.** (b)	**33.** (d)	**34.** (a)	**35.** (c)	**36.** (d)	**37.** (d)	**38.** (a)	**39.** (b)	

CHAPTER 09

Languages and Literature of Haryana

Haryana has a rich heritage of literature and language through all the ages. The evidence of its language and culture can be seen before the Mahabharata period.

Most sacred Hindu religious book **Srimad Bhagvad Geeta** was written here. It is believed that the creation of the Vedas was started here on the bank of Saraswati river. Later, Jain and Nath poets contributed a lot to make Haryana rich in literary terms.

Languages of Haryana

- Language is the means of communication through which we present our ideas. Generally, Haryanvi, Hindi, Punjabi, Urdu, English, etc. languages are spoken in Haryana.
- Hindi is the official language and is spoken by 89% population of the state. Punjabi is the second official language in the state.

Haryanvi Language

- Haryanvi is a dialect of Hindi. It is widely spoken, particularly in rural areas and is the most common dialect in the state. It is also known as **Bangaru** or **Jatu**.
- The Devanagari script is used to write the Haryanvi language.
- The origin of the Haryanvi language is believed to be from **Khari Boli** or **Kauravi**.
- Most of the words of the Haryanvi language are derived from the Brajbhasha.
- The Haryanvi language has developed from the Shaurseni Apabhransh.

> According to the famous scholar **Nanak Chandra Sharma**, Haryanvi language was born from Western Hindi i.e. Haryanvi language is the dialect of Western Hindi.

- British linguist Dr. Grierson calls the Haryanvi language **Bangaru.**
- Generally, Haryanvi language is divided into two parts based on the region – the language spoken in North Haryana and the language spoken in South Haryana.
- The language of South Haryana is called **typical Haryanvi.** There are a total of 10 vowels in the Haryanvi language - अ, आ, इ, ई, उ, ऊ, ए, ऐ, ओ, औ, while the number of **consonants** is 32.
- Haryanvi language was the origin language of Aryan in 1500 B.C.
- In the Haryanvi language, the consonants get converted into pre-consonants i.e. voiceless consonants while pronunciation. For example, use of 'gar' at the place of 'ghar' (house), the 'daram' at the place of 'dharma' (religion), 'janda' at the place of 'jhanda' (flag), etc.

> **Cultural Influence**
>
> Turkish and Persian intruders came to India and developed modern Hindi language with combination of Persian on the foundation of Haryanvi language. It provided foundation to many Indian languages.

Major Dialects of Haryanvi Language

The main dialects of Haryanvi language are:

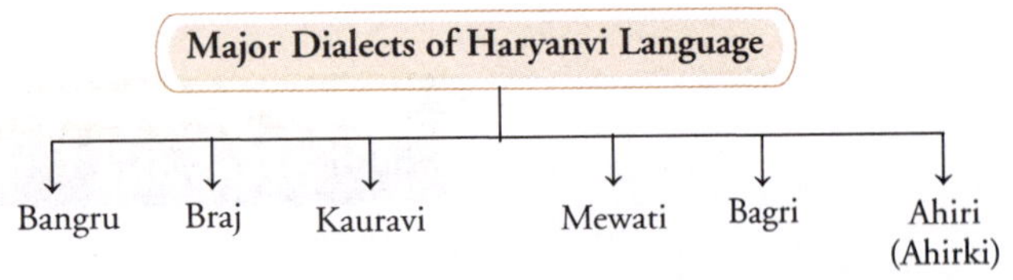

Bangru

- Spoken in — Rohtak, Hisar, Jind, Bhiwani, Sonipat, Kaithal, Karnal and Panipat
- Typical area — Rohtak
- It is the most spoken dialect in Haryana.
- Dr. Satya Gupta and Dr. Dhirendra Verma have also called Bangru synonymous with the Haryanvi language.
- Bangru is also referred to as the **native dialect.**

Kauravi

- Spoken in — Kurukshetra, Thanesar, Ambala, Jagadhri, Kalka, Pinjore, Panchkula, Morni, Narayangarh, Kalesar and Tajewala
- Major sub-dialects — Western Kauravi, Eastern Kauravi, Pahartali and Bijnori
- Purest form of Kauravi — Bijnori
- According to Dr. Vikram Singh, Khadi Boli is called Kauravi after the district. The name Kauravi is derived from **Kuru Janapada.**
- The famous Hindi language scholar Pt. Rahul Sankrityayan has named the Khadi dialect as **Kauravi.**
- Dr. Kailashchandra Singhal has prepared a list of 650 words on the Kauravi dialect.
- The Kauravi dialect is also called **Ambabali** because it is spoken in most of the areas of the Ambala division of Haryana.
- The Kauravi dialect has made an important contribution to the development of standard Hindi.

Ahiri (Ahirki)

- Spoken in — Kosli, Rewari, Mahendragarh, Narnaul, Pataudi and Khadi Khatiwas of Jhajjar
- The language of Ahirs in Haryana is called Ahiri or Ahirwati. The rural area of Ahirwati is referred to as Hiri.
- In the development of the Ahiri dialect, Dr. Shyamsunder Das has played a leading role and in his research, he identified 200 words as Ahiri.

Bagri

- It is spoken in Bahal Western part of Bhiwani, Siwani, Western part of Hisar, Ellenabad, Chautala, Dabwali, Rori and adjoining areas of Sirsa.
- Prof. Mathura Prasad Aggarwal has prepared a list of 81 words related to the Bagri dialect spoken in the Bagar region of Haryana.

Mewati

- It is spoken in Ferozepur-Jhirka, Nagina, Nuh, Hathin, Sohna, Bawal, Uchana, Bichhor, Tawadu, etc.
- Ishwari Prasad Sharma identified 300 words as Mewati.

Braj

- It is spoken in Eastern part of Faridabad, Gurgaon (Gurugram) and Mewat (Nuh) districts.
- The vocabulary of the Braj language is similar to that of Bangru.

Haryanvi Literature

- The literature of Haryana is very comprehensive in nature. Many philosophical texts and Vedic legends have been composed in the state of Haryana.
- Haryana literary texts have been composed in many languages, such as Sanskrit, Hindi and Urdu languages.

Sanskrit Literature of Haryana

- Essays are the main part of Haryanvi Sanskrit literature. **Ramdutt Sharma**, a resident of Bhiwani, Haryana, has composed 30 essays.
- Dr. Vedprakash Vedalankar, Dr. Ram Gopal, Dr. Bhimsingh Vedalankar, Dr. Raghunam Ari, Jayadev Arya, etc. are also Sanskrit essayists.

Leading Sanskrit Litterateurs and their Compositions

Litterateur	Composition
Dr. Vidyadhar Dhasmana	Nibandha Saptakam (This book contains a compilation of 7 essays)
Dr. Madan Lal Sharma	Vicharvithi (This book contains a compilation of 16 essays which are based on ancient and new topics)
Vedh Shankarlal Sharma	Madiya Karmabhoomi (This book is a compilation of 14 essays. This essay is related to Ayurveda)
Dr. Mahesh Chandra Sharma	Shri Harshadevasya Natakeshu Nari

Sanskrit Epic, Long Narrative Poetry and other Compositions

Epic	Author
Daduramadoy	Swami Haridas (Dadu Sampradaya)
Shrimastram Charitam	Haridutt Shastri
Harishchandra epic	Dr. Balbir Dutt Shastri
Shri Shankaracharyacharitam	Nigam Bodh Tirtha
Shri Krishnanand Mahakavyam	Mahakavi Vanmalidas
Gangayya Mahakavyam	Pt. Chandrabhanu Shastri
Amarcharita Mahakavyam	Pt. Rameshwar Lal
Shri Harishreshtha Mahakavyam	Mahakavi Vanmalidas

Sanskrit Long Narrative Poetry and Composers of Haryana

Composer	Long Narrative Poetry
Pt. Radhakrishna Shastri	Haryana Vaibhavam
Vanmalidas Shastri	Sankhya Sudhakar
Shri Laxman Singh Aggarwal	Vigyan Geetam, Ritambhara, Kalchakram
Hansraj Nagar	Guru Prashasti, Saraswati Vandana
Smt. Shanti Rathi (first fragment writer of Haryana)	Indira Prashastishatkam
Pt. Hazari Lal Shastri	Shiv Pratap Virudavli, Maharishi Dayanand Prashastishatkam, Kadambarishatkam, Sagunabrahmashatkam, Indira Vijaya Vajayntishatkam, Shiv Stotram
Vedh Shankar Lal Sharma	Ritu Vihar
Dr. Shankarlal Saraswat	Yug Bharti

Prose Literature of Haryana

- Prose literature consists of novels and language literatures, biographies, plays, fictions, etc.

Novels

- Sanskrit novels have also been written by litterateurs of Haryana.
- **Vaidya Shankarlal**, a resident of Dholra, Haryana, wrote the Sanskrit novel 'Shashiprabha', which was published in the year 1985.
- **Pt. Sayanudatta Sharma** wrote the language of Haryana.
- **Pt. Vidyadhar Shastri** wrote on Vedic literature.
- **Shivnarayan Shastri** wrote philosophy and grammar related literature.
- **Dr. Ram Gopal** composed literature related to Vedic language and grammar.

Biographies and Plays

- **Pt. Madhvacharya** composed Kathashtakam (narration of Dhanna, Raidas and Meera etc.) and Kabir Charitam. There are 100 stories in Kathashtakam which are written in simple language.
- **Acharya Vidyanidhi** composed Sri Dayanandarshi Charitam (Dayanand Chandrodaya). In this text, he has given a biography of Maharishi Dayanand.

> **Bhikharam Shastri** composed Gandhi Charitam and **Pt. Hazarilal Shastri** composed Maharishi Dayanand Prashastishatkam.

- **Pt. Chhajuram Vidyasagar** was the principal playwright of the state. He composed the Durgabhyudaya Natakam.
- The story of all these plays is religious and mythological.
- 'Shiva Samadhirupam', composed by **Prof. Satyadev**, is a famous play which has four parts and sixteen scenes.

Leading Playwrights and their Compositions

Playwright	Composition
Dr. Baldev Singh	Harshdarshanam
Dr. Vidyadhar Dhasmana	Paanchjanyam
Dr. Sudhikant Bhardwaj	Vyan ke Swam
Dr. Ram Dutt Sharma	Petika Rahasyam
Dr. Naubatram Bhardwaj	Patiprayan
Dr. Mathuradatta Pandey	Ekank Panchadashi (It has won President's award)

Fictions

- According to Shri Harikrishna Devsare, **Man ki Chanchalta**, composed by Pandit Madhav Prasad Mishra, is the first Hindi story in Haryana.
- According to Pandit Murari Goyal Prasad, the **Ladki ki Bahaduri**, composed by Pandit Madhav Prasad Mishra, is the first Hindi story in Haryana. The theme of this story is based on society.
- The second story of Haryana is **Daki Dabh Khana**, written by Dr. Nanak Chand Sharma.
- Important fictionists of Haryana are as follows
  - **Shamim Sharma** is a famous litterateur in Hisar district of Haryana. He started the first research work on short stories in Haryana. His major compositions include Panchnad, Chaupal ka Makhol, Chaupal Pattau, Chaupal ke Chale, etc.

– **Meenakshi Jijeevisha** is associated with Faridabad in Haryana. She has been active in short story writing for the last decade. Two of his fiction collections have also been published, of which the first collection is 'Is Tarah se Bhi'.

Leading Fictions and their Fictionists

- Pandit Madhavaprasad Mishra — Man ki Chanchalta, Ladki ki Bahaduri, Akhyayika Saptaka
- Vishambharnath Kaushik — Rakshabandhan ,Tai, Gulp Mandir, Sadh ki Holi, Chitrashala, Paris ki Nartaki, Pratishodh
- Mohan Chopra — Adha Kata Hua Surya, Peele Patte, Shyam aur Akela Aadmi, Band Darwaza, Toota Hua Aadmi
- Jaynath Nalin — Jhurmut, Sikke, Asli-Nakli, Jawani ka Nasha
- Dr. K.P. Singh — Samantar
- Rajendra Mohan Bhatnagar — Gandi Basti, Chanakya ki Haar, Gaurraiyya, Palash ke Phool
- Swadeshi Deepak — Ashwarohi, Maatam, Tamaasha, Maskhare, Kabhi Nahin Rote
- Sasibhushan Sinhal — Yeh Jag We Sapne
- Rakesh Vats — Pahar Ek Roz Ka, Antim Prajapati, Abhiyukta, In Halat Mein

Modern Literature of Haryana

The modern literature of Haryana is expressed in various typologies as follows

Essay

- The essay falls under the prose style. Dr. Harishchandra Verma, Jagdish Kaushik, Dr. Pushpa Bansal, Dr. Roopnarayan Sharma, Dr. Brajlal Goswami, Dr. Jayabhagwan Goyal, Dr. Yogeshwar Dev, Dr. Krishna Madhok, Dr. Shashibhushan Singh, etc. are prominent essayists of Haryana.
- **Balmukund Gupt** occupies a prominent position among the litterateurs of Haryana. Initially, he was an Urdu journalist, but later he started writing Hindi literature, influenced by the lectures of Deen Dayalu Sharma.
- Balmukund Gupt introduced the political, religious, and social problems of the nation to the public by his satirical writing through a letter called **'Bharat Mitra'**. One of his classics is **Shivshambhu ka Chittha**.

Famous Essayists and their Compositions

Essayist	Composition
Acharya Vinay Mohan Sharma	Drishtikon, Sahityavlokan, Sahitya Shodh, Rekha Aur Rang, Avlokan, etc.
Pt. Madhav Prasad Mishra	Madhav Mishra Niyamavali, Madhav Mishra Granthavali
Bhadant Anand Kausalyayan	Jo Bhul na Saka
Jayanath Nalin	Prastav Prabha, Chintan aur Kala, Majhdar ke Par

Novels

- Rajaram Shastri was **the first novelist of Haryanvi language**. He has written many poems in Haryanvi and Hindi languages.
  He is the creator of **Jhaadufiri**, the first novel of the Haryanvi language. He has also written a novel called Fafa Kuttani. Rajaram Shastri founded the **Haryana Lokmanch.**
- Prominent Novelist Mr. Mohan Chopra is the first successful novelist of Haryana.
  His major compositions are – Baahen, Need ke Agey, Ek Chhanya Main and Tuta Hua Aadmi, Subha Ke Pehle and Ye Naye Log.

Other Novelists and their Compositions

Novelist	Composition
Vishambharanath Kaushik (Ambala)	Maa, Bhikharini (published in 1923)
Rakesh Vats	Madhukan, Jeevit Chattane, Sagar aur Kalpana, Maryada, Phir Lautte Hue, Jangal Ke Aas Paas.
Swadesh Deepak	Number-57 Squadron (During Indo-Pak war related to the story of Air Force) Mayapot, Court Martial
Subhash Rastogi	Tute Sapne
Bhishma Pitamah	Chaudhary Sahab
Madhukant	Gaon Ki Aur
Rajkumar Nyal	Saye Apne Apne
Jayanarayan Kaushik	Maati Ka Mol, Budhi Suhagan
Krishna Bachhal	Amaanat Ek Shaheed Ki
Urmi Krishna	Van Aur Pangdandiya
Krishna Madhosh	Andha Safar

Novelist	Composition
Amritlal Madan	Lal Dhoop, Apne-Apne Andhere, Sindhu Putra
Shuganchand 'Muktesh'	Shesh- Ashesh, Ab Nahi, Aprajya, Maine Nahi Likha Mahabharat
Shashibhushan Singhal	Apne Paraye, Jani Anjani Raahen
Hemraj Nirgum	Mujhe Bhul Jana, Basant Phir Ayega, Tut te Bandhan, Seep Ka Moti, Jaal or Mukti, Laal Bahadur, Prateeksha or Tarashe Hue Patthar
Abhimanyu Anant	Laal Paseena
Rameshchandra Jain	Mehendi Rache Haath
Devishankar Prabhakar	Kharagputra, Ganputra
Kanhaiyalal Mishra 'Prabhakar'	Kanun Ka Kabeer, Agyeya ka Patta
Santosh Goyal	Hindi Upanyaskar Kosh

Court Literature of Haryana

Court literature occupies an important section in the literature of Haryana. **Birbal** occupies a prominent position in 'Navratnas' of the court of Mughal Emperor Akbar, whom Akbar gave the title of **Kavi rai.**

Litterateur	*Court*	*Composition*
• *Dev*	Seth of Dadri Sita Ram	Bhawani Vilaas
• *Jugal Kishore Bhatt (Kaithal)*	Muhammad Shah 'Rangeela'	Alankar Nidhi and Kavitt Sangrah
• *Bhai Santosh Singh*	Naresh Bhai Uday Singh of Kaithal	Amar Kosh (Bhashanuvad), Nanak Prakash, Atmapraa (Bhashanuvad), Guru Pratap Suraj
• *Mukund Das (Rewari)*	Maharaj Karam Singh of Patiala	Rasik Shiromani, Surya Sangrah
• *Kavi Banga Singh*	Dhanik Teeka Nihal Singh of Ladwa	Ramkatha
• *Shambhu Dayal (Dadri)*	Maharaja of Jind	Rukmani Mangal, Krishna Leela, Jogan Leela, Bhajan Sagar
• *Manmohan (Dadri)*	Raja Ranbir Singh of Jind	Ranbeer Prakash

Hindi Literature of Haryana

There are many famous writers of Hindi literature in the state. Their details are as follows

Siddha Chauranginath

- Considered as — **First Hindi litterateur** in Haryana
- Original name — Puranmal
- Writing — **Pranasamkali**, Srinaath-Ashtak

Balmukund Gupt

- Born on — 14th November, 1865
- Place — Gudiyani, Rewari district
- Famous as — Essayist, journalist and had a strong hold on Urdu
- He edited Urdu newspaper 'Akbare Chunar' in 1886 AD and '**Kohinoor**', an Urdu letter from Lahore, in 1888-89 AD. He successfully edited three **Hindi** letters Hindustan, Bangwasi and Bharat Mitra. He also compared the works of Lord Curzon with those of Nadir Shah.
- In addition to journalism, his two works full of humour and satire are famous namely Shivshambhu ke Chitthe and Urdu Bibi ke Naam Chitthi. Haridas, Khilona, Khel Tamasha, Sphutvatika, Gupt Nibandhawali, etc. are his major creations.

Hindi Litterateurs and their Compositions

Litterateur	Composition	Litterateur	Composition
Chauranginath	Vayutribhuvnopdesh, Pran- Sankali, Shrinath Ashtak	*Shridhar*	Chandraprabha, Shantinath, Parshvanath, Vardhman Mahavir, Shrimad Bhagwat Tika
Isardas	Angadpege, Bharat Vilap, Satyavati Katha	*Manikya Raj*	Amarsen Charitra
		Thakur Pheru	Vastusar, Ratna Pariksha
Samrat Harshvardhan	Priyadarshika, Ratnavali, Nagananda	*Dant Kavi*	Barahkhadi
Banabhatta	Chandishatak, Parvati Parinay, Harshacharita, Kadambari	*Nemichand*	Trilok Darpan
		Bhagwati	Sitasetu
Mayur	Mayurshatak Suryashatak, Matang Diwakar	*Manbhavan*	Brij Vinod
Garuddhwaj	Dharamdhwaj	*Nishchal Das*	Vichar Sagar, Vritti Prabhakar, Yukti Prakash

Litterateur	Composition
Madhav Prasad Mishra	Madhav Mishra Nibandhawali
Surdas	Sursagar, Sursaravali, Sahitya Lahari, Nal Damayanti, Vyahlo, etc.
Pt. Shri Ram Sharma	Haryana Ka Itihas, Navratna of India
Chandra Trikha	Jhutha- Sachaa, Tamas
Balmukund	Tara, Ashrumati, Tulsi Sudhakar, Adhkhila Phool Hindi Bhasha ki Bhumika, Hindi Bhasha, Ek lipi ki Zarurat, Devnagari Akshar, Hindustan Mein Rasmukhat
Ram Pratap	Swadesh Darshan
Brij Lal Sendhi	Nimbark Sampraday Prakash
Jaynarayan Kaushik	Maati ka Mol
Rajaram Shastri (Prose)	Eekh ki Kheti (Praharsan)
Swami Haridas	Daduramodya
Pt. Nandbhanu Shastri	Gangay Mahakavyam
Pt. Rameshvar Dayal	Amarcharit Kavyam
Dr. Balvir Datta Shastri	Harishchandra Mahakavyam
Buchraj	Santosh Jaytilak, Neminath, Vasantu, Nemishvar ka Barahmasa, Tandana Geet
Ramchandra	Kurukshetra Mahatmayam
Hardwari Lal	Saraswat

Litterateur	Composition
Jinndutt Suri	Gashdhar Sapttika, Purchari
Suganchand Muktesh	Maine Nahi Likha Mahabharat, Mahakavya Hazrat Muhammad
Harishchandra Verma	Hindi Sahitya ka Itihaas
Yash Gulati	Kavita aur Sangharsh Chetna
Liladhar Viyogi	Sihi ka Ant
Pushpa Bansal	Prativad Parv
Devishankar Dwivedi	Bhasha aur Bhashiki, Devnagari
Chandrakanta	Katha Satisar
Nandlal Mehta 'Vageesh'	Sanskriti Tatva Mimansa
Sunita Jain	Sunita Jain: Samagra (14 Parts)
Santosh Goyal	Hindi Upanyaskar Kosh
Hardatt Shastri	Mastram Charitam
Santosh Singh	Ramkosh, Shri Guru Nanak Prakash, Garav Ghajini, Valmiki Ramayana, Atma Purana, Guru Pratap Suraj
Gulab Singh	Bhavar Samrit Maakshe Panth and Prabodh Chandrodaya

Urdu Literature in Haryana

- Haryana has made significant contributions to the growth of Urdu language and literature. **Maulana Hali** and his family members like - Khwaja Ahmad 'Abbas', Salika Abid Hussain Begum, Mumtaz Mirza, Zahida Zaidi, etc. are the most important contributors to the growth of Urdu language and literature in Haryana.

Urdu Litterateurs and their Compositions

Litterateur	Composition
Pratap Singh Rana Ginnauri	Urdu translation of Kalidas, famous composition, Meghaduta
Shiv Prasad Javed	Shola - A- Tishnagi, Ghazal- a - Rana, Roop Ras
Uttamchand Sharad (Hali Awardee)	Phool aur Kaate
Vimal Kumar 'Ashq'	Aansu-Ansu, Geet Vatan Ke, Dukh ke Phool, Aaina or Parchnai
Balbir Singh Rathi	Katra-Katra
Bhagirath Lal 'Zakhmi'	Dastane Mazdur and Sarshak
Mohinder Pratap Chand	Harf-e-Raaz
Jwala Prasad Shahi	Jhola Awaz
Ramkrishna Tamanna	Nakshe Tamanna

Famous Litterateurs of Haryana

Litterateur	Details	Major Works
Khwaja Ahmad 'Abbas'	A renowned Urdu poet, recognised both in India and abroad. He was honoured with the President's Award for his contributions to Urdu literature.	Ababil, Ek Ladki, Musafir ki Diary, Mein Kaun Hoon, Paon Mein Phool and others.
Altaf Hussain Hali	Born in 1837 in Panipat, made remarkable contributions to Urdu literature. In 1904, the British Government honoured him with the title 'Shamsul Ulema' for his literary excellence.	Hayat-e-Saadi, Safarnama, Najm-e-Hali, Makatib-e-Hali, Makalat-e-Hali, Yadgar-e-Galib, Hayat-e-Javed, etc.
Naubhar Sabir	A famous Urdu poet from Tohana honoured by the Haryana Government in 1970-71 for his literary achievements.	Rajkumari, Lalita, Payam-e-Bedari, Krishna-Darshan, Karvaan Khayalo Ke, Lahu Tarang and others.
Jaimini Sarshar	One of the country's prominent poets, recognised by the Government of Haryana in 1971-72 and 1973-74 for his contributions to Urdu poetry.	Jajbat-e-Sarshar, Nagmat-e-Sarshar, Nigarshat-e-Sarshar, Tusarrat-e-Sarshar and others.
Prof. RP Shokh	He was an English teacher at Markandeya National College, Shahabad in Kurukshetra. He had a deep love for Urdu, especially Ghazals. His Ghazals were translated and published in Devanagari script in the book 'Zindagi ke Shishe Mein'.	Gamja-be-Gamja, Munakkash Khandahar (Jabin)
Dr. Sultan Anjum	He was a famous Urdu editor, poet and critic, edited the monthly Urdu magazine **Tamir-e-Haryana** for 35 years. He received accolades such as the Khwaja Ahmad Abbas Award and the Hali Award.	Doobte Manzar ka Safar, Khwahishein Khwab Hain, Sarabe Aarju, Haryana ki Hindi Kahaniyan.
Kashmiri Lal Zakir	He was the former Secretary of the Haryana Urdu Academy and the Chairman of Chandigarh Sahitya Academy.	Sindoor ki Rakh, Chhatthi ka Dudh, Mujhe Jeene Ka Haq Mil Gaya, Chaar Meel Lambi Sadak, Mera Gaon Meri Atma Hai and Puranmasi and so on. Besides these, he also composed Chirag ki Lau, Zakir ki Teen Kahaniyan, (a story collection of Hum Sab Sakshi Hain).

Sufi Literature of Haryana

- Panipat, Ambala, Thanesar, Kaithal, Narnaul and Hansi are main centres of Sufi Sect in Haryana.
- In the 12th century, **Chishtiya Saint Baba Fareed** (Sheikh Fariduddin)arrived in Hansi and established an education and literary centre. His efforts popularised **Fareedwani** in the region.

Key Contributors to Sufi Literature

Litterateur	Explanation
Sheikh Muhammad Turk	He was the first Sufi Saint of Haryana, who started Sufism in Haryanvi Society and Literature.
Rajaram Shastri	He discovered 'Barahmas' composed by Sufi Saint Hazrat Khairushah.
Shah Gulam Jilani Rohtaki	He was quite popular for his creation Chaupayi in Haryanvi language.
Shah Muhammad Ramzan 'Shaheed'	He composed in both prose and poetry styles. He is also known as Hadi - e - Haryana. His famous compositions are Akayade Azim, Akhirgat, Bulbule Bagenabi and Vasiyatnama.
Gulam Qadir	He was a litterateur related to Sufi ideology, but his Hariyanvi Chaupayi has also been quite famous. His main compositions are Prem Neher, Prem Vaani, Prem Pyaala, Inetkabh and Joysagar.

Jain Literature of Haryana

- Some historians states that **Pushpadanta** was the Aadi Jain poet of Haryana.
- According to Acharya Chatursen, Aadi Jain poet Pushpadanta was a native of Rohtak. He used to add adjectives with his name like *Abhimanmeru*, *Kavyaratnakar* and *Kavikultilak*.
- The most sacred Jain text **Satkhandagama** is the famous composition of Pushpadanta.
- This scripture has six parts. These are as follows
  - Jivasthana – Bandhasvamitva – Kshudraka Bandha
  - Vedana – Vargana – Mahabandha

Major Jain Litterateurs and their Compositions

Litterateur	Composition
Kavi Sudharu or Sadhas	Pradyumn Charit
Kavi Bhojraj Alias Bulb	Namishwar (Barhamas), Santosh Jaytilak, Chetan Pudgal Dhal, Neminath Vasantu, Futkar Basant, Tandana Geet, Yan Juice
Roopchand Pandey	Parmarthi Shatak, Geet Parmarthi, Mangal Geet Prabandh, Rupchandra Shatak
Rajkumar	Mahavir Charit
Banarsidas	Ardh Kathanak, Nam Mala, Moh Vivek Yudh, Banarasi Vilas, Navras Rachna
Jagat Rai	Sabhyakatv Kaumudi, Agam Vilas and Padamanandi Patr Vishantika
Vijayanand Suri	Aatmbavni, Jain Tatvadarshan, Agyantini Bhaskar, Navtatva, Ratnavali Shrutpanchami Raas, Aadinath Satvan
Nirdosh Hisari	Mrityunjay Mahavir
Anand Ghan	Anandghan Bahotari
Govardhan Das	Shakun Vichar
Dharampal	Shrut Panchami Ras, Aadinath Satvan
Shridhar Aggarwal	Pasnaah Chariu, Sukumal Chariu and Bhanvisayat Chariu
Sundar Das	Sundar Satsai, Sundar Shringar, Sundar Vilas, Pakhand Panchasika and Dharam Saheli
Bhagwati Das	Sitasetu, Jogirasa, Madhu Bindak Chaupai, Tandana Ras, Mrinank Lekhacharit, Aneko Arthmala, Mugtiraman, Chunari Manak-Rahsas, Chatur Banjara
Nayaymat Singh	Shiva Sundari Natak, Swamin Raksha Natak, Sati Menasundari, Sati Kamal Shri Natak, Bhavishdutt Tilka Sundari Natak
Maldev	Bhoj Prabandh, Sthulbhadra, Fagu, Purandar, Chaupai, Sur, Sundari Chaupai, Virangat Chaupai, Devdutt Chaupai

Saint Literature of Haryana

- The famous scholar **Dr. Surajbhan** has discussed the study of Saints in his book **Haryana Ka Sant Sahitya.**
- In this book, he has made a special mention of the Garib sect of Saint Garibdas in this book.

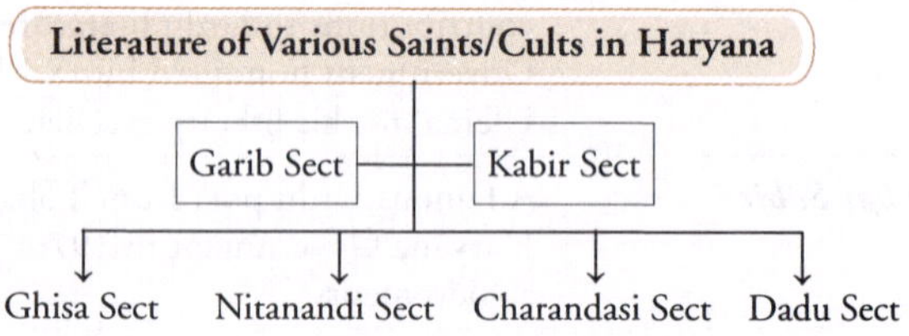

Garib Sect

- Originator — Sant **Garib Das**
- Born in — 1717 in a village called Chhudani of Jhajjar tehsil in Rohtak district
- Literary work — **Amritvani** in the Haryanvi language
- Recognition — First saint poet of Nirgunadhara in Haryana, composed 24,000 couplets
- Worship — Nirgun Rama
- Publication — Vaani published in the Granth Sahib from Haridwar in 1964

Ghisa Sect

- Promoter — Sadguru Ghisa Saheb
- Incarnation — Kabirdas
- Teachings — Speech and sermon compiled in **Granth Sahib**
- 1, 14 and 16 verses of his disciples Mahant Premdas, Shri Ram Kishan Das and Mahant Achaladas are available, respectively.

Nitanandi Sect

- Founder — Sant Nitanand, real name Nandlal
- Contemporary — Sant **Garib Das**
- Literary work — **Satya Siddhant Prakash** by Shri Bholadas
- There are many centres of this sect in Haryana.

Dadu Sect

- Founder — Sant Dadudyal
- Classes of Sadhus — Khalsa Sadhu (related to Narayana Gaddi), Virakta Dadu Panthi, Dakhanadha Sadhu, Uttarari Sadhu, Naga Dadu Panthi
- Haryana's tradition — **Uttaradi tradition**
- Chief Dadu Panthi Saint — Banwari Das, composed three verses and three Aartiyan

Prominent Litterateurs and Compositions Related to Dadu Sect

Litterateur	Composition
Nischal Das	Vichar Sagar, Vritti Prabhakar
Anaath Das	Vichaarmala
Chaturdas	Bhagwat Ekadash Skandh

Kabir Sect

- Founder Sant **Indraj** of Badli
- Key saint Harde Das, (compiled Vaani, included in second part of *Hriday Prakash*)

Prominent Litterateurs and Compositions of Kabir Sect

Litterateur	Composition
Durgadas	Vaani
Baba Dulan Das	Vaani
Surajdas	Panth
Baba Girdhari Das	Vaani
Asadas	Geetanuvad
Madhodas	Itihas Satishobha Devi
Sheetal Das	Bhajan

Charandasi Sect

- Founder Charan Das
- Region Mewat region of Haryana
- Key text The Bhakti Sagar epic (compiles the Vaani of Shri Charan Das)

Prominent Litterateurs and Compositions of Charandasi Sect

Litterateur	Composition
Ramswaroop	Guru Bhakti Prakash
Lala Sagar	Jog Jeet
Mahant Ganga	Shri Shyam Charan Das Charitawali

Nath Literature of Haryana

- **Chaurangi Nath** and Siddh Yograj Purnnath of Haryana have important place in Nath (Siddha) literature.
- Famous compositions of Chaurginath are – Pran-Sankli, Sri Nath Ashtak and Tattva-Bhavnopdesh, etc.
- The famous compositions of Siddh Yograj Purnath are Siddha Siddhanta Padhati, Goraksh Siddhanta Sangrah, etc.
- Gorakhnath composed many ragas and hymns in the Haryanvi language. He compiled a total of 49 ragas and 182 verses.
- Five texts of Nath sect, written in Sharda script, have been kept in manuscript museum of Kurukshetra University. These texts are Vivek Martand, Amrodh Shasanam, Shadchakra Nirnay, Hathyog Pradipika and Ashtang Yog.

Ramkavya Tradition in Haryana

- It is believed that the Ramkavya tradition in Haryana is started from Vikram Samvat 1029.
- Ramakavya can be seen in the creation of Pushpadanta, the last poet of Apabhransh language.
- The composition of Pushpadanta has description of the Ramkatha in 69 to 79 sargas of the **Tistathi Mahapuris Gunalankara.**
- **Haryanvi Ramayana** was composed by **Khuda Baksh Ahmed.**
- The best period of Ramkavya tradition in Haryana is considered to be between 1375-1900.

Major Litterateurs and Compositions of Ramkavya Tradition

Litterateur	Composition
Isardas	Angad Per, Bharat Vilap, Bharat Milap, Saraswati Katha
Bhagwatidas	Sitasetu
Ramkavi Hridyaram	Hanuman Natak, Chitrakoot Vilas, Dharma Charitra, Bali Charitra, Rukmani Mangal
Kavi Ramdas	Ramayan, Kartik Tarang, Ganga, Byahalo, Tirtha Mahatmay, Sudama Charitra
Nirmala Sadhu Pandit	Adhyatma Ramayan, Karma Vilap, Bhav Rasamrit
Gulab Singh	Moksha Pantha Prakash, Prabodh Chandrodaya
Bhai Santosh Singh 'Darshanik' (Courtier and Historian of Kaithal ruler)	Namkosh, Guru Nanak Prakash, Guru Pratap Suraj, he also translated Valmiki Ramayan
Ram Singh	Laghu Ramayan
Banga Singh	Ramkatha
Lakshman Singh Aggarwal	Ramrasayanam
Ram Ratna Laghudas	Hanuman Jayanti
Vishnu Mitra Sharma 'Shastri'	Ramcharitam
Ramesh Chandra Shukla	Sugam Ramayan

Krishna Bhakti Kavya of Haryana

- Shri Krishna preached the Gita to Arjuna in Kurukshetra. The political and heroic depiction of Lord Krishna can be seen in Krishna Bhakti Kavya literature of Haryana.
- **Surdas** has presented Krishna Bhakti Kavya on the basis of Shri Krishna's Baal Leela.
- Surdas was born in a Brahmin clan in Sihi village of modern Faridabad district. However, some scholars believe, he was born in Runkata.
- He has written about 1.25 million padas and mantras. His major compositions are Sur Saravali, Sursagar and Sahitya Lahri etc.
- Sayyed Gulam Hussain Shah has also depicted his feelings in the padas of Krishna Bhakti.

Major Litterateurs and Compositions of Krishna Bhakti Kavya

Litterateur	Composition
Pushpdant (Rohtak)	Mahapurana
Kavi Sudharu (Agroha, Hisar)	Padmacharit
Mahakavi Hridayram (Gharonda, Karnal)	Rukmani Mangal
Sant Garib Das (Garib sect)	Krishna Stotra
Ramdas (Hisar)	Sudamacharit
Dhaukal Ram (Bhiwani)	Rukmani Mangal, Prem Sindhu, Mahabharat
Kavi Sahib Singh Mrigendra	Barhamasa Sri Krishna – Radha, Barhamasa Shriradha, Rasamandal Leela, Krishna Kautuhal
Umadas (Thanesar)	Sudama Charit (in Brajbhasha)
Jugatanand Gusai (Rata, Gurgaon)	Bhakti Prabodh
Shambhudayal (Charkhi Dadri) (Court poet of Jind ruler)	Rukmani Mangal, Krishna Leela, Jogan Leela, Bhajan Sagar
Laxminarayan Sharma Kripan (Bhiwani)	Shyam Bansi, Shishupala Vadh
Ramswaroop (Tawadu)	Krishna Leela (in Brajbhasha)
Tulsiram Sharma 'Dinesh' (Bhiwani)	Shyam Satsai, Purushottam
Brahmadatta 'Vaggim'	Medtani Meera
Pt. Madhav Kaushik (Bhiwani)	Laut Aao Paarth, Suno Radhika
Mangal Rama Atreya (Kurukshetra)	Yamuna ke Us Paar
Lakshminarayan Sharma (Kaithal)	Vatsala
Purushottam Das 'Nirmal' (Narnaul)	Mahabharata Ratna
Bharat Bhushan 'Sanghiwal'	Sudama Saurabh (10 Sarga and 384 Chhand)
Khushiram Sharma 'Vashistha'	Rann Nemantran

Important Poets and Khandakavya

Poet	Khandakavya
Bhagwan Das Nirmohi	Indiranjali
Ramnivas 'Manav'	Indrakeel, Angulimaal
Dr. Liladhar Viyogi	Betwa ki Lahren, Pratham Diwas Ashaa Ka, Peeda ki Pagdandiyan
Khushiram Vashistha	Rann Nimantaran (topics related to peace and treaty of Mahabharata)
Charan Lal 'Niras'	Bangloday
Dharmachandra Vidyalankar	Gokul Gaurav Nahar Singh Keertigatha

Development of Ghazals in Haryana

- According to the nature of Hindi and the culture of Haryana, the traditional Ghazals have been developed by Shri Vimal Krishna 'Ashk', B.D. Kalia 'Hamdam', Prof. R.P. Shokh, Mahendra Pratap Chand and Kundan Gudgavi.
- **Vijay Kumar Sinhal's** Ghazal Collection **Dhoop Hamare Hisse Ki** is considered as the first **Ghazal collection of Haryana**, which was published in 1982 in collaboration with Haryana Sahitya Academy.
- **Kanwal Haryanvi**, popularly known as Haryanvi Ghazalkaar, was born on 9th May, 1927, in Pai village of Kaithal district. He is considered the modern master of Haryanvi folk literature.

Ghazal Singers and their Ghazal Collection

Ghazal Singer	Ghazal Collection
• Vijay Kumar Sinhal	Dhoop Hamare Hisse Ki, Barf Se Dhaka Jwalamukhi, Saat Samundar Pyaase, Dhundh Se Guzarte Hue
• Surendra Verma	Aainon Mein Talash Chehre, Aaj Ke Dashrath, Aina Bolte Hain
• Madhav Kaushik	Aina Ke Shahar Me, Kiran Subah Ki, Sapne Khuli Nigaho Ke, Hath Salamat Rahne Do, Asman Sapno Ka
• Gyan Prakash 'Vivek'	Dhoop Ke Hastakshar, Ankho Par Asmaan, In Mushkil Dino Mein
• Rana Gannauri	Roshani Ki Lakeer
• Udaybhanu Hans	Dard Ki Bansuri

Famous Litterateurs of Haryana

Pandit Satyadev Vashishtha

- Birth — 24th August, 1912; Mahal-Mahila village of Jalandhar
- Father — Pt. Anantram
- He composed Satyagraha Niti Kavyaam, Naditattvadarshanam, Vishnusahasranam and Satyabhashyam etc.

Pandit Vidyadhar Gautam

- Birth — Sirsa Khedi village, Jind
- Studied in — Banaras, Uttar Pradesh
- Sons — Beniram Gaur and Daulatram Gaur (Sanskrit Scholars)
- Composed — Instinct of Katyayana Srautasutra
- Other works of Pandit Vidyadhar Gautam are Sulabh Sultravati, Devachayagya Paddhati, Shraddhasar, Upanayana Paddhati, Sanapaabhu, Shikshanayas Paddhati, Vastu Shanti Paddhati and Vivah Paddhati etc.

Acharya Vidyanidhi Shastri

- Birth — 18th September, 1911, Lohari village, Panipat
- Memorised — Yajurveda and Ashtadhyayi (Sanskrit texts)
- Education — Bhainswal Kalan
- He composed Vyavahar Bhanu, Dayanand Chandrodayam, Shri Gandhi Charitamritam, Bhakta Phool Singh Charitam, Indira Kirtishatakam, Rigveda Kavya Tatvani, Sankshipt Ramayana, Mahabharate and Maitrayanisahityokta. Also translated Samaveda in Hindi.

Pandit Shivnarayan Shastri

- Birth — 1885, Gautauli village, Jind
- Interests — Sankhya philosophy
- Joined — Khemraj Shri Krishnadas Press, Mumbai
- Commentaries — On Samkhya Granth Samkhyatatvaprabod-hini, Pushpika
- Pandit Shivnarayan Shastri spent nearly 50 years in teaching and later joined Khemraj Shri Krishnadas Press in Mumbai.

Pandit Shivram Shastri

- Birthplace — Berla village, Charkhi-Dadri
- Parents — Pandit Shivdutt and Dhapo Devi
- He was a prominent scholar and Haryana Vaibhavam was his first poem.
- He also composed 'Gandhicharitam' and 'Nehruvanshamahakavayam', although these works have not been published yet.

Sunita Jain

- Birth — 13th July, 1941, Ambala
- Expertise — Novelist, short story writer, Hindi and English poet
- Awards — Padma Shri (2004), Vyas Samman (2015, by KK Birla Sangathan)
- She composed Ek Aur Din, Kaha Miloge Kavita, Jane Ladki Pagli, Barish me Delhi and Saanjh Ki Bair etc.

Dr. Mukta

- Founder — State Women's University
- First Woman Director — Haryana Sahitya Akademi
- Award — Best Female Creator Award 2017 (by Haryana Government)
- She composed Harigandha, Aakhir Kaise, Ete Moun, Beti ka Dukh, Apnatva etc.

Swadesh Deepak

- Birth — 1942, Haryana
- Famous Drama — Court Martial

Pandit Madhav Prasad Mishra

- Birth — 1928, Kungar village, Bhiwani
- Works — Madhav Mishra Granthavali, Madhva Mishra Niyamavali
- He has left an indelible mark in various literary genres like poetry, story, drama, etc.

Prof. Hari Singh

- He has translated Nobel Laureate Rabindranath Tagore's Gitanjali in Haryanvi language in the name of **Haryanvi Gitanjali**.

Maharishi Ved Vyas

- Composed — Mahabharata (18 Parv and 1 lakh Shlokas), Puranas and Gita
- Ashram — Shamyapras (Pehowa), on bank of holy river Saraswati

Harshavardhana

- Belong to — Thaneshwar or Srikantha Janapada (modern Kurukshetra district)
- Wrote — Priyadarsika, Nagananda, Ratnavali (Sanskrit plays)

Banabhatta

- Court poet of — Harshavardhana
- Composed — Harshacharitam, Kadambari, Chandikasatakam, Parvati Parinaya Natakam, Mukundashtakam
- Harshacharitam is considered the most ancient fable of Sanskrit literature.
- In Harshacharitam, Banabhatta discussed the Maha Purana composed by Pushpadanta of Haryana. He also mentioned **Vayu Vicar** (a Prakrit poet) and **Venibharata** (a poet of lingua franca).

Kavi Mayur Bhatt

- Birth place — Thaneswar
- Contemporary of — Banabhatta; Harshvardhana (cout poet)
- Composed — Mayurashatak and Surya Satakam

Pandit Chhajuram Vidyasagar

- Birth — 1894 AD in Ritoli village, Jind
- Father — Pandit Moksharaj
- He composed Kurukshetra-shtakam, Durgabhyudayanam Natakam, Sultan Charitram and Shivkathamritam, etc.

Madhwacharya

- Birth — 1897 in Kaul village, Kaithal
- Studied in — Delhi and Lahor
- Established — Sanskrit Schools in many countries
- Principal of — Sanskrit School, Bahawalpur (1923)
- Composed — Today Smriti and Kabir Charitam
- Journals — Hitwadi Vriddhi, Sanatana Dharma-Shastraathpanchak

Other Litterateurs of the State

Litterateur	Description
Jaitaram	He was the son of Garib Das and he composed poetry in Haryanvi language.
Dayaldas	He was a disciple of Garib Das. He composed a book called Vichaar Prakash.
Haridas	He composed a Haryanvi book named 'Raja Ratansen'. He was a contemporary of Tau Sangi.
Saint Nitanand	His famous compositions are Satya Siddhant Prakash, Nitanand ke Bhajan, Barahkhadi (small book).
Tau Sangi	His important creation is Rukmani Vivah.
Bansi Lal	He composed Guru Gugga, Raja Gopichand, Raja Nal, etc. Haryanvi texts.
Kavi Samainath	His famous creations are Rana Pratap, Prithvi Raj Chauhan, Raja Harishchandra.
Kavi Shankar Lal Shukla	His famous creations are Bhakta Prahlad, Bhura Badal, Bhaktmal.
Sayyed Gulam Hussain	He belongs to Maham, Rohtak. His famous creations are Ram-Mala, Dahine Hath ka Shankh.
Krishna Goswami	His famous creations are Dilawar, Budhamal and Gulabkavli.
Gowardhan Saraswat	His famous creations are Krishna Leela, Mahabharata, Jodhpur Naresh Jaswant Singh, Madhav Nal, Dulla Kam Kandla.
Sadulla	He belongs to Mewat region of Haryana. He composed Mahabharata.
Ali Baksh	His main creations are Raja Nal and Krishna Leela Aadi Saang.
Yogeshwar Balakram	His main creations are Puran Bhakt, Ramayan, Kunjadi and Shilade.

Haryana Literary Academies and Awards

- Sahitya Akademi of Haryana, Department of Cultural Affairs, Literature, creative arts and other major departments have established various awards and honours to encourage development in these fields.
- To encourage culture and literature, the Haryana Government has established 6 academies, which are as follows

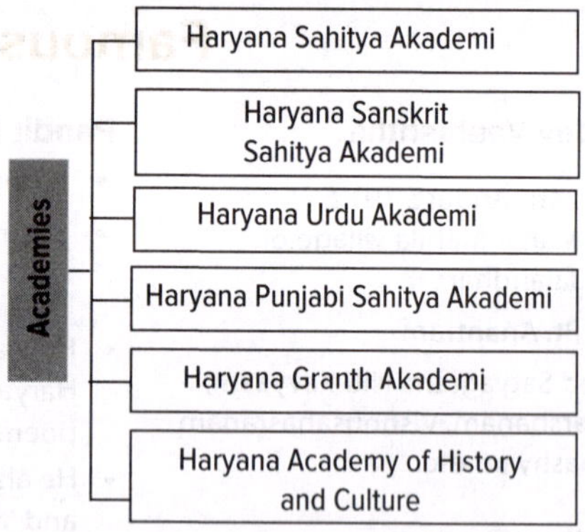

- These academies provide various awards and honours for promoting outstanding works of literature and culture in the state.

These are described as follows

Haryana Sahitya Akademi

- The State Government formed the Haryana Sahitya Akademi on 9th July, 1970, which is headquartered in **Panchkula**. It is established for the preservation, upliftment and promotion of literature in Haryana.
- Earlier, its administrative control was under the Education Department, but currently, it is under the Department of Information, Public Relations and Cultural Works.
- The Haryana Sahitya Akademi was reorganised after the transfer of the given administrative control on 26th August, 2011.
- The **Chairman** of this Akademi is the **Chief Minister of Haryana** and its two Senior Vice-Chairmen are the Minister of the Department of Public Relations and Cultural Work and the Education Minister of the state. There are also executive Vice-President, Director and Vice-President in this academy.
- The first prize of Haryana Sahitya Akademi was given to **Ashok Bhatia** for his book **Samudra Ka Sansar** in 1991.

Haryana Sahitya Akademi publishes regularly a monthly Literary Magazine, **Harigandha** in Hindi language.

Annual Awards and Honours given by Haryana Sahitya Akademi

Award	Description
Aajeevan Sahitya Sadhna Samman	• This award is given at the national level for the outstanding contribution to Hindi and Haryanvi literature. • It is not necessary to be a resident of Haryana to get this honour. • The minimum age to receive this honour is 65 years. The prize money is ₹ 7 lakh.
Pt. Madhav Prasad Mishra Award/Haryana Sahitya Ratna Award	• This award is given for distinguished contribution in Hindi and Haryanvi. • The litterateur should be a Haryanvi by birth or has been living in Haryana for 25 years. • The minimum age to receive this honour is 60 years. The prize money is ₹ 2.5 lakh.
Mahakavi Surdas Award	• This award is given for distinguished contribution in Hindi and Haryanvi language. • On 22nd May, 2006, it was renamed as **Surdas Samman**. The person should have published at least seven books and at least one book should be awarded by Sahitya Academy. • The minimum age to receive this honour is 65 years. The prize money is ₹ 5 lakh.
Babu Balmukund Gupt Samman	• This award is given in the field of Hindi and Haryanvi literature and journalism. • The author should be a resident of Haryana, have at least five published books, and at least one book should be awarded by Sahitya Academy. • The minimum age to receive this honour is 45 years. The prize money is ₹ 2.5 lakh..
Lala Deshbandhu Gupt Samman	• This award is given for outstanding contributions to Hindi journalism. • The author should be a resident of Haryana and have at least two published books. • The minimum age to receive this honour is 45 years. For this award, the prize money is ₹ 2 lakh.
Pt. Lakhmichand Award	• This award is given in the field of Haryanvi language, arts, culture, history and folk literature. • The litterateur can be from any region of India and must have at least five published books, with one awarded by Sahitya Academy. The minimum age to receive this honour is 45 years. The prize money is ₹ 2.5 lakh.
Lok Kavi Dayachand Samman	• This award was instituted in 2021 under the category of folk literature and culture. • It carries a prize money of ₹ 2.5 lakh.
Hindi Sevi Samman	• This special award has been started by the Akademi from the year 2021. It carries a prize money of **₹ 1 lakh.** • Its first recipients were **Dr. Shiv Mar Khandelwal, Ravi Sharma, Dr. Surendra Gupta, Asha Khatri Lata, Rajesh Chetan** and **Mahendra Jain** (2021).
Yuva Shrestha Kriti Puruskar	• The Akademi started such awards in various genres of Hindi and Haryanvi language from 2021. • Each award carries a prize money of ₹ 31,000.
Yuva Lekhak Samman Puruskar	• This award is now presented to 4 candidates. • Each award carries an honorarium of ₹ 1 lakh.
Swami Vivekananda Yuva Writer Award	• This award carries an amount of ₹ 1 lakh.
Jankavi Meher Singh Award	• This award is given for special contribution in art, culture, history and folk literature of Haryana. • The litterateur should be a Haryanvi by birth, with at least five published books. • The minimum age to get this honour is 45 years. The prize money is ₹ 2.5 lakh.
Haryana Gaurav Samman	• This award is given to litterateurs born in Haryana but living outside Haryana and making Haryana proud in the field of literature. The litterateurs must have at least five published books. • The minimum age to receive this honour is 50 years. The prize money is ₹ 2.5 lakh.
Aditya Alhad Hasya Award	• This award is given at the national level for making special contribution in the field of Hindi and Haryanvi humour and satire. The writer must have at least five original published books. • The minimum age to receive this award is 45 years. For this award, the prize money is ₹ 1 lakh.
Best Female Creator Award	• This award is given for notable contribution in Hindi and Haryanvi literature. • Women creators must be residents of Haryana. • The minimum age to receive this honour is 45 years. The prize money is ₹ 2.5 lakh.

Haryana Sanskrit Sahitya Akademi

- The Haryana Sanskrit Sahitya Akademi was established on 8th August, 2002 by the Haryana Government for the development and promotion of Sanskrit language.
- This academy publishes monthly magazine called **Hariprabha** related to Sanskrit language.
- The objective of the Akademi is to provide financial assistance for the upliftment of the Sanskrit language and literature, to preserve the literary work manuscript dictionary, to organise literary conferences, seminars and exhibitions and to encourage research in the Sanskrit language.

Haryana Urdu Sahitya Akademi

- Haryana Urdu Akademi was established on 22nd December, 1985 for promotion and development of under language and literature in Haryana.
- The akademi promotes Urdu language through Urdu centres, encourages Urdu folk litterateurs and preserves various works related to Urdu language.
- Haryana Urdu Akademi publishes two quarterly journals **Jamana Tat** (magazine of modern Urdu literature) and **Urdu Disha** (published in Devanagari script).
- Urdu Disha magazine also connects non-Urdu speaking people.

Awards and Honours given Annually by Haryana Urdu Sahitya Akademi

Award Name	Description
Fakhre-Haryana Samman	• This award is given to under poets for their outstanding work in Urdu poetry in Haryana. • It carries a prize money of ₹ 5 lakh.
Rashtriya Haali Samman	• This is the highest honour given by Haryana Urdu Sahitya Akademi, which is awarded to the nationally reputed Urdu litterateurs. An amount of ₹ 3,00,000 is awarded under this award.
Kanwar Mohinder Singh Bedi Samman	• This is a state-level award given annually. An amount of ₹ 21,000 is given under this award.
Munshi Gumani Lal Samman	• An amount of ₹ 21,000 is awarded under this honour.
Surendra Pandit Soz Samman	• An amount of ₹ 21,000 is awarded under this honour.

Awards given by Haryana Sanskrit Sahitya Akademi

Sanskriti Sahityalankar Samman

- This honour carries a prize money of ₹ 7 lakh.

Maharishi Valmiki Award

- This award is given annually to scholars and litterateurs of Sanskrit language.
- An amount of ₹ 3 lakh is awarded under this honour.

Maharishi Vedvyas Award

- This award is given to scholars and writers of Sanskrit language.
- A cash prize of ₹ 3 lakh is given to the person honoured under this award.

Banabhatta Award

- This award is also given to scholars and litterateurs of Sanskrit language.
- An amount of ₹ 2.5 lakh is given under this award.

Haryana Sanskrit Gaurav Samman

- This award is given to renowned Sanskrit litterateurs at National and International level.
- An amount of ₹ 5 lakh is given as prize money.

Guru Virjanand Acharya Samman

- This award is given every year for distinguished contribution in teaching Sanskrit grammar.
- An amount of ₹ 2 lakh is given as prize money.
- Acharya Swami Prasad Mishra of Panchkula received this award for the year 2021.

Pandit Yudhishthira Mimansak Acharya Samman

- This award is given for teaching in the field of Vedas, astrology or rituals. The prize money is ₹ 2 lakh.

Vidyamartand Pandit Sitaram Shastri Acharya Samman

- This award is given annually for outstanding work in the field of teaching Sanskrit literature.
- An amount of ₹ 2 lakh is as prize money.

Swami Dharmadev Sanskrit Samaradhak Samman

- This award is given for special contribution in the field of Sanskrit literature.
- An amount of ₹ 2 lakh is given as prize money.

Book Award Scheme

- This award is given for outstanding work in the field of prose and poetry genre.
- A cash prize of ₹ 51,000 is given as prize money.

Haryana Punjabi Sahitya Akademi

- Punjabi language is very popular in districts like Ambala, Kurukshetra, Karnal, Panchkula, Yamunanagar, etc. in Haryana.
- For the development and promotion of Punjabi literature, Haryana Punjabi Sahitya Akademi publishes the monthly Magazine **Shabd Boond**.
- The Shabd Boond magazine consists of 6 compositions, of child stories, whose primary purpose is to encourage child writers.

> Haryana Punjabi Sahitya Akademi, headquartered at **Panchkula**, was formed in October, 1996 with the objective of promoting the Punjabi language and literature in the state.

Awards and Honours given Annually by Haryana Punjabi Sahitya Akademi

Award Name	Description
Haryana Punjabi Gaurav Award	• Under this award, an amount of ₹ 5 lakh is provided by the Haryana Government.
Sant Taran Singh Vehni Award	• Under this award, an amount of ₹ 2 lakh is given annually by the Government of Haryana.
Mahakavi Bhai Santokh Singh Award	• Under this award, an amount of ₹ 2.5 lakh is provided annually by the Government of Haryana.
Baba Sheikh Farid Award	• Under this award, an amount of ₹ 2.25 lakh is given by the Government of Haryana annually.
Ragi/Dhodi/Folk Singer Award	• Under this award, an amount of ₹ 1 lakh is given annually by the Government of Haryana.
Book - Story Award	• Under this award, the Government of Haryana gives an amount of ₹ 21,000 each in the category of poetry, story, drama, novels, biography and children's literature annually.
Punjabi Journalism Award	• An amount of ₹ 1 lakh is given by the Haryana Government under this award. • **Harbans Singh Mander** received this award for the year 2022.
Kavi Harbhajan Singh Renu Award	• An amount of ₹ 1 lakh is given by the Haryana Government under this award.

Haryana Granth Akademi

- In the year 1963, the Government of India decided to make Hindi and other Indian languages a medium of higher education.
- Under this, it was decided to establish a textbook publication board/university cell and Hindi Granth Akademi for the creation of all university-level standard texts.
- The Haryana Granth Akademi was established in the year 1970 with its headquarters at **Panchkula**.
- It was set-up to produce university-level standard texts.
- The Haryana Granth Akademi was merged into with Haryana Sahitya Akademi, which was also established in the year 1970.
- Under this merger, an 'independent text division' was established in the academy.
- The Haryana Granth Akademi was reorganised on 1st September, 2011.
- So far, around 263 books on 23 subjects have been published by this academy, out of which the number of original books is 202 and translations of texts in 61 other languages.
- **Sapta Sindhu** quarterly and **Katha Samay** (monthly) magazine are published by Haryana Granth Akademi.
- Haryana Granth Akademi published Pandit Lakhmichand Granthawali, Pt. Mangeram Granthawali and Baje Bhagat Granthawali for the preservation of the culture of Haryana.

Haryana Academy of History and Culture

- The Centre for History, Culture and Social Development, Haryana was formed as part of the Haryana Institute of Public Administration in July 2006.
- The State Government reconstituted it on 27th July, 2010 as Academy of History and Culture.
- The academy gained statutory autonomy on 7th June, 2013. **Prof. K.C. Yadav** was the founding director.
- The academy was initially headquartered in Gurugram, but later shifted to Gulzarilal Nanda Centre, Kurukshetra in 2016.
- The main objective of the academy is to encourage research on the history of the state, economic development and social change, collecting and studying sources about various periods and civilisations of the state and setting up libraries, organising seminars and so on.

Famous Editors of Haryana

Newspaper	Editor
Jaat Newspaper (1889)	Kanhiyalal Mishra (Gurugrama)
Jaat Gazette (Urdu) (1916) Dainik Haribhoomi (first Hindi Newspaper of Haryana) (1996)	Ch. Chhoturam (Rohtak)
Haryana Jhajjar (first Newspaper of Haryana)	Deen Dayal Sharma
Nabh Chhor (Daily Evening from Hisar)	Rishi Saini

CHECK CHAPTER KNOWLEDGE

1 What is the official language of Haryana? *Haryana Clerk 2016*
(a) Urdu (b) English
(c) Punjabi (d) Hindi

2 How many per cent of people speak Hindi in Haryana? *HSSC 2020*
(a) 59% (b) 69%
(c) 79% (d) 89%

3 Haryanvi is a dialect of .... language. *HSSC 2020*
(a) Western Hindi (b) Punjabi
(c) Gurmukhi (d) Rajasthani

4 Haryanvi is originated from which script? *HSSC 2020*
(a) Brahmi script
(b) Devanagari script
(c) Gupta script
(d) Kalinga script

5 Haryanvi language is a part of which of the following languages? *PGT 2016*
(a) Khari Boli (b) Hindi
(c) Urdu (d) Sanskrit

6 In which of the following languages, you cannot find much Haryanvi literature? *HSSC 2020*
(a) Hindi (b) Braj
(c) Urdu (d) Pali

7 How many consonants are there in Haryanvi language?
(a) 12 (b) 28 (c) 32 (d) 40

8 Bijnori is the purest form of .... language. *HSSC 2020*
(a) Pahartali (b) Hindi
(c) Urdu (d) Kauravi

9 Which of the following languages is not spoken in Haryana? *HSSC 2020*
(a) Punjabi (b) Haryanvi
(c) Hindi (d) Gujarati

10 Which Hindi scholar gave the name Khadi dialect as Kauravi? *HSSC 2023*
(a) Prof. Mathura Prasad Aggarwal
(b) Pt. Rahul Sankrityayan
(c) Dr. Griyasen
(d) Pt. Shivram Shastri

11 Braj dialect is spoken in which district of Haryana?
(a) Gurugram (b) Mewat
(c) Faridabad (d) All of these

12 The ashram of Maharishi Ved Vyas was located on the banks of which river of Haryana?
(a) Indus (b) Setluj
(c) Saraswati (d) Yamuna

13 Which of the following is the famous play written by the King Harshavardhana? *HSSC 2024*
(a) Priyadarsika (b) Nagananda
(c) Ratnavali (d) All of these

14 Who wrote 'Harshacharitam'?
(a) Banabhatta (b) Ishadas Rachit
(c) Nath Sect (d) None of these

15 Who wrote Surya Satakam?
(a) Kavi Mayur Bhatt (b) Banabhatta
(c) Pt. Vidyadhar Gaur (d) Pt. Shivnarayan Shastri

16 Thaneshwar or Srikantha Janapada is located in which of the following districts of Haryana?
(a) Jhajjar (b) Kurukshetra
(c) Jind (d) Kaithal

17 Which monthly magazine is published by Haryana Sanskrit Sahitya Academy?
(a) Chandra Prabha (b) Satya Prabha
(c) Hariprabha (d) Pratibha

18 What is the highest honour given by Harayana Urdu Sahitya Academy?
(a) Kunwar Mohnider Singh Bedi Samman
(b) Rashtriya Haali Samman
(c) Munshi Gumani Lala Samman
(d) Surendra Pandit Soj Samman

19 Who authored 'Haryana Vaibhavam'? *HSSC 2023*
(a) Pt. Radhakrishna Shastri
(b) Vanmalidas Shastri
(c) Hansraj Nagar
(d) Pt. Hazari Lal Shastri

20 Which of the following works was written by Balmukund Gupt?
(a) Jo Bhul na Saka
(b) Shivshambhu ka Chittha
(c) Rekha Aur Rang
(d) Prastav Prabha

21 Who is regarded as the first novelist of the Haryanvi language? *HSSC 2024*
(a) Vishambharnath Kaushik
(b) Rakesh Vats
(c) Rajaram Shastri
(d) Mohan Chopra

22 Who authored "Maa" and "Bhikharini," published in 1923?
(a) Vishambharanath Kaushik
(b) Rameshchandra Jain
(c) Shashibhushan Singhal
(d) Devishankar Prabhakar

23 Fakhr-e-Haryana Award is given for *HSSC CET 2024*
(a) Hindi literature (b) Haryanvi literature
(c) Urdu literature (d) Sanskrit literature

24 Consider the following statements about Rajaram Shastri.
I. He authored "Jhaadufiri" and "Fafa Kuttani."
II. He wrote "Number-57 Squadron."
III. He was the founder of Haryana Lokmanch.
IV. His compositions include "Mujhe Bhul Jana."
Which of the above statements is/are correct?
(a) I and II (b) I and III
(c) I, II and IV (d) All of these

25 Who is the novelist of the novel 'Maati ka Mol'? *Haryana Shift Attendant 2017*
(a) Pt. Jasraj
(b) Jayanarayan Kaushik
(c) Sayyed Qasim Mahmud
(d) Parul Gulati

26 Who is the novelist of the novel 'Tutte Bandhan'? *HSSC 2019*
(a) Banabhatta (b) Sampraday
(c) Jaimini Saraswat (d) Hemraj Nirgum

27 The first novel of the Haryanvi Language is *HSSC 2020, 16*
(a) Heru ki Kahani (b) Jhaadufiri
(c) Dan Lula (d) Surahi Gaya

28 Who wrote the novel 'Toota Hua Aadmi'? *HSSC 2020*
(a) Mohan Chopra (b) Deedar Singh
(c) K.C Yadav (d) Prem Chaudhary

29 Who was the first Sufi Saint of Haryana? *HSSC 2016*
(a) Sheikh Muhammad Turk
(b) Swami Haridas
(c) Khwaja Ahmad Abbas
(d) Jemini Sarshar

30 Which famous ancient poet is from Haryana? *HSSC 2020*
(a) Rabindranath Tagore
(b) Mirabai
(c) Kabirdas
(d) Surdas

31 Who of the following is known as 'Hadi-e-Haryana'? *PGT 2016*
(a) Sufi Saint Shah Ghulam Jilani Rohtaki
(b) Shah Muhammad Ramzan 'Shaheed'
(c) Sheikh Muhammad Turk
(d) Hazrat Kherushah

32 Who is the author of literature 'Deshan mein Desh Haryana'? *Haryana Police 2018*
(a) Lakhmi Chand
(b) Udaybhanu Hans
(c) Dayachandra Mathan
(d) None of the above

33 Who is the composer of 'Rukmani Vivah'?
(a) Tau Sarngi (b) Kavi Saminath
(c) Haridas (d) Dayal Das

34 Who wrote 'Guru Gugga'?
(a) Tau Sarngi (b) Haridas
(c) Jaitram (d) Bansi Lal

35 Who wrote 'Krishna Leela Aadi Saang?
(a) Ali Baksh
(b) Sadullah
(c) Krishna Goswami
(d) Tau Sarangi

36 The famous creation 'Bhakt Prahlad' was written by *HSSC 2023*
(a) Tau Sarngi
(b) Dayaldas
(c) Haridas
(d) Kavi Shankar Lal Shukla

37 The headquarters of Haryana Sahitya Academy is located in
(a) Rohtak (b) Panchkula
(c) Hisar (d) Jind

38 Who authored "Pradyumn Charit (Paradvnu Chowpai)"?
(a) Jagat Rai (b) Kavi Sudharu
(c) Vijayanand Suri (d) Rajkumar

39 Who is the author of "Siddha Siddhanta Padhati" and "Goraksh Siddhanta Sangrah"?
(a) Siddh Yograj Purnnath
(b) Chaurangi Nath
(c) Gorakhnath
(d) Ram Singh

40 Match the following poets with their compositions.

List I (Poets)	List II (Compositions)
A. Ramkavi Hridayaram	1. Sudama Charit
B. Kavi Sudharu	2. Rukmani Mangal
C. Sant Garib Das	3. Padmacharit
D. Shambhudayal	4. Krishna Leela

Codes

	A	B	C	D		A	B	C	D
(a)	4	2	1	3	(b)	2	3	4	1
(c)	1	3	2	4	(d)	3	4	1	2

41 Who is known for composing "Angad Per" and "Bharat Vilap"?
(a) Isardas (b) Bhagwatidas Sitasetu
(c) Ram Ratna Laghudas (d) Ram Singh

42 Match the following poets with their compositions in the Ramkavya tradition.

List I (Poets)	List II (Compositions)
A. Kavi Ramdas	1. Kartik Tarang
B. Ram Singh	2. Ramkatha
C. Bhai Santosh Singh	3. Sudama Charitra
D. Kavi Ramavatar 'Abhilashi'	4. Hanuman Chalisa

Codes

	A	B	C	D		A	B	C	D
(a)	2	1	3	4	(b)	1	2	4	3
(c)	4	1	2	3	(d)	3	2	1	4

43 Who wrote the epic 'Surajmal Shaurya Katha'?
(a) Rajkavi Udaybhanu Hans
(b) Dharamchand Vidyalankar
(c) Tulsidas
(d) Bhagwan Das Nirmohi

44 Which poet is associated with the ghazal collection 'Dhoop Ke Hastakshar'?
(a) Vijay Kumar Sinhal
(b) Surendra Verma
(c) Gyan Prakash 'Vivek'
(d) Madhav Kaushik

45 What is the minimum age to receive Ajeevan Sahitya Sadhna Samman?
(a) 45 years (b) 50 years
(c) 55 years (d) 65 years

46 What is the prize money which is given under Madhavprasad Mishra Award?
(a) ₹ 50,000 (b) ₹ 1,00,000
(c) ₹ 2,50,000 (d) ₹ 3,00,000

47 Which prominent Hindi writer from Haryana compared the works of Lord Curzon with Nadir Shahi? *HSSC 2023*
(a) Hali
(b) Lala Lajpat Rai
(c) Balmukund
(d) Pandit Nekiram

48 Who is known as the 'Shakespeare of Haryana' and 'Suryakavi of Haryana? *HSSC 2023*
(a) Pandit Mangeram (b) Banshilal
(c) Ramsingh Nay (d) Dada Lakhmichand

49 Consider the following statements. *HSSC 2023*

I. Hindi is the official language of Haryana.

II. In the year 2010, Punjab was granted the status of official language of Haryana.

Which of the above statements are correct?
(a) Only II (b) Neither I nor II
(c) Both I and II (d) Only I

50 'Nabh Chhor' is a leading evening newspaper published from .... district of Haryana. *HSSC 2023*
(a) Palwal (b) Hisar
(c) Sonipat (d) Rohtak

CORRECT ANSWERS

1. (d)	2. (d)	3. (a)	4. (b)	5. (a)	6. (d)	7. (c)	8. (d)	9. (d)	10. (b)
11. (d)	12. (c)	13. (d)	14. (a)	15. (a)	16. (b)	17. (c)	18. (b)	19. (a)	20. (b)
21. (c)	22. (a)	23. (c)	24. (b)	25. (b)	26. (d)	27. (b)	28. (a)	29. (a)	30. (d)
31. (b)	32. (b)	33. (a)	34. (d)	35. (a)	36. (d)	37. (b)	38. (b)	39. (a)	40. (c)
41. (a)	42. (b)	43. (b)	44. (c)	45. (d)	46. (c)	47. (c)	48. (d)	49. (c)	50. (b)

CHAPTER 10

Archaeological Sites and Museums of Haryana

Archaeological forts and museums have a historically significant place. A fort is not only a structure made of bricks and stones, but also displays the valour of a ruler. Similarly, museums are our heritage while keeping our heritage safe.

Archaeological Forts of Haryana

In ancient times, the forts built by the kings were considered a symbol of their almighty fortifications. **Shukra Niti**, the major text of the sage Shukracharya, has mention of the seven major organs of the state in which the fort has also been included in the category of special organs.

The description of the archaeological forts built in Haryana is given below

Fort of Hansi

- The fort of Hansi was built by the Tomar ruler **Anangpal I.** This fort is also referred to as the fort of Prithviraj Chauhan. It was under the jurisdiction of the Mughals, Sikhs and British at different points in history.
- George Thomas made Hansi the capital of his empire and established it as the fortress of administrative headquarters.

- It is a **crescent-shaped** fort that includes a stable, a **step-well** and masjids. During the reign of George Thomas, a mint was also established here.

Fort of Asigarh

- The fort of Asigarh, located in Hansi, was built by **Prithviraj Chauhan** in the 12th century. It is also known as the **Fort of the Sword.**
- Prithviraj Chauhan also built another fort at Gohana.

Fort of Tohana

- This fort was constructed by **Anangpal Tomar**, the ruler of the Tomar dynasty of Delhi, in Tohana (Fatehabad).
- Emperor Anangpal originally named this place **Turana** after his dynasty, but later, it became known as Tohana.
- It is a crescent shaped fort featuring a **step-well** as its main highlight.
- Sultan Balban of the Delhi Sultanate renovated the fort, but it was completely destroyed in 1398 AD by Timur Lang. Currently, it remains in ruins.

Ramgarh Fort

- Ramgarh Fort, located in Panchkula, was built by the Rajput rulers of the **Chandel dynasty**. This fort is approximately 350 years old.
- Parts of this fort are still owned by the Chandel dynasty family, while the remaining sections are managed by the Haryana Tourism Department.
- The main gate of the fort, with a height of 37 feet, holds a record.

Taraori Fort

- Taraori Fort, situated in Karnal district, was built by **Prithviraj Chauhan**. It remains a preserved structure to this day.
- Taraori is renowned for the historic Battle of Tarain, fought in 1191-1192 AD.
- Aurangzeb constructed a pond and a masjid within the fort's boundary, which continue to attract tourists.

Fort of Hisar

- It was built by **Feroz Shah Tughlaq** in 1354 AD and has a crescent shaped structure.

- The fort has four gates - Dehli Gate, Nagauri Gate, Talaqi Gate and Mori Gate.
- Prominent attractions include the Jama Masjid, Lat Masjid, Diwan-i-Aam, Lal-Minar and Gujari Mahal.
- Gujari Mahal was constructed by Feroz Shah Tughlaq for his beloved Gujri. This palace is rectangular in shape and remains a major historical highlight.

Palwal Fort

- Palwal Fort is also known as **Matia Fort**. It was built during the reign of **Sher Shah Suri**. A lake was also constructed near this fort.
- Archaeological excavations reveal that there was a grand palace beneath the fort. Currently, the fort is in ruins.

Fort of Nivajpur

- This fort was built by **Nivaz Ali**, a Mughal Jagirdar, in the village of Nivajpur, about 10 km from Narnaul.
- The walls of the fort are made of stone, measuring 3 feet in width and about 20 feet in height. The entrance was 42 feet wide and the gates were adorned with pointed bars.
- The fort had systems for wells, warehouses and stables. At present, it stands in a ruined state.

Fort of Fatehabad

- Built in the 14th century by Feroz Shah Tughlaq, the fort was named after his son and is also called **Sher Shah's Fort**.

- The courtyard of the fort houses the tomb of the spiritual Guru Meerashah Pir of Feroz Shah Tughlaq. It is also referred to as **Humayun's Masjid** because Mughal Emperor Humayun offered Namaz here.
- The fort, constructed in 1868 AD, also includes a masjid built by Khairuddin Nambardar.

Loharu Fort

- Arjun Singh built this fort in 1570 AD. He was a descendant of Rao Narhar Das, the founder of Loharu. This fort is located in Bhiwani.

- The fort's main features include **Diwan-e-Khas** and **Sheesh Mahal**. The existing monuments here are the platform of Bhopal Singh and the mausoleum of a dog.
- From 1805 to 1947, the Loharu Princely State was ruled by Muslim rulers. After this period, the fort came under the control of Muslim rulers.

Fort of Taoru

- This fort is situated in Taoru town of Nuh district. It is referred to as the Fort of ruler **Nahar Singh**.
- High walls surround this fort. Several domes built in the West direction of Taoru are believed to have been constructed by the Mughal rulers.
- The Fort of Taoru has been converted into a police station. The fort, with its chambers and rooms, provides information about the history of Taoru.

Fort of Farrukhnagar

- This fort was built in 1732 AD by Faujdar Khan, the first Nawab of the Princely State of Farrukhnagar in Gurugram. **Faujdar Khan** served as Nawab under the Mughal Emperor Mohammad Shah Rangeela and built the Jama Masjid in Farrukhnagar.
- After the revolt of 1857, the British took control of this fort. At present, the fort is completely in ruins.

Fort of Madhogarh

- It was constructed in the first half of the 18th century by **Sawai Madho Singh** in the Aravalli Hills near Madhogarh in Mahendragarh.
- The fort is inaccessible due to its location on a hilltop and stairs have been carved into the hills for access. It served as an important defensive structure. In 1755 AD, Maratha rulers captured this fort.

Fort of Maham

- Maham Fort is located in the Rohtak district of Haryana. It was built in 1656 CE by **Saidu Kalal** during Shah Jahan's reign.

- This fort is made of gravel, sand and stone. A step-well is also located within the fort.

Bahadurgarh Fort

- This fort was constructed by **Bahadur Khan**. In 1793 AD, Bahadur Khan's army was defeated in a war with the Marathas, leading to the fort's capture by Maratha powers (Scindia).
- In 1803 AD, the Marathas were defeated by the British and had to accept the Treaty of Surji Anjan village. As part of this treaty, the Marathas handed over all conquered territories, including Bahadurgarh Fort, to the British.

- The fort of Bahadurgarh is also known as **Singh Dwar** or **the Gateway of Haryana**.

Fort of Kanod

- This fort was built in 1755 AD by the **Maratha rulers**. In 1860 AD, this area became part of the Princely State of Patiala.

- Maharaja **Narendra Singh** of the Princely State of Patiala renamed Kanod Fort to Mahendragarh in honour of his son, Mahendra. Later, the city came to be known as Mahendragarh.

Fort of Jind

- This fort was constructed in 1775 AD by **Gajpat Singh**, the then king of Jind. In 1844 AD, this fort came under the rule of **Jind Kaur**, the youngest queen of Naresh **Sarup Singh** of the Princely State of Jind.
- This fort contains the mausoleums of Maharaja Ranjit Singh and Maharaja Kharag Singh. Currently, this fort has been demolished.

Fort of Georgegarh (Jahazgarh)

- This fort was built by **George Thomas**, a resident of Ireland, at Georgegarh (Jahazgarh) in the Jhajjar district.
- This ruined fort is a reminder of the colonial period.

Sohna Fort

- This fort is located in the Gurugram district. It was built by Sohan Singh in the 18th century.
- At present, this fort is completely ruined.

Fort of Raja Nahar Singh

- The construction work of Raja Nahar Singh's fort was initiated by Raja Balram Singh of the Ballabhgarh Princely State. **Balram Singh** became the king of Ballabhgarh in 1739 AD.
- In 1850 AD, **Raja Nahar Singh** became the king and completed the fort's construction, giving it his name. The fort resembles the structure of **Bharatpur Fort**, with bastions at all four corners for cannon installations.
- The fort is now known as **Nahar Singh Palace**.

In 2003, the Tourism Department of the Haryana Government designated it as a Heritage Hotel.

Fort of Kunjpura

- This fort was constructed with small bricks at a place called Kunjpura in the Karnal district.
- At present, it houses a military school.

Other Forts

- During the Mahabharata period, 10 major fortifications were built in Rohtak, Hisar, Sirsa, Fatehabad, Jind, Farrukhnagar and Thaneshwar, earning the state the name **Dasharana**.
- Other prominent medieval forts in Haryana include the **Fort of Gokalgarh**, the **Fort of Thaneshwar**, the **Fort of Dhosi** and the **Fort of Sirsa**. However, these forts have lost their existence in the present time.

Other Archaeological Sites of Haryana

Archaeological Site	Location	Features
Chor Gumbad	Narnaul, Mahendragarh district	• This historic dome was built by Afghan **Sardar Jamal Khan** as his tomb. • It gives an appearance of a double-storeyed structure, but the upper part of the dome is just a verandah. • The verandah has 20 gates, which reflect the grandeur of the dome.
War Memorial in Ludesar Village	Ludesar, Sirsa district	• This memorial presents the immortal saga of martyrs who sacrificed their life for the country. • At present, the Haryana Government maintains this memorial.
Tosham's Baradari	Bhiwani	• This Baradari is also known as **Prithviraj Ki Kutcheri**. Not a single frame has been constructed in this Baradari. • It has 12 gates, which have been constructed in such a way that a person sitting in the central room can easily observe all four sides.
Salarganj Gate	Panipat	• It was constructed during the British period, offering an excellent specimen of ancient architecture. • The gateway consists of two arched openings at both ends of the passage. In ancient times, it served as the entrance to the town of Panipat.
Kishori Mahal and Barakhamba Chhatri	Hodal, Faridabad district	• This palace and Chhatri were constructed in 1754 to 1761 AD, respectively. • The Jat ruler **Suraj Mal** built these monuments in the name of his wife. It is a major historical monument of Haryana. • The royal palace, Kutcheri and Barakhamba Chhatri are more prominent in this palace.
Choron Ki Baoli	Meham	• Historic stepwell, built during Shah Jahan's reign, used for rainwater collection. It showcases Mughal-era architecture, which is now a tourist attraction.

Some Famous Museums in Haryana

Archaeological Museum

- It was established in the year **1959** by **Swami Omanand Saraswati** in **Gurukul Jhajjar**. This is the oldest and largest museum in the state.
- In this museum coins, seals, inscriptions, copper sheets, weapons, terracotta, pottery, stone sculptures, jewellery, manuscripts and beads have been preserved.
- Apart from this, the ancient statue of **Panchavati deer** associated with the Ramayana epic, Nilgiri drums made of camel skins, seamless chain and plows have been kept in this museum.

Home of Folk Arts Museum

- It was established in the year **1984** in **Gurugram**, district. **KC Aryan** is credited with establishing this museum.
- In this museum, ancient Indian sculptures, various types of utensils, items made of metal and glass have been stored.
- Apart from this, folk art, tribal and obsolete items have been kept in this museum.

Shri Krishna Museum

- Shri Krishna Museum was established in the year **1987** in **Kurukshetra** district of Haryana.
- The museum is three storeyed, which is 8885 sq. m. wide. The new campus of the museum was built in the year 1995.
- In addition to the remains found from the excavation at the Shri Krishna Museum, sculptures made of brass, bronze and wood, puppets made of leather, specimens of Madhubani painting, ancient coins and ancient manuscripts are also preserved here.
- Apart from this, special sculptures of elephant teeth made by artists of Odisha and Tamil Nadu are also kept in this museum.

Panorama and Science Centre

- A panorama has been established in the premises of Shri Krishna Museum in Kurukshetra, Haryana. Panorama is such a centre, where modern tools are used to provide audience information about science, culture, religion, human civilisation and history. In Kurukshetra Panorama, there is a complete system of displaying scientific interpretation related to the **Mahabharata** war.

- An exhibition has been organised in this science centre, the theme of which is 'India: A Heritage in Signs, Technology and Culture'. This exhibition showcases Indian knowledge related to geometry, arithmetic, medicine, surgery and astronomy.

Panipat Museum

- This museum was established in the year 2000 by **Panipat War Memorial Committee**.

- The purpose of setting up the Panipat Museum is to provide comprehensive information on the art, history, crafts and archeology arising out of the three Battles of Panipat.
- The pottery, ornaments, important documents, weapons, maps, manuscripts and sculptures in this museum are items of art and craft which have been stored here.
- In this museum, an attempt has also been made to explain the historical aspects through photos and slides through this museum.

Lila Dhar Dukhi Smarak Sarasvati Museum

- This museum was established in the year **2001**, in Sirsa district.
- The museum was dedicated to the general public on 26th April, 2001 by the Divisional Commissioner of Hisar, Umesh Nanda.

Dharohar Museum

- This museum was established in the year **2006** in the premises of **Kurukshetra** University in Kurukshetra district under the name Dharohar.
- In addition to various artifacts related to Haryanvi culture, this museum depicts the contribution of the Haryana people in the first freedom struggle of 1857 AD.

Jayanti Archaeological Museum

- This museum was established in the year **2007** in **Jind** district in Jayanti Tirth and Jayanti Devi Temple complex with the help of local people.
- This museum has a collection of ancient relics. The museum was inaugurated on 28th July, 2007 by the Governor of Haryana, Dr. A.R. Kidwai.

Sir Chhotu Ram Memorial Museum

- Sir Chhotu Ram Memorial Museum was established in the year **2013** at Garhi Sampla village in **Rohtak** district. In this museum, historical items related to Chaudhary Chhotu Ram have been kept.
- This museum was handed over to the Archaeological Department in September 2013. In this museum, on 9th October, 2018, Prime Minister Narendra Modi unveiled a 64 feet high statue of Chaudhary Chhotu Ram.

Archaeological Museum Thanesar

- This museum is established and operated by Archaeological Survey of India (Chandigarh Division), Chandigarh.
- This museum is located in the courtyard of the tomb of Sheikh Chilli.

Manuscript Museum

- This museum is located in the premises of **Kurukshetra University** in Kurukshetra district in Haryana. Pandit Sthanu Dutt Sharma played a major role in the establishment of this museum.
- Five texts of Nath Community written in Sharda script have been found in this museum.

Gulzarilal Nanda Museum

- It is located in **Kurukshetra** district, the museum has been established by the Kurukshetra Development Board under the aegis of Shri Krishna museum at Sadachar Sthal.

- It is the first personality museum of Haryana which is dedicated to Gulzarilal Nanda, the former Prime Minister (Bharat Ratna).

Other Museums

In order to preserve the cultural heritage of Haryana, two state-level museums have been constructed by the State Government at **Panchkula** and **Rakhigarhi** in Hisar at a cost of ₹ 30 crore and ₹ 5 crore, respectively. In addition to these museums, there are some other museums also in the state, which are as follows

- **Guru Govind Singh Martial Arts Museum** It is located at Kapalmochan in **Yamunanagar district**. The first Guru Nanak Dev Ji of Sikhs stayed here in the year 1584 AD and the tenth Guru, Guru Gobind Singh in the year 1686 AD, so it is a proud place for the arrival of two Sikh Gurus.
- **Guru Tegh Bahadur Memorial Museum** It is located at a place called Badkhalsa in **Sonipat district**. Guru Tegh Bahadur was the 9th Guru of the Sikhs. The museum is dedicated to him. It is also a major historical site of Sikhs.
- **Jahaj Kothi Zonal Museum** It is located in Hisar district. It was built in 1796 AD by George Thomas, a resident of Ireland. This is historically significant. Hence, this historical monument has been converted into a **regional archaeological museum.**

CHECK CHAPTER KNOWLEDGE

1 Who built the Fort of Hansi?
(a) Feroz Shah Tughlaq (b) Anangpal I
(c) Sultan Balban (d) Prithviraj Chauhan

2 Birbal ka Chhatta is located is which place of Haryana? *Haryana Clerk Exam 2016*
(a) Narnaul (b) Hansi
(c) Mahendragarh (d) Rewari

3 The Taraori Fort is located in which district of Haryana?
(a) Hisar (b) Panchkula
(c) Karnal (d) Fatehabad

4 Which fort was originally named 'Turana' by Anangpal Tomar?
(a) The Fort of Tohana
(b) The Fort of Hansi
(c) Ramgarh Fort
(d) The Fort of Asigarh

5 Who renovated the Fort of Tohana before its destruction?
(a) Sultan Balban (b) Timur Lang
(c) Aurangzeb (d) Anangpal Tomar

6 Consider the following statements about Ramgarh Fort.
I. It was built by the rulers of the Chandel dynasty.
II. Its main gate is 37 feet tall.
III. The entire fort is under Haryana Tourism Department.
Which of the statements is/are correct?
(a) I and II (b) II and III
(c) I and III (d) All of these

7 Consider the following statements about the Fort of Hisar.
I. It was built by Prithviraj Chauhan in 1354 AD.
II. It originally had deep water trenches.
III. It contains structures like Lal-Minar and Gujari Mahal.
Which of the statements is/are correct?
(a) I and II (b) II and III
(c) I and III (d) All of these

8 Which of the following statements about the Fort of Hisar is incorrect?
(a) It was built in 1354 AD by Feroz Shah Tughlaq.
(b) It was originally surrounded by deep water trenches.
(c) It has four gates, including Dehli Gate and Nagauri Gate.
(d) It is located in Karnal district.

9 In which century the Fort of Asigarh was built by Prithviraj Chauhan in Hansi? *HSSC 2017*
(a) 15th century (b) 12th century
(c) 14th century (d) 17th century

10 The Fort of Asigarh situated at Hansi which was built in 12th century is also known as *Haryana Clerk 2019*
(a) Fort of sticks (b) Fort of swords
(c) Fort of axes (d) Fort of knife

11 Which ruler has constructed the Fort of Gohana? *Haryana Clerk 2016*
(a) Akbar
(b) Hemchandra
(c) Harshavardhana
(d) Prithviraj Chauhan

12 Which fort was converted into a police station in the Nuh district?
(a) Fort of Jind (b) Fort of Farrukhnagar
(c) Fort of Taoru (d) Fort of Maham

13 What is the alternate name of Bahadurgarh Fort?
(a) Ferozi Lat fort (b) Jahazgarh fort
(c) Singh Dwar (d) Diwan-e-Khas

14 Which fort was built by Nivaz Ali, a Mughal Jagirdar?
(a) Fort of Madhogarh (b) Fort of Nivajpur
(c) Fort of Jind (d) Loharu fort

15 In which year was the Fort of Fatehabad built by Feroz Shah Tughlaq?
(a) 1732 AD (b) 1755 AD
(c) 1656 AD (d) 14th century

16 Consider the following statements about the Fort of Kanod.
I. It was built in 1755 AD by the Maratha rulers.
II. It was renamed to Mahendragarh Fort by Maharaja Narendra Singh.
III. The fort contains a mausoleum of a dog.
Which of the above statements are correct?
(a) I and II (b) I and III
(c) II and III (d) All of these

17 Famous fort of Mahendragarh was so named by ....in 1861. *HSSC CET 2024*
(a) Maharaja Maneendra Singh
(b) Maharaja Narender Singh
(c) Maharaja Ranjith Singh
(d) None of the above

18 Where is the Chaneti Buddhist Stupa located?
(a) Mahendragarh (b) Yamunanagar
(c) Hisar (d) Narnaul

19 Who constructed the Chor Gumbad in Narnaul?
(a) Rai Bal Mukund Das
(b) Jat ruler Suraj Mal
(c) Afghan Sardar Jamal Khan
(d) Kuli Khan

20 What is the significance of the War Memorial in Ludesar village?
(a) It is a residence of Mughal emperors.
(b) It is a Buddhist relic.
(c) It showcases British architecture.
(d) It honours martyrs who sacrificed their lives for the country.

21 Which Mughal emperor's Diwan built the Chatta Rai Balmukund Das?
(a) Akbar (b) Shah Jahan
(c) Jahangir (d) Aurangzeb

22 Gujari Mahal is located in which district of Haryana? *HSSC 2017*
(a) Hisar (b) Rewari (c) Hansi (d) Narnaul

23 The Jal Mahal in Narnaul is located in which district?
(a) Yamunanagar (b) Sirsa
(c) Mahendragarh (d) Faridabad

24 Consider the following statements regarding Tosham Baradari.
I. It is also known as Prithviraj Ki Kutcheri.
II. It has 12 gates, allowing observation from all sides.
III. It is located in Panipat.
Which of the statements is/are correct?
(a) Only I (b) I and III
(c) I and II (d) All of these

25 Consider the following statements about Salarganj Gate.
I. It was constructed during the Mughal period.
II. It served as an entrance to Panipat town in ancient times.
III. It is an example of British architecture.
Which of the statements is/are correct?
(a) Only I (b) I and III
(c) II and III (d) All of these

26 Consider the following statements.
I. Birbal ka Rang Mahal was constructed during the reign of Akbar.
II. Kishori Mahal was built in the name of Jat ruler Suraj Mal's wife.
III. Chatta Rai Balmukund Das is connected by a tunnel to multiple cities.
IV. Salarganj Gate was constructed in the Panipat district during the British period.
Which of the statements is/are correct?
(a) I and II (b) I, II and III
(c) I and IV (d) All of these

27 The ancient Fort of Madhogarh is located in which district of Haryana? *Haryana Panchayat Officer 2017*
(a) Jind (b) Hisar
(c) Sirsa (d) Mahendragarh

28 Who captured the Fort of Madhogarh in 1755 AD?
(a) Mughals (b) British (c) Marathas (d) Afghans

29 Maham fort is located in which district of Haryana? *Haryana Clerk 2016*
(a) Hisar (b) Kaithal (c) Rohtak (d) Jind

30 In which year was the Archaeological Museum (Gurukul Jhajjar Museum) established?
(a) 1960 (b) 1959
(c) 1984 (d) 2001

31 Who is credited with establishing the Home of Folk Arts Museum in Gurugram?
(a) Swami Omanand Saraswati
(b) KC Aryan
(c) Pandit Sthanu Dutt Sharma
(d) Bal Bhawan

32 What is the main objective of the Shri Krishna Museum in Kurukshetra?
(a) To preserve ancient artifacts
(b) To explain the three Battles of Panipat
(c) To showcase Haryana's freedom struggle
(d) To connect people with the philosophy and ideals of Lord Krishna

33 In which district is the Sir Chhotu Ram Memorial Museum located?
(a) Kurukshetra (b) Hisar
(c) Jind (d) Rohtak

34 Where is the Jahaj Kothi Zonal Museum situated?
(a) Panchkula (b) Rakhigarhi
(c) Hisar (d) Panipat

35 The fort of Raja Nahar Singh is located in which place of Haryana? *Haryana Police Sub-Inspector 2018*
(a) Mahendragarh (b) Rohtak
(c) Yamunanagar (d) Ballabhgarh

36 Constructed a palace in Narnaul who was the Diwan of Shah Jahan? *Haryana Group D 2018*
(a) Birbal
(b) Rai Mukund Das
(c) Rai Madhav Das
(d) None of these

37 Match List I with List II and choose the correct option. *HSSC 2023*

List I (Monuments)	List II (Location)
A. Gujri Mahal	1. Hisar
B. Seikh Chilli's Tomb	2. Kurukshetra
C. Choron ki Baoli	3. Rohtak
D. Jal Mahal	4. Mahendragarh

Codes

	A	B	C	D		A	B	C	D
(a)	1	2	3	4	(b)	2	3	4	1
(c)	3	1	4	2	(d)	4	1	2	3

38 Match List I with List II.

List I (Fort)	List II (Feature)
A. Palwal Fort	1. Converted into a Heritage Hotel
B. Fort of Nivajpur	2. Entrance was 42 feet wide
C. Fort of Farrukhnagar	3. Also known as Matia Fort
D. Fort of Taoru	4. Converted into a police station

Codes

	A	B	C	D		A	B	C	D
(a)	1	3	4	2	(b)	3	2	1	4
(c)	1	2	3	4	(d)	2	1	4	3

39 Match List I (Museums) with List II (Locations).

List I (Museum)	List II (Location)
A. Jayanti Archaeological Museum	1. Sirsa
B. Lila Dhar Dukhi Smarak Museum	2. Jind
C. Gulzarilal Nanda Museum	3. Kurukshetra
D. Guru Tegh Bahadur Memorial Museum	4. Sonipat

Codes

	A	B	C	D		A	B	C	D
(a)	1	2	4	3	(b)	3	4	2	1
(c)	2	1	3	4	(d)	1	3	4	2

40 Who played a major role in the establishment of Manuscript Museum in Kurukshetra University in Haryana? *HSSC 2017*
(a) Pt. Sthanu Dutt Sharma (b) Jairam Sharma
(c) Shri Sitaram Shastri (d) Kapil Dev Shastri

41 How many texts of Nath Community have been found in the Manuscript museum of Kurukshetra University? *HSSC 2020*
(a) Seven (b) Three
(c) Five (d) Four

CORRECT ANSWERS

1. (b)	2. (a)	3. (c)	4. (a)	5. (a)	6. (d)	7. (b)	8. (d)	9. (b)	10. (b)
11. (d)	12. (c)	13. (c)	14. (b)	15. (d)	16. (a)	17. (b)	18. (c)	19. (c)	20. (d)
21. (b)	22. (a)	23. (c)	24. (c)	25. (c)	26. (d)	27. (d)	28. (c)	29. (c)	30. (b)
31. (b)	32. (d)	33. (d)	34. (c)	35. (d)	36. (b)	37. (a)	38. (b)	39. (c)	40. (a)
41. (c)									

CHAPTER 11

Tourism in Haryana

- Haryana is an important place where various historical places made by different rulers exists at present. Kurukshetra being the place of Mahabharata, has witnessed the epic Battle of Mahabharata.
- Loharu, Rampur, Madhogarh, Ballabhgarh and Mahendragarh have many ancient forts.
- Tarawadi, Panipat and Kurukshetra are famous for battles.
- Historical sites in Haryana are maintained by **Haryana Tourism Department and Department of Archaeology**, India.
- In order to boost tourism in state, State Government constituted Haryana Tourism Corporation as a Public Limited Company under the Companies Act, 1956 on 1st May, 1974. It manages and maintains the existing centres and develops new tourist places. Its head office is located in Gurugram district.

Religious Places in Haryana

Most of the religious places of the state are located in Kurukshetra, Jind and Kaithal.

Some famous religious places of Haryana are discussed below

Religious Places of Kurukshetra

Pehowa

• Location	According to Mahabharata, it was situated on the bank of river Saraswati (Presently in district of Kurukshetra)
• Name	Prithudaka (derived from **King Prithu**)
• Present name	Town of Prithu, came to be called Pehowa

- According to ancient belief, on the death of his father Vena, King Prithu sat on the bank of river Saraswati, offering water to all visitors. As a result, the place came to be known as Prithudaka or Prithu's pool.
- Today, it is an ancient place of great devotion, where prayer and *pind daan* on the 4th day of Krishna Paksha in the Chaitra month for ancestors is believed to grant *moksha* or redemption from the cycle of birth and death.
- The place is renowned for having the same significance as Gaya in Bihar. The place is famous for temples of Lord Shiva and Kartikeya.

Amin Teerth

• Location	Village of Amin in Thanesar
• Mythological significance	Bhishma Pitamah chose Aditi Van (forest) for the Battle of Mahabharata

- Aditi Van is also called **Detwan**. The hermitage of sage Aditi was also there. This place is also called **Abhimanyu Kheda**.
- A holy place called 'Surya Kund' is also there, where mother Aditi gave birth to the Sun God **Surya Dev**.
- A strong myth prevails about this kund that if a pregnant woman takes a bath in this kund, then the upcoming male child will have excellent qualities like bravery and strength.

Arunai Teerth Temple

• Location	Near Pehowa, Kurukshetra
• Religious significance	Important places of pilgrimage associated with the saints Vashishta and Vishwamitra

- This place is the meeting point of Saraswati and Aruna rivers, which gives it more importance.

- The significance of this pilgrimage is vividly described in the Mahabharata, Vamana Purana, Skandapurana and Padma Purana.

Papantak Teerth

- Other name — Kaleshwar teerth, Pap-Antak teerth
- Mythological significance — Here, Kartikeya, after killing a demon, bathed in the Saraswati river.

Karnal Nabha Teerth

- Location — Kurukshetra district
- Religious significance — Believed that Lord Brahma had made his appearance here
- There is a pond at this place, where males and females take a bath (at separate places).

Kamodha

- Location — Forest area located at a distance of 14 km from Thanesar
- Mythological significance — Pandavas had stayed here
- Here, a temple and math of **Kameshwar Mahadev**, both are made of bricks.
- There is another small room made of bricks in this area, called Draupadi's store. Draupadi had cooked food for the Pandavas here.

Dukh Bhanjan Mahadev Temple

- Location — Near Sannihit Sarovar in Kurukshetra
- People worship Dukh Bhanjan Mahadev in this temple to attain peace and prosperity.

Jyotisar Sarovar

- Location — Jyotisar village in Kurukshetra district
- Significance of name — Symbolically signifies 'the essence of enlightenment'
- Shiva temple — Built by ruler of Kashmir
- Jyotisar is a very important pilgrimage site of Kurukshetra, situated on the bank of Saraswati river.

- It is also called **Geeta Sthali**. It is here under the holy banyan tree, that Lord Krishna is believed to have delivered the eternal message of Bhagwad Gita to Arjuna before the commencement of the Battle of Mahabharata.
- A beautiful marble Chariot of Krishna-Arjun and **Shankracharya temple** built by Kamkoti Trust in the year **1967** is also present at the site.
- It is believed that Shankaracharya also contemplated the philosophy of Bhagwad Gita at this place.

Aapga Teerth

- Location — 5 km from Dayalpur, Kurukshetra
- Significance — Has religious importance as mentioned in Puranas
- According to Puranas, a person who offers ***Pind Daan*** at this place in Bhadrapad month, attains salvation.
- The remains of late-Harappans culture have been found near this teerth.

Brahma Sarovar

- *Built by* — Raja Kuru
- *Located* — Thanesar, Kurukshetra
- *Other name* — Sarveshwar Mahadev Temple
- The Sarovar is also mentioned in the memoirs written by Al-Biruni in 11th century AD called *'Kitab-ul-Hind'*.

- It is believed that Lord Brahma used to worship Lord Shiva in this temple. This temple is dedicated to **Lord Shiva**.
- It is believed to be the site where Lord Brahma created the universe after performing a yajna.
- According to Vamana Purana and Matasya Purana, bathing in its holy water is a ritual followed by people during **Makar Sankranti** and **Purnima**.
- A '**Deep Daan**' and 'Aarti' ceremonies are held in November-December, where earthen lamps are floated in the water of the Sarovar.

Devikoop Bhadra Kali Temple

- Location — Thanesar Kurukshetra
- Devoted to — Sati or Bhadra Kali
- Other name — Devi Koop
- It is believed that Goddess Sati's lower limb ankle fell here, granting the area the sanctity of a Siddha Peeth or a place where wishes are fulfilled.
- Thousands of devotees visit the temple on the holy days of **Navratra** and every **Saturday**.
- Renovated in recent times, the temple has a white amla (fruit-shaped) dome. A large water body has been designed before the temple.

Sthaneshwar Mahadev Temple

- Location — Thaneswar Nagar
- Built by — King Pushyabhuti, ancestor of Emperor Harshavardhan
- It was the place where the Pandavas prayed to Lord Shiva and received the blessings of victory in the war of Mahabharata. The existing temple was constructed by Raghunath Rao Peshwa.

Laxmi-Narayan Temple

- Location — Near Sannihit Sarovar
- Constructed by — Baba Shiv Giri of the Giri community near the Sarovar
- Construction style — Dravidian style of architecture

Sarveshwar Mahadev Temple

- Built by — Baba Shravan Nath
- Idols — Garuda, Narayan, Shiv-Parvati, Ganesha and Shiv Linga

Birla Temple

- Location — Thanesar, Kurukshetra
- Built by — Jugal Kishor in 1952
- Made-up of — White Marble
- Other name — **Bhagwad Gita Temple**

▲ Birla Temple

Sannihit Teerth

- Location — Thanesar, Kurukshetra on Kaithal road and is deemed as a permanent abode of Lord Vishnu
- Spiritual importance — Believed to be meeting point of seven sacred Sarasvatis
- Bathing in the water of the tank on the day of Amavasya or during an eclipse is believed to bestow blessings, equivalent to performing '1,000 Ashvamedh Yajna'.
- The place is believed to be formed by King Ravana for establishing a Shiva temple during the Ramayana period. Fairs are organised here during solar eclipses.

Gaudiya Math

- It is located in Thanesar, Kurukshetra.
- It is one of the largest religious groups in India, formed by Bengali disciples who worship Lord Krishna and Chaitanya Mahaprabhu.

Valmiki Ashram

- It is located in Thanesar, Kurukshetra.
- Baba Lakshman Giri's Samadhi is also situated here. The shrine is considered to be the rarest among three Loks.

Markandeya

- It is located on the banks of Saraswati river at Kurukshetra.
- Rishi Markandeya achieved a divine status by carrying out meditation here.

Prachi Teerth

- It is located in Pehowa, Kurukshetra.
- It is considered a sacred site to carry out the rituals of Pitra Tarpan.
- It is believed that Bhishma's mother Ganga attained enlightenment here after taking bath.

Kuber Teerth

- It is located on the banks of Saraswati river, near Bhadra Kali temple.
- It is a shrine where it is believed that Kuber had performed Yajnas. It is also believed to be the residential place of Chaitanya Mahaprabhu.

Chandrakoop

- It is a well near which a temple is constructed.
- It is believed that Yudhisthir, after winning the Battle of Mahabharata, constructed the Chandrakoop well and temple in Kurukshetra.

Narkatari Teerth and Bhishma Kund

- It is located on the banks of Saraswati river.
- According to Mahabharata and Purana, this place has great significance. Its relationship has been established with Brahma, Vishnu, Mahesh and the wife of Rudra.
- **Baan Ganga** river is located here. It is believed that bathing in Baan Ganga river frees a person from all sins.
- **Bhishma Kund** is situated at Narkatari site in Kurukshetra. It is believed that Arjun created a bed of arrows for Bhishma, to quench the thirst of Pitamaha. Arjuna shot an arrow into the ground and a stream of gushing water formed, which led to the formation of Bhishma Kund. A temple also exists near this kund.

Religious Places of Jind

Pandu Pindara

- It is located on the Jind-Gohana road.
- The place is believed to be where Pandavas carried out the ritual of Pind-Daan for 12 years.
- A fair is held every year on the day of Somvati Amavasya at this place.
- It is also known as Laghu Haridwar.

Jamni

- It is located near Jind-Safidon road.
- A temple of a sage is situated at this place.

Varah

- It is located on Jind-Gohana road in Barah village.
- Varah Teerth is dedicated to Lord Varah as it is believed that all the 12 Avatars of Lord Vishnu appeared here.
- This is a sacred sarovar and taking a bath in the shrine pool provides blessings of Lord Vishnu.

Pushkar Teerth

- It is located in village Pokar Kheri, Jind district.
- A temple and a sarovar are located here near which Lord Parshuram's father **Jamadagni** is believed to have prayed.

Ramrai

• Location	Ram Raya village on the Jind-Hisar road
• Religious significance	Considered the South-West gate of the Kurukshetra battlefield

- It is believed that this place was visited by Lord Rama, Sita and Lakshman and a Yajna was performed by Parshuram here.

> **Dhundwa** is located nearby Ramrai where Duryodhana hide himself after being defeated in battle. Bheem killed him after locating him at the spot.

Safidon

• Also known as	Sarpdaman
• Religious significance	There is a sacred pond

- Parikshit died at this place due to snakebite. Parikshit's son Janmeyjay performed a Yajna.

Bhuteshwara Temple

• Location	Jind
• Religious significance	Dedicated to Bhuteshwara, a manifestation of God Shiva

- As per Hindu mythology, the Pandavas had an encounter with Prajapati Daksh, the father-in-law of Lord Shiva.

▲ Bhuteshwara Temple

- This temple was constructed by the ruler of Jind, Raghbir Singh. It has a large water tank all around it, and this is the reason that the **Bhuteshwar temple** is also recognised as **Rani Talab**.

Hatkeshwar

- It is located in Hatt village of Jind.
- It is believed that sage Dadhichi collected holy waters from 68 places and confluenced them here.
- He then bathed in the Sangam of holy waters. A fair is organised on the last **Sunday of the month** of **Shravan**.

Hansdehar

- It is believed that Lord Brahma descended here on his hans (goose) to attend the marriage of Rishi Kardam.
- Rishi Kardam meditated here and his son Kapil Muni was also born here.
- An ancient sarovar and a magnificent temple of Kardam Rishi is located here. Pandavas offered Pind-Daan to their ancestors here.

Some Religious Places of Yamunanagar

Surya Kund

- It is in Bilaspur area of Yamunanagar.
- It was built by **King Suraj Mal** of Tomar dynasty.
- Many religious beliefs are associated with it.

***Kapaal Mochan** (Som Sarovar)*

- It is a sarovar (a pond) located at a distance of 20 km from Jagadhri at a place called Bilaspur.
- The pond is considered sacred and bathing in it washes away all sins.
- The place gets its mention in Mahabharata and Puranas.

Shri Kaleshwar Mahadev Math

- It is located in Yamunanagar near **Kaleshwar**, on the bank of Yamuna river.
- It is one of the 12 oldest Hindu mathas of India.
- It is situated on the confluence of Saraswati, Yamuna and Sukhna. Surya Yajnas are held at this place.

Chitta Mandir

- It is located in **Bhatianagar** in the district of Yamunanagar.
- It is believed that Pandavas, while going for Mahabharata War, met Hanuman Ji at this place.
- There is a statue of Hanuman in white marble, which is why it is called **Chitta Mandir** (White Temple).

Parshuram Sarvdharam Temple

- It is situated in Jagadhri.
- This temple has a height of 55 feet and 11 storeys.
- The architecture depicts the medieval architecture of India.

Adi Badri Narayan Temple

- It is located in Kathgarh, 40 km from Jagadhri.
- The temple was built by Adi Shankaracharya in the 8th century.
- This temple was rebuilt by Purushottam Ashram in 1823.
- A fair is organised every year on Akshaya Tritiya in Vaisakh around April or May.

Surya Narayan Temple

- It is located in Aamadalpur.
- The first rays of the Sun fall on this temple.
- It was rebuilt in 1983 by Swami Akhilananda.

Pancham Kallen Jain Temple

- It is located in Buria town in Yamunanagar.
- This is a Digambar Jain temple built around 500 years ago.
- It is an important temple to Jainism.

Religious Places of Kaithal

Nava Graha

- Location — Kaithal
- Belief — 9 kundas believed to be built by Lord Krishna
- Also known as — **Chhoti Kashi** due to importance of bathing in these kunds or pool

Pundarik Sarovar

- Location — Pundarik, Kaithal
- Basis of name — Named after Rishi Pundarik who performed yajna
- Attractions — Vrindawan Ghat, Triveniwala Ghat, Ganga Ghat, Naghardiya Ghat etc.

Phalgu Teerth

- Location — 25 km from Kaithal in Feral (Pharal) village
- The nomenclature of Feral village appears to have originated from Falaki forest, where Phalgu Rishi lived.
- It is believed that this pilgrimage holds a special place as a site of penance for the gods.
- People perform last rites, **Pind-Dan** and other pujas here. The **Phalgu fair** is also held here.

> Offerings in the form of Pindadana on Amavasya in the month of Ashwin are believed to satisfy the ancestors' souls.

Gyarah Rudri Shiva Temple

- Location — Kaithal, Haryana
- Established — Believed to be built after Mahabharata War by Lord Krishna for peace
- Krishna established eleven Rudras (Shivlingas) in Kaithal.
- The temple structure was rebuilt 250 years ago by the queen of King Uday Singh of Kaithal.

Ambakeshwar Mahadev Temple

- Location — Kaithal
- Dedicated to — Lord Shiva
- Also known as — Pataleshwar and Swayamlinga
- Rebuilt — By the king of Shilakher

Ancient Hanuman Mandir

- Location — Centre of Kaithal city at a height of one storey from the ground level
- A mosque is also located behind this temple. It is around 500 years old.

Vradh Kedareshwar Mandir

- Location — Kaithal
- Built by — Maharaja Uday Singh
- Significance — Considered equivalent to Kedarnath temple of Uttarakhand

Radheshyam Mandir

- Location — Pundarik, Kaithal
- Consists of — Beautiful idols of Radha-Krishna
- Other important temples in the area include the Shiva temple in Pundarik and the Shiva-Parvati temple.
- The mausoleum of Lala Das is also located near this temple.

Old Shiva-Parvati Temple

- Location — Pundarik, Kaithal
- Religious significance — Water and sweets are offered to Shiva and Parvati during Mahashivratri

Some Religious Places of Bhiwani

Place	Description
Tosham Ke Teerth	It is located at the foot of the Tosham hill range in Bhiwani. The place is considered sacred due to the presence of 8 kundas. One of the oldest kunds is Pandava Teerth. Pandavas are believed to have stayed here for 13 days during their Agyatvas.
Devsar	The temple of Goddess Durga is situated on a hillock in Bhiwani, on the Loharu road. People visit this place to perform various religious ceremonies.
Dhanana Pahari	It is located in Loharu. Fairs are held in the months of Chaitra and Ashwin. Goddess Sheetala is worshipped here.
Mahendragarh Dhosi	It is located in Narnaul in the hills of Dhosi. The temple of Rishi Chawan is present here, who is believed to have prayed at this place for 7000 years. The place also has a Shiva temple and many kunds (ponds). People take a dip in the kunds during Somvati Amavasya.

Religious Places of Rohtak

Asthal Bohar

- Location — Bohar village in Rohtak district
- Religious significance — Place adorns the social, cultural and religious achievements of its time

- It is famous for Darshani Sadhus, who consider Gorakhnath to be their first teacher. These Sadhus have split ears.
- The Ashram was established at this place in 8th CE by Chaurangi Nath. Nearly 250 years ago, it was separated by Baba Mastnath.
- This holy place has a temple called **Siddh Smriti Mandir**.
- There is an Ayurveda College and an eye hospital, which was established in the year 1948.

Shiva Temple

- Location — Kiloi village
- Historical significance — 300-year-old Shiva temple
- It is said that Lord Shiva appeared in someone's dream and asked him to create a temple at that place.
- A fair is organised twice a year around the temple on the occasion of Shivratri.

Chaurangi Nath Ka Dhuna

- Location — Bailiana village of Rohtak
- Bailiana village is famous for Chaurangi Nath Ka Dhuna and Dokhar Johad (pond).
- It is believed that Balram, brother of Lord Krishna, meditated here. Baba Chaurangi Nath also meditated near the pond.

Some Religious Places of Palwal

Place	Description
Panchvati	• It is located in **Palwal**. • It is believed that the **Pandavas stayed here** during their period of **secret exile** (Agyatvas).
Sati Temple	• The **Sati temple** is located in Hodal. • Women come here to **worship the Goddess**. • **Fairs** are held here regularly.

Some Religious Places of Mahendragarh

Religious Place	Description
Modewala Temple	• This is situated in Narnaul. It is a temple dedicated to Lord Shiva. Fair is organised during the festival of Rakhi in this temple.
Ancient Shiva Temple	• It is located at Badhot in Mahendragarh district. It is associated with King Dilip of Ikshawaku dynasty. • It is believed that King Dilip got it constructed and named it Bagheshwar. Later, this name was changed to Badhot, large fairs are held on Shivratri in the month of Sharavan.

Chamunda Devi Temple

- This temple is situated in Narnaul. It is believed that **Raja Naun Karan**, the ruler of the area was a devotee of Chamunda Devi.
- He constructed a temple of Devi at the bottom of a hill. This temple is heart of the city. The temple building has 84 pillars which has inscriptions of Ashokan era.
- It is an ancient temple. After the fall of the regime of Raja Naun Karan, this area came under the control of the Mughals. They built Jama Masjid on the temple of Chamunda Devi.
- After independence people found that the temple is in bad condition and renovated it. Now, it is visited by many devotees. A big fair is held on Ram Navami.

Some Religious Places of Gurugram

Shri Mata Sheetla Devi Temple

• Location	Gurugram
• Religious significance	Dedicated to Mata Kripi, wife of Guru Dronacharya, who was the teacher of the Pandavas and Kauravas

- This temple is visited by a large number of people during **Navaratras**. Fairs are organised in this temple in the month of **March** and **October**.
- The temple was built by the Maharaja of Bharatpur in 1650.

▲ Ancient Shri Mata Sheetal Devi Temple

Shiva Temple

• Location	Sohna
• Built	16th CE by the rulers of Gwalior

- Fairs are organised on Mahashivratri and Shiv Chaudash.
- There are **Sulphur springs** near this temple.

Some Religious Places of Ambala

Bhawani Amba Temple

- This temple in Ambala district has derived its name from the Goddess of the temple, **Amba Devi** or **Bhawani Devi**.
- There is a popular belief that the city of Ambala has been named after **Devi Amba**.

Kali Mata Temple

- This temple is situated near **Rambagh** or cremation ground of Ambala.
- It has a 6-feet tall statue of Kali Mata installed here.
- The temple has been decked up with figurines of birds and animals, which depict the culture of the medieval times.

Some Religious Places of Panchkula

Bhima Devi Temple

- This temple was established during the reign of Gurjar-Pratihars. It is located in Pinjore (Panchkula), is also known as **Khajuraho of North India** for its erotic sculpture.
- Next to the temple complex is Pinjore Garden which is also known as Mughal Garden established by Aurangzeb's foster brother.

Chandi Devi Temple

- This temple is located 10 km from Mata Mansa Devi shrine in Panchkula. It is a small but famous temple worshipped as a Siddh Peeth.
- It is after this temple, that the town of Chandigarh gets its name. The temple falls on the Chandigarh-Kalka stretch of NH-22.
- Thousands of devotees visited the temple during Navratras.

Mata Mansa Devi Temple

- It is located in Panchkula district. This sacred temple is dedicated to mother Mansa Devi. According to Hindu mythology, the head of Goddess Sati fell down here.
- Maharaja Gopal Singh of Manimojra constructed the present main temple of Shri Mansa Devi in village Bilaspur, Panchkula, during the period of 1811-1815. It is one of prominent Shakti temples of North India.

Some Religious Places of Jhajjar

Thakurdwara of Kutani

- This temple was built in **1901 by Shauji Singh**.
- The idol of Radha-Krishna in Ashtdhatu (8 metals) is placed in the temple.
- The idol of Thakur Shalu Singh, which is 50 ft tall, is also installed in the temple.

Shiva Temple

- This ancient Shiva temple is located in Dighal village of Jhajjar.
- It was built by **Lala Dhani Ram**.
- The temple has a tall peak and is built of brick and limestone.

Rudh Mal Temple

- It is located in Beri village of Jhajjar.
- This temple was built by Lala Rudh Mal, Suraj Bhan and Girdhari Lal in 1892.
- The temple was rebuilt and renovated in 1953 and 1990.
- The temple complex has many small temples of Digambar Jain saints and one Shiva temple with a height of 116 ft.

Other Temples in Haryana

Temple	Location	Description
Gita Mandir	Kaithal	Belongs to the period of Mahabharata.
Devi Talab and Shiva Temple	Panipat	Built by Maratha Chief Sadashivrao Bhau during the 3rd Battle of Panipat.
Karneshwar Temple	Karnal	Temple houses Shiva idol having 5 heads and idol of Goddess Kali. Temple associated with the Karna, an important character of Mahabharata.
Shiv Temple	Karnal	It is believed that Kauravas and Pandavas worshipped here.
Jeet Giri Temple	Jind	Situated in Kakrod village. Also has Samadhi (mausoleum) of Baba Jeet Giri.
Ghanteshwar Temple	Rewari	Temple is dedicated to Lord Shiva.
Hanuman Temple	Rewari	Temple is situated near to large pond in Rewari Fair on every Tuesday is also organised here.
Panch Mukhi Hanuman Temple	Yamunanagar	Situated in Chhachhrauli. Idol of Hanuman is believed to be made 350 years ago.
Dauji Temple	Faridabad	Temple is dedicated to Balram, Krishna's elder brother. Dau Ji is the other name of Balram.

Major Gurudwaras in Haryana

Gurudwara Mastgarh

- It was originally a mosque built by the Mughal Emperor, **Shah Jahan** in 1630. It was converted into a Gurudwara much later after the matter was amicably settled after independence.
- It is located in **Shahabad Markanda**, 20 km South of Ambala Cantonment along the Sher Shah Suri Marg.

Gurudwara Navin Patshahi

- It is located in Kurukshetra.
- It is dedicated to the ninth Sikh Guru, Tegh Bahadur.
- It is believed that the Guru stayed at this place for a while on his way to meet Aurangzeb in Delhi.

Gurudwara Kapal Mochan

- It is located in Bilaspur of Yamunanagar district.
- It is dedicated to Guru Gobind Singh.
- It is believed that the Guru stayed here for 52 days during his battle with the kings of the Northern hills. At this place, Guru washed his weapons in **Rinmochan Sarovar**, so the place is also called **Shastra Ghat**.

Gurudwara Dhamtan Sahib

- It is located on Narwana-Tohana road in district of Jind.
- It is dedicated to the 9th Sikh Guru, Guru Tegh Bahadur.
- It is believed that Guru Tegh Bahadur stayed there on his way to Delhi before his martyrdom.

Gurudwara Shri Damdama Sahib and Gurudwara Jora Sahib

- It is located in Siana-Saidan, Kurukshetra.
- Shri Guru Gobind Singh Ji used to reside in this village. The Gurudwara was rebuilt in the early 21st century.

- A Gursikh of Guru Gobind Singh was living in the village Saina-Saidan. When he heard that Guru Gobind Singh was nearby, he took Guru Sahib to his house and looked after him very well.

> The Gursikh presented Guru Sahib with a fine pair of wooden shoes and in return, Guruji gave him his leather shoes. These shoes are still preserved in the Gurudwara. The name 'Jora Sahib' means a pair of shoes.

Gurudwara Lakhan Majra

- It is located in Rohtak district.
- It is dedicated to the 9th Sikh Guru, Guru Tegh Bahadur.
- He stayed at this place for 13 days.

Gurudwara Manji Sahib

- It is located in Kaithal.
- The name of this Gurudwara comes from **Tarkhan Singh Manji**, who invited Guru Tegh Bahadur to that place.
- He was a carpenter, so the place is known as **Manji Sahib Gurudwara**.

Gurudwara Neem Sahib

- It is located in Kaithal, near Dogra gate.
- It is dedicated to Guru Tegh Bahadur.
- Guruji sat in meditation under a neem tree at this place where he met a devotee suffering from fever. He offered his neem leaves and the devotee was cured. The place then came to be known as **Neem Sahib**.

Badshahi Bagh Sahib Gurudwara

- It is located in Ambala.
- It is commemorates the visit of Guru Gobind Singh in 1670.
- On returning from Lakhnaur, the Guru rested in a garden here, which belonged to **Pir Amir Din**.
- Pir Amir Din threw a challenge for a fight between his black hawk and Guru's white hawk. But Guruji called upon two sparrows to fight with the hawk and uttered the famous words 'Chirion se baaz larun, tabe Gobind Singh Naam Kahaun.'
- The black hawk fell to its death about a kilometer away, where Gurudwara Gobindpura is built.

Famous Churches in Haryana

Cantonment Church Tower

- Location — Historical church situated in Karnal
- Built in — 1806
- Religious significance — Dedicated to St. James, one of the disciples of Jesus Christ
- The church was built when an army cantonment was established by the British in Karnal. It has a tower 35 m tall, which can be seen from 7 km distance. The church was dismantled in 1841 when the cantonment was shifted to Ambala, but the tower was allowed to stay.

St. Paul's Church

- Location — Ambala Cantonment area
- Built in — 1857
- It was bombed severely during the Indo-Pak war, which partly destroyed the beautiful church building.

St. Thomas Church

- Location — Hisar
- Founded in — 1860
- This church is considered one of the historical sites in the district.

Major Mosques in Haryana

Name	Location	Description
Jama Masjid	Panipat, Rohtak	• Believed to be built by **Humayun** in 1531. • Largest mosque situated in the middle of Panipat. • Also located in the Rohtak district.
Lal Masjid	Rohtak	• Built by **Haji Aashiq Ali** in 1939. • Located in Rohtak. • Constructed atop a 10-feet tall platform. • Made of red sandstone.
Shishewali Masjid	Rohtak	• Located in Chameli Market of Rohtak district. • Entrance made of white marble. • A corridor has 14 pillars on one side and rooms on the other.

Name	Location	Description
Dini Masjid	Rohtak	• Situated in the middle of Rohtak district. • Also known as Adina Mosque. • Believe to have been a Jain temple, later turned into a mosque by Aurangzeb. • Mosque pillars depict writings of Mughal heroes. • Rebuilt into a temple in 1947.
Humayun Mosque	Fatehabad, Hisar	• Situated in Fatehabad, Hisar district. • Erected by Mughal Emperor Humayun on an already standing Lat (stone pillar) placed by Sultan Feroz Shah Tughlaq. • Humayun is believed to have stayed here while going to Amarkot after being defeated by Sher Shah Suri. • He offered Friday Namaz at this place.
Mosque of Alivardi Khan	Gurugram	• Built in the 18th century by Nawab Alivardi Khan. • Located in Gurugram. • Includes a sarai (rest house). • Believed to be a resting place of Alivardi Khan.
Kabuli Mosque 	Panipat	• Built by Babur in 1527 AD after his victory over Ibrahim Lodhi in the First Battle of Panipat. • Named after Babur's wife, **Mussmat Kabuli Begum.** • A garden and a reservoir were also built alongside the mosque. • The prayer hall is square-shaped with semi-spherical domes and line-plastered walls.
Kazi Masjid	Dujana Village, Jhajjhar District	• It was constructed by Qazi (Kazi) Sayeed Hafizuddin of Dujana princely state. • White stones were used in its construction.
Ibrahim Barah Hazari Mosque	—	• It was constructed by Ibrahim Barah Hazari, who was the general of Mohammad Ghori. • This masjid was built after defeating Chauhans of Rewari.
Lal Masjid	Rewari	• It was located near Purani Kacheri of Rewari. • It was constructed by Akbar around, 1570. • There are two tombs located near this mosque.
Sarai Alivardi Mosque	Gurugram	• It was constructed during the reign of Alivardi Khan. • A sarai is located near mosque, which was considered as rest house of Alivardi Khan.
Ranishah Mosque	Bhiwani	• From tourism point of view it is considered as an important mosque. • It is also known as Chhoti Masjid, Vyapariyon wali Masjid and Nayi Masjid.

Shrines and Dargahs in Haryana

Dargah Naugaja Peer

- It is located at Shahabad in Kurukshetra on NH-1.
- It is the shrine of **Baba Naugaja Peer,** whose real name was Sayed Ibrahim Badshah. He originally belonged to Iraq.
- There is a Shiva temple situated in the vicinity of the shrine. People visit both places.
- Devotees often offer chaddar (cloth), incense sticks and watches on the tomb of the peer.

Shrine of Mira Nau Bahaar

- It is located at Guhla-Cheeka in the district of Kaithal
- This shrine is believed to be 1000 years old. Baba Mira is also called **Bada Peer** as he was the eldest among his siblings.

- Baba Mira wrote many Sufi hymns, which are very popular. The shrine is the Samadhi place of Baba Mira.
- A fair is held at the shrine in June, five days after Nirjala Ekadashi.

Char Qutab Shrine

- It is located at Hansi in Hisar district.
- The shrine has tombs of four Sufi saints *i.e.* Jamal-ud-Din Hanswi (1187-1261 AD), Burhan-ud-Din (1261-1303 AD), Qutab-ud-Din Munawwar (1300-54 AD) and Nur-ud-Din (1325-97 AD).
- A large mosque was constructed by Feroz Shah Tughlaq on the Northern enclosure of the shrine.

Shrine of Mama Bhanja

- It is located in Sonipat.
- The tombs of **Imam Nasiruddin** and his nephew **Ibrahim Abdullah** are situated here.
- There is an ancient temple dedicated to Lord Shiva, which was built by regional Emperor Shiv Chandra. The place denotes Hindu-Muslim unity.

Shrine of Hamza Peer

- It is located in Dharsu village at Narnaul in Mahendragarh district
- The shrine contains the tomb of **Hamza Peer**, who was a disciple of Hazrat Shamsuddin Auliya. There are other tombs of Hazrat Shavbal Pir and his disciples.
- The entire shrine has many tombs and each dome is painted in white and green colours.

Shrine of Sheikh Musa

- It is located in Palla village of Nuh district
- The shrine is a 700-year-old building containing the tomb of Hazrat Sheikh Musa, a disciple of Sheikh Nizamuddin Auliya.
- It is built in a blend of Rajasthani and Mughal architectural styles. One of its gateways has shaking minarets that vibrate synchronously.

> In May 2012, an MoU was signed between the Waqf Board and ITRHD (Indian Trust for Rural Heritage and Development) for the conservation of Shrine of Sheikh Musa. From 2016, its conservation was taken over by the Archaeological Department.

Shrine of Five Peer

- It is located in Madhuban area of Karnal
- Peers are Sufi saints who preach unity, universal brotherhood and tolerance. Haryana has many tombs of Peers, as the region was inhabited by Sufi saints.
- The shrine consists of five tombs belonging to Hazrat Ali Ilahi Bakshsh, Bahadur Khan Durrani, Mohammad Ali, Sabar Singh Bori and Kesar Mal Bori.

Shrine of Bu Ali Shah Qalandar

- It was built in 14th century in Panipat.
- The shrine contains tombs of **Sheikh Sharafudeen Bu Ali Qalandar, Hakim Mukaram Khan** and **Urdu poet Maulana Altaf Hussain Ali.**
- It was constructed by Mahabat Khan, a general in the service of Mughal Emperor Jahangir.
- People come to offer prayers every Thursday.

▲ Dargah of Bu Ali Shah Qalandar

Tomb of Peer Baba Shah Mir

- It is located in Fatehabad.
- The town of Fatehabad was built by Feroz Shah Tughlaq. It is believed that he built the tomb of Shah Mir in white marble.

Other Tombs in Haryana

Tomb	Location
Baba Muquaddam	Hisar
Jamal Khan	Sonipat
Sheikh Hazrat Jalaluddin	Panipat
Baba Alishad	Kurukshetra
Baba Chetanshah	Kaithal
Hazrat Khwaja Shamsuddin	Panipat
Kabir Ul Auliya	Panipat
Sayyed Roshan Ali	Panipat
Sheikh Aman Ullah	Panipat
Sheikh Junaid	Hisar

Mausoleums or Samadhis in Haryana

Baba Pranpir Mausoleum

- It is located in Southern part of Hisar.
- The upper part of the mausoleum is made of white kankar stones. The upper portion is made of lakhauri bricks.
- There are four doorways around the mausoleum.

Altaf Hussain Hali Tomb

- It is located near Bu Ali Shah's dargah in Panipat district.
- Altaf Hussain was born in 1837. He was an Urdu scholar and knew Persian, Arabic and English. He was a contemporary of **Mirza Ghalib**. His pen name was **Maulana Khawaja**.

> Altaf Hussain Hali encouraged the formal system of education, built a library and established Hali High School.

Ibrahim Lodhi Tomb

- It is located in Panipat.
- Ibrahim Lodhi died on the battlefield during the first Battle of Panipat, fought between Babar and Ibrahim Lodhi. Therefore, his mausoleum is built there.
- At this place, a high double terraced platform was built by the Britishers. An inscription fixed in a niche near the grave declares that in 1866 AD, the Britishers rebuilt the tomb during the construction of Grand Trunk Road.

Sheikh Chilli Tomb

- It is located at Thanesar in Kurukshetra district
- Sheikh Chilli's real name was **Abdul Rahim Abdul Karim Razak**. He was the spiritual teacher of Dara Shikoh, the eldest son of Shah Jahan.
- The tomb was built in memory of Sheikh Chilli by **Dara Shikoh**. It includes two tombs, a Madrasa and Mughal gardens.
- It is a beautiful monument made of marble and is also referred to as the **Taj Mahal of Haryana.**

▲ Sheikh Chilli's Tomb

Salar Fakhruddin and Hafiz Jamala Tomb

- It is located in old Panipat.
- Salar Fakhruddin and Hafiz Jamala were the parents of Bu Ali Shah Qalandar.
- The mausoleum was built in their memory. However, the place is ruined now.

Muqarrab Khan

- The real name of Muqarrab Khan was Sheikh Hasan.
- Muqarrab was a prominent physician in the court of Jahangir.
- After his death, Jahangir erected a mausoleum in Panipat, where he breathed his last.

Khwaja Khizr Tomb

- It was built by Ibrahim Lodhi in 1522-24 AD.
- It is located in Sonipat.
- It is made up of red sandstone and has a hemispherical dome.
- It is presently under the conservation of the Archaeological Department of India.

Razia Sultan Mausoleum

- It is located in Kaithal district.
- The mausoleum had a boundary wall, a closed arch and is made of baked bricks and lime mortar.
- But, the place is ruined now.

Shah Wilayat Mausoleum

• Location	Beside the mausoleum of **Ibrahim Khan Suri** in **Narnaul**, Mahendragarh
• Built	During the tenure of **Feroz Shah Tughlaq**

- The tomb is surmounted by a hemispherical dome. It is a big tomb.
- The interior has paintings. Architecture from the Tughlaq era to the British period can be seen in this tomb.

Ibrahim Khan Suri Tomb

- It is located in South of Narnaul, in the district of Mahendragarh.
- Built by Sher Shah Suri in memory of his grandfather Ibrahim Khan Suri.
- Red and grey stones are used in its construction. The walls are artfully sculpted.

> The main attraction of Ibrahim Khan Suri tomb is its huge domed-shaped structure.

Modern Tourist Centres in Haryana

There are many tourist centres in Haryana that are developed recently. They are as follows

Aravalli Golf Course

- It is located in Faridabad, closer to NH-2.
- It is a 18-hole golf course and is designed on the model of Stephan Golf Course of the US.

Surajkund

- It is situated in Faridabad, 20 km from Delhi.
- It was originally constructed by King Surajmal of the Tomar dynasty. The shape of Surajkund resembles the rising sun.
- There is a hemispherical dam built on the beach of Surajkund to collect and conserve rainwater.
- The lake close to Surajkund is known as **Mayur lake**.
- Archaeological excavations have revealed the existence of a Sun Temple here based on ruins that can be seen even now.
- In modern times, Surajkund is developed as a place for crafts fair where craftsmen display their items.

Yadavindra Garden

- Location — Pinjore, Panchkula on the Chandigarh-Shimla road
- Also known as — Pinjore gardens
- It was built in the 17th century by Fidai Khan, an architect appointed by Aurangzeb.
- The name Yadavindra is in the name of Maharaja Yadavindra of Patiala who renovated this garden.
- This beautiful garden was also known as the Mughal garden in the medieval period. The entire garden is divided into four floors.
  - The first floor has **Sheesh Mahal**.
  - The second floor has **Rang Mahal**.
  - The third floor has cypress trees, flowerbeds and groves of fruit trees.
  - The fourth floor has the **Jal Mahal** with a square fountain bed.
- Yadavindra gardens are built in the style of Shalimar Bagh of Srinagar and reflect a combination of Rajasthani-Mughal style of architecture.

- Special festivals like Pinjore Baisakhi festival in April, Pinjore Mango Mela in July and Pinjore Heritage Festival in December are major annual celebrations at the garden.

Morni Hills

- It is located in Panchkula.
- It is the only hill station in Haryana.
- Morni hills geographically lies on the outer fringe of the Shiwalik hills.

Mountain Quail

- It is located in Morni hills of Panchkula district.
- It is developed as an eco-tourism spot by the Government of Haryana.

Kingfisher

- It is a resort with a health club, swimming pool, situated on Delhi-Ambala-Amritsar highway (NH-1).
- The place was used as a stable for military horses and a cantonment during the British rule.

Parakeet

- It is located at Peepli, Kurukshetra.
- It has been constructed on the road going to Kurukshetra.
- Restaurants and hotels etc. are constructed here for the convenience of tourists.

Jyotisar

- It is located on Pehowa route in **Kurukshetra** on the banks of Saraswati river.
- Pure and fresh water is available from the Narwana canal for bathing of tourists.

Kala Amb Park

- It is located 5 km from Panipat, on Sinauli road.
- Kala Amb historical war memorial is established by tourism department.

Blue Jay

- It is located in Samalkha, Panipat which is situated 18 km away from Panipat.
- It includes hotels motels along with other facilities.

Shama

It is located in Gurugram. It is established by Haryana Tourism Department, which is equipped with all the modern facilities. This tourist spot attracks a lot of tourist travelling on the Delhi-Gurugram route.

Gauraiya Tourist Place

- It is located in Bahadurgarh, Jhajjar of Haryana.
- It has been constructed by Haryana Tourism Corporation on National Highway No. 10 from Delhi to Hisar.

Sohna

- This tourist centre is constructed on the outer fringes of the Aravalli hills. It is situated at Delhi-Alwar road in Gurugram.
- In the month of February, a vintage car rally is organised here. It is also known for its hot springs (kunds).
- During the winter season, this tourist destination attracts many tourists.

Tilyar Lake

- It is a man-made lake developed in Rohtak district. It is spread over an area of 123 acres.
- There is a cafeteria, a zoo and green lawns for picnics around Tilyar lake.

Tajewala, Hathnikund, Kalesar Complex

- Tajewala, Hathnikund and Kalesar are at a distance of 5 km from each other at Jagadhri-Paonta road.
- Tajewala and Hathnikund are on the Western Yamuna Canal System. Both the places provide ample fishing opportunities.
- From Hathnikund, a glance at the Yamuna river is awesome. It is also developed as a common area for camping, rafting and other water sports.
- Tajewala and Hathnikund have rest houses.
- Kalesar is a sal forest reserve area having a good concentration of sal trees and chinar trees to a certain extent. It is good for hiking. It is spread over an area of 5100 hectare. The place has rest houses and a restaurant.

Dabchik

- It is situated on Delhi-Agra National Highway in the district of Palwal.
- It has a resort, entertainment park and camel rides for children.

Jaltarang

- It is located in Loharu, Bhiwani.
- It is established by Bhiwani Municipal Committee.

Chokki Dhani

- It is situated in Sonipat on National Highway No. 1.
- The place is developed as village tourism, where artists showcase their arts and crafts. It offers pure ethnic and traditional food and culture.

Other Modern Tourist Locations in Haryana

Name	Location	Description
Skylark Complex	Panipat	This complex is established by Haryana Tourism Department on Grand Trunk (GT) Road.
Red Robin Tourist Complex	Bhiwani	This is a hotel and restaurant established by PWD, Bhiwani.
Darango	Dadri	It is a hotel located in Dadri tehsil.
Oasis	Karnal	Located at Uchana, Karnal. Promotion of civilisation is the main intention to develop this place.

District-wise Tourist Location

District	Tourist Sites
Ambala	Kingfisher (Ambala), Yadavindra Garden (Pinjore)
Bhiwani	Red Robin, Darango (Dadri), Rajghat Gurudwara
Faridabad	Badkhal Lake, Arawali Golf Course, Dabchik (Hodal), Surajkund Megpai.
Gurugram	Sultanpur Bird Sanctuary, Damdama Lake (Sohna)
Hisar	Blue Bird
Jind	Bulbul Hariyal (Narwana)
Kaithal	Koyal, Sheikh Tayyab's Tomb, Manjhi Sahib Gurudwara, Kalayat (related to Kapil Muni)
Karnal	Karna Lake, oasis (Chana)
Panipat	Skylark, Black Ant, Blue Jay (Samalkha)
Kurukshetra	Neelkranti Krishna Dam, Parakeet, Tomb of Sheikh Chilli
Rewari	Jungle Babbler (Dharuhera) Sandpiper
Rohtak	Tilyar Lake, Maina, Naurang (Maham) Shri Krishna Sahib Gurudwara, Lakhna Majra Shivalaya of Dighal
Sirsa	Black Partridge (Abushor)
Sonipat	Chakaur
Yamunanagar	Tajewala, Hathnikund, Kalesar
Panchkula	Red Bishop, Morni Hills
Narnaul	City of stepwells and ponds, Tomb of Ibrahim Khan
Mahendragarh	Kanod Fort, Baghat of Pilgrimage, Chyavan Rishi Gupt

Haryana Tourism Policy, 2008

It was announced with the view to speed up development of tourism in Haryana. The new Tourism Policy envisages the creation of an environment conducive to increase private investment in the tourism sector.

The focus shall be on the following areas

- To promote tourism as a major engine of economic growth and capitalise on the potentials of sustainable tourism for economic and employment generation.
- To develop tourism, the establishment of Council of Tourism Development and Hotel Management Institutes in Rohtak and Faridabad.
- To encourage the private sector in the development of tourism by providing water, electricity and transport facilities.
- Developing heritage hotels, health clubs, adventure islands, entertainment parks, adventure farms, medical tourism, exhibition centres and sports complexes.

Haryana Stage Home Policy, 2022

- It was approved by the then Chief Minister Manohar Lal Khattar in 2022.
- Tourists from both India and abroad will have the opportunity to stay in a simple rural setting to experience rural tourism.
- This policy was first introduced in Morni Hills, Panchkula.
- Haryana holds significant potential for the development of sites such as Adibadri, Lohgarh, Kalesar, Buddhist Stupa the Aravali forest area, Kurukshetra, Shivalik etc. village tourism has great growth prospects here. To accomodate tourists, people in these villages will build two room limits.
- Haryana government plans to train villagers in this regard.

Tourism Divisions

The HTDC has divided the state into various divisions so as to encourage tourism. The divisions are as follows

- **Highway Tourism** The areas adjoining the national highways are developed into tourist centres. They are Kurukshetra, Karnal, Panipat, Sonipat and Palwal. An estimated 65 lakh tourists visit these centres annually.
- **Weekend Tourism** Haryana Government has designed the weekend tourism complexes to cater to the business class and upper income groups. They are developed in Faridabad, Rohtak, Gurugram, Hisar and Panchkula.
- **Pilgrim Tourism** Many sites are developed to cater to the pilgrim segment in Haryana. They are Kurukshetra, Kaithal and Panchkula. Kurukshetra is being developed as an international tourism centre.

Heritage Tourism The areas having significant heritage sites are developed in heritage tourism. They are Pinjore in Panchkula and Ballabhgarh in Faridabad. Under the Heritage Circuit of Swadesh Darshan Scheme, the Rewari-Mahendragarh-Madhogarh Circuit would be developed as a global tourism destination.

- **Eco Tourism** Morni Hills, Sultanpur and Kalesar Complex are developed as eco-tourism centres.

Haryana Tourism Corporation Limited

- It is the government-owned official tourism agency of Haryana in India. It began its operation with one resort in 1966 and now owns and operates tourist complexes all over the state. These complexes offer lodging, fooding and recreational activities.
- Haryana Tourism Corporation also offers adventure tourism and farm tourism. To promote the ancient heritage of Pinjore, the **Pinjore Heritage Festival** is also celebrated every year.
- Several tourist spots were opened along the national highways crossing through the state to centre to the travellers.

Tourist Destinations Developed by HTCL

Tourist Spot	Place	Formation
Aravalli Golf Course	Faridabad	1966
Yadavindra Gardens	Pinjore (Panchkula)	1967
Badkhal Lake	Faridabad	1969
Sultanpur Lake	Gurugram	1972
Karna Lake	Karnal	1972
Tilyaar Lake	Rohtak	1973
Surajkund	Faridabad	1988
Damdama Lake	Gurugram	1989
Chokhi Dhani	Sonipat	2013

Tourist Complexes in Haryana

- The Government of Haryana has set up a network of 44 tourist complexes in all over the state.
- Tourist complexes have been set at strategic points along the highway passing through the state.
- Further, tourist complexes have been developed around Delhi to promote leisure tourism and conference tourism.

Resorts Developed by HTDC

Name	Place	Year
Blue Jay	Panipat	1972
Parakeet	Kurukshetra	1972
Bulbul	Jind	1972
Jungle Babbler	Rewari	1974
Dabchick	Palwal	1974
Barbet, Saras, Shama	Gurugram	1974
Myna	Rohtak	1975
Skylark	Panipat	1976
Surkhab	Sirsa	1980
Sandpiper	Rewari	1982
Magpie, Rajhans, Sunbird	Faridabad	1982
Baya	Bhiwani	1983
Grey Pelican	Yamunanagar	1984
Koel	Kaithal	1984
Kingfisher	Ambala	1986
Neelkanthi	Kurukshetra	1987
Mountain Quail	Panchkula	1987
Gauriyya	Jhajjar	1990
Jatayu Yatrika	Panchkula	1993
Papiha	Fatehabad	1994
Black bird	Hansi	1999
Anjan	Pehowa	1999
Highway Golf Club	Uchan	1999
Ethnic Indian	Rai (Sonipat)	2000
Nahar Singh Palace	Ballabhgarh	2003
Adventure Resort	Tikkantal (Panchkula)	2003

CHECK CHAPTER KNOWLEDGE

1 Which of the following religious sites is associated with the belief that offering 'pind daan' grants moksha?
(a) Kamodha (b) Pehowa
(c) Brahma Sarovar (d) Jyotisar Sarovar

2 The temple known as Kaleshwar teerth is also called
(a) Papantak teerth (b) Brahma Sarovar
(c) Gaudiya math (d) Valmiki ashram

3 The place in Haryana where Lord Krishna delivered the Geeta-Updesh to Arjun? *HSSC 2015*
(a) Markandeya (b) Kaleshwar
(c) Jyotisar (d) Brahma Sarovar

4 Who built the Brahma Sarovar in Kurukshetra? *HSSC Auction Record 2016*
(a) Raja Kuru (b) Raja Bharat
(c) Ashoka (d) Pandavas

5 Sannihit Teerth is situated in the district of .... in Haryana. *HSSC 2020, 18*
(a) Gurugram (b) Kurukshetra
(c) Ambala (d) Rewari

6 Chaitanya Mahaprabhu is related to which pilgrim site in Haryana? *HSSC Division Account 2016*
(a) Kamalnath (b) Kuber
(c) Markandeya (d) Aapga

7 After winning the battle, Yudhisthir constructed which well? *HSSC Division Account 2016*
(a) Chandra koop (b) Surya koop
(c) Dharma koop (d) Mangal koop

8 Religious site Narkatari is near which river in Haryana? *HSSC Taxation Inspector 2017*
(a) Vyas (b) Yamuna
(c) Satluj (d) Saraswati

9 Which place in Haryana is known as 'Laghu Haridwar'? *HSSC 2020*

(a) Hatkeshwar (b) Pandu-Pindara
(c) Safidon (d) Debsar

10 The temple dedicated to Sati or Bhadra Kali, where Sati's ankle is believed to have fallen, is

(a) Sthaneshwar Mahadev temple
(b) Devikoop Bhadra Kali temple
(c) Sarveshwar Mahadev temple
(d) Dukh Bhanjan Mahadev temple

11 Shri Sheetala Mata temple is situated in which district of Haryana? *HSSC 2021, Taxation Inspector 2014*

(a) Rewari (b) Mahendragarh
(c) Gurugram (d) Hisar

12 Where in Haryana is Navgraha Kund located? *PGT 2016*

(a) Kaithal (b) Kurukshetra
(c) Hansi (d) Jagadhari

13 Phalgu tourist place is located in which district? *HSSC 2019*

(a) Mahendragarh (b) Kaithal
(c) Jind (d) Jhajjar

14 Which place in Haryana is known as Chhoti Kashi? *Haryana Patwari 2016*

(a) Hisar (b) Bhiwani
(c) Kaithal (d) Nuh

15 Religious place of Panchvati is located where in Haryana? *Haryana Bus Conductor 2017*

(a) Palwal (b) Rohtak
(c) Yamunanagar (d) Devsar

16 Modewala mandir at Mahendragarh district is dedicated to whom? *Haryana State 2017*

(a) Brahma (b) Rama
(c) Krishna (d) Shiva

17 Consider the following statements regarding Brahma Sarovar:

I. It was built by Raja Kuru.
II. Al-Biruni mentioned it in 'Kitabul-Hind'.
III. It is a sacred site for rituals during Makar Sankranti and Purnima.

Which of the above statements is/are correct?

(a) I and II (b) I, II and III
(c) II and III (d) All of these

18 Where is Pandu Pindara located?

(a) Jind-Safidon road
(b) Jind-Gohana road
(c) Jind-Hisar road
(d) Pundarik town

19 Which religious site in Jind is associated with all the 12 Avatars of Lord Vishnu?

(a) Pushkar teerth (b) Bhuteshwara temple
(c) Varah teerth (d) Safidon

20 Bhuteshwara temple is situated in the district of *HSSC 2017, Police Constable 2016*

(a) Bhiwani (b) Jind
(c) Jhajjar (d) Panipat

21 Consider the following statements regarding Adi Badri Narayan temple in Yamunanagar:

I. It was originally built by Adi Shankaracharya in the 8th century.
II. It was rebuilt by Purushottam Ashram in 1823.
III. A fair is organised here every year on Baisakh month.

Which of the statements are correct?

(a) I and II (b) I and III
(c) II and III (d) All of these

22 The Madhewala temple in Narnaul is dedicated to which God? *Haryana Senior Scale Steno 2017*

(a) Sun God (b) Vishnu
(c) Brahma (d) Shiva

23 Which district in Haryana has the Manjhi Sahib Gurudwara? *PGT 2016*

(a) Karnal (b) Ambala
(c) Kaithal (d) Jind

24 In Kaithal city of Haryana, which Gurudwara is situated near Dogra Gate? *HSSC 2016*

(a) Gurudwara Neem Sahib
(b) Ragdhar Gurudwara
(c) Gurudwara Chhati Patsahi
(d) Gurudwara Hanji Sahib

25 Which religious and historical place is situated in Lakhan Majra? *HSSC 2016*

(a) Neem Sahib Gurudwara
(b) Manji Sahib Gurudwara
(c) Sri Singh Sahib Gurudwara
(d) Kapal Mochan Gurudwara

26 Consider the following statements regarding religious places in Bhiwani.

I. Tosham Ke Teerth is known for its 8 Kundas, with Pandava Teerth being the oldest.
II. The temple of Goddess Durga at Devsar is located on a hillock on the Hisar road.
III. Fairs are held at Dhanana Pahari in the months of Chaitra and Ashwin.

IV. Rishi Chawan is believed to have prayed for 7000 years at Mahendragarh Dhosi.

Which of the above statements are correct?

(a) I, III and IV (b) I and II
(c) II and III (d) All of these

27 What is the historical significance of Charangi Nath ka Dhuna?

(a) It was established by Baba Mastnath.
(b) It is believed that Balram, brother of Lord Krishna, meditated there.
(c) It was built during the Mughal era.
(d) It was constructed by King Dilip of the Ikshvaku dynasty.

28 Where is Shishewali mosque, Dini mosque and Lal mosque in Haryana? *Haryana Bus Conductor 2016*

(a) Kurukshetra (b) Rohtak
(c) Palwal (d) Kaithal

29 What is a significant feature of Chamunda Devi temple in Narnaul?

(a) It is located near a lake
(b) It is dedicated to Lord Vishnu
(c) It has 84 pillars with inscriptions from the Ashokan era
(d) It was built in the 19th century

30 Sheikh Chilli's tomb is situated where in Haryana? *HSSC 2019, Haryana Police 2016*

(a) Thanesar (b) Hansi
(c) Pundarik (d) Narnaul

31 Where is Ibrahim Khan's Mausoleum located in Haryana? *TGT 2016*

(a) Rewari (b) Kaithal
(c) Narnaul (d) Hodal

32 Mausoleum of Ibrahim Lodhi is situated where in Haryana? *Haryana Forest Department 2017*

(a) Pinjore (b) Rewari
(c) Gurugram (d) Panipat

33 Where is the Panchvati temple located?

(a) Gurugram (b) Palwal
(c) Rohtak (d) Ambala

34 Which temple is located in Sohna, Gurugram?

(a) Mata Mansa Devi temple
(b) Bhima Devi temple
(c) Ancient Shiva temple
(d) Panchvati temple

35 The Gurudwara Mastgarh was originally built as a mosque by which Mughal emperor?

(a) Shah Alam (b) Shah Jahan
(c) Akbar (d) Aurangzeb

36 Where is the Cantonment Church Tower located?

(a) Ambala (b) Hisar
(c) Karnal (d) Rohtak

37 Who built the Kabuli mosque in Panipat?

(a) Humayun (b) Sher Shah Suri
(c) Babur (d) Akbar

38 The Humayun mosque in Fatehabad is associated with which Mughal emperor?

(a) Akbar (b) Humayun
(c) Shah Jahan (d) Aurangzeb

39 India's biggest Ashoka Chakra was recently unveiled in district of Haryana. *HSSC 2021*

(a) Gurugram (b) Yamunanagar
(c) Jind (d) Faridabad

40 Nek Chand Saini is associated with the *HSSC 2020*

(a) Novel, Lalpasina
(b) Literary work, Seep ka Moti
(c) Film, Chandrawal
(d) Rock Garden

41 Pipli mini zoo is situated in the district of .... in Haryana. *HSSC 2020*

(a) Bhiwani (b) Kurukshetra
(c) Rohtak (d) Panchkula

42 Which year did the Haryana Tourism Corporation (HTCL) begin operations?

(a) 1972 (b) 1980
(c) 1966 (d) 1990

43 Consider the following statements:

I. Sheikh Chilli's tomb was built in 1650 on a raised plinth.
II. It was built by Dara Shikoh.
III. This tomb is popularly known as Taj Mahal of Haryana.

Which of the above is/are correct?

(a) I and II (b) II and III
(c) I and III (d) I, II and III

44 Which of the following is/are a building constructed during the modern period?

I. Open Hand Monument
II. St. Paul Church
III. Jama Masjid
IV. Birla Mandir

(a) I and II
(b) I, II, III and IV
(c) I, II and IV
(d) I, III and IV

45 The famous mosque Lat Ki Masjid, located in Hisar was built by which of the following rulers?
(a) Shah Jahan
(b) Babur
(c) Muhammad bin Tughlaq
(d) Feroz Shah Tughlaq

46 Chokhi Dhani, a famous place for village tourism is located in which district?
(a) Rohtak (b) Sonipat
(c) Yamunanagar (d) Gurugram

47 Match List I with List II and choose the correct answer.

List I (Religious Site)	List II (Associated Feature)
A. Amin Teerth	1. Pandavas stayed here
B. Kamodha	2. Meeting point of Saraswati and Aruna
C. Arunai Teerth	3. Kartikeya bathed after killing a demon
D. Papantak Teerth	4. Bhishma Pitamah's battle site

Codes

	A	B	C	D		A	B	C	D
(a)	1	2	3	4	(b)	4	1	2	3
(c)	1	3	4	2	(d)	3	2	1	4

48 Match the Gurudwaras with their significance.

List I	List II
A. Gurudwara Navin Patshahi	1. Dedicated to Guru Gobind Singh
B. Gurudwara Kapal Mochan	2. Dedicated to Guru Tegh Bahadur
C. Gurudwara Dhamtan Sahib	3. Dedicated to Guru Tegh Bahadur
D. Gurudwara Shri Damdama Sahib	4. Dedicated to Guru Gobind Singh

Codes

	A	B	C	D		A	B	C	D
(a)	4	3	2	1	(b)	2	4	3	1
(c)	1	2	3	4	(d)	4	2	1	3

49 Match List I with List II and choose the correct option. *HSSC 2023*

List I (Monument)	List II (Location)
A. Gujri Mahal	1. Hisar
B. Seikh Chilli's tomb	2. Kurukshetra
C. Choron Ki Baoli	3. Rohtak
D. Jal Mahal	4. Mahendragarh

Codes

	A	B	C	D		A	B	C	D
(a)	1	2	3	4	(b)	2	3	4	1
(c)	3	1	4	2	(d)	4	1	2	3

50 Match the distinctive aspects given in List I with the correct districts of Haryana given in List II and select the correct answer using the options below.

List I	List II
A. This district has the Tomb of Sheikh Chilli	1. Rohtak
B. This city is associated with the temple called Panchvati	2. Jind
C. This district is associated with the temple of Jayanti Devi	3. Kurukshetra
D. This district is associated with the ancient town of Khokrakot	4. Palwal

Codes

	A	B	C	D		A	B	C	D
(a)	3	4	2	1	(b)	1	2	3	4
(c)	2	3	1	4	(d)	4	1	3	2

CORRECT ANSWERS

1. (b)	2. (a)	3. (c)	4. (a)	5. (b)	6. (b)	7. (a)	8. (d)	9. (b)	10. (b)
11. (c)	12. (a)	13. (b)	14. (c)	15. (a)	16. (d)	17. (d)	18. (b)	19. (c)	20. (b)
21. (d)	22. (d)	23. (c)	24. (a)	25. (b)	26. (a)	27. (b)	28. (b)	29. (c)	30. (a)
31. (c)	32. (d)	33. (b)	34. (c)	35. (b)	36. (c)	37. (c)	38. (b)	39. (b)	40. (d)
41. (b)	42. (c)	43. (d)	44. (c)	45. (d)	46. (b)	47. (b)	48. (b)	49. (a)	50. (a)

CHAPTER 12

Cultural Heritage of Haryana

- Cultural Heritage is an expression of the ways of living developed by a community which passed from generation to generation.
- The people of Haryana reflect their culture through their different colourful costumes and ornaments. Women wear very colourful attires which make them more elegant and beautiful whereas men's costumes are very simple but graceful.

Men's Traditional Costumes

The traditional costumes of men in Haryana are as follows

- **Pagri** It is a long fabric wrapped around the head in Marwari style. It is also known as 'Paagadi,' 'Pagdhar' and 'Saafi' in Haryanvi.

Types of Pagri

Paag

- Rajputi style pagri is called 'Paag'. It symbolises pride in Haryana.

Khandka

- A type of pagri worn by elderly men in
- Haryana, considered a symbol of prestige.

- **Safa** A type of pagri, specifically tied by soldiers in a distinct pattern.
- **Muretha** A type of cap worn by men in Haryana.
- **Guliband** A woolen muffler known as 'Guliband' or 'Gulband' in Haryana, worn around the neck during winters.
- **Mirjai** A modified version of a flowing robe (jama) fastened on the right. It is an underjacket with long, loose sleeves and open cuffs.
- **Angarakha** A long Kalidar garment with a traditional appearance. It can be both short or long.
- **Kamari** A half sleeved waistline jacket, usually worn by elderly men.
- **Khes** A coarse, hand woven, voluminous cotton sheet worn by men during winters.
- **Kurta and Kameez** Kurta, also called 'Kudta' in the local language, is a long, collarless shirt worn with dhoti or pajama.
- **Chaddar** A cloth tied around the waist or kept on the shoulders as a mark of honour and respect. It is often gifted by sisters and newlywed brides to male family members.
- **Blanket/ Woollen Sheet** (Dushala) A thick woollen sheet mainly worn by elderly men and farmers during winters.
- **Dohar** A fine, hand woven, large sized cotton sheet, also called 'Dhor,' worn by men during winters.
- **Dhoti** The primary attire of men in Haryana, usually made of white cotton.
- **Jutis** Traditional footwear, similar to 'Mojaris,' made of leather with golden and silver silk thread designs. Popular in Rohtak, Kalanaur, Jind and Julana.

Women's Traditional Costumes

The traditional costumes of women in Haryana are as follows

Costume	Description
Koti	It is a cut sleeved or sleeved jacket for women.
Kamari	It is half or full sleeved jacket normally worn by girls.
Kameez	This is a long straight kurta with collar worn by women in Haryana.
Angia	It is made of cotton and wear under kameez or suit by women of Haryana.
Odhani	It is worn by womenfolks on their head. The corners of odhani are often decorated with golden laces.
Chundhri	It is a thin muslin odhani which is dyed with red colour on edges and has blue colour in the middle part.
Gumati	It is a coloured cotton odhani embroidered with silk bundi work.
Chhyama	It is a type of odhani with yellow pat kashidakari embroidery.
Dimach	It is silk odhani which is gifted in marriages to the bride.
Sopali	It is a dark red coloured odhani which has prints on its edges. It is considered 'Manglik odhani'
Dukaniya	It is a type of odhana which is made of dark red coloured khaddar fabric with yellow thread embroidery work. Embroidery work is done only on its edges. It is also called **Dubla**.
Lahariya	It is a type of dyed odhana which is prepared by 'Bhandej method'.
Peeliya	This odhani has red edges with large prints on its central part. It is sent by parents to their daughter after birth of a male child. '**Kuwa Poojan**' ceremony is done by wearing this odhani.
Mandiya	It is a thin odhana which is dyed on edges with blue or black colour.
Bol	It is a type of cotton odhana which is prepared by silk pattidar embroidery.
Kangh	It is a deep red coloured odhana and has lots of different embroidery pattern in it.
Phulkari	Odhani with box like phulkari work is known as 'Phulkari'. It has dense embroidery work. Phulkari is an art of making shawl.
Borda	It is a floral printed long skirt (ghagra) which is made of khaddar fabric.

Costume	Description
Daaman	It is a type of ghagra which is worn by women. It is made of red or black cotton fabric.
Leh	It is a blue coloured ghagra, which is embroidered by blue and yellow coloured yarns.
Kairi	It is a type of ghagra which is made of blue khaddar along with red tika work.
Gulda Ki Leh	It is a type of ghagra made of dyed khaddar by Bandhai method.
Khara	It is a type of khaddar ghagra which is woven by a combination of four red and four blue threads, without Kali work.
Chand Tara Ghagra	It is made of khaddar (duff) fabric. It is printed with stars and new moon.
Sameej	It is a girls' vest or a loose-filling innerwear top.
Jumpher	It is a form of shirt or suit, highly popular in present time.
Ulti Lamman Ka Ghagra	It is mainly worn by Gujari women. This Ghagra is higher than the normal Ghagra.
Silwar	It is also known as salwar. It is more popular among new generations.

Traditional Costumes for Children

- **Phargal** It is cap worn by children during winter season. The cap has colourful frills.
- **Jhugla** It is also called 'Jhagla' and is worn by infants and babies. It is made of cotton.

Traditional Ornaments in Haryana

- Haryana is well-known for its jewellery, crafted in silver, gold, bone and lac. Folk jewellery follows traditional designs which have remained unaltered.
- Techniques of ornamentation like **repousse**, **chase**, **filigree** and **enamelling** are common here.
- People in Haryana wear ornaments as per their tradition, rituals, beliefs and lifestyle.

Ornaments Worn on Feet

Name	Description
Payal	It is also called Payjeb, Ramjhol, etc. It produces a tinkling sound and is worn on the ankle.
Tanka	It is made up of silver and round in shape. It sounds sweetly.
Aawla	It is silver or golden ornament worn on the ankle.
Kadi and Chalakde	These are ring-shaped silver ornaments. These are worn on the foot above the ankle. Kadi is heavy jewellery while chalakde are light in weight.
Galya	It is a broad ring made of silver worn on toes.
Jhanjhar	It is an anklet that is broader than payal.
Newari	It is a ring-shaped silver ornament which is worn by women on their feet. It makes the sound of Ghunghru.
Pagpan	It is an anklet and a toe ring connected with a thin chain. Brides wear it.
Pali	It is made of silver and worn on top of Newari.
Bichhiya/ Bichhudi	It is a silver ornament which is worn by married women on their toes.
Hirnami	It is made of silver and worn on feet.
Toda/Langer	It is made by tying silver wires and is worn like a large anklet.
Nazariyan	It is worn on feet. It is made of silver.
Angootha	This is in the shape of a ring made of silver but bigger than that of a round shaped ornament which is worn on the toe.
Gajriyan	It is worn by women on their feet. It is made of silver.
Chhail Kada	It is made of silver and worn on the upper part of the ankle. It is smaller than the bangle of hands.

Ornaments Worn on Hands, Arms and Fingers

Name	Description
Tadiya	It is worn on **arms**. It is a heavy jewellery made of silver.
Aarsi	It is a **finger ring** which has a mirror in it. It is worn by women on their righthand thumb.
Kangni	It is a light Kangan which is worn on **wrists**.
Kangan	It is worn by women on their **wrists**.
Dastband	It is worn by women on their **hands**.
Kadulla	It is worn by women on their **arms**.
Hathphool	It is a bracelet that has rings and is connected with a chain. Women wear this on their wedding day or special occasions. 
Anant	It is worn on the **arms** and has a design of a cobra snake made on it.
Gajra	It is tightly worn on the **wrist** by women.
Chhan-Kangan	It is worn by women on their **hands**. It makes a sound when struck together.
Tadiye	Generally made of silver or gold, worn on the **arms** and has a tinkling bell hanging.
Langar	It is a **hand** ornament made of broad silver wires tied together.
Ponche	These are bangles worn by women on their **wrists**. These bangles have small round-shaped balls on them.
Nogri	It is a bangle made of pearls. Women wear it in the middle of bangles.
Gokhru	It is like a bangle made of gold or silver.
Chuud	It is a broad bracelet made of solid gold.
Daman	It is a ring that can be worn on two fingers together.
Mudrika	It is a ring that has a precious stone.
Bajuband	It is also known as 'Bajuphal' and 'Baju bank' in Haryana. It is worn on upper arm. 

Ornaments Worn on Ears, Nose and Forehead

- **Karanphool** Women wear it in the lower part of their **earlobes**. It is mainly made of gold or silver.
- **Phool** It is worn by women on their **head**. It is made of gold or silver.
- **Singar Patti** It is also called kori, jura, viralta, bandini, etc. and is worn on the **head**.
- **Tika/Mang Tika** It is worn on the **head** and hangs till the **forehead**. It is composed of a chain with a hook and a beautiful pendant on the other.
- **Sahr and Borla** The Haryanavi bride wears Borla and Sahr on her **head**. Sahr is silver jewellery which is attached with the Borla. Borla is spherically shaped with a string of gold.

- These are heavy jewellery. Now the Haryanvi bride has switched to Mang Tika, which is made of gold with red and green stones.

▲ Women of Haryana wearing Borla on their Head

- **Sheesh Phool** It is worn by women on their **head**.
- **Jhumka** It is worn in the lower part of the **ears** and is generally dangling.
- **Nath** It is worn by women in their **nose**. It is made of gold. Haryanvi brides look beautiful and elegant in this jewellery.
- **Purli** It is worn by women of Haryana in their **nose**. It is made of gold.
- **Balaak** It is worn in the septum (**nose**). It is made of gold with gems studded in the bottom.

> **Chhaj** It is an ornament made of silver or gold. It is worn by womenfolk on their **forehead**.

- **Koka** It is also known as 'Long' in the local language. It is a grain sized ornament made of gold, silver or diamond. It is worn by women in their **nose**.
- **Boojali** It is worn by women in their **ears**. It is made of silver or gold.
- **Modh** It is worn by both the bride and bridegroom during marriage. It runs from **ears to the forehead** and looks like a crown.
- **Maimad** Women wear it on the **forehead**.
- **Gofan** Women wear it in their **hair**.
- **Jhumki** It is just like jhumka, but the danglers consist of tiny bells.
- **Kudak** Children wear this in their **ears**; it is a very thin gold or silver wire.
- **Magar and Kundal** These earrings are made of gold. Many women wear them daily and prefer the traditional designs.
- **Bhawra** It is worn by women on their **nose** and is much bigger than laung (nosepin).

> **Nakesar** It is worn usually by unmarried girls in their **nose**. It is a very thin wire made of gold or silver with a pearl in the centre.

- **Rakhdi** It is a round ornament made of gold, worn by women on the parting of their hair, hanging towards their forehead.
- **Ognya** It is worn by women on the upper portion of the **ear**. It is made of gold or silver and is designed like a betel leaf.
- **Bessar** It is a ornament worn on the forehead, which is also called chholi nath.
- **Gurda** It is a golden ornament for the **ear**.

Ornaments Worn on the Neck

- **Galshri** It is also known as 'Galsri'. It is made of three or five lines of gold thick beads which are stitched on a cotton fabric strip.
- **Chandan Haar** It is worn by women, which also covers their chest. It is also known as **Raani Haar**. It is made of many golden threads which are linked by rectangular or circular pieces.
- **Gulband** It is made on a gold strip which has small golden beads with a flower petal design.
- **Hasla, Panchmora** Hasla is heavy jewellery meant for brides and given to them at the time of their marriage. It is made of gold, which is heavy but loose around the neck. Panchmora is usually worn by women who are married.
- **Kanthi** Gold ornament worn around the neck and has very small hangings carved in the shape of leaves.
- **Kanthla** Gold ornament worn around the neck of small children.
- **Jhalra** It is a long necklace (haar) which is made of silver coins. These coins are linked together with a gap of 3-4 inches.
- **Mohan Maala** It is also known as **Matarmaala**. It is made of gold with pea-shaped beads. It is worn by women on traditional occasions.
- **Khungali or Hansli** It is made of silver or gold and is worn by women. It keeps the neck bone (Hanseli) safe. It is also known as 'Hansla'.

> **Patri** It is used by both men and women folk. This neck ornament has a design of betel or shahtoot leaf.

- **Hamel** It is a traditional ornament for the neck.
- **Ram Navami Jewellery** It is made of gold. It is a long, heavy ornament for the neck.
- **Tussi** It is like a necklace but is heavier than it.
- **Aad** It is a gold ornament given to the bride by her in-laws.
- **Mantilaya** It is an amulet worn around the neck by tying it with a thick black thread.
- **Jangira** It is a necklace, made of gold which is worn by both men and women. It is also made of silver.
- **Haar** It is a neck ornament made of silver or gold.
- **Muktmaala** It is a neck ornament made of round gold seeds. Ordinary people also wear a necklace of pearls.
- **Chowki** This is an ornament with the image of Gods which is string on a thread and worn around the neck.

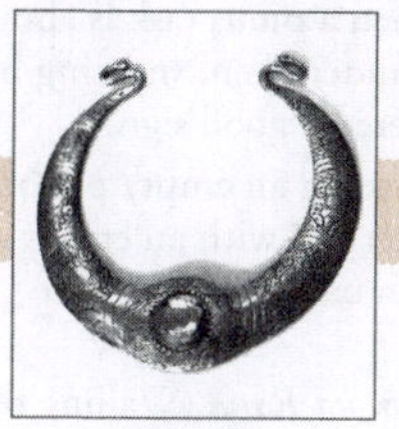
Hansli

Mohan Mala

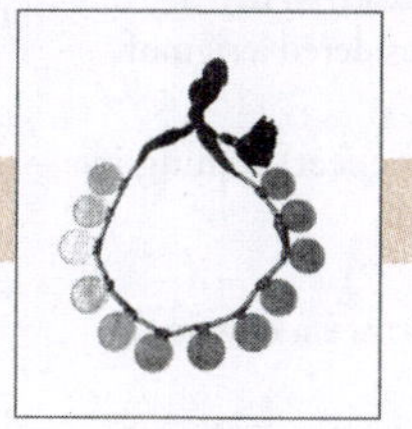
Jhalra

Ornaments Tied around the Waist

Name	Description
Tagari or Tagdi	It is a bread chain with beautiful designs on it, made of gold or silver and tied around the waist.
Naara	It is a silver fuzzy ornament which is worn with Ghagra.
Satka	It is usually a golden or silver ornament with hanging keys. Women tuck one end of this on their waist cloth.
Kandora	It is made of gold or silver and worn by women on their waists. The designs are more complex and intricate than Tagari.
Pallu	It is a silver ornament which is tied with the edge of Odhana by women.

Men's Ornaments

Ornament	Description
• *Gofya*	It is a gold necklace (Haar) which is worn around their neck.
• *Murki*	It is a stud worn in ears by menfolk.
• *Kathla*	It is a gold ornament which is worn around the neck.
• *Zanjira*	It is an ornament worn in the ears.
• *Chauth*	It is an ornament worn on the waists.
• *Patri*	It is an ornament worn on their neck.

Some Famous Dishes of Haryana

Dish	Description
Kachri Ki Chutney	Kachri is a vegetable of cucumber variety and is round in shape, brown or green in colour. A chutney (sweet and sour sauce) is made of Kachri by mixing and grinding it with garlic, onion, aniseed, cumin seeds, etc.
Bajra Aloo Roti	It is a staple diet of Haryana. It is prepared with a mix of bajra flour, mashed potatoes, ginger, garlic, onion and spices. The rotis are served hot with butter on top.
Alsi Ki Pinni	It is a popular sweet prepared with gram alsi seeds (flax seed), flour, sugar, ghee and nuts. It is eaten in winters.
Malpua	It is an Indian version of sweet pancakes. They are fluffy and are served hot. Malpua is made and garnished in ghee.
Bathua Raita	It is a yogurt recipe in which fresh Bathua leaves are added along with cumin powder, red chilli and salt.
Besan Masala Roti	It is a roti made up of gram flour (besan), wheat flour, ghee, mango powder (aamchur) and other spices. It is served with curd or raita.
Bajara Khichdi	It is very famous in Haryana. In this Khichdi, Bajra is used instead of rice.

Good and Bad Omen in Haryana

Good Omen

An good omen is an event or a sign of something good to happen before starting a work or journey.

Some of these are given below

Hiran Darshan (Seeing a deer) During a foreign journey, if a deer crosses the way or runs from left to right, it is considered a good omen. In the local language, it is called as 'Hiran ki Bukkal Kholna'.

Kowe ka Bolna (Crow making a sound) When a crow makes a sound while sitting on the roof, it is considered a sign of the coming of a guest.

Paani Bhara Ghada (Seeing a filled pitcher) It is considered good to see a water bearer girl (Paniharin) along with a filled pitcher outside the home.

Brahman Kanya Ka Darshan (To see a Brahmin girl) To see a Brahmin girl early in the morning is considered good.

Hatheli ka Khujlana (Itching on palm) It is a sign of gaining wealth when a man has itching on his right palm and a woman on her left palm.

Juti pe Juti Chadhna (Sandals above one another) When a sandal is one above the other sandal, it is expected that the person may go for a long journey.

Aankh ka Phadakna (Twitching of eye) It is considered a good sign when the right eye of a man and the left eye of a woman twitches.

Dahi Athwa Chandi ka Sikka (Curd or silver coin) To see curd or a silver coin in the morning is considered a good omen.

Billi ka Muh Dhona (Face of a cat) To see a cat while washing the face in the early morning is a sign of the coming of a loved one.

Doob ka Darshan (Seeing green grass) To see green grass (doob) after getting up from bed is considered to be a pleasant day.

Sadhwa Darshan (Meeting a married woman) To meet a fully made-up married woman on the way is considered auspicious.

Hast Darshan (Seeing own hands) After getting up in the morning, without seeing anybody's face, to see one's own hands in the form of Anjali is considered auspicious (the cup-shaped hollow formed by the joining of the two palms together).

Bhishti ka Jal Liye Milna (Meeting a bearer with filled pitcher) To meet a water bearer with a filled pitcher.

Roti Ka Mud Jana (Folding of bread) When a bread (Roti) is folded, it is considered a sign of the coming of a guest.

Pair Ka Khujlana (Itching in the feet) Itching in the feet is considered a sign of a journey.

Gau Darshan (Seeing a cow) To see a cow is considered a good omen.

Neelkanth Darshan (Seeing an Indian Roller) It is considered very auspicious to see the Neelkanth bird in the morning. On Dussehra seeing the Neelkanth is considered a sign of freedom from all sins.

Chiriya ka Ret me Nahana (Bird bathing in sand) If a bird is seen bathing in sand, then it is predicted that it will rain.

Jhadu Liye Hue Mehtar (Sweeper with broom) It is auspicious to meet a black coloured sweeper on the road with a broom in his hand.

Bad Omen

A bad omen is an event or a sign of something bad to happen before starting a work or journey. The mention of bad omens can even be found in books written by **Banabhatta** in the 6th CE.

Some of these are given below

Gwale ka Bhens ki Sawari (Seeing a milkman riding a buffalo) To see a milkman riding a buffalo is considered a bad omen.

Kutton ka Rona (Wailing of dogs) Wailing of dogs is considered the premonition of a tragedy that may strike in the coming event.

Kaali billi ka Rasta Katna (Crossing of a black cat) If a black cat crosses a person from his right to his left, then it is considered a bad omen for that person.

Ankh Phadakna (Twitching of an eye) It is considered a bad omen when the right eye of a woman and the left eye of a man twitches.

Chhikna (Sneezing) When a pious task is about to be done or being undertaken, sneezing by anyone is not considered a good sign.

Khali Ghara Dekhna (Seeing an empty pitcher) To meet a water bearer girl with an empty pitcher is considered a bad omen for that person.

Shamshan Mein Gidaron ka Rona (Wailing of jackals in cremation ground) Wailing of jackals in the cremation ground is considered a premonition for the death of someone in a colony.

Indhan ka Tokra (Fuel Crate) Crossing someone's path with a fuel crate is considered inauspicious.

Suar ka Milna (Meeting a pig) Seeing a pig on the road is inauspicious.

Cultural Beliefs in Haryana

There are many cultural beliefs in Haryana. Some of them are described below

Beliefs Related to Journey

- Eating of **curd** and **jaggery** is considered good before starting a journey.
- Consuming milk just before starting a journey or undertaking a journey on Wednesday is not considered auspicious.
- It is considered unpleasant and unsafe to see a married woman with a filled pitcher of water and to hear a sound of a partridge bird on the left side and a kotri bird on the right while starting a journey.
- To see a dog with a bone, a mongoose, a bird eating an insect sitting on a cactus plant or sneezing just before starting a journey is not considered auspicious.
- Brooming just after someone has gone out is **not** considered auspicious.

Beliefs Related to the Society

- Not purchasing anything made of iron on Saturday.
- Males not cutting their hair on Thursday and mothers not washing the hair of their children on Saturday.
- Sleeping towards the South direction and doing some work facing South is not considered good.
- Wednesday is considered an auspicious day to start a new work, but Friday is not a good day to begin some new work.

- Digging the Earth on Tuesday is not considered good.
- During Amavasya, it is not considered good to plough the fields using oxen, milk cows or run flour grinders at home. Milk is neither sold nor set to curding during Amavasya and Ekadashi.
- Sneezing and hiccups are considered signs of someone remembering you.
- Kutumbi-Jan-Shartejeev is said on the sneezing of a sick person.
- If children and people sneeze generally, then people around say Chhatrapati, Cheenk Mata, Mathe Rati Tel, etc.

Beliefs Related to Sickness

- To ward off the evil eye and prevent young children from falling ill, mothers put kajal or mascara dot on their child's forehead or behind the ears.
- If a person is bitten by a snake, then he/she is tied with an amulet of Gaugaji, Dadi Gauri, etc. to lower the effect of poison.
- A blue thread is tied on the feet of calves to prevent them from the evil eye.
- Weighting a newborn baby frequently retards the physical growth of the baby.
- During solar or lunar eclipses, pregnant women should not eat or drink anything and should not go out, otherwise, the foetus will develop some kind of deformity.
- Infants should not be put to sleep in baby cots at 12 PM (noon).

Haryanvi Proverbs and Sayings

Proverb Gaaye Ki Bhens Taley, Bhens Ki Gaaye Taley *(गाँ की भैंस तले, भैंस की गाँ तले)*
Meaning Living a life even in difficult conditions.

Proverb Gaam Basya Nahi Mangate Pahlyaan Firange *(गाम बसया नहीं, मँगते पहल्याँ फिरंगे)*
Meaning Achieve benefits by people before the work is done.

Proverb Jhotyan Ki Ladai Mein, Jhundo Ka Kho *(झोट्याँ की लड़ाई में झुण्डों का खो)*
Meaning Loss of weak people in the struggle of powerful ones.

Proverb Tawla Se Bawla *(तावला से बावला)*
Meaning The hasty person's discretion becomes zero.

Proverb Doodh Ki Rakhwali Billi *(दूध की रखवाली बिल्ली)*
Meaning To entrust a confidential task to a deceitful person.

Proverb Nayiyon Ki Barat mein Sab Thakur *(नाईयों की बारात में सब ठाकुर)*
Meaning Among ignorant people all think themselves as great.

Proverb Nekki Nau Kos, Badi Sau Kos *(नेक्की नौ कोस, बदी सौ कोस)*
Meaning Evil spreads faster than good.

Proverb Aapna Bharya Tey Jagat Ka Bharya
(अपणा भरया तै जगत का भरया)
Meaning Selfish people do not care for others.

Proverb Aapna Maare Cha Main Gere *(आपणा मारै छां में गेरे)*
Meaning Everyone has spiritual attachment with their loved ones.

Proverb Aape Maare Bina Swarg Kisne Dekhya *(आपै मारे बिना स्वर्ग किसनै देख्या)*
Meaning Success cannot be achieved by relying on others.

Proverb Chhaaj Te Baje-se-Baje, Chhalni bi ke Baje-Jisme Bahttar Chhed *(छाज तै बाजे रे बाजे, छालणी बी के बौले जिसमें बहत्तर छेद)*
Meaning Guilty person should not find fault in others.

Proverb Thaali baithi naan Katde Munde *(ठाली बैठी नाण, काटडे मुँड़े)*
Meaning In absence of useful work doing unusable work.

Haryanvi Idioms and Phrases

Idiom	Meaning
Anghayi Karna (अंघाई करना)	To be pride due to satisfaction
Aal Karna (आल करना)	To do some mischievous work
Imli Ke Patya Pe Dand Karna (इमली के पातयाँ पै डंड करणा)	To be delighted only by the imagination of the prosperity
Ek Handi Me Do Pet Karna (एक हाँडी में दो पेट करणा)	To show biased behaviour
Kulhon Mein Gur Phodna (कुल्हों में गुड़ फोड़ना)	An unsuccessful attempt to keep something secret
Khuri Khodna (खुरी खोदना)	To show forceful act
Ghar Ka Khodya Paani Pina (घर का खोद्या पाणी पीणा)	To become fully self-dependent
Thekli Chadana (थेकली चढ़ाना)	Spend days in poverty
Dhiktana Karna (धिकताना करना)	To coerce or to force someone
Chee Bolna (ची बोलना)	Deciding not to do a work
Churne Ladna (चुरने लड़ना)	Getting excited
Thada Chhikana (ठाडा छिकणा)	To get satisfied
Thoddi Pakadna (ठोड़ी पकड़ना)	To plead, making an emotional appeal
Palle Gaanth Marna (पल्ले गाँठ मारना)	To learn a lesson after much humiliation
Chillam Bharna (चिलम भरना)	To persuade or do flattery
Kolle Lathi Dharna (कोलै लाठ्ठी धरणा)	Be ready for fight
Tang Talai se Nikarna (टांग तलै से निकड़ना)	Accept defeat
Akar Jana (अकड़ जाना)	Stubborn
Anguli Pakar Kar Pahocha Pakarna (ऊँगली पकड़कर पहौंचा पकड़ना)	Trying to grab everything by taking little by little.

Caste System in Haryana

Haryana is ranked 6th in the country on the basis of scheduled castes population. There are 37 castes in the category of Scheduled Castes in Haryana. These are given below

S. No.	Scheduled Castes	S. No.	Scheduled Castes	S. No.	Scheduled Castes	S. No.	Scheduled Castes
1.	Addharmi	11.	Drain	21.	Marija, Marecha	31.	Sansi, Bhedkut, Manesh
2.	Balmiki	12.	Deha, Dhaya, Dhea	22.	Mazhabi	32.	Sansoi
3.	Bengali	13.	Dhank	23.	Megh	33.	Sapela
4.	Berar, Burar, Virar	14.	Dogri, Dangir, Siggi	24.	Nat	34.	Sarera
5.	Batwal	15.	Dumn, Mahasha, Doom	25.	Odh	35.	Sikligar
6.	Bauria, Bawaria	16.	Gagra	26.	Pasi	36.	Sirkiband
7.	Baazigar	17.	Gandhila, Gandil	27.	Perna	37.	Sanhal
8.	Bhanjra	18.	Kabirpanthi, Julaha	28.	Pherera		
9.	Chamar, Jatav	19.	Khatik	29.	Sanhai		
10.	Dagi	20.	Kori, Koli	30.	Chanal		

Backward Class 'A' Category Castes

S. No.	Category	S. No.	Category	S. No.	Category	S. No.	Category
1.	Aheri, Aheria, Heri	19.	Faquir	37.	Lakhera, Manihar, Kachera	55.	Teli
2.	Barra	20.	Gwaria, Gauria	38.	Lohar, Panchal	56.	Bajra, Banjara
3.	Beta, Henis, Hesi	21.	Ghirath	39.	Madari	57.	Jullaha
4.	Bagria	22.	Ghasi, Ghasiara, Ghosi	40.	Mochi	58.	Bhattu
5.	Barwar	23.	Gorkhas	41.	Mirasi	59.	Bedi
6.	Barai, Tomboli	24.	Gawala, Gowala	42.	Nar	60.	Meena
7.	Baragi, Swami Sadh	25.	Gadaria, Pal	43.	Noongar	61.	Rahbari
8.	Battera	26.	Garhi Lohar	44.	Nalband	62.	Charan
9.	Bharbhunja, Bharbhuja	27.	Hajjam, Nai	45.	Pinja, Penja	63.	Mahabrahman
10.	Bhat, Bhatra, Darpi, Ramiya	28.	Jhangra, Brahman, Khati	46.	Rehar, Rehara	64.	Ramgarhia
11.	Bhuhalia, Lohar	29.	Joginath, Jogi, Yogi	47.	Raigar	65.	Udasin
12.	Changar	30.	Kanjar	48.	Rai Sikh	66.	Rangrez, Lilgar, Nilgar, Lallari
13.	Chirimar	31.	Kurmi	49.	Rechband	67.	Dawala, Soni-Dawala, Nyaaria
14.	Chang	32.	Kumhar, Prajapati	50.	Shorgir, Shergir	68.	Bhar, Rajbhar
15.	Data	33.	Kamboj	51.	Soi	69.	Nat (Muslim)
16.	Dhobi	34.	Khanghera	52.	Singhikant, Singiwala	70.	Jangam
17.	Dakaut	35.	Kuchband	53.	Sunar, Zargar, Soni	71.	Chimba, Chhipi, Chimpa, Darzi, Rohilla
18.	Dhosali, Dosali	36.	Labana	54.	Thathera, Tamera	72.	Dhimar, Malhad, Dhinwar, Kashyap, Rajput, Kahar, Jhiwar, Khewat, Mehra, Nishad, Sakka, Bhishti, Sheikh-Abbasi.

Castes of Backward Class 'B' Categories

- Ahir, Yadav
- Saini
- Gujjar
- Lodha, Lodh
- Meo

CHECK CHAPTER KNOWLEDGE

1 In Haryana, the turban worn by the males is called as *HSSC 2024*
(a) Pagdhar (b) Munetaa
(c) Khandwa (d) Tomar

2 Rajputi Style Pagadi is also known by which name in Haryana? *TGT 2016*
(a) Safa (b) Topi (c) Paag (d) Dohar

3 Which of the following is a type of pagadi?
(a) Khandwa (b) Paag
(c) Safa (d) All of these

4 'Kurta', which is worn by menfolk of Haryana, is also known by which name? *TGT 2015*
(a) Angrakha (b) Kamari
(c) Kudta (d) Kameez

5 Muffler is known by which name in Haryana?
(a) Guliband (b) Paag
(c) Safa (d) None of these

6 A cap which is worn by menfolk of Haryana is known as *PGT 2016*
(a) Tora (b) Muretha
(c) Paggad (d) Khandwa

7 A coarse hand woven, coarse cotton sheet, which is worn by men during winter in Haryana, is known by which name? *HSSC 2023*
(a) Topi (b) Khes (c) Kamari (d) Loi

8 Dohar is a
(a) Sheet (Chadar) (b) Pagadi
(c) Kamari (d) Pajama

9 Mirjai is a
(a) cotton kamari (jacket)
(b) hand ornament
(c) bridal wear
(d) pagadi

10 A type of Odhani with yellow pat Kashidkari embroidery is known as *HSSC 2023*
(a) Sopali (b) Chhyama
(c) Dimach (d) Phulkari

11 This is a traditional costume of women in Haryana which is given to her at the time of marriage. This is known as *Haryana CET 2022, HSSC 2020*
(a) Dimach (b) Lahariya
(c) Gumati (d) Mandiya

12 A dark red coloured Odhani which has prints on its edges is known as
(a) Dakaniya (b) Chhyama
(c) Sopali (d) Aangi

13 An Odhana made of dark red coloured Khaddar fabric with yellow thread embroidery work is known as *PGT 2016*
(a) Dakaniya (b) Chhyama
(c) Sopali (d) Gumti

14 The meaning of Phulkari is *PGT 2016*
(a) a large part of villages of Haryana
(b) art of making clay pots
(c) the art of flowers on edifices
(d) art of shawl making

15 A blue coloured Ghagra which is embroidered by blue and yellow coloured yarns is known by which name?
(a) Daman (b) Leh (c) Kairi (d) Ghaghri

16 Chandtara is a type of Ghagra which is worn by women of Haryana. It is made of which fabric in Haryana? *HSSC 2023*
(a) Silk (b) Duff (Khaddar)
(c) Deru (d) None of these

17 Nazariyan ornament is worn in which part of the body by women?
(a) Arm (b) Foot (c) Neck (d) Ears

18 Kadulla ornament is worn by women in which part of their body? *HSCC 2016*
(a) Fingers (b) Neck (c) Arm (d) Foot

19 Kangan is worn on which part by women of Haryana? *HSSC 2020*
(a) Wrist (b) Ears (c) Neck (d) Nose

20 Chhaj ornament is worn on which part by women? *HSSC CET 2022*
(a) Neck (b) Forehead (c) Hand (d) Waist

21 Phool is a traditional ornament of Haryana worn by women on their *HSSC 2020*
(a) ears (b) head (c) chest (d) wrist

22 Where is Boojali ornament worn? *HSSC CET 2023, Patwari 2016*
(a) Ear (b) Nose (c) Neck (d) Hand

23 Purli is worn in
(a) ear (b) neck (c) nose (d) hand

24 Balaak ornament is worn in which part of the body?
(a) hand (b) foot
(c) wrist (d) nose

25 Kadulla is worn by women in their *HSSC 2016*
(a) fingers (b) neck
(c) arms (d) nose

26 Haryana is known as the land of *HSSC 2020*
(a) rice (b) rotis
(c) pulses (d) fruits

27 Some famous dishes of Haryana are
(a) mixed dal and bajra aloo roti
(b) makki roti and sarson ka saag
(c) chole bhature and dal makhani
(d) All of the above

28 Which one is a famous dish of Haryana?
(a) Methi Gajar (b) Bajra Khichri
(c) Urd rice (d) Both (a) and (b)

29 Famous sweet of Haryana is
(a) alsi ki pinni (b) malpua
(c) gajar ka halwa (d) Both (a) and (b)

30 Which of the following is a Omen?
(a) Seeing a dear
(b) Crow making sound
(c) Pitcher filled with water
(d) All of the above

31 Pair ka Khujlana is a sign of
(a) journey (b) tragedy
(c) disease (d) marriage

32 Which of the following is considered as a bad-omen?
(a) Wailing of dogs
(b) Twitching of eye
(c) Crossing of a black cat
(d) All of the above

33 The meaning of the Haryanvi Proverb 'Tawla se Bawla' is *HSSC CET 2022*
(a) doing an unimportant work in the absence of an important work
(b) the hasty person's discretion becomes zero
(c) evil spreads faster than good
(d) selfish people do not care for others

34 A belief in Haryana is that one should not do any work facing .... direction.
(a) South (b) East (c) West (d) North

35 .... is considered as a bad-omen by people of Haryana.
(a) Hiran Darshan (b) Ankh Phadakna
(c) Juti Pe Juti Chadhna (d) Doob ka Darshan

36 The most appropriate meaning of the idioms 'Bahati Ganga Mein Hath Dhona' is *Haryana CET 2023*
(a) to make more and more progress
(b) to make the impossible work possible
(c) taking advantage of opportunity
(d) washing hands with holy water

37 Which day is considered auspicious to start a new work in Haryana?
(a) Monday (b) Sunday
(c) Wednesday (d) Friday

38 Match the following *PGT 2016*

	List I		List II
A.	Koti Ghagra	1.	Underwear
B.	Daman Dupatta	2.	Jacket
C.	Peeliya	3.	Dupatta
D.	Aangi	4.	Ghagra

Codes

	A	B	C	D		A	B	C	D
(a)	4	2	1	3	(b)	4	1	2	3
(c)	2	3	1	4	(d)	1	2	3	4

39 Match the following. *PGT 2016*

	List I		List II
A.	Chuud	1.	Ornament for ears
B.	Sahr	2.	Ornament for head
C.	Tagdi	3.	Ornament for waist
D.	Karnaphool	4.	Ornament for hand

Codes

	A	B	C	D		A	B	C	D
(a)	1	2	3	4	(b)	2	3	4	1
(c)	3	2	1	4	(d)	4	3	2	1

CORRECT ANSWERS

1. (a)	**2.** (c)	**3.** (d)	**4.** (d)	**5.** (a)	**6.** (b)	**7.** (b)	**8.** (a)	**9.** (a)	**10.** (b)
11. (a)	**12.** (c)	**13.** (a)	**14.** (d)	**15.** (b)	**16.** (b)	**17.** (b)	**18.** (c)	**19.** (a)	**20.** (b)
21. (b)	**22.** (a)	**23.** (c)	**24.** (d)	**25.** (c)	**26.** (b)	**27.** (a)	**28.** (d)	**29.** (d)	**30.** (d)
31. (a)	**32.** (d)	**33.** (b)	**34.** (a)	**35.** (b)	**36.** (c)	**37.** (c)	**38.** (b)	**39.** (a)	

HARYANA

Geography

and Environment

This section contains all the important topics of Haryana Geography like Geographical Structure, Soil, Climate, Rivers, Lakes, Waterfall National Park, Wildlife, etc.

CHAPTER 13

Geographical Structure of Haryana

- The geographical structure of Haryana has evolved due to endogenic and exogenic forces, along with horizontal structure of the plate.
- Haryana lies in the vast plains between the Ganga river system (East) and Indus river system (West).
- Yamuna, a tributary of Ganga is the only major river flowing through the state. There are other small non–perennial rivers and lakes in the state.

Location and Extent of Haryana

• Location	In North-Western part of India and in the Southern part of Indus plains (Punjab plains).
• Geographical overviews	Haryana is a landlocked state, mostly covered by Indus-Ganga Plain and is 300 miles North of the Tropic of Cancer and forming an uneven quadrilateral shape.
• Latitudinal extension	27°39′ to 30°55′ North
• Longitudinal extension	74°27′ to 77°36′ East
• Area	44,212 sq km (1.34% of Country's Total Area)
• Position in the country in terms of area (statewise)	20th
• Total length from North to South	281 km
• Total length from East to West	200 km
• Easternmost district	Yamunanagar
• Westernmost district	Sirsa
• Northernmost district	Panchkula
• Southernmost district	Nuh
• Largest district	Sirsa (4,277 sq km)
• Smallest district	Faridabad (743 sq km)
• Number of district	22

Extend of Boundary of Haryana

Haryana shares its border with 5 States and 2 Union Territories.

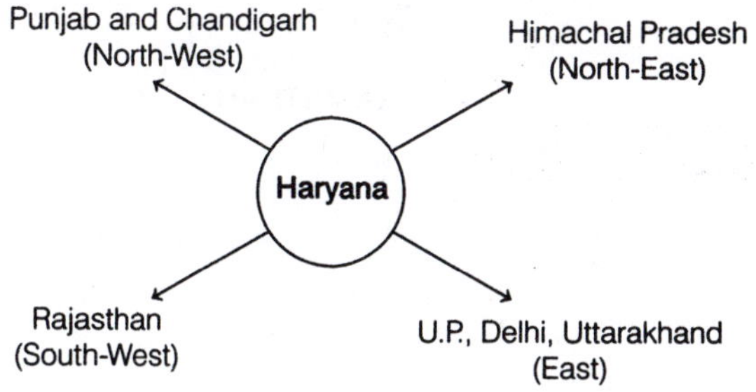

• Capital	Chandigarh (Union Territory)
• Delhi	Surrounded by Haryana from three sides
• Rajasthan	Shares longest boundary with Haryana (1,262 km)
• Uttarakhand	Shares shortest boundary with Haryana (12 km)

• Natural boundaries	Include the Shivalik ranges (North-East), Aravalli hills (South), Yamuna river (East) and Rajasthan desert (South-West)
• River Yamuna	Demarcates boundary between Haryana and Uttar Pradesh. Flows towards Eastern border of Haryana
• Ghaggar river	Flows in the North-West of Haryana
• Rohtak and Charkhi-Dadri	Only districts of Haryana not sharing any State or Union Territory's borders
• Rohtak	Shares border with Jind, Hisar, Bhiwani, Charkhi-Dadri, Jhajjar and Sonipat
• Hisar	Shares border with districts Fatehabad, Jind, Rohtak and Bhiwani
• Noteworthy	14 districts (57% area of state) of Haryana are part of the National Capital Region

- Five largest districts areawise (sq.km) are – Sirsa (4,277), Hisar (3,983), Bhiwani (3,283), Jind (2,702) and Fatehabad (2,538)
- Five smallest districts areawise (sq. km) are – Faridabad (743), Panchkula (898), Gurugram (1,258), Panipat (1,268) and Palwal (1,359).

Districts of Haryana Sharing Border with Different States and UTs

District	Border Sharing States
• Nuh (Mewat)	Rajasthan, Uttar Pradesh
• Yamunanagar	Himachal Pradesh, Uttarakhand, Uttar Pradesh
• Panchkula	Punjab, Himachal Pradesh, Chandigarh (UT)
• Jind	7 Haryana districts – Fatehabad, Hisar, Rohtak, Sonipat, Panipat, Karnal, Kaithal
• Mahendragarh	Surrounded by Rajasthan from three sides
• Hisar	Rajasthan

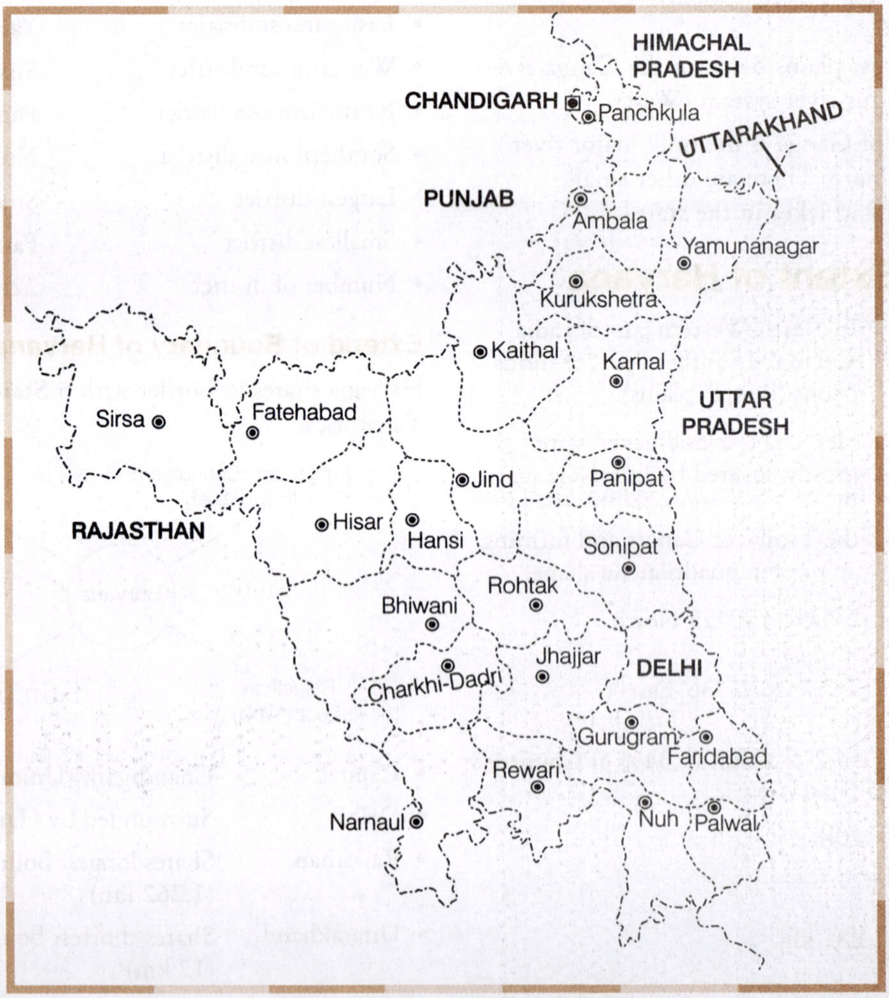

▲ Districts and Neighbouring States of Haryana

Neighbouring States/UT and Districts Sharing Border with Haryana

Neighbouring State/UT	No. of Districts Sharing Border	Name of the Districts
Rajasthan	8	Gurugram, Nuh, Rewari, Mahendragarh, Bhiwani, Hisar, Fatehabad, Sirsa (South-West)
Punjab	7	Sirsa, Fatehabad, Jind, Kaithal, Kurukshetra, Ambala, Panchkula (North-West)
Uttar Pradesh	7	Yamunanagar, Karnal, Panipat, Sonipat, Faridabad, Palwal, Nuh (East)
Himachal Pradesh	3	Panchkula, Ambala, Yamunanagar (North-East)
Uttarakhand	1	Yamunanagar
Delhi	4	Sonipat, Jhajjar, Faridabad, Gurugram (South-East)
Chandigarh	1	Panchkula

Geological Structure of Haryana

- Haryana's geological structure has been unstable since the day of formation and has changed with time.
- There has been no change in the geological structure of Haryana during **Azoic period** and **Palaeozoic period.**
- The important changes in its geological structure occurred during **Mesozoic period.**
- During **Cenozoic period** (about 4 crore to 6 lakh years ago), rivers, mountains and other geographical features were formed.
- It is believed that the geographical location and climate of Haryana has also been determined during this period.

> According to famous writer Colonel **M.L. Gill Bhargav**, in the geological past, Southern part of state was bordered by the sea. These seas were **Saraswati** in the West and **Akhawat** in the East.

- In Mesozoic period, this part of the state also emerged above along with the other regions of North India.
- In the past, Aravalli ranges, which are located in Haryana, were quite lofty and covered with snow. A number of rivers is believed to have been originated from these hills.
- In the past, climate of state was different and the state used to receive heavy rainfall. The winter season was very cold and the summer season was not so long. However, the climate of state changed with the change in geological structure.
- Based on the geological structure of the state, it can be said that by cutting the sedimentary rocks of the Himalayan Mountains, the rivers have changed their route to form the fertile plains of **Ghaggar Yamuna** rivers.
- In Delhi Group, rocks of Purana series are found, which are famous for minerals. The rocks of this series are found in the **Narnaul region.** This region is known as **Museum of Minerals.**

Divisions of Haryana

On the basis of geographical area, Haryana in divided into following three parts

Kurukshetra

- It is situated between 29°52' to 30°12' North latitude and 76°26' to 77°04' East longitudes. Jind and Karnal are part of this division.
- This area is quite important from the point of view of religion. Chautang river flows in this division and soil of Kurukshetra district is not sandy.

Haryana

- It is situated between 29°30' to 30° North latitude. Fatehabad, Hansi, Hisar, Bhiwani and Rohtak districts lie in this division.
- This division is mainly inhabited by Jat people, thus, it is also called Jatiyaat area.

Bhattiana

- This geographical division is situated between Fatehabad and Batu tehsils.
- This division is dominated by the Bhati Rajputs from ancient time, thus, this area is known as Bhattiana.

Physiography of Haryana

• Terrain	Includes flat plains, hills, etc.
• Flat plains	93.76% of the state, located between Ghaggar and Yamuna rivers.
• Also known as	Ghaggar-Yamuna plains. It is largest physiographic region of state.
• Distribution	68.21% of this area is flat and 25.55% is undulating
• Average altitude	200-300 m above sea level

- Formation — Created by sediment deposition from Himalayan rivers. Sand stumps and mounds found on 6.24% area besides this plain.
- Aravalli hills — Cover 3.09% area of the state in Southern part, with an altitude over 300 m
- Physiographic region — Mahendragarh, Rewari, Gurugram, Bhiwani, Charkhi-Dadri, Palwal and Faridabad districts are hilly and rocky.
- Shivalik hills — Found in the North-Eastern part of the state

Geographical Division of Haryana

Dr. Jasbeer Singh in his book **An Agricultural Geography of Haryana**, has divided the state into eight geographical divisions. These are

- Shivalik
- Piedmont Plains
- Alluvial Plains
- Flood Plains
- Plains with Sand Dunes
- Rocky Plains of Aravalli Hills
- Undulating Sandy Plains
- Marshy Land

Shivalik

- Location — Situated in the North-Eastern part, including parts of Panchkula (only hill station of state), Ambala and Yamunanagar.
- Post-Pliocene age — Shivalik which is also known as Sub-Himalaya, is the youngest Himalayan range formed in this age.
- Deposition — The range is formed due to deposition of sediments by Southern Himalayan rivers.
- Rainfall — The highest rainfall occurs in the Shivalik region.
- Area — Covers 1.38% of the state, with an average altitude of 300-600 m (some areas exceed 600 m).
- Sub-Himalaya coverage — 0.56% by Shivalik hills and 0.92% by Sub-Shivalik hills.
- Altitude — On this basis, Shivalik hills have been categorised into two parts, i.e. upper Shivalik ranges and lower Shivalik ranges.

Shivalik Hills

↓

Upper Shivalik Ranges

The average height of these ranges is more than the 600 m. Morni hills, the highest hills in the state is a part of these ranges.

Morni hills lie at a distance of 35 km from the district of Panchkula. The highest point on these hills is the **Karoh Peak** (1,514 m). Morni hills play a vital role in connecting Himalayan plains. Morni and Tipra hills are separated by the Ghaggar river.

↓

Lower Shivalik Ranges

The average height of these ranges is between 400-600 m. These ranges are formed due to deposition of silt, pebbles, conglomerates, etc.

Ghaggar, Markanda, Tangri and Saraswati rivers originate from Shivalik ranges. Shivalik hills have intense slopes due to which these rivers erode these hills.

Piedmont Plains

- Location — South of Shivalik hills, extending from Yamuna to Ghaggar rivers.
- Coverage — Spread over 25 km, including Ambala, Panchkula and Yamunanagar; average height of 300-375 m.
- Transition zone — Serves as a transition between Shivalik hills and plain areas, locally known as **Ghar**.
- Geographical features — Pits, known as Cho in Pahari language, formed by Himalayan rivers and streams.
- Main rivers — Ghaggar and Markanda
- Alluvial fans — Formed due to deposition of silt, pebbles and gravels by rivers.
- Fertility — Plains are less fertile; slope runs from North-East to South-West.

Alluvial Plains

- Location — Between Piedmont Plains of Shivalik (North) and Aravali hills, Yamuna and Ghaggar rivers (South); this plain is also known as **Bhangar**.
- Coverage — Spreads across districts like Ambala, Yamunanagar, Kaithal, Karnal, Kurukshetra, Panipat, Sonipat, Rohtak, Jind, Hisar, Fatehabad, Sirsa, Gurugram and Faridabad.
- Slope — Gentle slope from North-East to South-West.
- Altitude — Average of 220-280 m above sea level.

- Rivers — Markanda, Saraswati and Chautang flow through these plains
- Fertility — Highly fertile, supporting crops like wheat and paddy

Flood Plains

- Location — Found in the Eastern and North-Western parts of the state
- Eastern plains — Undulating with interlinked valleys and marshy lands
- Formation — Created by sediment deposition from the Yamuna river and its tributaries, flowing from Yamunanagar to Faridabad
- North-Western plains — Formed by sediment deposits from Ghaggar and Markanda rivers
- Local names — Known as **Naili** and **Bet** in local language

Plains with Sand Dunes

- Location — Found in the South-West, along the Rajasthan border, covering Southern districts Sirsa, Hisar, Bhiwani, Mahendragarh, Rewari and Jhajjar.
- Formation — Created by sand deposition from hot, dry winds from Rajasthan.
- Sand dunes — Generally, 3-6 m high, reaching up to 15 m in some areas; shift in the direction of wind.
- Low basins — Formed between sand dunes, locally, known as **Tal**, fill with water during monsoon, forming temporary lakes called 'Thooth or Bawdi'.
- Infertility — Infertile due to sand dunes; groundwater is deep and saline.
- Green belt — Trees planted to prevent further sand dune expansion.
- Drip and sprinkle irrigation — With the help of the method crops such as maize, jowar, wheat and pulses are grown in these plains.

Undulating Sandy Plains

- Formation — Created by wind-driven sand deposition.
- Location — Spread across Mahendragarh, Rewari and Gurugram districts.
- Troughs — Found between ridges, filling with water during rains.
- Soil composition — Contains sand, alluvial soil and pebbles.
- Sand mounds — Present near the Aravalli hills.

Marshy Land

- Location — Found in the Western part of Sirsa district
- Elevation — Lowest in the state, below 200 m above sea level
- Formation — Created due to waterlogging
- Cause — Narrow and shallow Naili area with a very gentle slope

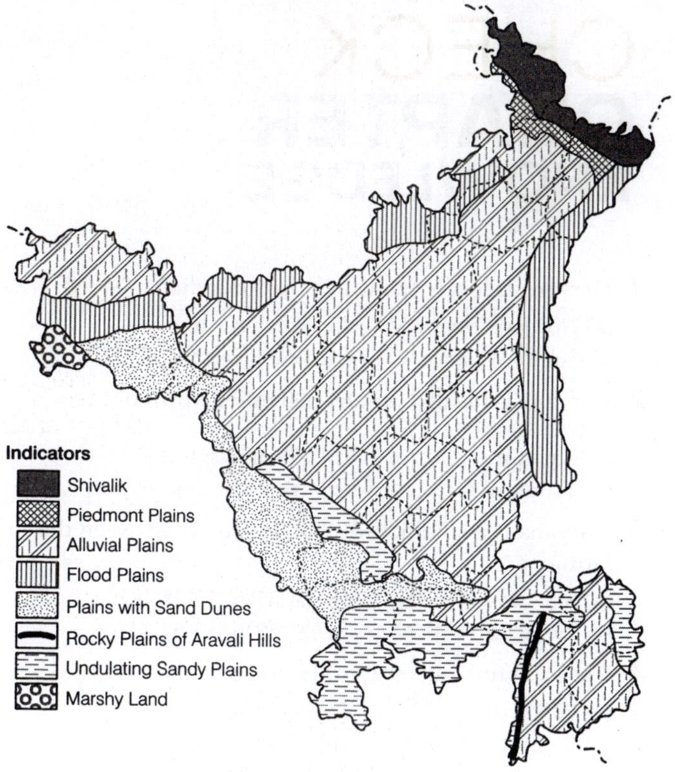

▲ Physical Divisions of Haryana

Rocky Plains of Aravalli Hills

• Location	Found in Southern Haryana, part of the Aravalli hills in Rajasthan
• Elevation	Ranges from 225-500 m above sea level
• Coverage	Includes Gurugram, Faridabad, Rewari, Nuh (Mewat), Bhiwani and Mahendragarh districts
• Terrain	Rugged with low, broken and scattered residual Aravalli hills
• Erosion	Circular, bare rocks showcase wind erosion in the semi-arid region
• Climate and vegetation	Receives low rainfall; has thorn bushes and trees
• Resources	Limestone is extracted from these hills
• Highest point	**Dhosi hills** in Kultajpur village (Narnaul) at 652 m
• Main stretch	Found in Gurugram district
• Key hills	Tosham hills (Bhiwani) and Indori hills (Mewat) are part of the Aravalli range
• Local name	Southern Aravalli hills are called **Mewat hills**
• Minerals	Rich in rock phosphate, asbestos and other minerals
• Delhi ridge	A branch of the Aravalli extending from Haryana to Delhi, running from Dhaula Kuan to Delhi University *via* Karol Bagh
• Low-lying hills	Found West of Bawal and Rewari towns of Haryana
• Rock disintegration	Due to continues Solar radiation
• Debris accumulation	Excessive rock debris has gathered in the foothills

CHECK CHAPTER KNOWLEDGE

1 Haryana is located in which part of India? *HSSC 2024*
(a) North-Western (b) North-Eastern
(c) South-Western (d) South-Eastern

2 Haryana is located around 300 miles North of the *HSSC CET 2022*
(a) Equator (b) Greenwich line
(c) Tropic of Capricorn (d) Tropic of Cancer

3 Haryana is a landlocked state, which lies between the latitudes *HSSC 2017*
(a) 8°37' to 31° 35' N (b) 24°26' to 27°28' N
(c) 29°20' to 31°30 N (d) 27°39' to 30°55' N

4 The longitudinal extent of Haryana is *HSSC 2022*
(a) 70°28' to 77° 36' E (b) 74°27' to 77°36' E
(c) 71°28' to 77°36' E (d) 77°28' to 84°38' E

5 What is the total area of Haryana? *HSSC 2018*
(a) 33,212 sq km (b) 44,212 sq km
(c) 55,212 sq km (d) 44,000 sq km

6 In the total area of country, Haryana's share is *Haryana Junior Engineer 2020*
(a) 1.34% (b) 2.58%
(c) 3.26% (d) 2.76%

7 In the terms of area, which one of the following is the biggest district of Haryana? *Haryana Clerk 2021*
(a) Sirsa (b) Gurugram
(c) Rewari (d) Mahendragarh

8 Haryana shares boundary with how many states?
(a) 3 (b) 5 (c) 6 (d) 4 *HSSC 2015*

9 Which state lies to the South-West of Haryana? *Haryana CET 2022, 18*
(a) Gujarat (b) Punjab
(c) Rajasthan (d) Uttar Pradesh

10 Which of the following neighbouring states of Haryana lies in its East? *HSSC 2016*
(a) Rajasthan (b) Uttar Pradesh
(c) Himachal Pradesh (d) Punjab

11 The state located in North-West of Haryana is *HSSC 2016*
(a) Gujarat (b) Punjab
(c) Rajasthan (d) Uttar Pradesh

12 Which among the following states shares boundary with Haryana? *HSSC 2024*
(a) Himachal Pradesh (b) Sikkim
(c) Arunachal Pradesh (d) Mizoram

13 Haryana has bounded Delhi from .... sides. *Haryana Lab Attandant 2021, HSSC 2017*

(a) 2 (b) 1 (c) 3 (d) 4

14 The river Yamuna flows on the .... boundary of the Haryana. *HSSC 2020*

(a) Eastern (b) Northern
(c) Western (d) Southern

15 Consider the following statements *HSSC CET 2023,22*

1. Sonipat and Jhajjar share border with Delhi.
2. Rohtak does not share its border with Delhi.

Which of the statements given above is/are correct?

(a) Only 1 (b) Only 2
(c) Both 1 and 2 (d) Neither 1 nor 2

16 Which of the following districts of Haryana shares border with Punjab and Rajasthan? *Haryana CET 2023*

(a) Hisar (b) Sirsa (c) Kaithal (d) Jind

17 Given below is a list of districts along with district's touching its boundaries. *HPSC HCS 2023*

1. Jind	Hisar, Kaithal, Panipat, Karnal
2. Rohtak	Jind, Charkhi-Dadri, Hisar, Rewari
3. Rewari	Mahendragarh, Gurugram, Nuh, Jhajjar
4. Hisar	Bhiwani, Rohtak, Sirsa, Fatehabad

Which of the above is/are correctly matched?

(a) 1, 2 and 3 (b) 2, 3 and 4
(c) 2 and 4 (d) 1 and 3

18 The most important change in the geological structure of Haryana was occurred during which period?

(a) Cenozoic (b) Paleozoic (c) Mesozoic (d) Ozoic

19 Which one of the following districts of Haryana is not sandy? *HSSC 2016*

(a) Sirsa (b) Kurukshetra
(c) Bhiwani (d) Bhattiana

20 The Bhattiana division had been dominated by whom in ancient time? *PGT 2016*

(a) Jats (b) Rajputs
(c) Both (a) and (b) (d) None of these

21 Which of the following physiographic regions covers largest area? *PGT 2016*

(a) Shivalik hills (b) Sandy area
(c) Plains (d) Aravalli hills

22 The .... is the largest part of the Haryana state. *HSSC Field Cadre 2020*

(a) Aravalli range in the South
(b) Yamuna-Ghaggar Plain
(c) Shivalik hills to the North-East
(d) Semi-desert sandy plain

23 On how much area of Haryana, the remnants of Aravalli hills are extended?

(a) 25.6% (b) 6.24%
(c) 3.09% (d) 4.57%

24 Shivalik hills are not found in which among the following districts of Haryana? *HSSC CPT 2023, 22*

(a) Ambala (b) Yamunanagar
(c) Sirsa (d) Panchkula

25 Shivalik hills are present in which part of Haryana? *SSC 2020, 18,16*

(a) Northern (b) North-Western
(c) North-Eastern (d) Western

26 Shivalik hills are located in which district of Haryana? *Haryana Accountant 2018*

(a) Rohtak (b) Ambala
(c) Gurugram (d) Sonipat

27 Morni hills are located in which district of Haryana? *HSSC 2022, 20*

(a) Mahendragarh (b) Panchkula
(c) Ambala (d) Karnal

28 The highest point of the Morni hills is known as *Haryana Field Cadre 2020*

(a) Karoh peak (b) Garoh peak
(c) Tosa peak (d) Grasher peak

29 The highest mountain peak in Haryana, located in Panchkula and is part of the Shivalik hill range of greater Himalayas is .... *HSSC Field Cadre 2020*

(a) Karoh Peak (b) Nanda Devi
(c) Saltoro Kangri (d) Kamet

30 Which of the following hills acts as a bridge between plains of Himalaya? *HSSC 2018*

(a) Tipra (b) Morni (c) Aravalli (d) Ambala

31 Morni and Tipra hills are separated by .... river. *Haryana Accountant 2018*

(a) Yamuna (b) Ghaggar
(c) Saraswati (d) Markanda

32 Which of the following hill ranges is not in Haryana? *HSSC Field Cadre 2020*

(a) Aravalli range (b) Morni hills
(c) Shivalik hills (d) Satpura range

33 .... serves as a connecting link between Himalayas and Haryana plains. *HSSC CET 2023*

(a) Aravalli hills (b) Morni hills
(c) Mewat hills (d) Tipra hills

34 Piedmont Plains are locally known by the name

(a) Bangar (b) Khadar
(c) Ghar (d) Tal

35 The Alluvial Plains in Haryana extend in which among the following districts?
(a) Kaithal (b) Panchkula
(c) Karnal (d) Both (a) and (c)

36 What are the flood plains of Ghaggar river called in Haryana?
(a) Bangar (b) Khadar
(c) Terai (d) Bet and Naili

37 .... is the main geographical feature of Haryana in southern part of the state. *HSSC 2024*
(a) Shivalik hills (b) Ghaggar plane
(c) Semi desert (d) Aravalli hills

38 Aravali hills are located in which part of Haryana? *HSSC 2021, Haryana Field Cadre 2020*
(a) Northern (b) Southern
(c) Eastern (d) Western

39 The main presence of Aravali hills is found in the district of *HSSC 2018*
(a) Ambala (b) Rohtak
(c) Gurugram (d) Yamunanagar

40 Tosham hills are located in *PGT 2015*
(a) Rohtak (b) Hisar
(c) Mahendragarh (d) Bhiwani

41 Indori hills are located in *PGT 2015*
(a) Mewat (b) Palwal
(c) Rewari (d) Mahendragarh

42 The Southern part of Aravalli hills is known by which name? *Haryana Clerk 2019*
(a) Marshal hills (b) Mewat hills
(c) Bhangar (d) Yamunanagar

43 Undulating sandy plains have been formed by which agent of erosion?
(a) Wind (b) Glaciers
(c) Water (d) Wave

44 Where are the undulating sandy plains found in Haryana? *PGT 2016*
(a) Gurugram (b) Rewari
(c) Mahendragrah (d) All of these

45 Which of the following regions has the lowest elevation in Haryana?
(a) Semi-desert Plains (b) Marshy Land
(c) Alluvial Plains (d) Piedmont Plains

46 Consider the following statements.
1. Haryana lies between the longitude of 74°27″ to 77°36′.
2. Shivaliks and Aravali hills lie in the Southern part of the state.

Which of the statements given above is/are correct? *TGT 2016*
(a) Only 1 (b) Only 2
(c) Both 1 and 2 (d) None of these

47 Match List I with List II and choose the correct option. *HPSC-HSC 2023*

	List I		List II
A.	Dagar	1.	Parts of Hisar, Bhiwani and Sirsa
B.	Bet	2.	Flood plains of Markanda
C.	Nall	3.	Flood plains of Ghaggar
D.	Khadar	4.	Flood Plains of Yamuna
E.	Bangar	3.	Old alluvial plains

Codes

	A	B	C	D	E
(a)	1	2	3	5	4
(b)	2	1	3	4	5
(c)	1	2	3	4	5
(d)	2	4	5	1	3

48 Match the divisions in Haryana given in List I with two of the selected districts in each one's jurisdiction given in List II and select the correct answer using the options given below the columns. *HPSC HCS 2019*

	List I		List II
A.	Karnal	1.	Jind, Sirsa
B.	Hisar	2.	Panipat, Kaithal
C.	Ambala	3.	Jhajjar, Bhiwani
D.	Rohtak	4.	Kurukshetra, Yamunanagar

Codes

	A	B	C	D		A	B	C	D
(a)	4	1	3	2	(b)	1	3	2	4
(c)	3	4	1	2	(d)	2	1	4	3

CORRECT ANSWERS

1. (a)	2. (d)	3. (d)	4. (b)	5. (b)	6. (a)	7. (a)	8. (b)	9. (c)	10. (b)
11. (b)	12. (a)	13. (c)	14. (a)	15. (c)	16. (b)	17. (d)	18. (c)	19. (b)	20. (b)
21. (c)	22. (b)	23. (c)	24. (c)	25. (c)	26. (b)	27. (b)	28. (a)	29. (a)	30. (b)
31. (b)	32. (d)	33. (b)	34. (c)	35. (d)	36. (d)	37. (d)	38. (b)	39. (c)	40. (d)
41. (a)	42. (b)	43. (a)	44. (d)	45. (b)	46. (c)	47. (c)	48. (d)		

CHAPTER 14

Climate of Haryana

- The long-term weather conditions of an area are called **climate.**
- In other words, climate is the average weather condition for a particular location over a long period of time.
- The climate of any state is determined by the distance from the sea, the latitudinal position, the North-Western disturbance and the South -West monsoon.
- India has a tropical monsoon type of climate. Therefore, the climate of Haryana also falls under the **monsoonal climate.**
- The state of Haryana has a **sub-tropical dry** continental climate due to its location far from the sea.
- The Northern region of Haryana, bordering Himachal Pradesh, has **sub-humid** climate and the Southern region bordering Rajasthan has **dry climate.**
- The climate of Haryana can also be called as the climate between the semi-arid climate of the Eastern part of Rajasthan and the humid climate of the Ganga plains.
- Due to the diversity in the climate of Haryana, there is a considerable difference in temperature and rainfall across regions.

Classification of Climate in Haryana

According to the climatic classification of **Koppen,** Haryana has mainly two types of climate. The description of these climates is as follows

Classification of Haryana Climate

↓

Humid Sub-tropical Climate (Caw)

- The extension of this type of climate is found in a 72 km wide strip spread in the South of the Shivalik range. Thus, the climate of Shivalik has an impact on the climate of the state.
- The average winter temperature in this region is found to be less than 18° C and the January temperature reaches 3°-4°C.
- The temperature of the Northern part of Shivalik range reaches freezing point at night.

↓

Hot Steppe Climate (Bsh)

- This type of climate is found in most parts of Haryana.
- This climatic region receives rainfall from the South-West monsoon coming from the Bay of Bengal.
- This climatic region does not receive excess rainfall, due to which high temperature and evaporation prevail in summers.

Climatic Features of Haryana

- Haryana's climate is influenced by its location, i.e. lies North of the **Tropic of Cancer** due to which the centre of low pressure is made by the effect of high temperature.
- In India after **21st March**, the Sun shifts northward and after **21st September**, the temperature starts falling due to southward shift of the Sun.
- North-West disturbance and South-West monsoon have a direct effect on the continental condition of the state.

- From July, when the isobars of **998 millibars** pass through the Western part of Haryana, the direction of the winds turns from West and South-West to North-East.
- In January, when the isobar line of **1018 millibars** crosses the Eastern part of the state, then the direction of winds is towards North and North-West.
- Diversified dry, semi-arid, sub-humid tropical climate is found from South to **North in the state.**

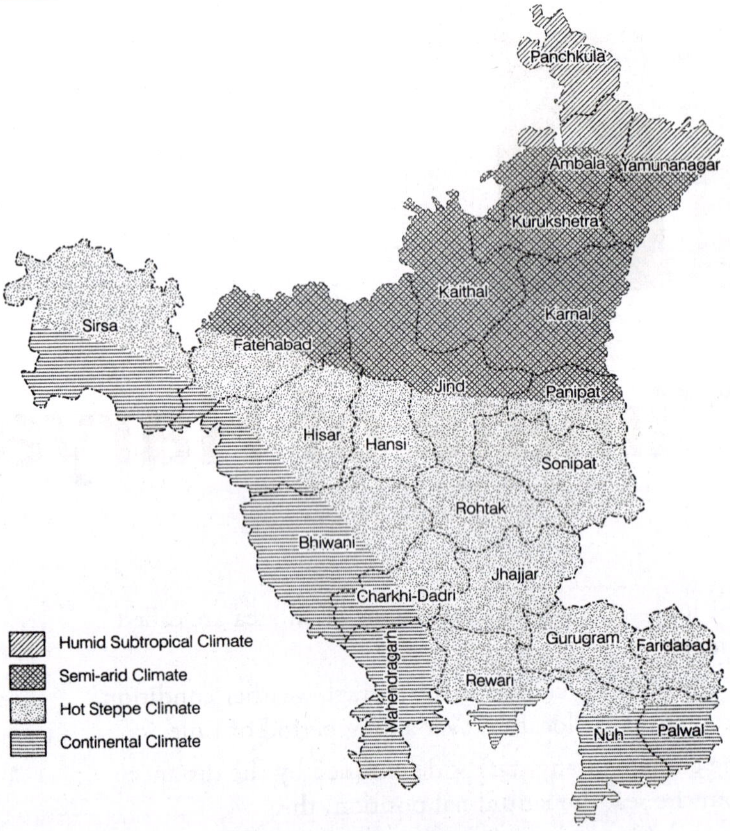

▲ Climatic Zones of Haryana

Temperature in Haryana

- Haryana's temperature undergoes significant changes throughout the year.
- **Temperature Rise** (March-June) Sharp increase in temperature, with averages varying across regions.
- Northern parts experience higher temperatures, while South-Eastern areas remain relatively cooler.
- **Summer Extremes** (May-June) Daily temperatures can soar up to 49°C-50°C in desert-affected areas.
- **Monsoon Impact** (June) Arrival of monsoon leads to a sudden drop in temperature. July temperatures are relatively lower.
- **Second Summer Season** (September-October) Clear skies bring a slight increase in temperature.
- **Winter Chill** (October-January) Temperature continues to fall, with significant variations between winter and summer temperatures in Northern parts.
- **Southern-Western part** of the state experiences a relatively low annual temperature range, resulting in higher temperatures throughout the year.
- The **Northern Shivalik** region can drop below 0°C in January.

Major Seasons of Haryana

In each season, there is a difference in temperature, pressure, direction of winds, amount of rainfall and its duration. The following are the three major seasons of the state of Haryana

Summer Season

- Duration — April to June
- Average temperature — in 35°C (avg) and goes up to 49°C
- Highest temperature is recorded in May-June.
- Season is generally dry, i.e humidity is very low.
- Due to high temperatures in this season, dust storms or loo blows in the state, which is hot, dry and strong wind.
- This storm blows in the South and South-West of the state.

> **Loo** normally blows in North India during summers. Loo or storm absorbs the moisture of the crops, causing damage to crops.

- This storm also affects human health as it causes dehydration and fever.
- **Hisar** is the **hottest district** (46°C) of the state.

Winter Season

- Duration Mid-September to March
- Average temperature 12-14° C
- Lowest temperature recorded in December-January (3-4° C).
- A dry winter season is found in the South-Western part of the state.
- **Mahendragarh district** lies in this part. During this season Ambala records about 12.8° C and Hisar records about 13.6° C temperature in the state.
- **Narnaul** and **Hisar** are the **coldest places** in Haryana.

Rainy Season

- Duration July to mid-September
- Average rainfall 40-60 cm (400-600 mm)
- Rainfall in the state is irregular, erratic and uneven.
- Haryana comes under the states with low rainfall.
- Substantial difference in temperature is observed in the months of July and August.

> The foothills of Shivalik in Haryana receive more rainfall than other regions of the state. For example, districts in the South-Western part along the border of Rajasthan receive less than 30 cm of rainfall, while the Shivalik region receives 110 cm of rainfall.

- Rainfall in Haryana occurs mainly in **two seasons.** The first is during the Indian monsoon period in the months of June to September and the second in the winter season from December to February.
- 80% of the rainfall in the state occurs from the South-West monsoon coming from the **Bay of Bengal** in the months of July to September.
- 10-15% rainfall in the state occurs in the rainy months of January-March (winter) due to the Western Disturbance coming from the **Persian Gulf.** It is called **Maavath** in the local language.
- Winter rains are significant for rabi crops. The North-Eastern part of the state receives the **highest** rainfall.
- The South-Western part of the state receives the **least** rainfall (about 25-28 cm).

District with Highest and Lowest Rainfall

Highest Average Rainfall
The districts with highest average rainfall in the state are – Ambala, Yamunanagar, Kurukshetra, Kaithal, Karnal, Jind and Sonipat.

Lowest Average Rainfall
The districts of the state with lowest annual rainfall are – Sirsa, Hisar, Bhiwani, Rewari, Rohtak, Faridabad, Gurugram and Mahendragarh.

- **Chhachhrauli** town of Yamunanagar is called **Cherrapunji of Haryana** due to excessive rainfall.
- **Ambala** in the state receives the **highest rainfall.**
- **Sirsa** district of the state receives the **least rainfall.**

Distribution of Rainfall in Haryana

- Haryana is divided into Eastern and Western divisions.

Eastern Division

- Districts falling under this division are – Panchkula, Ambala, Yamunanagar, Kurukshetra, Karnal, Kaithal, Panipat, Sonipat, Faridabad, Mewat, Palwal and parts of Jind, Rohtak, Jhajjar and Gurugram.
- It covers 49% of Haryana's total land area.
- Its average rainfall is between 500-1100 mm. 75-80% rainfall occurs between July-September.
- It receives 10% rainfall in summer and 10-15% in winter. Normal temperature is around 20° C for 8-10 months, with May-June being warm (above 40° C) and December-January being cold.

Western Division

- Districts falling under this division are – Sirsa, Hisar, Fatehabad, Bhiwani, Mahendragarh, Rewari and parts of Jind, Jhajjar, Rohtak and Gurugram.
- 80-85% rainfall occurs from South-West monsoon. Normal rainfall is less than 400 mm in South-Western part. October to mid-April months are usually dry.
- **Mahendragarh** is the **driest region** in Haryana.

Variability of Rainfall in Haryana

- The amount of rainfall exceeding or less than the average is known as variability of rainfall.
- Low variability ensures sufficient water for crops, while high variability makes irrigation necessary for agriculture activities.
- Variability of rainfall in Haryana increases from North-West to South-East, affecting the Southern region with drought.
- State receives frequent floods due to 80% rainfall in July to September. Thus, both flood and draught conditions are found due to hight variability.

Geographical Variations in Rainfall

Shivalik Foothills The Shivalik foothills in Haryana receive relatively higher rainfall, with some areas receiving up to 110 cm of rainfall. This is due to the orographic lift of moisture-laden winds, resulting in enhanced precipitation.

South-Western Part In contrast, the South-Western part of Haryana receives significantly lower rainfall, with some areas receiving less than 30 cm. This region's rainfall is influenced by the arid conditions of the neighbouring Rajasthan state.

CHECK CHAPTER KNOWLEDGE

1 Haryana has sub-tropical dry continental climate due to *HSSC 2023*
(a) being a land-lock state
(b) distance from the Himalayan mountains
(c) distance from the sea
(d) lack of rivers

2 The climate of Haryana is *HSSC CET 2022*
(a) sub-humid temperate type
(b) sub-humid sub-tropical type
(c) sub-tropical continental type
(d) continental type

3 Which type of climate is found in the Northern region of Haryana?
(a) Sub-humid climate
(b) Dry climate
(c) Humid-evergreen climate
(d) Temperate-humid climate

4 According to Koppen's classification, what type of climate is found in a 72 km wide strip South of the Shivalik range in Haryana?
(a) Hot Steppe Climate (Bsh)
(b) Humid Sub-tropical Climate (Caw)
(c) Tropical Monsoon Climate
(d) Continental Climate

5 According to Wladimir Koppen, Haryana has how many types of climate? *HSSC 2024*
(a) 1 (b) 2
(c) 3 (d) 4

6 What are the two main seasons that influence the climate of Haryana, according to the text?
(a) Summer and winter
(b) Monsoon and post-monsoon
(c) North-West disturbances once and South-West monsoon
(d) Pre-monsoon and monsoon

7 Which of the following is correct in association of Warm Steppe climate?
(a) High temperature in Summer
(b) High rate of evapouration
(c) Both (a) and (b)
(d) None of the above

8 In which part of Haryana, the average temperature is found high in the state?
(a) Northern part
(b) Southern part
(c) South-Western part
(d) Eastern part

9 Which months record higher temperature in Haryana?
(a) March-April (b) May-June
(c) June-July (d) July-August

10 Which month is known as the 'Second Season of Summer' in Haryana?
(a) July-August (b) August-September
(c) October-November (d) September-October

11 What is the average winter temperature in the Humid Sub-tropical Climate region of Haryana?
(a) Less than 10°C (b) Less than 18°C
(c) More than 20°C (d) More than 25°C

12 Which month is the coldest in Haryana when the temperature goes below the freezing point? *HSSC 2016, Haryana Patwari Exam 2015*
(a) January (b) December
(c) November (d) February

13 When is the Summer season in Haryana? *HSSC 2019*
(a) April to June (b) January to March
(c) March to May (d) July to September

14 What is the main factor that influences Haryana's climate due to its location?
(a) Proximity to the equator
(b) Presence of the Himalayas
(c) Location North of the Tropic of Cancer
(d) Coastal influence

15 Which of the following months is the hottest in Haryana? *Haryana Field Cadre 2020*
(a) July (b) May (c) March (d) April

16 Which of the following is the hottest district in Haryana state?
(a) Sirsa (b) Hisar (c) Sonipat (d) Jind

17 During summer season, 'Loo' blows in which region of Haryana?
(a) Eastern part
(b) Northern part
(c) South and South-Western part
(d) Central part

18 Which district in Haryana is described as the driest region in the state?
(a) Mahendragarh (b) Sirsa
(c) Hisar (d) Bhiwani

19 During winter season, what is the average temperature in Haryana? *Haryana Police 2016*
(a) 5°C (b) 10°C
(c) 12°C (d) 20°C

20 In Haryana, which season is experienced from July to mid-September?
(a) Rainy season (b) Winter season
(c) Summer season (d) None of these

21 What is the average rainfall in the state of Haryana? *Haryana Accountant 2018, PGT 2016*
(a) 30-40 cm (b) 40-50 cm
(c) 40-60 cm (d) 80-100 cm

22 What is the reason behind the falling of temperature during rainy season in Haryana?
(a) Difference in rainfall
(b) Difference in humidity
(c) Lack of sunshine
(d) All of the above

23 The Shivalik region of Haryana receives how much rainfall during rainy season?
(a) 90 cm (b) 100 cm
(c) 110 cm (d) 150 cm

24 Around 80% rainfall in Haryana is due to
(a) South-West monsoon
(b) Eastern winds
(c) Western disturbances
(d) Cold waves

25 What is the duration of the Western Disturbance season in Haryana?
(a) December-February (b) January-March
(c) February-April (d) March-May

26 Which part of Haryana receives the least rainfall?
(a) North-Eastern Part (b) South-Western Part
(c) Shivalik Foothills (d) Eastern Part

27 Which part of Haryana receives highest rainfall? *HSSC CET 2022, Haryana Anganwadi 2017*
(a) South-Western (b) North-Western
(c) North-Eastern (d) Southern

28 Which area of Haryana is known as 'Cherrapunji of Haryana'? *HSSC CET 2023*
(a) Chhachhrauli (b) Kosli
(c) Rewari (d) Thanesar

29 Which of the following districts receives highest average rainfall in Haryana? *HSSC 2019, Anganwadi 2017*
(a) Sirsa (b) Mewat
(c) Hisar (d) Ambala

30 Which part of Haryana receives least rainfall? *HSSC 2017, 16*
(a) North-Western (b) North-Eastern
(c) South-Eastern (d) South-Western

31 Which district of Haryana receives least rainfall? *HSSC 2018*
(a) Sonipat (b) Ambala
(c) Sirsa (d) Rohtak

32 Which of the following is not a part of Eastern Division of Haryana?
(a) Sirsa (b) Kaithal
(c) Karnal (d) Sonipat

33 What is the main characteristic of the climate in the North-Eastern part of Haryana?
(a) Dry and semi-arid (b) Sub-humid tropical
(c) Continental climate (d) Oceanic influence

34 How much rainfall occurs in the Eastern division of Haryana during the summer season?
(a) 5-10% (b) 10-15%
(c) 15-20% (d) 20-25%

35 What is the name of the wind pattern shift that occurs in July in Haryana?
(a) North-East monsoon
(b) South-West monsoon
(c) North-West disturbance
(d) Shift from West/South-West to North-East

36 The driest region of Haryana is *HSSC 2017*
(a) Rewari (b) Mahendragarh
(c) Bhiwani (d) Rohtak

37 **Assertion (A)** Ambala receives the highest rainfall in Haryana.
Reason (R) It is surrounded by Shivalik hills. *HSSC 2018*

Codes
(a) Both A and R are true and R is the correct explanation of A.
(b) Both A and R are true, but R is not the correct explanation of A.
(c) A is true, but R is false.
(d) A is false, but R is true.

CORRECT ANSWERS

1. (c)	**2.** (c)	**3.** (a)	**4.** (b)	**5.** (b)	**6.** (c)	**7.** (c)	**8.** (a)	**9.** (b)	**10.** (d)
11. (b)	**12.** (a)	**13.** (a)	**14.** (c)	**15.** (b)	**16.** (b)	**17.** (c)	**18.** (a)	**19.** (c)	**20.** (a)
21. (c)	**22.** (d)	**23.** (c)	**24.** (a)	**25.** (a)	**26.** (b)	**27.** (c)	**28.** (a)	**29.** (d)	**30.** (d)
31. (c)	**32.** (a)	**33.** (b)	**34.** (b)	**35.** (d)	**36.** (b)	**37.** (a)			

CHAPTER 15

Soil Resources in Haryana

- Haryana is an agricultural state. The soil resources play an important role in determining the form of its vegetation and agriculture.
- The soils found in the state determine its agricultural land use, regional distribution of crops, quantity of production, variation of vegetation, etc.
- In the state, the expansion of hilly area is less and the plain area is more, which affects the distribution of soil. Hence, uneven distribution of soil is found in the state.

Regional Distribution of Soil in Haryana

- Haryana is mostly a plain area. Most of the soil in the plains of Haryana is formed from sediments brought by rivers, which are called **alluvium**. This soil is more fertile.
- Sand and sandy soils are present in the South-Western part of Haryana which are brought here by winds blowing from Rajasthan.
- Bet soil is also present in Haryana along the flood plains of **Markanda** river.

Classification of Soils

The soils can be classified on the basis of topography as well as physical and chemical properties.

Soils on the Basis of Topography

Soils of Mountainous Area

- The soil of mountainous area is hard, thin and rocky. Colour of this soil is dark brown.
- This type of soil can be seen on the **Morni Hills** in Haryana.

Soils of Plain Area

- Most of the soil in the plain area comes under **Khadar area,** due to which the soil is more fertile.
- Colour of this soil is pale brown.
- The soil of the plains in the state is spread through the rivers Yamuna and Saraswati.
- The plains in the state are made up of sand, mud, silt and hard calcarea gravels. Hence, the soil of this region is locally known as **Kankers.**

Sandy Soil

- The sandy soil is mostly spread in the **South-Western** part of Haryana. Colour of this soil is light brown.
- The spread of sandy soil in the state is due to the strong winds blowing from the neighbouring state of **Rajasthan.** The soil is not very fertile.

On the Basis of Physical and Chemical Properties

- A renowned agricultural scientist of Haryana, **Dr. Jasbir Singh** has said that the soils of Haryana can be divided into six major parts on the basis of the zinc, chemical and fertiliser properties of the soil.

These parts are as follows

1. Light Soil

- Light soil mainly consists of sandy-loam and loam soils. According to Dr. Jasbir Singh, this soil is characterised by the presence of silt, sand and clay.
- The ratio of silt, clay and sand is almost equal in this soil.
- It can be divided into the following two categories

Types of Light Soil

↓

Sandy-Loam Soil

- This soil is soft and has low water holding capacity.
- Adequate irrigation system is required to get more productivity in this soil.
- Found in some villages of Sirsa tehsil and in Dabwali tehsil.
- The ratio of silt, clay and sand is almost equal in this soil.

↓

Relatively Sandy-Loam Soil

- It is a mixture of loam soil and sandy-loam soil.
- This soil is also called Rosali in local language.
- Found in the districts of Hisar, Bhiwani, Rewari, Gurugram and Jhajjar (some part) of Haryana.
- This soil has more water holding capacity, this. This soil can be made more fertile by drip irrigation and sprinkler irrigation. It has more sand than silt and clay to which it is considered as useful for agriculture.

2. Extremely Light Soil

- It is **sandy and loam-dominated soil.**
- The quantity of lime is high in this soil.
- This soil is found in the arid region of the state, because the soil lacks vegetative elements and the soil particles are unorganised.
- The extension of this soil is found from the Southern part of Sirsa to Fatehabad, Bhiwani, Mahendragarh and Hisar.
- Wind erosion is more in this soil due to its lightness. The area of this soil is dominated by **sand dunes**.
- This soil has less ability to absorb water.

3. Heavy and Very Heavy Soils

- This soil is found on the banks of rain-fed rivers of the state.
- This soil has a predominance of **clayey silt.**
- This soil becomes sticky in the rainy season and hardens in the dry season.
- In the Ghaggar area of Thanesar and Fatehabad, hard clay is found which is known as **Solar** and **Ferruginous** clay is found in Jagadhri which is known as **Dakar.**
- In this soil, rice, wheat, gram and barley can be grown.

4. Medium Soil

This soil is more fertile than other soils. This soil consists of three type of sub-soils, which are as follows

Type	Feature
Thick Loam	• The particles of this soil are thick. • This soil is found in the Nuh tehsil of the state and in the lower areas of Western Firozpur Jhirka.
Light Loam	• This soil is mainly found in South-Western Ambala and Southern part of Narayangarh tehsil of the state. • Along with this, it is also found in the Northern part of Mewat, North-Western part of Nuh and in the areas of central Rewari.
Loam Soil	• It is found in a very large part of Yamuna-Ghaggar plain in the state. This soil is highly fertile. When there is sufficient rainfall, this soil produce good harvest. • Red chestnut soil is a type of loam soil which is found in Yamunanagar district of Haryana. • Wheat, rice, cotton, sugarcane, etc. are produced more in this soil. This soil is found in central parts of the state, mainly Jind, Kaithal, Sonipat, Panipat, Gurugram, Kurukshetra, etc.

5. Shivalik, Piedmont and Foothills Soils

The occurrence of these soils in the state is the expansion of the **Shivalik** in the North-Eastern part and the **Aravalli hills** in the South. These soils are mainly found in the districts of Panchkula, Ambala, Yamunanagar, etc.

The description of these soils are as follows

Shivalik Soil	→	*Foothills Soil*
• It contains sandstone, sand, clay, gravel and other elements. • This soil is found in the Kalka of Panchkula and Narayangarh tehsil of Ambala.	→	• Rocky and sandy soils are found in the region of Aravalli range in the Southern part of Haryana. • This soil is less fertile and shallow. • This soil is limited to areas like Bhiwani, Dadri, Gurugram, Faridabad, Palwal,

↓

Piedmont Soil

- This soil is found in the piedmont region of Shivalik. This soil is of low quality due to the predominance of sand and gravel elements.
- This soil is found in the Kalka of Panchkula, Narayangarh tehsil of Ambala and Jagadhri tehsil of Yamunanagar.
- In Kalka and Narayangarh tehsils, piedmont soil is called Dhar and in Jagadhri tehsil, it is called Kandhi.
- This soil is eroded on a wide scale through rain-fed drains and streams.

6. Generally Heavy Soil

- This soil with silt is also called **Khadar soil**. This soil has low water holding capacity, thus it hardens when the soil dries.
- This soil is mainly found in Yamunanagar, Kurukshetra, Karnal, Panipat, Sonipat and Faridabad.
- This soil is also called **New Khadar** as it receives flood water every year.

Khadar Soil (New Alluvium)

- Renewed annually by flood deposits, in the plains of Yamuna making it highly fertile.
- Rich in lime, potash, magnesium and other nutrients.
- Locally known as **balua-silt, balua-matiyar domat, matiyar domat,** etc.
- No chemical fertilisers required; ideal for jute and rice cultivation.
- Nali soil is a sub-type of Khadar soil, mainly prevalent in the floodplains of Ghaggar river.

Bangar Soil (Old Alluvium)

- Found in Doab regions between two rivers.
- Lacks nitrogen and phosphorus.
- Locally known as **uphar, domat, matiyar domat, matiyar-balui-domat**, etc.
- Suitable for rabi crops; this soil is found in Hisar, Bhiwani and Sirsa districts of Haryana.

Soil Degradation in Haryana

- Soil degradation means decrease in the fertility of the soil. Decrease in the fertility of the soil is caused by the increase in alkaline and saline elements and decrease in organic elements (humus).
- **Soil erosion** is the **main problem** in the state. It destroys the top fertile layer of soil.
- Soil erosion is also called **Nirdayi Shatru** or **Rengati Mrityu** of agriculture.
- Soil erosion in the state is mainly occurred through water and wind.

> Soil erosion by water in the state occurs mainly in the **piedmont** part of Shivalik in the North-Eastern mountainous region, as the annual average rainfall of this region is more than 100 cm. Here, the intensity of seasonal rainfall is more than 2.5 cm per day.

- Soil erosion by water occurs mainly in **Panchkula, Ambala** and **Yamunanagar** districts.
- Soil erosion by wind occurs in the state mainly in the Southern and South-Western districts located near Rajasthan. It mainly occurs in **Hisar, Sirsa, Bhiwani, Mahendragarh, Rewari** and **Gurugram.**

Soil Salinity and Alkalinity in Haryana

- The main reason for the problem of salinity and alkalinity is **over-irrigation.** Due to irrigation by taking more and more water from the canals, the underground water level in this area starts rising.
- This leads to a situation of **waterlogging.** In such a condition, soluble salts start accumulating in the soil.
- Due to insufficient leaching and less rainfall, the process of accumulation of salts and alkalis in the soil continues.
- In the rainy season, the salts of the soil dissolve in water and get leached towards the underground water.
- In hot and dry weather, the moisture of the soil evaporates on a large scale and as a result, the salty solution starts coming from bottom to top on the surface through capillary action.
- On the surface, the water evapourates, but the salt remains on the soil in the form of white crystals.
- The **problem of alkalinity** is more common in clay soil. Both salt and alkali are present in the loam soil.
- The presence of salts and alkalis on the top surface of the soil destroys the fertility of soil.
- The local names of saline and alkaline soils are **Reh** and **Kellar.** These soils are found in the area of few rainfall and poor drainage.

Affected Districts of Haryana

Reason	Affected Districts
Salinity and Alkalinity	Southern part of Ambala, Kurukshetra, Kaithal, South-East Karnal, Jind, Panipat, Sonipat, Jhajjar, Rohtak, Gurugram and Faridabad
Salinity	Eastern Hisar, North-Eastern Bhiwani and Rohtak
Potential Saline Soils	Northern Jind, Hisar, East Bhiwani, Jhajjar, Gurugram, Rewari and Mahendragarh
Thur and Kallar	Hisar, Fatehabad, Jind, Kaithal, Kurukshetra, Panipat and Sonipat

Other Soil Problems in Haryana

↓

Lack of Moisture in the Soil

Haryana has semi-arid climate, hence the soil lacks moisture for a long period of hot weather. Due to this, soil evaporation is high. Evaporation of water by trees and plants is called evapotranspiration. Excessive amount of evaporation creates a condition of drought in the soil.

↓

Depletion of Soil Fertility

Due to the cultivation in fertile plains of Haryana since the ancient time, the natural fertility of the soil is decreasing in the state. Another reason for the decrease in soil fertility in the state is the adoption of faulty method of agriculture.

Measures of Soil Conservation in Haryana

- The efforts are being made at both government and private levels to prevent soil erosion and conserve them in the state.
- The measures being taken for soil management in the state can be divided into two categories, which are as follows
  - Measures to prevent soil erosion
  - Measures to maintain soil fertility

Measures to Prevent Soil Erosion

Tree Plantation Tree plantation is the most appropriate measure for soil conservation.

- There is a lack of forests in the Southern and South-Western regions of the state. Therefore, the problem of soil erosion arises due to rainwater.
- If trees are planted in this area, the roots of the trees can hold the soil and can prevent soil erossion.
- It is also necessary to stop unplanned cutting of trees in this area.

Control over Animal Grazing Along with agriculture, animal husbandry is also an important economic activity in the state. Animal grazing is necessary, but special pastures should be developed for this purpose.

- Herding in empty fields should be controlled, because the animals roaming freely loosen the soil with their hooves, which gets eroded over time.

Linear Plantation In the dry areas of Hisar, Bhiwani, Sirsa and Mahendragarh districts, the plants should be planted in linear pattern for conservation of fields. This can also prevent soil erosion.

Construction of Dams The 4 dams should be constructed in the areas of the state where there is flood. It will control the flow of water and also soil erosion.

Measures to Maintain Soil Fertility

Controlling Excessive Water Flow

- Improving drainage infrastructure and implementing water management techniques to regulate irrigation.
- Terracing or contour plowing on sloped land to slow down water runoff.

Drought Management

- Planting crops that are naturally adapted to survive in dry conditions.
- This is crucial in regions like Southern and South-Western Haryana, where rainfall is scarce.

Soil Fertility Enhancement

- Planting manure crops that are later plowed into the soil to improve its fertility like Red Clover, Clover Fodder, Sweet Clover and Alfalfa.
- It also increases water-holding capacity and provides nutrients to subsequent crops.

Crop Rotation with Leguminous Crops

- Crop rotation should be implemented which involves alternating different crops in a planned sequence.
- Leguminous crops like peas, beans and pulses have a unique ability to fix nitrogen from the atmosphere into the soil and also increases water holding capacity.

Soil Salinity and Alkalinity Control

- Barley, compass and maize should be grown because these crops can withstand higher salt levels, allowing for agricultural production in affected areas.
- Adding gypsum to the soil also reduces salinity.

CHECK CHAPTER KNOWLEDGE

1 What is the reason for the soil fertility of the plain areas of Haryana?
(a) Due to abundance of nutritions in the land.
(b) Due to sediments brought down by rivers.
(c) Due to application of organic fertilisers.
(d) Due to mixed farming.

2 The soil of mountainous area of Haryana is *Haryana Police Sub-Inspector 2018*
(a) black (b) yellow
(c) clay (d) rocky

3 Which region of Haryana has abundance of mountainous soil?
(a) Aravalli hills (b) Morni hills
(c) Shivalik hills (d) South-Western hills

4 Most of the soils of the plain area come under which area of Haryana?
(a) Khadar (b) Bangar
(c) Doab (d) All of these

5 Which of the following rivers does not deposit sediment in the plain areas of Haryana?
(a) Yamuna (b) Ghaggar
(c) Saraswati (d) None of these

6 The plains in the state are made up of sand, mud, silt and hard calcarea gravel. Hence, the soil of this region is locally known by which name? *HSSC 2019*
(a) Kankers (b) Saras
(c) Bunkars (d) Karnals

7 .... is the main feature of sandy soil. *HSSC 2023*
(a) Brown soil
(b) Red soil
(c) Light brown colour
(d) None of the above

8 The soil found in the South-Western part of Haryana is
(a) Alluvial soil (b) Sandy soil
(c) Piedmont soil (d) All of these

9 What is the reason of the spreading of sandy soil in Haryana? *HSSC 2023*
(a) Flow of rivers
(b) Strong winds blowing from the neighbouring state of Rajasthan
(c) Weathering of rocks
(d) All of the above

10 What is the characteristic feature of Light soils according to Dr. Jasbir Singh?
(a) Presence of high clay content
(b) Presence of silt, sand and clay
(c) Presence of high water holding capacity
(d) Presence of low nutrient content

11 Which type of soil has low water holding capacity and requires adequate irrigation system?
(a) Relatively Sandy-Loam soil
(b) Sandy-Loam soil
(c) Loam soil
(d) Clay soil

12 Which soil is known as Rosali in Haryana? *PGT 2016*
(a) Relatively sandy-loam soil
(b) Sandy-loam soil
(c) Light loam
(d) Loam soil

13 In which districts is relatively Sandy-Loam soil found?
(a) Sirsa, Dabwali and Fatehabad
(b) Hisar, Bhiwani, Rewari, Gurugram and Jhajjar
(c) Rohtak, Jind and Kaithal
(d) Ambala, Kurukshetra and Yamunanagar

14 Which of the following is the feature of extremely light soil? *HSSC 2024*
(a) Lack of sand and loam
(b) Lack of lime
(c) Lack of vegetative elements
(d) Lack of light matters

15 Which of the following statements is not correct about the extremely light soil of Haryana?
(a) This soil has less ability to absorb water.
(b) The extension of this soil is found in Mahendragarh and Hisar.
(c) The State Government is promoting dry land farming to increase productivity of this soil.
(d) None of the above

16 What is the main characteristic of the soil found in the Southern part of Sirsa to Fatehabad, Bhiwani, Mahendragarh and Hisar?
(a) High water holding capacity
(b) Low water holding capacity
(c) High clay content
(d) High sand content

17 Extremely light soil is found in which of the following districts? *HSSC 2016*

(a) Hisar (b) Bhiwani
(c) Sirsa (d) All of these

18 Which type of soil is prone to wind erosion due to its lightness?

(a) Loam soil (b) Extremely light soil
(c) Clay soil (d) Alluvial soil

19 Which soil type is most susceptible to the problem of alkalinity?

(a) Sandy soil (b) Loamy soil
(c) Clay soil (d) Alluvial soil

20 Which type of soil is found in a very large part of the Yamuna-Ghaggar plain in Haryana?

(a) Loam soil (b) Sandy Loam soil
(c) Clay soil (d) Alluvial soil

21 Which soil is mainly found on the banks of rain-fed rivers of Haryana?

(a) Khadar soil (b) Bangar soil
(c) Heavy and very heavy soil
(d) All of the above

22 Which soil is locally known as 'Dakar soil'? *HSSC 2017*

(a) Generally heavy soil
(b) Heavy and very heavy soil
(c) Shivalik soil
(d) Piedmont soil

23 What is the main crop that can be grown in the soil found in the Ghaggar area?

(a) Rice, wheat, gram and barley
(b) Cotton, sugarcane and tobacco
(c) Maize, jowar and bajra
(d) Pulses, oilseeds and spices

24 What is the main reason for the occurrence of Shivalik and Piedmont soils in Haryana?

(a) Expansion of the Shivalik in the North-Eastern part of Haryana.
(b) Expansion of Aravalli hills in the South of Haryana
(c) Both (a) and (b)
(d) None of the above

25 Shivalik soil contains which of the following elements in it?

(a) Clay (b) Gravel
(c) Sandstone (d) All of these

26 What is the main difference between Khadar soil and Bangar soil?

(a) Khadar soil is renewed annually, while Bangar soil is not
(b) Khadar soil lacks nitrogen and phosphorus, while Bangar soil is rich in these nutrients
(c) Khadar soil is found in Doab regions, while Bangar soil is found in floodplains
(d) Khadar soil is suitable for rabi crops, while Bangar soil is suitable for kharif crops

27 Which soil is also known as 'Khadar soil'?

(a) Generally heavy soil
(b) Thick and very heavy soil
(c) Foothill soil
(d) None of the above

28 Which of the following is not a characteristic of Khadar soil? *HSSC 2020*

(a) High fertility
(b) Renewal by annual flood deposits
(c) Presence of nitrogen and phosphorus
(d) Low organic matter content

29 Which element is found abundantly in Khadar soil?

(a) Lime (b) Potash
(c) Magnesium (d) All of these

30 Which crop is mainly cultivated in Khadar soil?

(a) Jute (b) Rice
(c) Both (a) and (b) (d) None of these

31 What is the primary reason for the suitability of Khadar soil for jute and rice cultivation?

(a) High organic matter content
(b) Presence of nitrogen and phosphorus
(c) Well-drained soil
(d) High fertility

32 In which of the following districts of Haryana, red chestnut soil is found? *Haryana Fire Station Officer 2018*

(a) Rohtak (b) Sirsa
(c) Yamunanagar (d) Bhiwani

33 Which of the following soil types is not found in Haryana? *HSSC 2020*

(a) Mountain soil
(b) Alluvial soil
(c) Red soil
(d) Black soil

34 .... is the main problem of soil erosion in Haryana. *Haryana Police Constable 2016*

(a) Drought (b) Wind erosion
(c) Earthquake (d) Flood

35 Which of the following facts is not true about soil erosion?

(a) Wind and water are mainly responsible for soil erosion.
(b) Soil becomes less fertile due to soil erosion.
(c) Soil erosion is also known as 'Rengati Mrityu'.
(d) None of the above

36 Which process contributes significantly to drought conditions due to excessive water loss from trees?
(a) Condensation (b) Precipitation
(c) Evapotranspiration (d) Infiltration

37 Wind erosion takes place in which district of Haryana?
(a) Sirsa (b) Hisar
(c) Rewari (d) All of these

38 Which of the following conditions is most likely to lead to the accumulation of salts and subsequent alkalinity in soil?
(a) Excessive wind erosion
(b) Prolonged waterlogging
(c) High organic matter content
(d) Frequent crop rotation

39 The accumulation of alkalis and salts on soil surface is found in Haryana due to which of the following?
(a) Less rainfall (b) Insufficient leaching
(c) Both (a) and (b) (d) None of these

40 Which soil is known as 'Kallar' and 'Reh'?
HSSC 2024
(a) Soil mainly affected by salts and bases.
(b) Soil deposited by wind and water.
(c) Soil which uses organic fertilisers.
(d) All of the above

41 Which of the following is responsible for the decrease in soil fertility?
(a) Construction of dams
(b) Adoption of faulty methods of agriculture
(c) Both (a) and (b)
(d) None of the above

42 Which of the following is/are an/the important measure(s) for soil conservation?
(a) Control on overgrazing
(b) Linear plantation
(c) Construction of dams
(d) All of the above

43 Match List I with List II and choose the correct option. *HCS Prelims 2023*

List I	List II
A. Bagar	1. Parts of Hisar, Bhiwani and Sirsa
B. Bet	2. Floodplains of Markanda
C. Nali	3. Floodplains of Ghaggar
D. Khadar	4. Floodplains of Yamuna
E. Bangar	5. Old Alluvial Soil

Codes

	A	B	C	D	E
(a)	1	2	3	5	4
(b)	2	1	3	4	5
(c)	1	2	3	4	5
(d)	2	4	5	1	3

44 Which soil lacks in nitrogen and phosphorous?
(a) Khadar (b) Bangar
(c) Medium soil (d) None of these

45 In Jagadhri tehsil, the piedmont soils of the Shivalik foothills are known as
(a) Khadar (b) Bangar
(c) Kandhi (d) Red Chestnut

CORRECT ANSWERS

1. (b)	2. (d)	3. (b)	4. (a)	5. (b)	6. (a)	7. (c)	8. (b)	9. (b)	10. (b)
11. (b)	12. (a)	13. (b)	14. (c)	15. (d)	16. (b)	17. (d)	18. (b)	19. (c)	20. (a)
21. (c)	22. (b)	23. (a)	24. (c)	25. (d)	26. (a)	27. (a)	28. (d)	29. (d)	30. (c)
31. (d)	32. (c)	33. (d)	34. (b)	35. (d)	36. (c)	37. (d)	38. (b)	39. (c)	40. (a)
41. (b)	42. (d)	43. (c)	44. (b)	45. (c)					

CHAPTER 16

Drainage System of Haryana

- Drainage generally means the flow of rivers. The rivers flow in various forms and these forms are called **drainage patterns.**
- The state of Haryana is a large plain area, which is situated as a water divide between the Ganges and the Indus river systems.
- The vast plains of Haryana state are drained by rivers like Yamuna, Ghaggar, Markanda, etc. Due to the abundance of plain area, no perennial river originates from the state.

Classification of Drainage System

Haryana's drainage system is classified into two parts based on geographical features

Drainage System
→ Northern Drainage System
→ Southern Drainage System

Northern Drainage System

- The rivers originate from the Shivalik ranges of the Himalayan mountains.
- The rivers are mostly perennial. Major rivers in this system are as follows

Yamuna River

• Ancient name	**Yami** or Kalindi
• Origin	Yamunotri Glacier, Banderpunch range, Garhwal Himalayas, Uttarakhand
• Altitude	6,316 m above mean sea level
• Forms	320 km (long) boundary between Uttar Pradesh and Haryana
• Entry into Haryana	**Kalesar** in **North of Tajewala, Yamunanagar** district
• Flows through	Yamunanagar, Karnal, Panipat, Sonipat, Delhi, Faridabad, then enters Aligarh district, Uttar Pradesh

- Tributaries in plains include Tons, Giri, Asan.
- Tributaries in state include Somb, Pathrala, Buddhi Ganga.
- It is the largest tributary of the Ganga; perennial river.

> **Hathnikund barrage** was constructed at Tajewala, Yamunanagar where the East Yamuna canal and Western Yamuna Canal originate.

- Western Yamuna Canal supplies water to several Haryana districts i.e Yamunanagar, Kurukshetra, Karnal, Panipat, Sirsa, Jind, Sonipat, Rohtak.
- Somb and Pathrala originate from Shivalik hill on border of Haryana and Himachal Pradesh and meet Yamuna at Mehramajra.

Saraswati River

- Ancient river — Cradle of Vedic Civilisation
- Rigveda description — Mentioned as a strong river
- Historical significance — Sage **Ved Vyasa** composed **Mahabharata** on its banks
- Origin — Shivalik Hills, on border of Sirmaur district, Himachal Pradesh
- Entry into Haryana — **Adi Badri, Yamunanagar** district
- Joins — Ghaggar river in Sangrur district, Punjab
- Flows through — Kurukshetra, Ambala, Kaithal, Sirsa, etc.
- Tributary confluences — Chautang river joins near Bhaini and Markanda river joins at Pehowa, forming modern Saraswati
- Extinction — Near Sirsa at **Bhatner**
- Major tributaries — **Tangri, Markanda** and **Chautang**

Ghaggar River

- Type — Large rain-fed river in the Sutlej-Yamuna plains
- Origin — Dagshai, Solan district, Himachal Pradesh (1,927 m above sea level)
- Length — 291 km (in Haryana)
- Entry into Haryana — Near **Kalka, Panchkula** district
- Flows through — Panchkula, Ambala, Kaithal, Fatehabad, and Sirsa districts
- Disappearance — In Rajasthan's Hanumangarh desert region
- Major tributaries — **Markanda Chautang, Jhajra** and **Kaushalya** rivers
- Local features — Small drains joining the river are called **Chau** locally. The river forms a floodplain known as **Naili**.
- Ottu barrage (Sirsa district) — Diverts water into two canals for irrigating Rajasthan and Houses **Chaudhary Devi Lal Ottu Weir**, a large reservoir and tourist spot
- Downstream name — After Ottu Weir, the river is known as **Hakra river**

Two Streams Originated from Ghaggar River

- **Zoya** — Originates at Phulad in Punjab, flows through Fatehabad and Bhatinda, rejoins Ghaggar in Sirsa district
- **Sukar** — Originates from the Ghaggar river to the South

Tangri River

- Origin — Shivalik Range, possibly near Dagshai in Solan district, Himachal Pradesh or **Morni Hills** in **Panchkula** district
- Significance — Main tributary of the Markanda river
- Type — Rain-fed river in Haryana
- Flows parallel to — Umrah drain in Ambala
- Confluence — Joins Markanda river near Mulana
- Path — Passes through Southern Ambala and enters Patiala district, Punjab, at Nihasari, flowing South-West
- Tributaries — Balaiali and Aamri

Balaiali River

It originates from Morni Hills and joins Tangri near Chhajju Majra village, Ambala.

Aamri River

It originates near **Radaur, Yamunanagar** and joins Tangri, also known as Dadari or **Shahzadpur Wali river.**

Apaga River

It is considered a sacred river in Vedic texts. It is currently a rain-fed stream. It is known as **Nichli Khand** (lower division) in Haryana.

Markanda River

- Mythological name — Aruna
- Named after — **Maharishi Markandeya**
- Type — Rain-fed river in Haryana
- Origin — Lower Shivalik Hills, Himachal Pradesh
- Entry into Haryana — **Kalaamb, Ambala** district
- Flows through — Kurukshetra, Ambala and Kaithal districts
- Confluence — Joins Saraswati river at Sanisa Lake (near Pehowa)
- Disappearance — Vanishes in the Rajasthan desert

- Flooding — Causes floods in Ambala and Kurukshetra districts during the rainy season
- Major tributaries — **Tangri, Nakti, Ran** and **Begna**

Chautang River

- Also known as — Chitang, Chautang and **Drishadvati** (mentioned in Rigveda)
- Origin — **Shivalik Hills** (lower region)
- Flow — Parallel to Saraswati river
- Tributary — **Rakshi**
- Significance — Previously a tributary of the Ghaggar river
- Flows through — Yamunanagar, Kurukshetra, Karnal, Kaithal, Jind and Hisar districts
- It joins Ghaggar river near Bhatner, Rajasthan. Siswal village (Hisar) is situated on its bank.

Rakshi River

- Origin — **Shahpur** village near Bilaspur, Yamunanagar district
- Also known as — **Raka** river
- Type — Rain-fed river
- Flow — South-West direction
- Confluence — Joins Chautang river at Ladwa, Kurukshetra

> Siniwali, Brihad Diu, Kaushiki, Ambumat are the **other rivers in Northern Haryana**.

Southern Drainage System

The rivers in this system originates from Aravalli range in the Southern Haryana. Major rivers in this system are

Sahibi River

- Also known as — **Sabi** river
- Type — Rain-fed river
- In Delhi — Known as **Najafgarh drain**
- Origin — **Mewat hills**, Aravalli Range, Rajasthan
- Entry into Haryana — From Rewari near Kot-Kasim
- Flows through — Rewari, Jhajjar and Gurugram districts
- Major tributaries — Sota and Indori

  Sota river meets Sahibi in Jaipur, Rajasthan.

  Indori river is the **largest tributary** and a major river of Southern Haryana.
- Infrastructure — Masani Barrage built near Dharuhera, Rewari district
- After leaving Jhajjar district, Sahibi river enters Gurugram district near Khedi Sultan. After covering some distance (about 13 km) in Gurugram, it again enters Jhajjar district near Kutani village and finally joins Yamuna river through Najafgarh drain in Delhi.
- Most of the rivers originating from Aravalli flow towards the South, but Sahibi river, as an exception, flows to the North of Jaipur and Alwar.

Indori River

- Origin — **Mewat hills** near Nuh district (earlier Mewat district)
- Ancient name — **Anshumati**
- Named after — Indori Fort
- Type — Rain-fed river
- Runoff area — 198 km
- Length in Haryana — 50 km
- It is divided into two branches.
- One branch joins Sahibi river near Pataudi, Gurugram district after taking water from some fain-fed drains.
- Other branch joins Sahibi river on Southern border of Rewari district.

Kasaunti or Krishnawati River

- Origin — Mewat Hills, 1.6 km from Neem Ka Thana, North of Jaipur, Rajasthan
- Initial flow — Moves in a North-East direction
- Entry into Haryana — Enters **Jhajjar** district near Kosli village, flowing West
- This river is divided into two branches near the Surehti village. Its one branch disappears near the Southern part of Jhajjar district and the other branch turns towards Chhuchhakwas village (Jhajjar district) and drains into Behror drain.

Dohan River

- Origin — Neem Ka Thana area, in the district of Sikar, Rajasthan
- Entry into Haryana — Mahendragarh district
- Disappearance — Vanishes at Basai
- Total Length in Haryana — 50 km

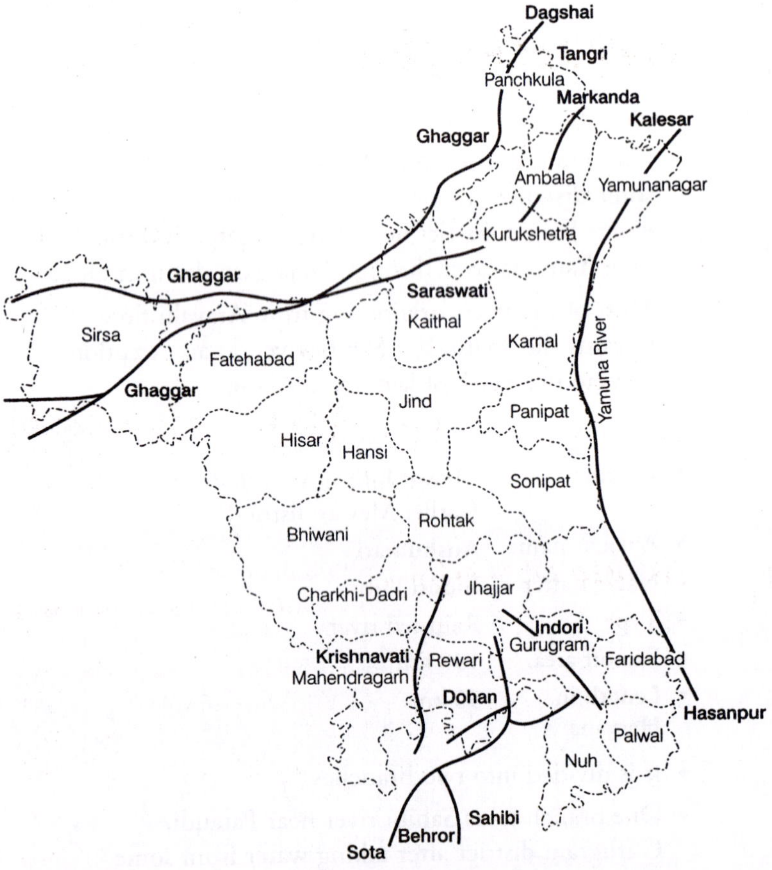

▲ Rivers of Haryana

Major Lakes of Haryana

- The Shivalik range is located in the North-Eastern part and the Aravalli hills in the Southern part of Haryana. Due to this, there is abundance of lakes in the state.
- These lakes have special significance in the state's agriculture, tourism and environment.

The major lakes of the state are as follows

Lake	Features
Badkhal Lake	• It is located near **Badkhal** village, Faridabad, surrounded by Aravalli hills (206 acres). • In ancient times, this lake was main reason of floods. A dam was built in 1947 to control the water of this lake. • It hosts a **Flower Show** during spring seasons. • **Peacock lake** is located near this lake.
Kotla Lake	• It is located in **Nuh** (spread over an area of 108 acres). It is a man-made lake. • It is used for rainwater collection. A dam is constructed here which also benefits Kotla, Akora, Mohammadpur, Khanpur and Nuh.

Lake	Features
Damdama Lake	• It is the located in Sohna, Gurugram district, built in 1919 by British to collect rainwater. • It is **largest natural lake in Haryana** (spreadover an area of about 3000 acres). • It is Amoeba-shaped and home to around 190 bird species. • Water Polo Sports Centre is being constructed on this lake.
Sultanpur Lake	• It is located in **Farukhnagar**, 15 km from Gurugram (spread over an area of about 353 acres). • It is major bird sanctuary with about 250 bird species. More than 100 migratory species visit from Siberia, Europe and Afghanistan. • It was included in Ramsar list in 2021.
Khalilpur Lake	• It is located in Gurugram district (spread over an area of 1,500 acres). • Seasonal lake; receives water during rains, dries in summer.
Chandni Lake	• It is located 16 km from **Khalilpur Lake** (spread over an area of 988 acres). It is a permanent water body.
Karna Lake	• It is located 5 km from Karnal, on NH-1 (spread over an area of 17 acres). • It is a man-made lake (1972) and circular-shaped. Other names of this lake are **Karnar** and **Chakravati**. • Karnal city named after this lake.
Tilyar Lake	• It is located in **Rohtak** on Delhi-Fazilka NH-10 (spread over an are a of 132 acres). • A zoo has been built on this lake by the Haryana Government.
Bhindawas Lake	• It is located in **Jhajjar** spread over an area of 1016 acres. It is a **largest wetland** in Haryana. • It was declared a Wildlife Sanctuary on 5th July, 1986, Bird Sanctuary on 3rd June, 2009 and Ramsar site on 25th May, 2021. • It is home to 266 bird species.

Other Lakes of Haryana

Lake	Place
Brahma Sarovar lake	Thanesar (Kurukshetra)
Surajkund lake	Faridabad (formed by Raja Suraj Pal. Part of Asola Bhathi wildlife sanctuary)
Ujina lake	Nuh (Mewat)
Bibipur lake	Kurukshetra (It is located in the plains of Haryana)
Blue Bird lake	Hisar
Tikkar Taal lake	Panchkula
Dhauj lake	Faridabad
Peacock lake	Faridabad
Chilli lake	Fatehabad (Golden Jubilee Heritage Park has been constructed under Chilli lake)
Dabchick lake	Palwal(This is a dead lake, that dried up in 1985-86)
Anangpur lake	Faridabad
Basai lake	Gurugram

Drains of Haryana

Following are the main drains of Haryana

Lake	Features
Badshahpur Drain of Ghata	• Origin Hills of Delhi (near Mehrauli) • Enters Gurugram through Gwal Pahari village • Falls into Najafgarh lake (near Dhankot village of Gurugram tehsil
Landoha Lake	• Origin Alwar, Rajasthan • Enters Haryana from Ferozepur tehsil • Falls into Ujina drain • Recharges groundwater in Ferozepur Jhirka and Nuh tehsils
Buriya Drain (Tilpat Drain)	• Origin Hills near Mewla Maharajpur village (Ballabhgarh tehsil, Faridabad) • Flows East and joins Yamuna river near Maujpur village.This drain is also known as Tilpat drain.
Mehendi Bari Nala	• Origin near a village named Gosai Johar in Rajkha Hills of Gurugram district. • Merges into Khalilpur lake in Nuh Tehsil of Mewat district.

CHECK CHAPTER KNOWLEDGE

1 Yamuna enters Haryana from the district of *HSSC 2016*
(a) Yamunanagar (b) Kaithal
(c) Bhiwani (d) Karnal

2 Which among the following districts of Haryana is not drained by Yamuna river? *HSSC CET-2023*
(a) Hisar (b) Panipat
(c) Yamunanagar (d) Sonipat

3 Which of the following is the perennial river of Haryana? *HSSC Clerk 2016*
(a) Saraswati (b) Sahibi (c) Markanda (d) Yamuna

4 The Yamuna river does not cross the boundary of which of the following districts of Haryana? *Computer Operator 2016*
(a) Ambala (b) Yamunanagar
(c) Karnal (d) Panipat

5 Which district of Haryana does not have a border with the Yamuna river? *HSSC 2016*
(a) Panipat (b) Rohtak
(c) Yamunanagar (d) Sonipat

6 In Haryana, Tejewala Barrage is built on which river? *HSSC JE 2024*
(a) Saraswati (b) Yamuna
(c) Krishnavati (d) Chautang

7 The Yamuna river flows in which part of Haryana? *HSSC 2021*
(a) Southern (b) Eastern
(c) Western (d) Northern

8 Which of the following rivers forms the boundary between Haryana and Uttar Pradesh? *Haryana Junior Engineer 2018*
(a) Saraswati (b) Ghaggar
(c) Yamuna (d) Sahibi

9 Which river defines the Eastern border of Haryana with Uttar Pradesh? *HSSC 2020*
(a) Narmada (b) Ganga
(c) Yamuna (d) Kaveri

10 The Hathnikund barrage is located on which river? *HSSC 2020*
(a) Yamuna (b) Ghaggar
(c) Saraswati (d) Ganga

11 Western Yamuna Canal originates from which place on Yamuna river? *Mandi Supervisor 2017*
(a) Salhawas (b) Karnal
(c) Tajewala (d) Bhakra-Nangal

12 Vedic Civilisation flourished on the banks of .... river. *HSSC 2018*
(a) Saraswati (b) Ganga (c) Yamuna (d) Kaveri

13 Adi Badri place is associated with which holy river? *Haryana Lab Attendant 2018*
(a) Yamuna (b) Saraswati (c) Markanda (d) Ganga

14 At which place of Punjab, Saraswati river flows into the Ghaggar river? *HSSC CET 2023*
(a) Mansa (b) Patiala
(c) Sangrur (d) Sasnagar

15 Ghaggar river is a *HSSC Clerk 2016*
(a) seasonal river (b) large rains-fed river
(c) Both (a) and (b) (d) None of these

16 The Ghaggar river does not passes through which of the following districts of Haryana? *Anganwadi 2017*
(a) Kaithal (b) Bhiwani
(c) Fatehabad (d) Sirsa

17 Ottu barrage is located on which river? *Haryana CET 2023, HSSC 2020*
(a) Tangri (b) Yamuna
(c) Ghaggar-Hakra (d) Sahiba

18 Which river was known as 'Aruna' in mythology? *Haryana Accountant 2018*
(a) Ghaggar river (b) Drishadvati river
(c) Markanda river (d) Sharda river

19 Markanda river enters Haryana from the district of *PGT 2016*
(a) Ambala (b) Faridabad
(c) Hisar (d) Sonipat

20 The important tributary of Markanda river is *PGT 2016*
(a) Sahibi (b) Tangri
(c) Krishnavati (d) Dohan

21 During rainy season, Markanda river becomes major cause of floods for which district of Haryana? *Haryana CET 2022*
(a) Ambala (b) Kurukshetra
(c) Both (a) and (b) (d) None of these

22 The Tangri river begins its journey at......... in Haryana. *HSSC CET 2023*
(a) Kalka (b) Aravali hills
(c) Chandigarh (d) Ambala

23 What is the name of the river which originates from the Shivalik range near a place called Dagshai in Solan district? *HSSC 2019*
(a) Saraswati (b) Ghaggar
(c) Tangri (d) Markanda

24 Shivalik hills are the source region of many rivers. One of these rivers is *HSSC 2019*
(a) Tangri (b) Ganga (c) Kaveri (d) Kapila

25 Tangri is the tributary of *HSSC 2018*
(a) Markanda river (b) Sahibi river
(c) Indori river (d) Yamuna river

26 Chautang river originates from which of the following places? *PGT 2016*
(a) Aravalli hills (b) Shivalik hills
(c) Mewat hills (d) Neem Ka Thana

27 The name of Chautang river in Rigvedic period was *PGT 2016*
(a) Saraswati (b) Shatradi
(c) Krabhu (d) Drishadvati

28 The source region of Indori river is near *HSSC 2018*
(a) Indore (b) Kaithal
(c) Bhiwani (d) Karnal

29 Which non-perennial river flows for about 50 km in the state of Haryana? *HSSC 2019*
(a) Dohan (b) Chautang
(c) Rakshi (d) Indori

30 Following are the rivers of Haryana, except *PGT 2016*
(a) Ghaggar (b) Dohan
(c) Kotla (d) Indori

31 Which of the following rivers does not flow in Haryana? *HSSC 2021*
(a) Ghaggar (b) Sahibi
(c) Dohan (d) Beas

32 Which of the following rivers does not go through Haryana? *HSSC 2020*
(a) Sarsuti/Saraswati (b) Kashalya
(c) Ganga (d) Yamuna

33 Which of the following lakes is situated in Haryana? *PGT 2016*
(a) Damdama lake (b) Kotla lake
(c) Khalilpur lake (d) All of these

34 Badkhal lake is located in the district of *HSSC 2020,18, Haryana Clerk 2016*
(a) Sirsa (b) Panipat
(c) Faridabad (d) Kurukshetra

35 This lake is a part of the Asala Bhatti wildlife sanctuary in Haryana *HSSC CET 2024*
(a) Brahma Sarovar lake (b) Karna lake
(c) Surajkund lake (d) Badkhal lake

36 Damdama lake is situated in the district of *HSSC 2016*
(a) Faridabad (b) Gurugram
(c) Rohtak (d) Hisar

37 Which of the following lakes is present in Gurugram? *HSSC 2020*
(a) Badhkal lake (b) Karna lake
(c) Damdama lake (d) Dhauj lake

38 Which is the largest natural lake in Haryana? *HSSC 2020*
(a) Surajkund lake (b) Sukhna lake
(c) Damdama lake (d) Tilyar lake

39 Where is Brahma Sarovar situated? *HSSC CET 2023*
(a) Fatehabad (b) Kurukshetra
(c) Hisar (d) Sirsa

40 Damdama is the name of the .... in Haryana. *HSSC 2020*
(a) highest mountain peak (b) longest river
(c) biggest lake (d) largest tiger reserve

41 Kotla lake is located in *PGT 2015*
(a) Nuh (Mewat) (b) Palwal
(c) Rewari (d) Mahendragarh

42 What is the name of the famous lake situated in Karnal district of Haryana? *HSSC 2019, HSSC Clerk 2019*
(a) Parakeet lake (b) Karna lake
(c) Sultanpur lake (d) Abhimanyu lake

43 Which among the following is the largest wetland of Haryana? *HSSC CET 2024*
(a) Badkhal (b) Surajkund
(c) Bhindawas (d) Damdama

44 Who built the Surajkund lake in Faridabad district of Haryana? *HSSC 2021*
(a) Raja Nahar Singh (b) Raja Gurdit Singh
(c) Raja Siraj Dev (d) Raja Suraj Pal

45 Blue Bird lake is located at which place of Haryana? *Haryana CET 2022, HSSC Clerk 2015*
(a) Faridabad (b) Fatehabad
(c) Hisar (d) Jind

46 Famous Bibipur and Najafgarh lakes are located in which natural region of Haryana? *PGT 2016*
(a) Plain region
(b) Desert region
(c) Shivalik hills region
(d) Arid area of Aravalli hills

47 Which among the following lakes is located in Rohtak District of Haryana? *HSSC CET 2023*
(a) Karna lake (b) Brahma sarovar
(c) Tylyar lake (d) Blue Bird lake

48 Which of the following is correctly matched? *Auction Recorder 2016*

Lakes	District
(a) Badkhal	Faridabad
(b) Bhindawas	Kurukshetra
(c) Brahma Sarovar	Rohtak
(d) Damdama	Sirsa

49 'Sahibi river' is also known as .... *HSSC 2018*
(a) Drishadvati (b) Kumudvati
(c) Kaveri (d) Sabi

50 Match the following

List I	List II
A. Karna lake	1. Palwal
B. Surajkund lake	2. Karnal
C. Dabchick lake	3. Gurugram
D. Damdama lake	4. Faridabad

Codes

	A	B	C	D		A	B	C	D
(a)	2	4	1	3	(b)	1	2	3	4
(c)	3	4	1	2	(d)	2	1	4	3

CORRECT ANSWERS

1. (a)	2. (a)	3. (d)	4. (a)	5. (b)	6. (b)	7. (b)	8. (c)	9. (c)	10. (a)
11. (c)	12. (a)	13. (b)	14. (c)	15. (b)	16. (b)	17. (c)	18. (c)	19. (a)	20. (b)
21. (c)	22. (a)	23. (c)	24. (a)	25. (a)	26. (b)	27. (d)	28. (c)	29. (d)	30. (c)
31. (d)	32. (c)	33. (d)	34. (c)	35. (c)	36. (b)	37. (c)	38. (c)	39. (b)	40. (c)
41. (a)	42. (b)	43. (c)	44. (d)	45. (c)	46. (a)	47. (c)	48. (a)	49. (d)	50. (a)

CHAPTER
17

KNOW YOUR STATE
HARYANA

Forest Resources in Haryana

- About 80% of Haryana's land is under cultivation, making it primarily an agricultural state.
- Tropical forests are found in abundance in the state, with diverse species due to variations in climate, temperature, soil and rainfall.
- In addition to mango, jamun, sal, sheesham, pine, the state also has different varieties of medicinal plants like kurand, kherti, bathua, ashwagandha, shakhawali, shati, sadabahar, makoi, etc. and different types of grass like dubach, dhaman, dilla, dubh, bhurat, etc.
- There is an abundance of cane in the state, which is used for rope making. The cottage industry based on cane is also popular in the state.
- The forest wealth of the state has environmental importance as well as economic importance, so important measures have also been taken by the government for its conservation.

Forest Cover in Haryana (ISFR 2023)

- Target (As Haryana State Forest Policy, 2006) — 20% of geographical area
- Current status — 3.65% of total geographical area is under forest cover (India State of Forest Report 2023)
- Forest area — 1,614.26 sq km
- Very Dense Forest (VDF) — 27.17 sq km(0.06%)
- Moderately Dense Forest (MDF) — 441.18 sq km (1%)
- Open Forest (OF) — 1,145.91 sq km (2.59 %)
- Scrub area — 174.38 sq km (0.39%)
- Highest forest area — **Panchkula** (390.12 sq km)
- Lowest forest area — **Palwal** (13.82 sq km)
- Five districts with maximum forest areas in decreasing order are
  - Panchkula (390.12 sq km)
  - Yamunanagar (188.99 sq km)
  - Gurugram (113.11 sq km)
  - Mahendragarh (111.31 sq km)
  - Mewat (108.96 sq km)
- Five districts with minimum forest areas in increasing order are
  - Palwal (13.82 sq km)
  - Rohtak (14.54 sq km)
  - Panipat (15.97 sq km)
  - Fatehabad (21.31 sq km)
  - Sonipat (22.64 sq km)

District-Wise Forest Cover in Haryana

- According to the India State of Forest Report 2023, the district-wise information about forests of Haryana is as follows

District Wise Forest Cover in Haryana

District	Geographical Area (GA) (in sq km)	Total Forest Cover (in sq km)	% of GA
Ambala	1,574	56.67	3.60
Bhiwani	3,386	62.61	1.85
Charkhi-Dadri	1,382	45.92	3.32
Faridabad	741	78.43	10.58
Fatehabad	2,538	21.31	0.84
Gurugram	1,258	113.11	8.99
Hisar	3,993	58.54	1.47
Jhajjar	1,834	25.56	1.39
Jind	2,701	26.43	0.98
Kaithal	2,318	54.32	2.34
Karnal	2,494	32.95	1.32
Kurukshetra	1,536	46.03	3.00
Mahendragarh	1,899	111.31	5.86
Mewat	1,507	108.96	7.23
Palwal	1,359	13.82	1.02
Panchkula	898	390.12	43.44
Panipat	1,288	15.97	1.24
Rewari	1,594	61.45	3.86
Rohtak	1,704	14.54	0.85
Sirsa	4,277	64.58	1.51
Sonipat	2,163	22.64	1.05
Yamunanagar	1,768	188.99	10.69

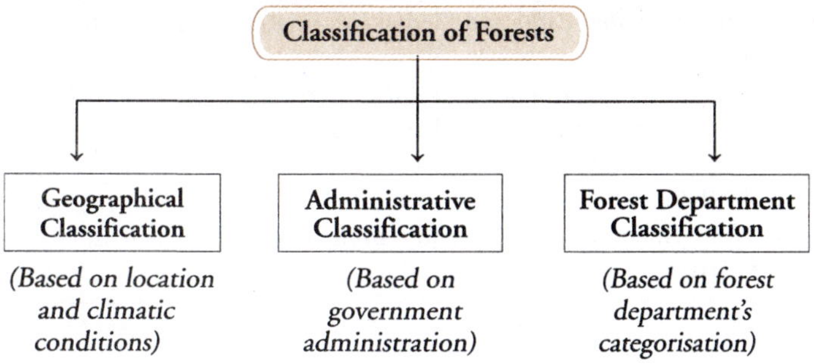

Geographical Classification of Forests

As per **Champion and Seth**, Haryana's forests are divided into following categories. These are

1. Tropical Dry Deciduous Forests

- Location — Found in Mahendragarh, Rewari, Yamunanagar, Gurugram, Bhiwani, Kaithal, Karnal and Sonipat districts.
- Rainfall — Found in areas with less than 100 cm rainfall.
- Tree species — Indian rosewood (sheesham), sacred fig, peepal, neem, mango, jamun, tamarind, kendu, lasoda, semal.
- Sub-types — Moist deciduous forests in wet areas and thorn forests in dry areas.

> Tropical thorn forest trees like babool, kikar, firas, jharberi, pilu, khair, oak, patha, jala, thuhar, sarkanda, bui are found in dry regions like sirsa, Fatehabad etc.

2. Sub-Tropical Pine Forests

- Location — Found in hilly areas of Ambala, Panchkula, Yamunanagar and Rohtak districts.
- Rainfall — Found in the areas with rainfall of 100 cm or above.
- Tree Species — Dominated by pine, sal and chir trees cirrus, jamun, kachnar, khair, amaltas, mahua, kalka, bahera, jhingan, etc.
- Sal trees are specifically found in Rohtak's forests.

Administrative Classification of Forests

Haryana's forests are divided into three classes on the basis of administration

1. Reserved Forests

- Control — Completely under government control
- Restrictions — Grazing and tree cutting are banned
- Objectives — Land reclamation, flood control, wood supply, wildlife protection and valuable forest products
- Top 5 districts with maximum area — Yamunanagar, Kaithal, Ambala, Jind and Hisar
- Bottom 5 districts with minimal area — Sirsa, Nuh, Bhiwani, Palwal and Faridabad
- Districts with No Reserved Forests — Fatehabad, Hisar, Jhajjar, Panipat, Sonipat and Rohtak

2. Protected Forests

• Control	Under government control with special care to prevent damage
• Restrictions	Conservation and limited production activities
• Local Resident Permissions	Cutting firewood, grazing and pastoral activities
• Top 5 districts with maximum area	Panchkula, Yamunanagar, Bhiwani, Sonipat and Karnal
• Bottom 5 districts with minimal area	Faridabad, Nuh, Gurugram, Palwal and Mahendragarh

Panchkula ranks 1st in both reserved and protected forest areas.

3. Unclassified Forests

• Control	Forests outside of reserved and protected forests, with shared authority among government, community and people
• Restrictions	No restrictions on wood cutting and pastoralism, with some conservation measures
• Top 5 districts with maximum area	Kaithal, Rohtak, Yamunanagar, Jind and Palwal
• Bottom 5 districts with minimal area	Bhiwani, Hisar, Panchkula, Nuh, and Gurugram
• Districts with No Unclassified Forests	Ambala, Faridabad, Karnal, Kurukshetra, Panipat and Sonipat

- The reserved forest area, protected forest area and unclassified forest area of Haryana are classified as closed areas under Section 38 of Indian Forest Act, 1927 and Section 4 and 5 of Punjab Land Conservation Act, 1980.

Forest Department Classification

The Haryana Forest Department categorised the state's forests into three types

1. **The State Forests** These are the forest areas over which the government has full control.
2. **Community Forests** These are the forest areas that are under the authority of local bodies such as District Council, Municipality and Nagar Panchayat, etc.
3. **Private Forests** These are the forest areas over which individuals have rights, i.e. they are under the control of the people.

Haryana State Forest Policy, 2006

- In order to promote sustainable development of forests in the state, the Government of Haryana formulated a forest policy in 2006, known as the Forest Policy, 2006.
- According to this policy, the government has targeted to increase the forest and tree cover from 10% to 20%.

Highlights of the Forest Policy, 2006

Objectives

- Promote afforestation to maintain environmental stability and restore ecological balance.
- Conserve and develop water resources, biodiversity and medicinal plants in forest areas.
- Promote tree cover, wood production and eco-tourism while controlling soil erosion and sand dune expansion.

Key Strategies

- Promote plantation, agricultural forestry and social forestry.
- Encourage research, education and training in forestry.
- Ensure proper management and conservation of forest resources.
- Build institutions for joint management and participation in forest development.

Measures for Implementation

- Plantation is being promoted along with agricultural forestry and social forestry.
- Research work is being promoted in the field of forestry.
- Industries based on agro-forestry are being encouraged, as well as better education and training arrangements have been made.
- Proper management and conservation of forest resources is being done.
- Preservation and expansion of medicinal plants is being done through **Herbal Parks** and **Herbal Information Centers** in the state.
- Along with the promotion of agro-forestry and farm forestry, several important schemes and programmes have been implemented to increase forest cover in the state.
- Arrangement of education and training for the expansion of forestry.

Schemes Related to Forest Development in Haryana

A number of schemes are being run to promote forest conservation and forest development in the state of Haryana.

Centrally Sponsored and External Sector Schemes

Scheme	Explanation
Kandi Project	• Launched in 2008, funded by the World Bank. • Focuses on re-plantation in the Shivalik hills of Ambala and Yamunanagar districts. • Integrated scheme involving Forest, Agriculture, Animal Husbandry and Horticulture departments.
National Afforestation Programme	• Lanunched in 2000 • It aims to restore degraded forests and develop forest resources with community participation, focusing on improving livelihoods of forest fringe communities.
Aravalli Rehabilitation Scheme	• Implemented in Haryana since 1990-91. • Founded by the European Economic Community. • Aims to re-plant and rejuvenate the Aravalli hills, with 33,000 hectares of tree planting completed within 6 years.
Social Forestry Scheme	• Started in 1982 with World Bank collaboration, estimated at ₹ 33.32 crores. • Completed in 2006-07, covering 338 villages in 11 districts with prominent women's participation. • **Aim** encourage citizens to plant trees and develop pastures. • Objectives include raise awareness about plantation, creating rural employment, maintaining environmental balance, promoting cottage industries based on forest products.
Van Mitra Scheme	• Launched in 2024 to promote afforestation in non-forest areas through community participation. • Aims to increase green cover and sapling survival rate. • Eligible for persons of 18-60 years of age having annual income below ₹ 1.80 lakh.

State Government Sponsored Schemes

Scheme	Explanation
Har Ghar Hariyali Yojana	• Launched in 2015, focusing on local species development. • Plants indigenous species like peepal, neem and pomegranate. • 141.01 lakh saplings planted in 18,412 hectares in 2016-17. • 3 crore plants were to be planted in Haryana. • Biodiversity Board formed to conserve biological resources .
Greening of Haryana Scheme	• Launched in 1989-90 for large-scale tree plantation. • Tree belts have been made on the banks of rivers, canals, roads, railways and around villages. • Planted medicinal trees and herbs like giloy, kherti, kurand, kukuruda, kataan, chaulai, bathua, gokharu, jalabhangara, indrayan, muruyali, ashwagandha, shakhawali, etc. • Under this scheme different types of herbs are obtained from the state forests which are used as medicine. The state observes **Tree Day** on 15th July every year since 2014.
Environmental Education and Awareness Programmes	• This programme aims to educate local people, especially youth, women, students and teachers, about natural resources.
Haryana Community Forestry Project	• Co-founded by the Government of Haryana and the European commission. • Implemented in 338 villages to conserve and rejuvenate natural resources through forestry development with community participation, especially women.
Nature Camps	• Set up by the Haryana Forest Department to promote environmental adaptation and eco-tourism . • Located in Thapli, Morni, Ban Santour and Chuharpur.

Herbal Parks in Haryana

- The Government of Haryana has set up herbal parks with the objective of bringing awareness to the people about the natural ecological system in each district of the state.
- According to Economic Survey 2024-25, a total of 59 herbal parks have been established in the state, which encourages people to do environmental friendly work.
- The **first and largest herbal park of the state** is **Chaudhary Devi Lal Herbal Nature Park** located in Chuharpur village of Yamunanagar district.
- The state is going to establish the world's largest herbal park. This park will be built on the land of the Forest Department in Morni.
- This park will promote environmental balance by conserving species as well as acting as gene pool for native and exotic species.

Nature Camp Thapli

Northern Region Herbal Parks

Name	Location
Cantt Herbal Park	Ambala
Thapli Herbal Park	Panchkula
Adibadri	Yamunanagar
Kapur Vatika	Panchkula
Harar Vatika	Ambala
Rudraksh Vatika	Yamunanagar
Jamun Vatika	Kaithal
Arjun Vatika	Kurukshetra

Southern Region Herbal Parks

Name	Location
Kadipur Herbal Park	Mahendragarh
Kakodia Herbal Park	Rewari
Kariya Herbal Park	Mahendragarh
Amla Herbal Garden	Gurugram
Ratanjot Vatika	Faridabad
Guggal Vatika	Mahendragarh
Chawan Rishi Vatika	Mahendragarh
Indira Gandhi Memorial Herbal Park	Rewari
Ghritkumari Vatika	Mewat (Nuh)
Khalilpuri Vatika	Rewari

Western Region Herbal Parks

Name	Location
Ch. Surendra Singh Memorial Herbal Park (Tosham)	Bhiwani
Ch. Surendra Singh Memorial Herbal Park (Kairu)	Bhiwani
Chandan Vatika	Jind
Mulethi Vatika	Fatehabad
Baheda Vatika	Sirsa
Shatavari Vatika	Hisar

Central Region Herbal Parks

Name	Location
Indri Herbal Park	Karnal
Khanpur Kalan Herbal Park	Sonipat
Herbal Park Bhindawas	Jhajjar
Ashok Vatika	Karnal
Amaltas Vatika	Sonipat
Putranjiva Vatika	Jhajjar
Bilva Vatika	Panipat
Neem Vatika	Rohtak

Forest and Environment-related Institutes in Haryana

Institute	Explanation
Haryana State Pollution Control Board	It was established in 1974 to prevent industrial and local body residues and control pollutants.
Haryana Forest Development Corporation	It was founded in 1989 to develop forests in the state, headquartered in Panchkula.
State Medicinal Plants Board	It was established in 2002 to promote medicinal plants and implement National Medicinal Plant Board projects, also headquartered in Panchkula.
The Environment Club	It aims to establish 5250 Environment Clubs across Haryana's districts, with 2850 already set up.
Clonal Safeda Nursery	A Clonal Safeda Enhancement Centre has been set-up in 2016 in Kurukshetra district in Silothi village.
Swarna Jayanti Environment Training Institute	It offers training programmes for environmental conservation and sustainability.
Forest Training Institute (FTI)	It provides training for forest officers, forest guards and other stakeholders .
Directorate Environment and Climate Change	It oversees environmental policies, projects and initiatives in Haryana .

CHECK CHAPTER KNOWLEDGE

1 What is the reason for diversity in forests found in Haryana?
(a) Variation in climate
(b) Variation in temperature
(c) Variation in rainfall
(d) All of the above

2 What is the name of the medicinal plant mentioned in the text that is commonly found in Haryana?
(a) Ashwagandha (b) Shakhawali
(c) Makoi (d) All of these

3 Which of the following vegetation is found abundantly in Haryana, which is used for rope making?
(a) Cane (b) Dubach
(c) Dola (d) Bhur

4 What is the target forest cover in Haryana as per the State's Forest Policy, 2006?
(a) 10% (b) 15%
(c) 20% (d) 25%

5 What percentage of Haryana is officially recognised as being under forest cover? *HPSC HCS 2019*
(a) 5.5% (b) 3.65% (c) 3% (d) 4.5%

6 What is the total forest area in Haryana in square kilometers as per ISFR, 2023?
(a) 1,414.26 sq km (b) 1,514.26 sq km
(c) 1,614.26 sq km (d) 1,714.26 sq km

7 Which district has the highest forest area in Haryana? *HSSC 2020*
(a) Karnal (b) Kurukshetra
(c) Panchkula (d) Faridabad

8 Which district of Haryana has the lowest forest area in the state? *HSSC 2017*
(a) Fatehabad (b) Palwal
(c) Faridabad (d) Bhiwani

9 What is the percentage of Very Dense Forest (VDF) in Haryana as per ISFR, 2023?
(a) 0.01% (b) 0.03%
(c) 0.06% (d) 0.09%

10 Which district has the lowest forest area in respect of geographical area in Haryana? *Haryana Police Constable 2018*
(a) Rewari (b) Fatehabad
(c) Gurugram (d) Jind

11 Forests of Haryana are divided into which categories on the basis of geographical criterion?
(a) Tropical Dry Deciduous Forests
(b) Tropical Thorn Forests
(c) Sub-Tropical Pine Forests
(d) All of the above

12 Which type of vegetation is most prevalent in Haryana? *HSSC 2020*
(a) Tropical evergreen rain forest
(b) Deciduous forest and thorny bushes
(c) Mountain forest
(d) Mangrove forest

13 What is the total scrub area in Haryana in square kilometers?
(a) 74.38 sq km (b) 124.38 sq km
(c) 174.38 sq km (d) 224.38 sq km

14 Which of the following is a type of tree species of Haryana?
(a) Semal (b) Kendu
(c) Lasoda (d) All of these

15 Sub-tropical Pine Forests are found in which district of Haryana?
(a) Ambala (b) Panchkula
(c) Yamunanagar (d) All of these

16 Sal trees are found in .... district of Haryana. *HSSC 2018*
(a) Gurugram (b) Sonipat
(c) Rohtak (d) Kalesar

17 Which types of forests are covered under the administrative classification of forests?
(a) Reserved forests (b) Protected forests
(c) Unclassified forests (d) All of these

18 What is the percentage of Moderately Dense Forest (MDF) in Haryana as per ISFR, 2023?
(a) 0.5% (b) 0.8%
(c) 1% (d) 1.2%

19 Which district in Haryana has the lowest forest area after Palwal as per ISFR, 2023?
(a) Rohtak (b) Panipat
(c) Fatehabad (d) Sonipat

20 Which district of Haryana has its maximum area under protected forests?
(a) Panchkula (b) Kaithal
(c) Bhiwani (d) Sonipat

21 What is the main objective of Reserved Forests in Haryana?
(a) Conservation and limited production activities
(b) Land reclamation, flood control, wood supply, wildlife protection and valuable forest products
(c) Promotion of tourism and recreation
(d) Generation of revenue through timber sales

22 Which districts of Haryana have highest forest cover in the state? *HSSC 2010*
(a) Yamunanagar, Panchkula, Gurugram, Kaithal
(b) Panchkula, Yamunanagar, Gurugram, Bhiwani
(c) Yamunanagar, Panchkula, Kaithal, Gurugram
(d) None of the above

23 According to Haryana State Forest Policy, 2006, the government targeted to increase the forest cover around
(a) 10% (b) 20% (c) 30% (d) 40%

24 Haryana Government has promoted which of the following activities to achieve the goal of Haryana State Forest Policy, 2006?
(a) Ago-forestry (b) Farm-forestry
(c) Afforestation (d) All of these

25 Kandi Project in Haryana was funded by which of the following organisation?
(a) World Bank (b) European Union
(c) UNICEF (d) America

26 In which year, Social Forestry Scheme was started in Haryana?
(a) 1980 (b) 1982 (c) 1996 (d) 1999

27 In which year, 'Har Ghar Hariyali Yojana' was launched in Haryana?
(a) 2015 (b) 2016
(c) 2017 (d) 2018

28 In which year, 'Greening of Haryana Programme' was started in Haryana?
(a) 1985-86 (b) 1990-91 (c) 1989-90 (d) 1986-87

29 In Haryana, 'Tree Day' is observed every year on
(a) 15th July (b) 17th August
(c) 20th September (d) 21st October

30 With the help of which of the following international organisations, Haryana Community Forestry Project was started? *HSSC-CET 2023*
(a) World Bank
(b) European Commission
(c) South Asian Association for Regional Cooperation (SAARC)
(d) None of the above

31 The largest herbal park in Haryana is located in which district of the state? *HSSC 2019*
(a) Karnal (b) Jind
(c) Yamunanagar (d) Gurugram

32 'Arjun Vatika' is located in which district of Haryana?
(a) Panchkula (b) Ambala
(c) Kurukshetra (d) Rewari

33 Ashwagandha Vatika is located in which district of Haryana?
(a) Rewari
(b) Mahendragarh
(c) Hisar
(d) Bhiwani

34 World Herbal Forest Project has been inaugurated at *HSSC 2020*
(a) Panchkula (b) Ambala
(c) Mahendragarh (d) Yamunanagar

35 Neem Vatika is located in the district of ....
(a) Panipat (b) Rohtak
(c) Karnal (d) Sonipat

36 The headquarters of Haryana Forest Development Corporation is located in which district of Haryana?
(a) Panchkula (b) Yamunanagar
(c) Rohtak (d) Bhiwani

37 A Clonal Safeda Enhancement Centre has been set up in which district of Haryana?
(a) Jind (b) Kurukshetra
(c) Fatehabad (d) Kaithal

38 Match the following.

List I		List II	
A.	Chandan Vatika	1.	Jind
B.	Baheda Vatika	2.	Sirsa
C.	Indri Herbal Park	3.	Karnal
D.	Amaltas Vatika	4.	Sonipat

Codes

	A	B	C	D		A	B	C	D
(a)	1	2	3	4	(b)	4	3	2	1
(c)	2	3	1	4	(d)	2	4	1	3

CORRECT ANSWERS

1. (d)	**2.** (d)	**3.** (a)	**4.** (c)	**5.** (b)	**6.** (c)	**7.** (c)	**8.** (b)	**9.** (c)	**10.** (b)
11. (d)	**12.** (b)	**13.** (c)	**14.** (d)	**15.** (d)	**16.** (c)	**17.** (d)	**18.** (c)	**19.** (a)	**20.** (a)
21. (b)	**22.** (b)	**23.** (b)	**24.** (d)	**25.** (a)	**26.** (b)	**27.** (a)	**28.** (c)	**29.** (a)	**30.** (b)
31. (c)	**32.** (c)	**33.** (a)	**34.** (a)	**35.** (b)	**36.** (a)	**37.** (b)	**38.** (a)		

National Parks and Wildlife Sanctuaries in Haryana

- Haryana has rich biodiversity with about 1614.26 sq km of 'Forest Cover' as per the India State of Forest Report 2023.
- The state has around 500 species of birds and also welcomes large number of migratory birds during the winter season.
- For the conservation of wildlife, the state has about 33,000 hectares under protected area network which includes 2 national parks, 8 wildlife sanctuaries and 2 conservation reserves.
- The state has 8 Wildlife breeding centres, 3 Zoos, 1 Elephant rehabilitation centre and 1 Deer park.

National Parks in Haryana

National parks are forests which are reserved for the protection of vegetation and wildlife.

Two national parks in Haryana are as follows

Sultanpur National Park

• Location	Sultanpur, **Gurugram** district
• Area	142.52 hectares
• Named after	**Dr. Salim Ali**, famous Indian Ornithologist
• Bird species	About 250 species, including Siberian cranes
• Migratory birds	Siberian crane, wood sandpiper, Eurasian wigeon, etc.
• Common bird species	Hoopoe, Indian cormorant, francolin, spoonbill, crested lark, etc.
• Protected area status	**Bird Sanctuary** 2nd April, 1971, **National Park** 1991, Ramsar Site, 2021
• Significance	Bird Watcher's Paradise, **Lake Bird Sanctuary**
• Wildlife	Siberian crane, greater flamingo, spot-billed pelican, wood sandpiper, grey heron.

Kalesar National Park

• Location	**Yamunanagar** district
• Area	4682.32 hectares (largest in Haryana)
• Named after	**Kalesar** (Shiva) **temple**
• Protected area status	National Park on 8th December, 2003
• Significance	Famous for **Red Jungle Fowl**
• Wildlife	Leopard, barking deer, sambar, chital, python, king cobra, monitor lizard, etc.
• Other facts	**Largest national park** in Haryana, shares boundaries with Himachal Pradesh, Uttarakhand and Uttar Pradesh

Wildlife Sanctuaries in Haryana

An area designated for the protection of animals and birds in their natural habitats is known as a wildlife sanctuary.

The eight Wildlife Sanctuaries in Haryana cover around 23,441.17 hectares of land. These Wildlife Sanctuaries are as follows

- Bhindawas Wildlife Sanctuary
- Chhilchhila Wildlife Sanctuary
- Nahar Wildlife Sanctuary
- Bir Shikargarh Wildlife Sanctuary
- Abubshahar Wildlife Sanctuary
- Khaparwas Wildlife Sanctuary
- Kalesar Wildlife Sanctuary
- Khol Hi-Raitan Wildlife Sanctuary

National Parks and Wildlife Sanctuaries in Haryana

Bhindawas Wildlife Sanctuary

• Establishment	1986
• District	**Jhajjar**
• Area	411.55 hectares

- It was declared a bird sanctuary by Indian Government on 3rd June, 2009.
- It attracts around 35,000 variety of migratory birds belonging to over 250 species during winter.
- This sanctuary is famous for brown goose, duck, red nightingale, kingfisher, neelgai, jackal, langur, peafowl, hornbill, coppersmith barbet, etc.
- It was designated as a Wetland of International Importance, i.e., Ramsar site in May, 2021.

> Bhindawas Lake of Bhindawas Wildlife Sanctuary is the largest wetland in Haryana.

Chhilchhila Wildlife Sanctuary

• Establishment	November, 1986
• District	**Kurukshetra**
• Area	28.92 hectares

- It is the **smallest wildlife sanctuary** in Haryana in terms of area.
- In 2009, the Ministry of Environment and Forests declared the sanctuary as **Eco-Sensitive Zone** (ESZ) for conservation of flora and fauna.
- The sanctuary attracts wide variety of winter migratory birds. Blue peafowl, ducks, starks, hornbill, barbet, rufous treepie, greater coucal, etc. are also found here.

Nahar Wildlife Sanctuary

• Establishment	1987
• District	Rewari
• Area	211.35 hectares

- This sanctuary was the pasture of the Nawab of Dujana.
- It was known as **Nahar Wildlife Reserve Forest** before it was declared as a sanctuary.
- It was declared as Eco-Sensitive Zone in 2009 by Indian Government.
- Black buck, jackal, monitor lizard, neelgai, fox, black deer, brown pheasant, langur, blue peafowl, etc. are found here.

Bir Shikargarh Wildlife Sanctuary

• Establishment	May, 1987
• District	**Panchkula**
• Area	767.30 hectares

- In 2009, Government of India declared it an Eco-Sensitive Zone (ESZ).
- This sanctuary is famous for its variety of flora and fauna like Cheetal, sambar, neelgai, etc.

Abubshahar Wildlife Sanctuary

• Establishment	January, 1987
• District	Sirsa
• Area	11,530.56 hectares

- In terms of area, it is the **largest Wildlife Sanctuary of Haryana.**
- The main attraction of the wildlife sanctuary are blue bull, partridges and black buck.

Khaparwas Wildlife Sanctuary

• Establishment	January, 1987
• District	Jhajjar
• Area	82.70 hectares

- It was also declared as Eco-Sensitive Zone by the Indian Government.
- Water birds are main attraction of this sanctuary. It is famous for various breeds of migratory birds.

Kalesar Wildlife Sanctuary

• Establishment	December, 1996
• District	Yamunanagar
• Area	11,570 Acre

- It was also declared as Eco-Sensitive Zone by the Indian Government.
- This area has dense sal forests, khair forests and patches of grasslands.
- Cheetal, sambhar, neelgai, barking deer, wild boar, etc. are found here.

Khol Hi-Raitan (Morni Hills) Wildlife Sanctuary

• Establishment	2004
• District	Panchkula
• Area	4,882.96 hectares

- At the time of its establishment, the area of this sanctuary was 2,226.56 hectares, but in the year 2007, an area of 2,656.38 hectares was also added in this sanctuary.
- Cheetal, spotted deer, jackal, wild cat, Indian fox, brown pheasant, bear, wild monkey, etc. are found here.

Asola-Bhatti Wildlife Sanctuary

- It covers an area of 3200 hectares. It starts from Sariska National Park in Alwar, Rajasthan and is spread over **Mewat, Faridabad** and **Gurugram** districts of Haryana.
- Tourist destinations around this sanctuary are Surajkund, Anangpur dam, Tughlaqabad fort, Adilabad ruins, Chhatarpur temple, etc.
- This protected area contains one of the last surviving remnants of Delhi Ridge (hill range), its semi-arid forest habitat and its dependent wildlife.
- The Ministry of Environment and Forests has declared the 1 km area around Asola-Bhatti Wildlife Sanctuary in Gurugram and Faridabad as Eco Sensitive Zone.
- About 200 species of local and migratory birds are found in this sanctuary.

Conservation Reserves in Haryana

- There are 2 conservation reserves in Haryana which covers around 4872.11 hectares of land in the state.

Conservation Reserve

↓

Saraswati Wildlife Sanctuary

- It is also known as Seonsar Forest and is spread over Kaithal and Kurukshetra districts of Haryana.
- It covers an area of 4452.85 hectares. It was established in the year 2007.
- It is the third largest Wildlife Sanctuary of Haryana. Deers are found more in this sanctuary.

↓

Bir Bara Ban Wildlife Sanctuary

- It is located in Jind district. It covers an area of 419.26 hectares. It was established in the year 2007.
- Neelgai, jackal, langur and birds like rufous treepie, coucal, hornbill and coppersmith barbet are found here.

Animal Rehabilitation, Research and Conservation Centres of Haryana

Deer Park

It is situated on Hisar-Dhansu Road of Hisar district. It was established in 1970-71. The area of this park is around 42 acres. Blackbuck, chital, spotted deer and sambar are found in this park.

Elephant Rehabilitation Centre

The Ch. Surinder Singh Elephant Rehabilitation Centre (ERC) is situated at Ban Santour forest of Yamunanagar district. It is a project undertaken by the Haryana Forest Department, Government of Haryana in collaboration with Wildlife SOS. The injured, sick and saved elephants are rehabilitated in this centre.

National Research Centre on Equines (NRCE)

It was established in Hisar district on 7th January, 1986. In the year 1989, a sub-centre of the National Research Centre on Equines (NRCE) was established in Bikaner of Rajasthan.

Jatayu (Vulture) Conservation and Breeding Centre (JCBC)

It was established in 2001 for protection of vultures in Pinjore. This is a joint effort of Haryana Forest Department and Bombay Natural History Society. The world's maximum number of vultures are found here. It is also Asia's first vulture breeding centre.

Hisar Bovine Sperm Station and Research Centre (HBSSRC)

It is a bovine semen production bank and provides services like veterinary care, breeding, etc.

Zoos of Haryana

There are 3 zoological parks (zoos) in Haryana

Mini Zoo, Pipli

- Establishment 1982-83
- Location National Highway 1
- District **Kurukshetra** (Pipli)
- Area 27 Acres

Front View of Pipli Zoo

Mini Zoo, Bhiwani

- Establishment 1982
- Location Bhiwani
- Area 7 Acres

- Deer park was established in this zoo on 3rd October, 1982 and Bear park on 5th September, 1983.
- Horses and crocodiles are also being kept in this zoo since 1987.
- It received the status of Mini Zoo on 14th August, 2008.
- In this zoo, animals like crocodile, black bear, fox, spotted deer, sambar, hippopotamus, red wild rooster, leopard, tiger, etc. are found.

Rohtak Zoo

- Establishment 1985-86
- Location Rohtak
- Area 44 Acres

- The zoo was approved by the Central Zoo Authority on 28th March, 2005.
- The Rohtak Zoo has different animals like crocodile, hippopotamus, tiger, hyena, wolf, jackal, beaver, black deer, sambar, langur, monkey, etc.

Important Breeding Centres in Haryana

Name	District
Crocodile Breeding Centre	Kurukshetra (Bhor Saidan)
Black Buck Breeding Centre	Kurukshetra (Pipli)
Chinkara Breeding Centre	Bhiwani (Kairu)
Pheasant Breeding Centre	Panchkula (Morni)
Vulture Conservation and Breeding Centre	Panchkula (Pinjore)
Peacock and Chinkara Breeding Centre	Rewari (Jhabua)
Red Jungle Fowl Breeding Centre	Panchkula (Pinjore)
Central Horse Breeding Centre	Hisar
Central Sheep Breeding Centre	Hisar
Central Buffaloes Breeding Centre	Hisar
Pig Breeding Centre	Hisar

CHECK CHAPTER KNOWLEDGE

1 Approximately how much area of Haryana comes under wildlife protected area?
(a) 2000 hectares (b) 2700 hectares
(c) 3000 hectares (d) 33000 hectares

2 The total number of wildlife sanctuaries in Haryana are *HSSC 2020*
(a) four (b) six
(c) eight (d) ten

3 Sultanpur national park is situated in which district of Haryana? *HSSC 2024, 21, 19*
(a) Yamunanagar (b) Gurugram
(c) Rewari (d) Sirsa

4 What is the other name of Sultan national park? *Haryana Tehsildar 2019*
(a) Agha Khan bird sanctuary
(b) Dr. Salim Ali bird sanctuary
(c) Mushtaq Ali bird sanctuary
(d) None of the above

5 Sultanpur national park was established in the year
(a) 2003 (b) 2001
(c) 1999 (d) 1971

6 Kalesar national park is situated in which district of Haryana? *Haryana Accountant 2020, 18*
(a) Yamunanagar (b) Gurugram
(c) Bhiwani (d) Panchkula

7 During which year, Kalesar was declared as national park?
(a) 2000 (b) 2001
(c) 2002 (d) 2003

8 Bhindawas wildlife sanctuary is associated with which of the following districts of Haryana? *HSSC 2023, 20, Mandi Supervisor 2017*
(a) Jhajjar (b) Rewari
(c) Gurugram (d) Faridabad

9 .... was declared a bird sanctuary by Indian Government on 3rd June, 2009. *HSSC 2020*
(a) Kalesar (b) Abubshahar
(c) Bhindawas (d) Nahar

10 In which year, Bhindawas wildlife sanctuary was declared as a bird sanctuary by Indian Government?
(a) 2006 (b) 2008
(c) 2009 (d) 2011

11 Which of the following is not found in Bhinda was wildlife sanctuary?
(a) Red Jungle fowl (b) Jackel
(c) Peafowl (d) Brown goose

12 Chhilchhila wildlife sanctuary is located in which district of Haryana? *HSSC 2022*
(a) Rewari (b) Kurukshetra
(c) Panchkula (d) Jhajjar

13 Which of the following is the smallest wildlife sanctuary of Haryana in terms of area?
(a) Nahar wildlife sanctuary
(b) Abubshahar wildlife sanctuary
(c) Chhilchhila wildlife sanctuary
(d) Khaparwas wildlife sanctuary

14 Nahar wildlife sanctuary is situated in which district of Haryana? *Anganwadi 2017*
(a) Rewari (b) Mahendragarh
(c) Palwal (d) Nuh

15 During ancient time, which wildlife sanctuary of Haryana was the pasture land of the Nawab of Dujana?
(a) Bhindawas wildlife sanctuary
(b) Nahar wildlife sanctuary
(c) Chhilchhila wildlife sanctuary
(d) Abubshahar wildlife sanctuary

16 In which year, Nahar Wildlife Sanctuary was declared as Eco-Sensitive Zone by the Indian Government?
(a) 2007 (b) 2009
(c) 2013 (d) 2015

17 Bir Shikargarh sanctuary is situated in the district of .... Haryana. *HSSC 2023, 17, Haryana Patwari 2018*
(a) Karnal (b) Hisar
(c) Sirsa (d) Panchkula

18 In which year, Bir Shikargarh wildlife sanctuary was set up in Haryana?
(a) 1983 (b) 1987
(c) 1990 (d) 1995

19 Which of the following is the largest wildlife sanctuary in Haryana in terms of area?
(a) Khaparwas wildlife sanctuary
(b) Abubshahar wildlife sanctuary
(c) Bir Shikargarh wildlife sanctuary
(d) Khol Hi-Raitan wildlife sanctuary

20 In which year, Abubshahar wildlife sanctuary was set up in Haryana?
(a) 1985 (b) 1986
(c) 1987 (d) 1988

21 Which wildlife sanctuary of Haryana is an Eco-Sensitive Zone from the point of view of environment and pollution?
(a) Nahar wildlife sanctuary
(b) Chhilchhila wildlife sanctuary
(c) Khaparwas wildlife sanctuary
(d) Kalesar wildlife sanctuary

22 In which year, Kalesar wildlife sanctuary was set up in Haryana?
(a) 1994 (b) 1996
(c) 1998 (d) 2000

23 Which of the following trees is mainly found in the Kalesars forest? *HSSC 2020*
(a) Peepal (b) Sal
(c) Eucalyptus (d) Babul

24 Kalesar National Park is famous for *HSSC 2020*
(a) Boar (b) Barking deer
(c) Red Jungle fowl (d) None of these

25 In which year, an area of 2,226.56 hectares was added in Khol Hi-Raitan wildlife sanctuary?
(a) 2000 (b) 2003
(c) 2005 (d) 2007

26 This protected area contains one of the last surviving area remnants of the Delhi Ridge hill range *HSSC 2024*
(a) Bhindawas wildlife sanctuary
(b) Nahar wildlife sanctuary
(c) Asola-Bhatti wildlife sanctuary
(d) Abubshahar wildlife sanctuary

27 Which of the wildlife sanctuary is situated near Surajkund, Haryana? *HSSC 2020*
(a) Bir Shikhargarh wildlife sanctuary
(b) Asola-Bhatti wildlife sanctuary
(c) Khol Hi-Raitan wildlife sanctuary
(d) Saraswati wildlife sanctuary

28 How many conservation reserves are there in Haryana?
(a) 2 (c) 7
(b) 5 (d) 10

29 Saraswati Conservation Reserve is situated in the district of *Haryana Group D 2019, PGT 2016*
(a) Kaithal
(b) Kurukshetra
(c) Karnal
(d) Both (a) and (b)

30 What is the other name of Saraswati conservation reserve? *HSSC 2015*
(a) Seonsar Forest (b) Kalesar Forest
(c) Bhur Syeda (d) Bir Shikargarh

31 Bir Bara Ban conservation reserve is located in which district of Haryana? *PGT 2016*
(a) Hisar (b) Sirsa
(c) Jind (d) Palwal

32 Deer park is located in which district of Haryana?
(a) Hisar (b) Kaithal
(c) Rohtak (d) Jind

33 Elephant Rehabilitation Centre is located in Ban Santour forest of .... district of Haryana. *PGT 2016*
(a) Panipat (b) Yamunanagar
(c) Kurukshetra (d) Ambala

34 In which year, National Research Centre on Equines (NRCE) was set up in Hisar district of Haryana? *HSSC 2019*
(a) 1982 (b) 1985
(c) 1986 (d) 1988

35 Jatayu (Vulture) Conservation and Breeding Centre is located in which district of Haryana? *HSSC Clerk 2016*
(a) Kurukshetra (b) Panchkula
(c) Yamunanagar (d) Karnal

36 How many zoos are there in Haryana?
(a) 2 (b) 3 (c) 5 (d) 9

37 In which year, Bear park was established in Mini Zoo in Haryana?
(a) 1982 (b) 1983
(c) 1989 (d) 1991

38 Which zoo of Haryana is located on the National Highway No. 1?
(a) Pipli Zoo (b) Rohtak Zoo
(c) Mini Zoo (d) None of these

39 Rohtak Zoo was established in which year in Haryana?
(a) 1982-83 (b) 1984-85
(c) 1985-86 (d) 1987-88

40 Crocodile Breeding Centre is situated in the district of *HSSC 2023, 20*
(a) Panchkula (b) Kurukshetra
(c) Bhiwani (d) Hisar

41 Chinkara Breeding Centre is located in which district of Haryana? *HSSC 2009, 23, 22*
(a) Pipli, Kurukshetra (b) Morni, Panchkula
(c) Kairu, Bhiwani (d) Hisar

42 Consider the following statements.

I. Sultanpur national park is the biggest National Park of Haryana.

II. Earlier, it was a bird sanctuary which accorded the status of national park in 1991.

Which of the statements given above is/are correct?

(a) Only I (b) Only II
(c) Both I and II (d) None of these

43 Consider the following statements regarding of Haryana. *HPSC PRE 2022*

1. Bhindawas wildlife sanctuary-Jhajjar district
2. Nahar wildlife sanctuary - Rewari district
3. Chhilchhila wildlife sanctuary - Kurukshetra district
4. Bir Shikargah wildlife sanctuary - Mahendragarh district

(a) 1, 2 and 3 (b) 1, 2 and 4
(c) 2, 3 and 4 (d) 1, 3 and 4

44 The Forest Department of Haryana runs a Pheasant breeding centre in .... *HSSC 2024, 21*

(a) Kurukshetra (b) Bhiwani
(c) Panchkula (d) Pinjore

45 Match the Following *HSSC 2020, PGT 2016*

Breeding Centre	Location
A. Pheasant Breeding Centre	1. Kairu
B. Red Jungle Fowl Breeding Centre	2. Bhor Saidan
C. Crocodile Breeding Centre	3. Pinjore
D. Chinkara Breeding Centre	4. Morni

Codes

	A	B	C	D		A	B	C	D
(a)	1	2	3	4	(b)	2	1	3	4
(c)	3	2	1	4	(d)	4	3	2	1

CORRECT ANSWERS

1. (d)	2. (c)	3. (b)	4. (b)	5. (d)	6. (a)	7. (d)	8. (a)	9. (c)	10. (c)
11. (a)	12. (b)	13. (c)	14. (a)	15. (b)	16. (b)	17. (d)	18. (b)	19. (b)	20. (c)
21. (c)	22. (b)	23. (b)	24. (c)	25. (d)	26. (c)	27. (b)	28. (a)	29. (d)	30. (a)
31. (c)	32. (a)	33. (b)	34. (c)	35. (b)	36. (b)	37. (b)	38. (a)	39. (c)	40. (b)
41. (c)	42. (b)	43. (a)	44. (c)	45. (d)					

CHAPTER 19

Agriculture and Animal Husbandry

- Haryana is a leading agricultural state, with around 70% of its population depending on agriculture and allied activities.
- The state is **self-sufficient** in food production and is the **second largest contributor** to the Central Foodgrains Reserves.
- Food Production increased from ₹ 25.92 lakh tonne in 1966-67 to ₹ 208.8 lakh tonne in 2023-24.
- First Agriculture census was done in the state in **1970-71**.
- The **Green Revolution** started in the year 1966-67, significantly boosting wheat production and transforming the agricultural sector.
- The major crops of Haryana include rice, wheat, jowar, bajra, maize, sugarcane, cotton, pulses, oilseeds, potato, fruits and vegetables.
- Crop diversification through Soyabean, sunflower, peanuts and horticultural products is encouraged.

Agricultural Land Use

• Total cultivable area	86% of geographical area (44,212 sq km)
• Gross area sown	6570 thousand hectares (Economic Survey 2024-25)
• Cropping intensity	183.2% (higher than the national average of 155.41%)

- Land is the main source of agriculture. Adequate means of irrigation facilities in Haryana have led to agricultural expansion.

Agro-Climatic Zones

Haryana falls in the **Trans-Gangetic Plains Region** (Agro-climatic zone VI), divided into two agricultural zones based on climatic conditions. These are as follows

1. **North-Western Zone** In this zone, rice, wheat, vegetables and fruits of temperate zone are cultivated on a large number.
2. **South Western Zone** In this zone, vegetables, crops, medicinal plants, herbs and tropical fruits are cultivated.

Crop Seasons in Haryana

↓

Rabi

- Rabi crops in Haryana are sown in October-November and harvested in April-May.
- These crops are also known as **Asadhi crops** and are mainly winter crops.
- Wheat, barley, gram, mustard, peas are Rabi crops.

↓

Kharif

- Kharif crops in Haryana are sown in June-July and harvested in October-November. These crops require high temperature and high humidity.
- These crops are also called **Savani crops** as they are sown on the arrival of monsoon. It is also known as summer crop.
- Rice, sugarcane, maize, jowar, bajra, cotton, beans are Kharif crops.

Major Crops of Haryana

- The main crops of Haryana are wheat, rice, sugarcane, cotton, oilseeds, gram, barley, corn, millet, etc. which are grown according to their agro-climatic conditions in different crop seasons of Haryana.
- Other crops grown are food crops, cash crops, spices, herbs and horticultural crops.

> **Regional Specialisation**
> - Southern Haryana produces pulses and oilseeds.
> - Western Haryana produces cotton.
> - Northern Haryana produces rice and wheat.

Major food crops of Haryana are discussed below

Wheat

- Wheat is an important food crop of Haryana. Haryana is often referred to as **Wheat Bowl of India.**
- It has the largest area under cultivation.
- **First Grain Bank** is established in **Panipat** district.
- **Second largest grain market in Asia** is located **Kurukshetra** district.

Geographical Conditions for Wheat Cultivation

• Temperature	10-15°C during sowing, 15-28°C during ripening
• Grows in	Sub-temperate climate
• Annual rainfall	50-75 cm
• Suitable soil	Loamy, clayey loam and light clayey
• Ideal region	Plain areas with irrigation facilities (around 60% in Haryana).

- Moist soil during sowing, clear sky and bright sunshine during growth.

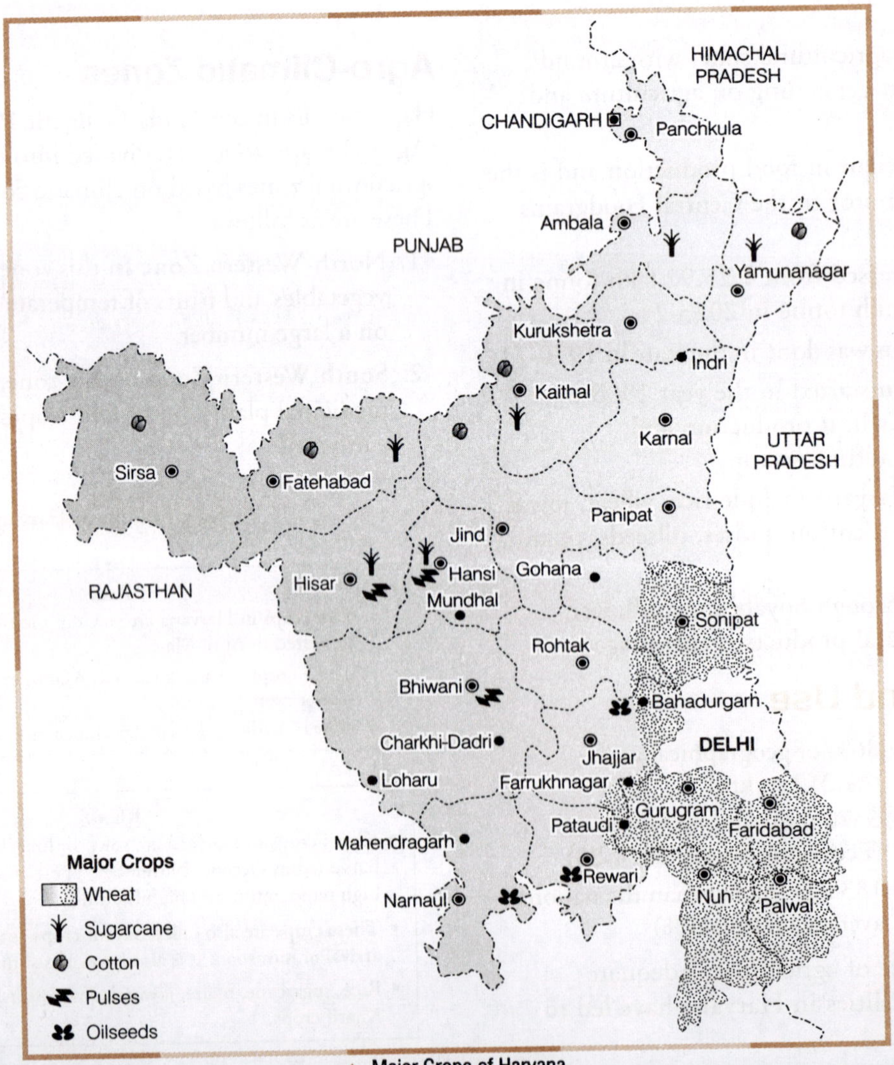

▲ Major Crops of Haryana

Wheat Production

- Haryana is known as the **wheat bowl** due to its high wheat production, exceeding its own needs.
- As per the Economic Survey 2024-25, Haryana produced 124.83 lakh tonnes of wheat in 2023-24.
- **Top wheat producing districts** Sirsa (largest producer), Faridabad, Kurukshetra, Jhajjar, Sonipat, Bhiwani, Gurugram and Mewat.
- Lowest wheat producing district **Panchkula**.
- Indian Institute of Wheat and Barley Research located in Karnal district.

Rice

- Rice is the second most important crop of Haryana after wheat.
- It is mostly cultivated in North-Eastern and Central Haryana.

Geographical Conditions for Rice Cultivation

- Temperature: >20°C during sowing, 27°C during ripening
- Grows in: Tropical climate
- Annual rainfall required: 150-200 cm
- Suitable soil: Loamy, clayey, gravel but thrives in alluvial soil
- Ideal region: Suitable for plain lands or gentle slopes
- It remains water cover for around 75 days.
- It needs heat, light and good irrigation facilities for its growth.
- It needs fertilisers like green manure, ammonium sulphate, super sulphate and compost.

Rice Production

- According to Economic Survey 2024-25 Haryana produced 69.88 lakh tonnes of rice in the year 2023-24.
- **Karnal** (a rice bowl of Haryana) is the largest producer, accounting for 14.11% of state's rice production. Karnal and Kurukshetra are famous for producing high-quality Basmati rice.
- Kaithal and Karnal districts export Basmati rice.
- Haryana exports 60% of India's Basmati rice alone.
- Kaithal, Kurukshetra and Jind other major rice producing districts together with Karnal.

Maize

- Maize is cultivated in places those receive less rainfall. It is also planted with Jowar and Bajra in many places.

Geographical Conditions for Maize Cultivation

- Temperature: 25°C to 30°C
- Annual rainfall: 50-100 cm
- Suitable soil: Deep loamy soil enriched with nitrogen
- Ideal region: Plain areas and gentle slopes
- Maize is cultivated in Haryana across multiple seasons.
- It is also grown for animal feeding and use in industries, for starch production.

Jowar

- It is grown in the dry regions with average or medium rainfall.

Geographical Conditions for Jowar Cultivation

- Temperature: 25°C to 30°C
- Annual rainfall: 60 cm or less
- Suitable soil: Less fertile soils (red, yellow, light, deep loamy) and alluvial soil
- Ideal region: Gentle sloping and plain areas
- Largest producer: Rohtak district
- Other major producers: Jhajjar, Sonipat and Palwal districts

Bajra

- It is considered as a coarse grain. It is also used as a fodder crop.
- Bajra is one of the indigenous plants of Haryana as hot and dry climatic conditions required for its growth are found here.

Geographical Conditions for Bajra Cultivation

- Temperature: 25°C to 30°C
- Rainfall: 40-50 cm (or 30-50 cm with loamy soil)
- Soil: sandy, loam, light sandy and sandy soil
- Ideal region: Plain and plateau areas, semi-arid region
- Growth period: 2-3 months
- Sowing time: After first monsoon showers
- Sunshine: Light sunshine during sowing
- Largest producer: Mahendragarh district
- Other major bajra-producing districts: Bhiwani, Gurugram, Jhajjar, Sirsa, Hisar, Fatehabad, Jind, Rohtak, Faridabad
- Indigenous to Haryana, thriving in the state's hot and dry climatic conditions.

Barley

- It is grown in Haryana since ancient times and the climatic conditions of the state are suitable for its cultivation.
- It is also known as Yav in Sanskrit and used in religious ceremonies.

Geographical Conditions for Barley Cultivation

- Temperature — 12-15°C during growth, up to 30°C during maturity
- Annual rainfall — 30-100 cm (moderate rainfall is ideal)
- Growth in — Sub-tropical climate
- Suitable soil — Well-drained loamy to sandy loam soil
- Ideal regions — Rain-fed plains and dry temperate regions
- Major barley producing districts — Mahendragarh, Hisar, Sirsa, Jhajjar

Gram

- Gram is sown both as a Rabi and as a Kharif crop. It replenishes the soil with nitrogen.

Geographical Conditions for Gram Cultivation

- Temperature — 20°C to 25°C during the growing period
- Suitable soil — Well-drained loamy to clayey soils, with moderate moisture retention
- Annual rainfall — 40-60 cm
- Ideal region — Rain-fed plains, particularly in semi-arid and dry regions.

Gram Production

- **Mainly produced in** Western Haryana.
- **Largest producer Bhiwani** district (54.42% state share).
- **Other major gram producing districts** Mahendragarh, Hisar, Sirsa and Rohtak.

Cash Crops

- Sugarcane, cotton and oilseeds are major cash crops of Haryana. These are discussed below

Sugarcane

- Haryana is major sugarcane-producing state in India.
- It is annual crop, used to produce sugar and jaggery.

Geographical Conditions for Sugarcane

- Temperature — 21°C to 27°C (grows best in warm and humid climates)
- Annual rainfall — 75 cm-150 cm
- Suitable soil — Well-drained, fertile loamy or alluvial soil with good organic content; slightly acidic to neutral pH (5.5 to 8.0)
- Ideal regions — Rain-fed plains, river valleys and coastal areas with adequate irrigation sources.

Sugarcane Production

- According to Economic Survey 2024-25 Sugarcane production was 72.03 lakh tonnes in the year 2023-24.
- It contributes around 3% to India's sugarcane production.
- Mainly produced in Yamuna basin, with **Yamunanagar** as the **largest producer** (1/3 of state's production)
- Other major producing districts include Ambala, Karnal, Kurukshetra, Jind, Sonipat and Rohtak.

Cotton

- It is an ancient crop, cultivated since Rigvedic period.
- It is also known as **White Gold.**
- Two varieties of cotton are grown i.e. **American** and **Indian.**
- The fibres of **American variety** are long, shiny and more durable. While fibres of **Indian variety** are small, less shiney and less durable. Coarse clothes are made with this cotton.
- Irrigation facilities are drawn from different canals of Haryana.

Geographical Conditions for Cotton

- Temperature — 21°C to 30°C
- Annual rainfall — 50 cm - 100 cm (requires irrigation in low-rainfall areas)
- Suitable soil — Black soil (Regur soil) and well-drained alluvial soil
- Ideal regions — Rain-fed plains

▲ Cotton Production

Cotton Production

- According to Economic Survey 2024-25 total production of cotton was 15.09 lakh bales in the year 2023-24.
- **Highest producer** Sirsa district
- **Other major cotton-producing districts** Hisar, Fatehabad, Jind, Rohtak, Bhiwani, Sonipat and Rewari.

Oilseeds: Mustard

- Mustard is the most important oilseed crop in the state.
- It is a Rabi crop.

Geographical Conditions for Mustard Cultivation

- Temperature 10°C to 25°C
- Annual rainfall 25 cm - 40 cm
- Suitable soil Well-drained loamy or sandy loam soil
- Ideal regions Rain-fed plains

Mustard Production

- According to Economic Survey 2024-25, total oilseeds production was 13.94 lakh tonnes in the years 2023-24.
- **Largest producer** Bhiwani district.
- **Other major mustard-producing districts** Mahendragarh, Sirsa, Jind, Rewari, Rohtak, Sonipat and Gurugram.

Crop Producing Districts of Haryana

District	Major Crops
Ambala	Wheat, Rice, Maize, Gram
Yamunanagar	Wheat, Sugarcane, Maize, Gram, Sunflower
Panchkula	Rice, Wheat, Gram, Maize
Kaithal	Wheat, Rice
Kurukshetra	Wheat, Rice (Basmati), Sugarcane
Karnal	Sunflower, Rice (Basmati), Sugarcane
Rohtak	Jowar, Bajra, Wheat, Sugarcane, Cotton, Gram Maize
Sonipat	Jowar, bajra, Wheat, Rice, Sunflower, Mushroom, Sugarcane, Pulses
Gurugram	Jowar, Bajra Wheat, Barley, Gram
Jhajjar	Wheat , Gram, Rice
Faridabad	Wheat, Bajra, Mustard
Palwal	Wheat, Bajra, Gram
Mewat (Nuh)	Wheat, Bajra, Mustard
Rewari	Wheat, Rice, Gram
Mahendragarh	Wheat, Mustard, Gram, Bajra
Hisar	Wheat, Rice, Cotton, Gram, Oilseed, Pulses.
Bhiwani	Wheat, Rice, Cotton, Gram, Mustard
Fatehabad	Wheat, Rice, Cotton, Gram
Jind	Wheat, Rice, Bajra, Cotton, Oilseed
Charkhi-Dadri	Wheat, Rice, Cotton, Gram, Mustard
Sirsa	Wheat, Rice, Cotton, Gram, Mustard

Largest Crop Producing Districts

Crop	District
Wheat	Sirsa
Rice	Karnal
Bajra	Bhiwani
Cotton	Sirsa
Sugarcane	Yamunanagar
Sunflower	Ambala
Gram	Bhiwani
Jowar	Rohtak

Targeted Area, Production and Average Yield of Major Crops for 2024-25

Crops (Kharif)	Area (000 hectare)	Production (000 Tonne)	Average Yield (Kg/hect)
Rice	1200	5040	4200
Jowar	80	50	625
Maize	50	140	2850
Bajra	530	1075	2025
Kharif Pulses	80	85	1050
Crops (Rabi)			
Wheat	2500	12500	5000
Gram	50	85	1700
Barley	20	70	3500
Rabi Pulses	10	12	1200
Cash Crops			
Sugarcane	120	10440	87000
Cotton (Lint)*	675	2144	540
Kharif Oil Seed	28	26	925
Rabi Oil Seed	750	1575	2100
Sun Flower	25	50	2000

**Cotton Production in '000' Bales of 170 kg each.*
***Source** Economic Survey 2024-25*

Horticulture in Haryana

- Haryana is emerging fast as one of the leading states in horticulture sector. In the state, almost all types of fruits, vegetables, spices, mushroom and flowers are grown.
- Out of the total area under horticulture cultivation, around 80% area is under vegetables and the rest is under fruits, spices, etc.

- According to Economic Survey 2024-25, the total area under the Horticulture crops is **4.12 lakh hectares** and total production on Horticulture crops in the state was 68.43 lakh metric tonnes in 2023-24.
- With a view to give a boost to the growth of horticulture Government created a separate Department of Horticulture in 1990-91.

Horticulture Zones of Haryana

Horticulture	Districts
North-Eastern Zone	Panchkula, Kaithal, Karnal and Jind
South-Western Zone	Fatehabad, Sirsa, Bhiwani and Rewari
South-Eastern Zone	Palwal, Mewat and Gurgaon
Central Zone	Kurukshetra, Panipat and Fatehabad

- The **important horticultural crops** like fruits, vegetables, spices, medicinal plants, aromatic plants and flowers are discussed in detail as follows

Fruits

- Total area — 70,218.92 hectares in 2023-24 (as per Economic Survey 2024-25)
- Total production — 8.56 lakh metric tonnes (2023-24)
- Important fruits — **Mango, Guava, Papaya, Citrus fruits** like (kinnow, amla)
- Government initiative — Department of Horticulture promoting cluster approach for better fruit cultivation development.

Top Fruit Producing Districts
- **Sirsa** Largest citrus fruit producer (orange, kinnow and grapes)
- **Sonipat** Largest guava producer
- **Fatehabad** Largest apple producer

Mango Cultivation

- Area — With more than 19% of total fruits area, it is a prominent fruit, cultivated in Haryana.
- Major varieties — Dashehari, Chausa, Langra, Mallika, Ramkela, Arunika and Ambika

Kinnow Cultivation

- Production — 22 tonnes per hectare
- Harvesting period — December-February
- Largest producer — Yamunanagar
- Leading producers — Sirsa, Fatehabad, Hisar, Bhiwani and Jhajjar districts
- Kinnow cultivation is gaining popularity in the state due to low water requirement and suitability for semi-arid region.

Fruits and Area of Production

Fruit	Main Production Area
Mango	Panchkula, Ambala, Yamunanagar, Karnal, Kurukshetra
Guava	Gurugram, Karnal, Hisar, Faridabad, Sonipat
Citrus	Sirsa, Hisar, Ambala, Gurugram, Fatehabad
Papaya	Yamunanagar, Karnal, Panchkula, Kurukshetra, Ambala
Berry	Sonipat, Gurugram, Hisar, Fatehabad, Rohtak
Amla	Sirsa, Gurugram, Hisar, Karnal, Faridabad, Ambala

Vegetables

- Total area — 3,34,995.34 hectares (in 2023-24 as per Economic survey 2024-25)
- Total production — 59.14 lakh metric tonnes (2023-24)
- Main vegetables grown — Potato, cauliflower, carrot, tomato, radish, onion
- Largest cultivated vegetable — Potato
- Sonipat district is the largest producer of vegetables in the state.
- **Turnip** is extensively cultivated, enhancing land fertility.

Vegetables and Area of Production

Vegetable	Main Production Area
Potato	Kurukshetra, Yamunanagar, Ambala, Karnal
Onion	Gurugram, Sonipat, Panipat, Panchkula
Cauliflower	Sonipat, Panipat, Kurukshetra, Yamunanagar
Tomato	Karnal, Sonipat, Panipat, Gurugram

Mushroom Cultivation

- Mushroom (Khumbi) cultivation in Haryana is rising. It requires less land and water. It is profitable to grow mushrooms seeing its high demand in country as it is a rich source of protein, vitamin, folic acid, iron, etc.
- The Haryana government has launched a new scheme for promoting mushroom production in four districts, viz, Kaithal, Jind, Rewari, Mahendragarh by giving ₹ 50 lakh as subsidy.
- There are export opportunities of processed mushrooms like canned and dried mushrooms.
- **Sonipat** is the largest producer of mushrooms in Haryana.
- In the year 2023-24, the production of mushroom was 15,339.50 metric tonnes. (Economic Survey 2024-25)

Top Producers of Vegetables in Haryana

Vegetable	Largest Producer
Potato	Kurukshetra, Sonipat
Onion	Ambala
Mushroom	Sonipat
Apricot	Sirsa

Spices

- Major spices grown: Green chillies, garlic, coriander, methi and turmeric
- Total area: 5,633.58 hectares in 2023-24 (Production of 0.37 lakh metric tonnes)
- Largest cultivated spice: Garlic
- Top spice-producing district: Yamunanagar, accounts for around 40% of total spice production in Haryana

Area and Production of Spices

Name	Achievement 2023-24	
	Area (Hect)	**Production** (MT)
Ginger	57.12	690.1
Garlic	3702.6	30465.5
Fenugreek	1042.6	1966.5
Others	831.26	4048.9
Total	5633.58	37171

As per Economic Survey of Haryana 2024-25

Spices and Area of Production

Spice	District
Coriander	Kurukshetra, Karnal, Gurugram, Panchkula, Ambala
Chillies	Yamunanagar, Karnal, Hisar, Jind, Fatehabad
Garlic	Karnal, Yamunanagar, Fatehabad, Sirsa, Gurugram
Methi	Gurugram, Hisar, Mahendragarh, Kurukshetra, Jind
Turmeric	Yamunanagar, Kurukshetra, Ambala, Panchkula

Medicinal and Aromatic Plants

Haryana state has a limited share in the cultivation of medicinal plants like Aloe vera (largest cultivated plant in Haryana) Stevia, Guggal, Tulsi, Mulethi, Arjun, Giloy, etc.

State Medicinal Plan Board

- Established on 13th August, 2002
- Objective: To promote medicinal and aromatic plants sector through promotional projects, schemes and contractual farming initiatives.
- Location: Panchkula
- Activity: Provides training, conduct workshops, seminars, resources for herbal parks, etc.

- Currently a project on 'Conservation and Development of Guggal in Haryana' and another project for 'Plantation of Amla and Moringa' are under implementation in the state by the Forest Department.
- The state has large number of herbal parks i.e., 59 herbal parks.
- Highest number of **herbal parks are in Rewari** (15) followed by Mahendragarh (11). World Herbal Forest is being developed in Morni Hills. New parks are created in Masudpur, Kheri Lohchab, Dharam Kheri and Khanda Kheri.

Area and Production of Medicinal and Aromatic Plants

Name	Achievement 2023-24	
	Area (Hect)	**Production (MT)**
Aloe vera	5.3	6.5
Stevia	0	0
Arandi	0	0
Others	341.4	223.9
Total	346.7	230.4

As per Economic Survey of Haryana 2024-25

Floriculture in Haryana

- Haryana mainly cultivates Gladiolus, Marigold, Rose and Tuber Rose.
- As per the Economic Survey 2024-25, the state's total flower production was 0.19 lakh metric tonnes (2023-24).
- Largest cultivated flower is **Gladiolus**, mainly produced in Faridabad.
- Focus is on **Gerbera** cultivation (red, pink, yellow, white) with plants sourced from Pune and Bengaluru.
- State Government is giving 50% grants for Gerbera cultivation.
- It is in high demand as it is used for decoration in wedding and other ceremonies.

- Lilliam flowers of white, red and yellow colours are also in great demand.
- Lilliam cultivation is done in Tosham of **Bhiwani** district. The sandy soil and climatic conditions of Bhiwani are suitable for the cultivation of Lilliam.
- Lilliam seeds are imported from Holland.
- The state has set up centre of excellence for flowers in assistance with Netherlands in Jhajjar district to encourage the farmers to take up floriculture.
- Shahbad town of Kurukshetra is gaining popularity for the high income it earns due to flower cultivation mainly of Marigold, Jaffrey Rose and Chrysanthemum.
- Flowers from Haryana are sent to Delhi, Chandigarh, Punjab, Himachal Pradesh and Rajasthan.

Flowers and Area of Production

Flower	Main Production Area
Rose	Panipat, Sonipat, Gurugram, Kaithal
Marigold	Gurugram, Sonipat, Jind, Jhajjar
Rajnigandha	Faridabad
Gladiolus	Faridabad, Gurugram, Karnal, Panchkula

Centre of Excellence in Horticulture

Institution	Location
Centre of Excellence for Fruit	Mangiana (Sirsa)
CoE Biotechnology	Shamgarh (Karnal)
CoE for Honey	Ramnagar (Kurukshetra)
CoE for sub - tropical Fruits	Ladwa (Kurukshetra)
Guava Technology Exhibition Centre	Bhuna (Fatehabad)
Coe for Flower	Jhajjar

Institutions for Agricultural Development

Haryana being an agricultural state, has dedicated departments for agricultural development.

These are discussed below

Haryana Cooperative Agriculture and Rural Development Bank

- Established on — 1st November, 1966 (under the Punjab Cooperative Association Act, 1965)
- Objective — Provides long-term loans to farmers
- Financed by — NABARD (90%), Haryana State Government (5%) and Central Government (5%)

Haryana State Cooperative Bank Limited (HARCO)

- Established on — 1st November, 1966
- Objective — Provides finance to farmers, marginal labourers and industrialists.
- Branches — 19 branches and 2 extension boards in **Chandigarh** and **Panchkula**.
- Services — Offers financial assistance and aid to its customers.

Haryana State Cooperative and Marketing Federation (HAFED)

- Established on — 1st November, 1966
- Headquarters — **Panchkula**
- Objective — Provide clean and hygienic food products
- Main products — Basmati rice, mustard oil, refined oil, soyabean oil, wheat, sugar, turmeric, etc.

Haryana State Cooperative Sugar Mills Limited

- Established in — 1966
- Objective — Set up new sugar mills and improve functioning of existing mills.

Haryana Warehousing Corporation

- Established on — 1st November, 1967
- Objectives — To provide scientific warehousing for farmers, government agencies and traders.
- Started with 16 warehouses (7,000 metric tonnes capacity); expanded to 111 warehouses (15.25 lakh metric tonnes) by 30th November, 2019.
- Operates an Inland Container Depot in Bawal, Rewari, with freight facilities and Electronic Data Interchange for import-export operations.

Haryana State Agriculture Marketing Board (HSAMB)

- Established on — 1st August, 1969 under the Punjab Agricultural Produce Market Act, 1961
- Headquarters — Panchkula
- Develops modern markets for grains, fodder, fish, cotton and wool, ensuring an efficient marketing system.
- Developing Agro Shopping Malls for easier agricultural product marketing, completed in Karnal, Rohtak, Panipat and Panchkula.
- Establishing an International Horticulture Market at Ganaur, Sonipat, with cold storage, ripening, grading and packaging facilities.
- Engaged in village road development to improve rural connectivity.

Haryana Seed Development Corporation (HSDC)

- Established in 1974 under the Companies Act, 1956
- Operates 6 seed processing plants in Umri, Hisar, Sirsa, Yamunanagar, Tohana and Pataudi
- Produces, distributes, imports, exports and sells certified seeds under the **Haryana Seeds** brand through 74 sale counters and institutional agencies like HAFED, HAIC and Mini Banks.
- Owns seed testing laboratories and supplies quality seeds to farmers at regulated prices under central and state schemes.

Haryana Land Reclamation and Development Corporation (HLRDC)

- Established on 27th March, 1974
- Headquarters Panchkula, with regional offices in Hisar, Karnal and Kaithal.
- Works on alkaline land reclamation, government farm management and agricultural input sales.
- Provides 50% grants for gypsum and 60% grants under the National Food Security Mission and National Mission for Oilseed and Oil Palm.

Haryana State Seed Certification Agency (HSSCA)

- Established on 6th April, 1976, registered under the Societies Act, 1860.
- Headquarters Panchkula; regional offices in Hisar, Karnal, Sirsa and Rohtak
- Certifies seeds as per Section 5 of the Seeds Act, 1966, and has expanded into organic production.
- Ensures certified seeds for farmers at reasonable prices.
- Seed certification is also conducted by HSDC, HAFED, HLRDC, Haryana Agricultural University, National Seed Corporation and private centers.

Haryana Farmer Commission

- Established on 15th July, 2012, with RS Paroda as the first Commissioner
- Members Vice-Chancellor of Agricultural University, Hisar, Finance Commissioner of Agriculture Department and two non-government members appointed by the Governor.
- Headquarters Hisar, with a camp office in Gurugram for farmer support.

The work done by the Commission are

- To know and understand about agricultural problems in the state.
- To advice on how to raise farmer's income and productivity.
- Formulate plans and projects on animal husbandry, horticulture, etc.
- To propose or recommend the management of seeds, manures, fertilisers, pesticides, etc. to the State Government.
- To prepare plans on proper use of irrigation resources.
- To encourage research and technical development in agriculture sector.

Important Schemes for Agriculture Development (Haryana Government)

Scheme	Explanation
Haryana Fasal Suraksha Yojana	• Launched in 2023 by Haryana State Government. • It is primarily designed to provide financial assistance to farmers to protect crops from natural calamities. • Under the scheme, farmers receive compensation for crops loss, which helps them meet their cultivation costs and continue production in the future.
Mukhya Mantri Kisan Evam Khetihar Mazdoor Jiwan Suraksha Yojana	• This scheme was launched in 2014 by the State Government of Haryana. • It aims to provide insurance cover to farmers and farm workers in the event of death or injury due to operation of farm machinery. • Under this scheme, the government provides a compensation of ₹ 3 lakh in case of death and ₹ 1 lakh in case of any disability.
Seed Scheme	• It started from 2011. This programme is implemented by Haryana Seed Development Corporation. • The farmers are provided assistance for the purchase of hybrid/certified seeds. They are provided subsidies for the purchase of seeds of wheat, barley, paddy and bajra.

Scheme	Explanation
Weather Based Crop Insurance Scheme	• It is implemented in 12 districts of the state from 2009-10. This scheme is based on several weather parameters such as deficit rainfall, excess rainfall, temperature and dry days instead of yield parameters. Main crops under this scheme are wheat and paddy.
Indo-Dutch Project	• It was started in 1994 in collaboration with Government of Netherlands and currently running in four areas namely Lakhan Majra (Rohtak), Safidon (Jind), Ghadwal and Gohana (Sonipat). • This project is undertaken by the Haryana Government to treat the waterlogged and saline soils for the reclamation of waterlogged and saline lands. It is part of the main project-**Haryana Operational Pilot Project**.
Tele Agriculture	• This is an agricultural helpline started by the State Government through which farmers can get relevant information related to weather, agricultural developments, new technology, seeds, etc. • Initially implemented in Hisar district, now this helpline is being available in other districts also.
E-NAM	• The State Government has launched e-National Agriculture Market (NAM) in Haryana and has linked 54 modes with e-NAM to promote online trading of agricultural commodities. • The government has also launched an 'e-Kharid' project to digitise the procurement process of foodgrains. The State Government gives agriculture awards **Chowdhary Devilal Award** to encourage the farmers. • It also provides financial assistance like Revolving Cash Credit Scheme, Easy Loan Scheme, etc. • The state celebrates **Farmers Day** every year on **23rd December** to mark the birth date of Chowdhary Charan Singh.
Mukhya Mantri Bagwani Bima Scheme	• The objective of this scheme is to keep farmers free from the risk of uncertainity of weather. • Under this scheme, farmers will have to pay 2.5% premium per acre.
Mera Pani Meri Virasat	• This scheme was launched in the year 2020. This scheme is to motivate farmers towards less water intensive agriculture option from paddy.
Khet Khali Phir Bhi Khushali	• This scheme was launched in the year 2021. The objective of this scheme is to provide benefits to farmers even if the paddy grown on that land-remains barren. • Under this, the government gives ₹ 7000 per acre to the farmers who do not sow paddy.

Central Government Schemes

Scheme	Explanation
Pradhan Mantri Kisan Maandhan Yojana	• It was launched on 12th September, 2019 by PM Narendra Modi at Ranchi, the capital of Jharkhand. • The farmers above 60 years are provided with a pension of ₹ 3,000. • The eligible farmer is required to contribute to a pension fund between ₹ 55 to ₹ 200 per month depending on the entry age. The Central Government contributes in equal amount to the pension fund.
Pradhan Mantri Kisan Samman Nidhi	• The scheme was launched in 2019. Under this scheme, a sum of ₹ 6,000 is being provided to each farmer in an year in three installments. • The PM-Kisan Scheme aims to supplement the financial needs of the Small and Marginal Farmers (SMFs) in procuring various inputs to ensure proper crop health and appropriate yields. This would protect them from falling in the clutches of moneylenders.
Pradhan Mantri Fasal Bima Yojna	• It was launched on 18th February, 2016 by the PM Narendra Modi. • According to Economic Survey 2024-25, under the scheme, the farmer's share of premium is 1.5% for Rabi crops, 2% for Kharif crops and 5% for horticultural and commercial crops. • The remaining share is paid by the Central and State Government in equal proportion.
Soil Health Card Scheme	• Prime Minister Narendra Modi launched Soil Health Card scheme on 19th February, 2015. • The main objective of this scheme is to recommend about the required nutrition or fertilizers for the fields so that farmers can increase their productivity. • In the first phase of this scheme (2015-17) 10.74 crore cards and in the second phase (2017-19) 11.69 crore Soil Health Cards were distributed to farmers.

Scheme	Explanation
Food and Nutrition Security (FNS) and National Food Security Mission	• It is a Centrally Sponsored Scheme running in the state from 2007-08. Its objective is to increase production of wheat and pulses through area expansion and productivity enhancement in a sustainable manner. • The scheme runs on 60:40 basis from the year 2015-16 where 60% is centre share and 40% is state share of the finances. Seven districts of Haryana are covered for wheat crop and 5 for pulses.
Rastriya Krishi Vikas Yojana	• It was started in 2007-08 in Haryana with a centre-state sharing pattern of 60 : 40. • Development works like irrigation through underground pipeline system, sprinklers, increasing soil health through provisions of manures, better seeds are undertaken under this scheme. • The scheme aims to set up ideal agricultural village by spreading awareness on farming practices.
National Organic Farming Project	• This project was launched under 10th Five Year Plan (2002-07) to encourage organic farming. • The project is being run by National Organic Farming Centre (Ghaziabad) and 8 regional centres are Patna, Bubneshwer, Bangluru, Panchkula, Gaziabad, Imphal and Nagpur.
Crop Diversification Scheme	• It is a sub-scheme of Rashtriya Krishi Vikas Yojana (RKVY), which aims to encourage farmers to shift away from water intensive crops to more sustainable water efficient alternatives. • They are educated on how to sow a variety of crops that improves soil fertility and productivity. • Farmers are encouraged to sow maize, moong and other pulses along with rice and wheat.
Meri Fasal, Mera Byora	• It is a flagship programme of State Government where farmers register themselves to sell their crops on MSP and to get other benefits of Agriculture and other allied departments, which is a single window platform for all farmers to take benefit of government schemes.

Haryana State Agriculture Policy

- The Government of India, formulated National Agriculture Plan in 2000 and in 2007, formulated plan for farmers to achieve high growth in the agriculture sector. Later, Haryana Government made a draft to improve the overall conditions of the farmers of the state.
- Haryana State Government has divided the entire state into **three agricultural zones** based on the geographic and climatic conditions.

  These zones are as follows

  - **Zone I** There are 8 districts in this zone. These are Panchkula, Ambala, Kurukshetra, Karnal, Yamunanagar, Kaithal, Panipat and Sonipat.
  - **Zone II** There are 7 districts in this zone. These are Fatehabad, Sirsa, Hisar, Jind, Rohtak, Faridabad and Palwal.
  - **Zone III** There are 7 districts in this zone. These are Bhiwani, Charkhi-Dadri, Mahendragarh, Rewari, Jhajjar, Gurugram and Nuh.

Agricultural Awards

The Haryana State Government provides the following awards for outstanding work in the field of agriculture

- **Jan Nayak Chaudhary Devi Lal Award** Under this Award, the highest producing farmer at the district level gets cash reward of ₹ 25,000 and the highest producing farmer at the state level gets ₹ 1 lakh cash prize.
- **Krishi Ratna Award** This award is given by the Haryana State Government for outstanding performance to the farmers of the state. The award is given at two levels - state and district.
- At the state level farmers are awarded ₹ 1,00,000 cash prize, a citation, and at the district level farmers are awarded ₹ 51,000 cash prize and a citation as an award.

Under the Krishi Ratna Award many awards are given in various fields of agriculture like, Fasal Ratna, Udhami Ratna, Matsya Ratna, Phool Ratna, Sabzi Ratna, Nursery Ratna and Mushroom Ratna Awards.

- Zone I and Zone II are specially marked for the production of sugarcane, cotton, wheat, pulses, rice, horticulture and dairy.
- Zone III is specially marked for cultivation of those crops that can survive in semi-arid climate such as mustard, pulses, wheat, bajra etc. Nuh is specially marked for animal rearing.

Government Initiatives in Horticulture

Crop Cluster Development Programme

- This scheme is launched by Horticulture department of the state which came into effect from 21st February, 2018.
- It is launched in 340 villages which will be developed into 'Horticulture villages'. These villages are made into 140 clusters.
- These clusters are given the facilities of pack house, polyhouse, packing machinery, cold house, primary processing units, sales centres, refer vans, solar energy facilities, etc.
- This cluster is developed at **Uncha Majra village** in Gurugram district.

Horticulture Vision 2030

- In the year 2017, Haryana State Government has prepared a long-term vision to increase the horticulture twice and production thrice by the year 2030.
- To give a boost in the horticulture sector, State Government has set up Bagwani Vishwavidyalya in Karnal district.
- Under this, State Government has been establishing centre of Excellence in each district of the state for the promotion of horticulture. Karnal, Sirsa and Kurukshetra has already set up three Centres.
- As per this vision, Haryana Government has planned to enhance the area under horticulture cultivation from 7 to 25%.

Bhavantar Bharpayee Yojana

- This scheme was launched on 30th December, 2017 and came into effect from 1st January, 2018.
- In this scheme, the farmers will be assured of compensation in case the prices go below the mentioned prices.
- This scheme is undertaken to diversify the farmers from producing traditional crops to vegetables.
- Presently, compensation assurance of four vegetables are given, i.e. tomato, potato, onion and cauliflower.
- This scheme is firstly launched at Ganger village in Karnal.

Horticulture University

- In order to develop state specific technologies that cater to the local needs, the State Government has set up **Maharana Pratap Horticultural University** at Karnal to carry on research in horticultural practices.
- It was established 28th November, 2016.

National Horticulture Mission

- The Government of India has launched National Horticulture Mission in 2005-06 as a Centrally Sponsored Scheme to promote holistic growth of the horticulture sector through area based regionally differentiated strategies.
- Under National Horticulture Mission, two centres have been established.
  1. Centre for Excellence for food, Sirsa.
  2. Centre for Excellence for vegetable, Karnal.

Indo-Israel Horticulture Project

- The Harayana Government has set up an Indo-Israel Horticulture Project at Gharaunda in Karnal district to enable farmers to grow off seasonal vegetables.
- Under the project, seedlings of various vegetables like tomato, seedless cucumber and capsicum would be prepared in the greenhouse, polyhouse, net house and these saplings would be provided to the farmers on subsidy.

International Horticulture Market

- To make a world class, modern, wholesale fruit and vegetable trading platform, the Haryana Government has decided to make use of French expertise in horticulture marketing and develop an International Horticulture Market (IHM) in Ganaur (Sonipat) and Panchkula.
- Horticulture crops are covered under the Pradhan Mantri Crop Insurance scheme.
- Now the State Government of Haryana will stand the Chief Minister Horticulture Insurance Scheme.
- A total of 20 horticulture crops (14 vegetable crops, two spice crops, four fruit crops) have been covered under this insurance scheme.

Modified National Agricultural Insurance Scheme (MNAIS)

- This scheme was first started in the Karnal and Kaithal districts of Haryana but now it is working in Rohtak and Jindh.
- There is a provision of 40 to 50 per cent grant in this scheme. Wheat and Rice crops are covered under this scheme.

Kisan E-Portal

- The department of horticulture in Haryana provides the facility to link the village with E-portals so that farmers can benefit from information related to weather, seed plantations, market rates, etc.

Farmer Clubs

- The farmer clubs are grassroot level informal forums run by individuals belonging to farming community. At present, 835 such clubs are running in the state with a membership of 1000 farmers in each club.

Technology Demonstration Centres

- The State Government has set up Technology Demonstration centres at seven places i.e. Shamgarh, Gharaunda, Mangeana, Ladwa, Ram Nagar, Jhajjar and Bhuna.
- **Real Time Data Acquisition System** (RTDAS) is the data of complete information of water level in canals.

Integrated Parasite Management

- A Biological Control Laboratory has been set up in Sirsa to decrease the dependency on chemical pesticides.
- State Government promoted bio-pesticides and bio-agents through which the use of bio-pesticides by the farmers of the state has been increased.
- Under this scheme, farmers will be provided free bio-agent in order to reduce crops diseases.

Animal Husbandry in Haryana

- Animal husbandry is an important sector to supplement the income of rural masses in the state. It is the **second most important activity** after agriculture in the state.
- The first Animal Survey of India was done in 1919-20 after which, it is conducted every five years.
- As per 20th livestock Census 2019, the livestock population of Haryana consists of 71.26 lakh including 19.32 lakh cattle and 43.76 lakh Buffaloes.
- The districts with highest number of cattle population is **Bhiwani.** It is followed by Hisar, Jind, Sirsa and Kaithal.
- Cow, buffalo, sheep, goat, pig, horse are reared in the Central, Eastern and Northern regions of the state.
- Donkeys, mules and camels are reared in the drier parts of Southern and Western regions of the state.
- The milk production in Haryana in the year 2023-24 was 119.65 lakh tonnes. (Economic Survey 2024-25)
- As per the Economic Survey 2024-25, there are 2,956 Veterinary Institutions in Haryana.

Important Facts Related to Animal Husbandry

- Semen Bank established at Narnaul in Mahendragarh district that has facilities of liquid nitrogen to keep safe.
- Hisar has artificial insemination centres.
- **Hisar** district has **Asia's largest animal farm.**
- Horse (stallion) breeding centre is located at Tohana in Hisar.
- Poultry Disease and Research Centre is at Thanesar in Kurukshetra. It was established in 1988-89.
- Gurugram has three poultry research and breeding centres.
- Sperm centres are at Hisar, Gurugram and Jagadhri.
- State animal wealth farms are situated in Hisar.

Livestock in Haryana

Buffalo

• Murrah Buffalo	Indigenous to Haryana, especially found in Rohtak, Hisar and Jind. Known for superior milk production (around 35 liters/day), it is often called **Black Gold** or **Asian Tractor.** Locally it is called as **khunds.**
• Highest population	Hisar, followed by Bhiwani and Jind
• Lowest population	Panchkula

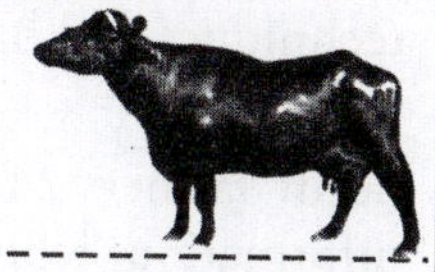

Cow

• Breeds	Hariana, Tharparkar and Sahiwal, originating from Rohtak, Hisar, Jind and Gurugram
• Jersey cattle and mix breed	Also found in the state
• Highest cattle population	Sirsa, followed by Hisar and Karnal
• Government protection	Abhyaranyas (sanctuaries) established in Hisar and Panipat

Sheep

• Breeds	Nali and **Hisardale**, found in Hisar and Rohtak.
• Highest sheep population	Bhiwani, followed by Hisar and Sirsa

- Most of the sheep flocks in Haryana are stationary. Only a few are migratory that follow a fixed route along Rajasthan and Madhya Pradesh.

Goat

• Breeds	Betal, Nagfani, Jamunapari, Boer and Nubian goats.
• Highest goat population	Sirsa, followed by Bhiwani and Mahendragarh

Other Animals

• Horses	They are found highest in Gurugram followed by Karnal and Kaithal.
• Donkey	They are found highest in Palwal followed by Gurugram and Rewari.
• Camels	They are found highest in Bhiwani followed by Bhiwani and Mahendragarh.

Major Districts with Livestock (in Descending Order)

Livestock	Districts
Cow	Hisar, Sirsa, Karnal
Buffalo	Hisar, Jind, Kaithal
Sheep	Bhiwani, Hisar, Sirsa
Goat	Mahendragarh, Bhiwani, Sirsa
Horse	Gurugram, Karnal, Bhiwani
Mule	Bhiwani, Jhajjar, Kaithal
Camel	Bhiwani, Sirsa, Mahendragarh
Pig	Sonipat, Jhajjar
Dog	Gurugram, Bhiwani
Donkey	Palwal, Gurugram

State Government Initiatives for Development of Animal Husbandry

The Department of Animal Husbandry, established in 1966, provides healthcare and breeding facilities for the livestock in the state. In order to improve the genetic merit of livestock, government has initiated many programmes. Some of the initiatives are discussed below

Haryana Pashu Kisan Credit Card Yojana 2021

- Under this scheme, farmers who has a cow, will be provided a loan of ₹ 40,783 and ₹ 60,249 will be provided to buffalo owner.
- In order to get this loan, cattle farmer has to get an **Animal Farmer Credit Card.**
- The loan amount will be provided in 6 equal installments.
- This amount will have to be returned to the beneficiary with a 4% interest rate in a span of 1 year.

Pashudhan Bima Yojana

- It was started on 29th July, 2016, to safeguard the interests of the farmers at Jhajjar. It was started from Jhajjar.
- Under this scheme, ₹ 100 for large mammals such as cattle, buffaloes, horses, donkeys, etc. and ₹ 25 for small ruminants such as sheep, pigs, etc is being paid for 3 years as premium.

- Farmers can insure either five big animals or 50 small ruminants under this scheme.
- The scheme is running in 15 districts of the state.
- Scheduled Castes can avail this scheme for free.

Haryana Gauvansh Sanrakshan and Gausamvardhan Act, 2015

- This act was launched on 27th October, 2015.
- Under this act, the State Government established institutions to accept, keep, maintain and care for the infirm, injured, stray and uneconomic cows in the state of Haryana.
- The institutions provide programmes for the conservation and upgradation of indigenous breeds of cows. It also bans cow slaughter with punishment of upto 10 years and ₹ 1 lakh fine.

Banjh Mukt Pashudhan

- To maximise per head productivity through regular breeding, a unique programme of Banjh Mukt Pashudhan was launched in 2009-10.
- This programme is undertaken by Rashtriya Krishi Vikas Yojana.

Pandit Deendayal Upadhyay Bharpai Scheme

- This scheme aims to make the livestock owner risk free.
- It offers subsidised premiums and provides coverage for a maximum number of large and small animals.

National Programme for Bovine Breeding

- To bring the indigenous cattle at par with buffaloes, **Systematic Breed Improvement Programme** through various organisations, especially Gaushalas in the state is being undertaken, where selective breeding through natural service as well as through artificial insemination with quality semen is performed.

> Indigenous breeds of cattle and buffalo namely Murrah, Sahiwal, Hariana, Tharparker are being maintained at state owned farms at Hisar.

- These breeds are supported with various programmes to encourage retention of high fielders.

Veterinary Services

- In order to provide quality veterinary services, selected district hospitals are being upgraded into specialised polyclinics in a phased manner.
- Three such polyclinics at **Sonipat**, **Bhiwani** and **Sirsa** in addition to one Pet Animal Polyclinic at Rohtak is also started.

Pandit Deen Dayal Upadhyay Bima Yojana

- In this scheme, farmers can insure their farm animals for one year.
- They can insure big animals (cow, buffalo, horse, camel). etc. for a sum of ₹ 10,050 each.
- Farmers can also insure their small animals (sheep, goat, pig etc.) for a sum of ₹ 25 each.

Biogas Plant Scheme

- The Government is providing financial assistance to farmers for the installation of biogas plants.
- The main purpose of this scheme is to use animal dung in order to obtain the necessary fuel and manure that can be used in agriculture also.

Pashudhan Vikas Vahini Yojana

- This facility is started by Haryana Government to provide information about animal husbandry techniques and breeding facilities.
- It is a State Government funded scheme that helps the needy farmers 24 hours by giving them educational information, telling them about available vaccination, nearby animal care centres, etc.

Important Facts on Livestock

- **Vaccination Programme** Joint vaccination for cows and buffaloes under Atmanirbhar Bharat Scheme to prevent cattle diseases.
- **Animal Insurance** Haryana is the first state to provide free animal insurance to Scheduled Tribes, along with a 50% subsidy for setting up dairy or rearing goats, pigs and sheep.
- **Gokul Gram** An ideal village at Hisar to promote and upgrade indigenous breeds like Sahiwal, Hariana and Tharparkar.
- **Cow Identification** Haryana is the first state to issue a 12-digit ID card for cows, tracking breed and growth.
- **Milk Grants** Farmers receive grants (₹ 1,000- ₹ 20,000) based on milk readings from their animals.
- **Livestock Shows** The state organises district-wise livestock exhibitions, offering cash awards for farmers under the Integrated Murrah Development Scheme.
- **Protection Acts** Haryana implemented the Haryana Murrah Buffalo and Milch Animal Breed Act, 2001 for breeding improvement.
- **Pashu Swasthya Kalyan Samiti** A committee promoting animal welfare, especially in veterinary hospitals and district diagnostic labs.
- **Medicines** Essential medicines available in **Pashudhan Aushadhi Stores** at every veterinary hospital.

Livestock and Daily Development Institute

National Dairy Research Institute

- It was established in 1923 in Bengaluru and was named as Imperial Institute of Animal Husbandry and Dairy.
- In 1947, the name was changed to National Dairy Research Centre. In 1955, the head office was shifted from Bengaluru to Karnal. Facilities at Bengaluru were retained to function as a regional station to serve the Southern states.

Haryana Dairy Development Cooperative Federation Limited

- It was established in 1970. This institution was operational till 31st March, 1977.
- After 1977, a three level Cooperative Dairy Federation was established on the pattern of Anand Cooperative of Gujarat.
  The three level cooperative management is done in the following ways : Milk producers centres at village level; Milk producers Cooperative Union at district level and Milk producers Federation at state level.

Lala Lajpat Rai University of Veterinary and Animal Sciences

- This university was established on 4th February, 2010. It is in Hisar district.
- Six higher education institutions are affiliated to this university. These are as under
  - Animal Veterinary Sciences College
  - Institute of Veterinary, Animal Health and Biotechnology
  - Institute of Fish Sciences
  - Institute of Animal Biotechnology
  - Institute of Dairy Technology
  - Animal Sciences College

YMCA University of Science and Technology

- It was established in 2009 by Haryana state Legislative Act 21 of 2009.
- Formerly, it was known as YMCA institute of engineering, established in 1969 as an Indo-German Project.

Livestock Development Award

- The Government of Haryana has started the 'Livestock Development Award' scheme with an aim to encourage the cattle rearers to preserve their high quality milch Murrah buffaloes.
- Under this scheme, cattle owners will be provided incentives ranging from ₹ 1,000 to 6,000 per buffalo as well as the owners of Murrah buffalo who have recorded milk of 19-22 kg, 22-25 kg and more than 25 litre will be given ₹ 15,000, ₹ 20,000 and ₹ 30,000 cash incentive, respectively.

Some Livestock Institutes in Haryana

Institute	Year	Centre
Central Buffalo Research Institute	1985	Hisar
National Horse Research Institute	1986	Hisar
Animal Vaccination Research Institute	—	Hisar
Animal Veterinary and Research Centre	—	Hisar

Poultry Farming in Haryana

- Poultry farming is a rapidly expanding sector in Haryana, providing a vital secondary income source and reducing reliance on traditional agriculture.
- The industry has seen a 12% growth in the last five years, with over 12,000 farms now operating state-wide.
- Broiler farms are concentrated in key districts like Jind, Panipat, Hisar, Fatehabad, Sirsa, Karnal, Kaithal and Yamunanagar.
- The government actively supports this growth through the Department of Animal Husbandry and Dairying, operating four poultry farms in Ambala, Rohtak, Bhiwani and Hisar.
- Further support comes from the Central Poultry Breeding Farm in Chandigarh, which focuses on poultry development and vaccination.
- The government also offers subsidy schemes for small landholders and BPL families.

Backyard Poultry Scheme

- This scheme was started in the year 2018.
- The primary goal is to create self-employment opportunities for small farmers, marginal labourers and landless workers.
- To initiate the programme, each beneficiary family is provided with a starter kit, which includes 80 chicks (8 to 10 days old), along with two feeders and two drinkers.
- Throughout the chick-rearing process, families receive continuous guidance and support to ensure successful outcomes.

Fisheries in Haryana

- The state of Haryana has great potential of fish culture and it is now on the threshold of Blue Revolution after Green and White Revolution.
- The important ones are **Katla, Mrigal, Chunni, Bata, Siriha, Mallee**, etc.
- Fish culture is also being accepted by the farmers of the state as subsidiary occupation along with agriculture.
- **Shrimp culture** is also taking place in man-made salt lakes in the state.
- The government is providing technical and financial assistance through **Fish Farmers Development Agencies** to the fish farmers, which have been set up in all the districts except Panchkula, Nuh and Palwal.
- It is proposed to establish new fish market at Bahadurgarh and Gurugram.
- According to the Economic Survey 2024-25, the total area under fish farming in rural water bodies is around 21,550.73 hectare.
- The Fish production in the state was 2,15,173.55 metric tonne in the year 2023-24.
- There are around 20 fish healthcare centres, 14 aqua polyclinics and 1 state diagnostic lab to cater to the demand of fish.
- Fisheries Department of Haryana aims to develop 2,500 acre of waterlogged area for pisciculture in Jind, Jhajjar, Charki-Dadri, Rohtak, Palwal, Sonipat, Nuh, Hisar, Fatehabad and Faridabad.
- Tikkar Tal of Panchkula and West Yamuna Canal of Yamunanagar are being developed for conservation of depleted fish species.
- Prawn chilling and its processing centre is established for shrimp production in the saline affected and waterlogged areas in the state.
- Haryana is declared by the government as fish disease free state.
- Fisheries Department declared to include 200 hectare water logged area utilising saline water for fish production.
- The Government will create a fish mandi, awareness amongst the common people regarding importance of fish conservation.

CHECK CHAPTER KNOWLEDGE

1 What service does the Tele Agriculture initiative provide to farmers?
(a) Free fertilisers
(b) Agricultural helpline with weather updates, farming info and seed advice
(c) Direct cash benefits
(d) Only irrigation support

2 First Agriculture census was done in Haryana in *Haryana Patwari 2016*
(a) 1968-69 (b) 1970-71
(c) 1975-76 (d) 1980-81

3 In which of the following discipline Haryana is most famous for? *HSSC 2020*
(a) Agriculture (b) IT industries
(c) Sports (d) Manufacturing

4 How many Agro Climatic Zones are there in Haryana?
(a) 1 (b) 2 (c) 3 (d) 4

5 What is Rabi crop locally called in Haryana?
(a) Asadhi crop (b) Savani crop
(c) Agphani crop (d) Kartik crop

6 During monsoon, which crops are grown in Haryana? *HSSC 2023, 17*
(a) Kharif (b) Rabi (c) Zaid (d) Cash

7 Kharif crops are grown in the month of *HSSC 2017*
(a) January-February (b) March-April
(c) June-July (d) July-August

8 Kharif crops are also known as .... crops. *HSSC 2020, 19*
(a) Cash (b) Food (c) Summer (d) Winter

9 Which crop is produced most in Haryana? *Haryana Lab Attendant 2018, Anganwadi 2017*
(a) Rice (b) Sugarcane
(c) Maize (d) Wheat

10 Which district is the largest producer of wheat in Haryana?
(a) Jind (b) Bhiwani
(c) Sirsa (d) Kaithal

11 Which of the following taxes has waived by the Haryana Government on wheat?
(a) Sales tax (b) Production tax
(c) VAT (d) All of these

12 Which Kharif crop covers the maximum agricultural area in Haryana?
(a) Rice (b) Wheat
(c) Bajra (d) Maize

13 Which district in Haryana is the largest exporter of Basmati rice?
(a) Fatehabad (b) Panipat
(c) Karnal (d) Kurukshetra

14 Which district is known as Rice Bowl of the state? *HSSC 2022, 17*
(a) Ambala (b) Sirsa (c) Hisar (d) Karnal

15 Best quality rice is grown in which two districts of Haryana? *Haryana Patwari 2015, HSSC 2017*
(a) Karnal and Kurukshetra
(b) Karnal and Rewari
(c) Hisar and Rewari
(d) Sirsa and Faridabad

16 Which crop in Haryana is grown both as Rabi and as Kharif crop?
(a) Jowar (b) Gram
(c) Bajra (d) Mustard

17 Which one of the following is not the main crop of Haryana? *Haryana Clerk 2016, Haryana Patwari 2015*
(a) Wheat (b) Rice
(c) Tea (d) Sugarcane

18 Haryana is called as *HSSC 2024, 20*
(a) Sacred land
(b) Land of temples and churches
(c) Land of flowers
(d) Wheat bowl of India

19 Which of the following commercial crops covers maximum area in the state?
(a) Sugarcane (b) Oilseeds
(c) Cotton (d) Sunflower

20 Which of the following districts is the highest producer of cotton in Haryana? *HSSC 2023*
(a) Ambala (b) Sirsa
(c) Rohtak (d) Rewari

21 Which is the most important oilseed grown in Haryana? *HSSC 2024, 17*
(a) Seasame (b) Mustard
(c) Groundnut (d) Soya

22 Apart from Bhiwani, which district of Haryana produces large quantities of mustard? *HSSC 2017*

(a) Karnal (b) Rohtak
(c) Faridabad (d) Mahendragarh

23 Which fruit is grown on largest area in Haryana? *HSSC 2017*

(a) Amla (b) Orange
(c) Guava (d) Mango

24 Which district is the largest producer of mangoes in Haryana? *HSSC 2016*

(a) Ambala (b) Karnal
(c) Panchkula (d) Yamunanagar

25 Mango is not produced in which district of Haryana? *HSSC 2016*

(a) Yamunanagar (b) Kurukshetra
(c) Karnal (d) Mahendragarh

26 Which districts is/are among the leading producers of Kinnow?

(a) Sirsa (b) Hisar
(c) Jhajjar (d) All of these

27 Which one of the following crops helps to enhance the fertility of the land? *HSSC 2017,16*

(a) Tomato (b) Wheat
(c) Turnip (d) Brinjal

28 Haryana ranks first in the production of *HSSC 2022, 18*

(a) Spices (b) Nuts
(c) Cabbage (d) Mushrooms

29 Which district of Haryana is the highest producer of mushrooms? *HSSC 2021,17*

(a) Ambala (b) Sonipat
(c) Sirsa (d) Kurukshetra

30 When was State Medicinal Plant Board set up in Haryana?

(a) 2016 (b) 2002
(c) 2019 (d) 1999

31 Which flower has the largest area under cultivation in Haryana?

(a) Rose (b) Gladiolus
(c) Lily (d) Tuber rose

32 In which year, Haryana State Seed Certification Agency was established? *TGT 2016*

(a) 1975 (b) 1976 (c) 1977 (d) 1978

33 Where is the Headquarter of Haryana land Reclamation and Development Corporation (HLRDC) located?

(a) Hisar (b) Karnal
(c) Kaithal (d) Panchkula

34 Seed scheme was started in Haryana in the year

(a) 2009 (b) 2011
(c) 2013 (d) 2015

35 Indo-Dutch project was launched in Haryana in collaboration with which country?

(a) Spain (b) Japan
(c) Portugal (d) Netherlands

36 How many markets in Haryana are linked to the e-National Agriculture Market (e-NAM)?

(a) 40 (b) 54 (c) 60 (d) 75

37 When was Rashtriya Krishi Vikas Yojana (RKVY) implemented? *HSSC 2016*

(a) 2011-12 (b) 2004
(c) 2007-08 (d) 2005

38 Which village in Gurugram district is developed as a horticulture cluster?

(a) Ganaur (b) Gharaunda
(c) Uncha Majra (d) Binola

39 Horticulture department of Haryana had planned to enhance the area under horticulture cultivation from 7 to .... percent by 2016. *Haryana HSSC 2020*

(a) 25 (b) 15
(c) 18 (d) 10

40 In which of the following districts International Horticulture Market was set up? *HSSC 2020*

(a) Gurugram (b) Panchkula
(c) Sonipat (d) Both (b) and (c)

41 When was the first animal survey of India conducted?

(a) 1919 (b) 1984 (c) 1965 (d) 1976

42 Which among the following is/are the breed of buffalo? *Patwari 2016*

(a) Murrah (b) Hariana
(c) Sahiwal (d) Both (a) and (b)

43 In which year Pashudhan Bima Yojana (Animal Insurance Scheme) started in Haryana? *HSSC 2023, 16*

(a) 29th July, 2016 (b) 31st March, 2016
(c) 1st August, 2016 (d) None of these

44 What is the age limit to join 'Chief Minister Kiran and Agricultural Labourer Life Security Scheme' in Haryana? *HSSC CET 2024*

(a) 10 years to 60 years (b) 20 years to 59 years
(c) 15 years to 75 years (d) None of these

45 Animal Insurance Scheme in Haryana was started from which district? *HSSC 2016*

(a) Panipat (b) Jhajjar
(c) Rohtak (d) Sirsa

46 'Banjh Mukt Pashudhan' has been launched in which of the following states? *PGT 2016*

(a) Haryana (b) Punjab
(c) Uttar Pradesh (d) Rajasthan

47 Asia's largest animal farm is in *HSSC 2016*

(a) Jind (b) Bhiwani
(c) Hisar (d) Karnal

48 In which year, National Dairy Research Institute's head office was shifted to Haryana? *Haryana Clerk 2016*

(a) 1960 (b) 1950
(c) 1955 (d) 1965

49 Where is National Dairy Research Institute situated in Haryana? *Haryana Clerk 2016, HSSC 2020*

(a) Hisar (b) Kurukshetra
(c) Rohtak (d) Karnal

50 Where is Central Research Institute for Buffaloes situated? *Patwari 2016*

(a) Rohtak (b) Karnal
(c) Hisar (d) None of these

51 Where is Central Buffalo Research centre situated in Haryana? *HSSC 2017*

(a) Hisar (b) Chandigarh
(c) Mahendragarh (d) Sirsa

52 The Government of Haryana has introduced a horticulture project in Karnal district with the asistance of *HSSC 2020*

(a) Japan (b) France
(c) USA (d) Israel

53 Which of the following pairs is correctly matched? *SSC-CTET 2023*

(a) National Diary Research Institute-Manesar
(b) YMCA University of Science and Technology-Faridabad
(c) Lingaya's University-Hisar
(d) National Brain Research Centre-Hisar

54 Match the following schemes portal of the Government of Haryana. *HPSC-HCS-2023*

List I	List II
A. Meri Fasal, Mera Byora Fatal	1. To free farmers from the risk of weather uncertainties
B. Uttam Seed Portal	2. Canals
C. Mukhyamantri Bagwani Bima Yojana	3. To prevent abritrainess of seed sellers.
D. Real Time Data Acquisition System	4. Allow farmers to sell their crops and provides financial assistance of fertilisers, seed loan and agricultural equipments from their home.

Codes

	A	B	C	D		A	B	C	D
(a)	1	2	3	4	(b)	2	3	4	1
(c)	3	4	1	2	(d)	4	3	1	2

55 Match the following schemes/yojanas of Government of Haryana. *HPSC-HCS-2023*

List I	List II
A. Khet Khali Phir Bhi Khushali	1. To make livestock owener's risk free
B. Mera Pani Meri Virasat	2. To make farmers free from risk at the time of a fall in the prices of fruits, vegetables
C. Bhavantar Bharpai Yojana	3. To encourage farmers to diversify from paddy to alternative less water intensive crop.
D. Pandit Deendayal Upadhayay Pashudhan Suraksha Yojana	4. Farmers get benefit even if the land where paddy is grown is kept fallow.

Codes

	A	B	C	D		A	B	C	D
(a)	1	2	3	4	(b)	2	3	4	1
(c)	4	3	2	1	(d)	4	1	2	3

CORRECT ANSWERS

1. (b)	2. (b)	3. (a)	4. (b)	5. (a)	6. (a)	7. (c)	8. (c)	9. (d)	10. (c)
11. (c)	12. (a)	13. (c)	14. (d)	15. (a)	16. (b)	17. (c)	18. (d)	19. (a)	20. (b)
21. (b)	22. (d)	23. (d)	24. (d)	25. (d)	26. (d)	27. (c)	28. (d)	29. (b)	30. (b)
31. (b)	32. (b)	33. (d)	34. (b)	35. (d)	36. (b)	37. (c)	38. (c)	39. (a)	40. (d)
41. (a)	42. (a)	43. (a)	44. (d)	45. (b)	46. (a)	47. (c)	48. (c)	49. (d)	50. (c)
51. (a)	52. (d)	53 (b)	54. (d)	55. (c)					

CHAPTER 20

Irrigation in Haryana

- Agricultural state Haryana, has irrigation facilities covering 60% of its land. The main sources of irrigation are **canals**, **tubewells**, **wells** and **ponds**.

Sources of Irrigation in Haryana

Source	Percentage
Tubewells	51.12%
Canal Irrigation	48.3%
Other Sources	0.52%

- **Kaithal** has the largest tubewell irrigation facility (185 hectare) and **Panchkula** has the lowest (15 hectare).
- **Sirsa** has the largest overall irrigation facilities (698 hectares), while **Panchkula** has the lowest (25 hectares).
- Around 5672 hectares of land is irrigated in Haryana. Some districts use windmills and some depends upon Canal Irrigation. They are as follows

Districts Using Windmills for Irrigation	Rohtak, Gurugram, Karnal, Bhiwani
Districts depend on Canal Irrigation	Ambala, Yamunanagar, Kurukshetra, Karnal, Jind, Panipat

- The countries like Holland (the Netherlands) and Germany have support the process of doing irrigation with the help of windmills.
- Most districts in Haryana lack adequate water resources for irrigation, relying on groundwater management and international water agreements for agricultural water supply.

Canal Irrigation System in Haryana

- According to the Economic Survey 2024-25, Haryana has a canal network of 1,503 channels covering **14,128 km.**
- The state's canal system consists of two major water systems, the **Western Yamuna Canal System** and the **Bhakra Canal System.**
- The Bhakra Canal System is the **largest** in **Haryana,** spanning 6,279.57 km with 558 canals. The Western Yamuna Canal System has 473 canals covering 4,295.35 km.

The main canal projects of Haryana are as follows

Western Yamuna Canal System

- The oldest canal in Haryana, started in 1879 at **Tajewala** on the Yamuna's right bank, was originally built by **Feroz Shah Tughlaq.** With a total length of 3,226 km, it irrigates 4 lakh hectare.
- Ambala, Kurukshetra, Karnal, Sonipat, Panipat, Rohtak, Hisar, Sirsa and Jind districts are covered under this canal system.
- It also irrigates about 1 lakh hectare land of Delhi and Rajasthan. It currently originates from the Hathnikund Barrage in Haryana.

Branches of Western Yamuna Canal

Branch	Description
Sirsa Branch Canal	This canal provides irrigation facilities in Jind, Fatehabad and Sirsa. It was constructed in 1896 and it is the longest branch of Western Yamuna Canal System.
Bhalaut Branch Canal	It is a sub-branch of Delhi branch of Western Yamuna Canal which flows from Khubru village to Jhajjar district. The Jhajjar canal is a sub-canal of the Bhalaut branch.
Barwala Branch Canal	It is a sub-branch of Sirsa of Western Yamuna Canal. The canal provides water to Hisar district.
Hansi Branch Canal	The canal was remodelled in 1959 but originally it was built in 1825. One of its main branch, Bhutana canal provides water to the Hansi area of Hisar district. This canal originate from paleochannel of Chautang river.
Jind Branch Canal	It flows through the Jind district of the state. Rohtak canal and Bhiwani canal are its main branches. These branches provides the water to Rohtak and Bhiwani districts for irrigation and other activities.
Munak Canal	It is 102 km long. It carries water from Munak village in Karnal to Haidarpur in Delhi. It is one of the main sources of drinking water for Delhi.

Bhakra Canal System

- The Bhakra Canal, built on the **Sutlej river** via Nangal dam, irrigates Punjab, Haryana and Rajasthan.
- The canal is a combined project of these three states and irrigates a large part of Northern India.
- It enters Haryana near **Tohana** and irrigates large part of Hisar, Rohtak, Fatehabad and Sirsa districts through its main branches i.e. **Ratia, Rori, Barwala** and **Fatehabad.**
- It is linked with the Western Yamuna Canal through the **Western Yamuna Feeder Project**. It ensures water supply to arid region of western Haryana during summer.
- The feeder has two branches i.e. **Narwana Link Canal** (capacity 2700 cubic feet) and **Barwala Link Canal** (capacity 1700 cubic feet).
- The Barwala Link Canal draws water from the Western Yamuna canal in summer and Bhakra canal at year end.

Gurugram Canal Project

- This canal takes off from **Okhla** (Delhi) by building a dam on Yamuna river. The construction work of this canal was started in 1970. It was completed during the time of 10th Five Year Plan.
- This canal irrigates 1.2 lakh hectare land in Gurugram, Faridabad and Palwal districts.

Jawahar Canal and Bhiwani Canal

- These two small canals are drawn out from Bhakra Canal System.
- Jawaharlal canal irrigates the area of Sonipat district and Bhiwani canal irrigates the area of Bhiwani district.

Agra Canal

- This canal draws water from Yamuna river and starts from **Okhla Barrage** near Delhi.
- This canal irrigates the area of Agra and Mathura in Uttar Pradesh, Bharatpur in Rajasthan and Faridabad in Haryana.

Sutlej-Yamuna Link Project

- Sutlej-Yamuna link Project (known as SARYU or SYL) is a proposed project to link the rivers Sutlej and Yamuna.
- The canal is being constructed in the state to divert the water of Ravi and Beas rivers.
- The project is 211 km long in which 90 km is expanded in Haryana and 121 km in Punjab.
- This project is the lifeline of Haryana. The construction of the link canal is on hold due to legal disputes between Haryana and Punjab.

Multipurpose River Valley Projects of Haryana

Some of the multipurpose river valley projects of Haryana are as follows

Lift Irrigation Projects

- Lift irrigation projects in Haryana serve hilly and dry regions, mainly in the Southern and Western areas.
- These areas are offshoots of the Aravalli hills, which receive low rainfall. Hence, Lift Irrigation System is used in these areas which is helpful for agriculture.
- The system supports agriculture with 493 canals spanning 3,702 km.

Important Lift Irrigation Projects in Haryana
Jui Canal Project • This Lift Irrigation Scheme is designed to irrigate the upper area of Bhiwani and adjoining areas. • This 170 km long canal irrigates about 32 thousand hectare of land. • The Jui Canal Project was started in 1969 and is successfully running in Haryana.
Jawaharlal Nehru Lift Irrigation Project • This irrigation project is built along the Bhakra canal. This project was first initiated in 1976 in the dry region of Mahendragarh district. • It irrigates the agricultural land areas of Mahendragarh and Bhiwani districts. • The project was specially helpful in saving Kharif crops during the drought of 1987.
Loharu Lift Irrigation Project • This project is also known as **Indira Gandhi Irrigation Project**. • Canal made under this project is 225 km long. • This project provides water to the **Bhiwani** and **Charkhi-Dadri** districts.
Bhiwani Lift Irrigation Project • It is also known as **Virendra Narayan Chakravarti Project.** • Canal made under this project is 200 km long. • This project irrigates about 1 lakh hectare of land in **Bhiwani.**
Nangal Lift Irrigation Project • The canal under this project is 80 km long and constructed in two phases. • The project irrigates **Ambala** and provides drinking water to Ambala canal and Ambala Cantt areas.

Hathnikund Barrage Project

- The 360-meter-long concrete barrage on the Yamuna river in Yamunanagar district of Haryana, was constructed between October 1996 and completed in June, 1999 at the cost of ₹ 220 crore to replace the old Tajewala Barrage.
- It started functioning from 2002. It aids irrigation and creates a wetland for 31 species of water birds.
- The barrage diverts excess water during Monsoon to the **Western and Eastern Yamuna Canals,** this preventing floods.

Narwana Irrigation Project

- The 37,500-feet-long Narwana Irrigation Project connects the **Salwan Feeder** with the **Dhamtan distributary.**
- It provides water for irrigation to areas including **Kaloda Khurel, Bhikhewala, Tulian Kalan** and **Sulehra** areas of the state.

Tajewala Barrage

- It was constructed in 1873 across the Yamuna river in Yamunanagar district. The barrage with a height of 24.73 m and length of 360 m, regulated flow for irrigation in Western Uttar Pradesh and Haryana through the Western and Eastern Yamuna Canals.
- It was decommissioned after the proper functioning of Hathnikund Barrage.

Other Irrigation Projects

Irrrigation Project	Irrigation Areas
Narwana Lift Irrigation Project	Jind
Nangal Lift Irrigation Project	Ambala
Loharu Lift Irrigation Project (Indira Gandhi Canal Project)	Bhiwani, Mahendragarh, Jhajjar
Mewat Canal Irrigation Project	Mewat
Dadupur, Shahbad Canal Irrigation Project	Yamunanagar, Ambala, Kurukshetra

Major Dams of Haryana

Haryana has several dams, which serve various purposes including water storage for irrigation and power generation. The major dams of Haryana are as follows

Pathrala Dam

- Built in — 1875-76
- Location — Near Dadupur village of Yamunanagar district
- Dimension — 460 m in length and 34 m height

Ottu Dam

- Built in — 1896
- Also known as — Ottu Weir and Ottu Head
- Location — Ghaggar-Hakra river near Sirsa
- It was a joint project by the Princely State of Bikaner and the British Government.
- It creates a large water reservoir out of the formerly-small Dhanur lake, located near the village of Ottu in **Sirsa district.**
- It provides water to **two Ghaggar canals** (the Northern Ghaggar Canal and the Southern Ghaggar Canal) that provide water to Northern Rajasthan state for irrigation.

- In 2002, a tourist complex was inaugurated at the barrage and it was renamed as **Chaudhary Devi Lal Weir** in honour of Haryana's former Chief Minister.
- The **Dhanur Lake reservoir** is now known as the Ottu Reservoir.

Anangpur Dam

- Location — Near Anangpur village, Faridabad
- Also known as — Gravity dam
- This dam was constructed by King Anangpal of Tomar dynasty in 8th century. It is an excellent example of **Indian Hydraulic Engineering.**

Kaushalya Dam

- Constructed in — 2012
- Location — Pinjore, Panchkula
- The Kaushalya dam, constructed on the **Kaushalya river** (a tributary of the Ghaggar-Hakra river), is 700 m long and 34 m high.
- Total catchment area of this dam is 75 sq km.

> Kaushalya dam controls the flow of excess water in Kaushalya and Ghaggar rivers during monsoon. It provides water to Panchkula district.
> Kaushalya dam is an important wetland that is home to many endangered migratory birds.

- It also helps in conservation of underground water level.

▲ Kaushalya Dam

Masani Dam

- This dam is constructed on **Sahibi river** which is a tributary of Yamuna river. It is located in **Rewari.**
- It prevents flooding of the nearby areas of Sahibi river during monsoons in the district of Rewari.

Other Dams

- The State Government has given go ahead to construct, **Dangrana, Dewanwala** and **Chhamla** dams on river Ghaggar and its tributaries.

Region-Wise Irrigation System in Haryana

Irrigation in North-Eastern Region

- The North-Eastern region, including the plains of **Ambala** and the **Shivalik** hills, receives sufficient rainfall, making the plains fertile.
- Rainfall irrigates the fields in most of the areas in this region.
- Canal irrigation in Ambala district was made possible after the **Nangal Lift Irrigation Scheme**, which covers 45,000 acres of land.

Irrigation in Central Region

- The Central region, including Kurukshetra, Karnal, Jind, Rohtak, Panipat and Sonipat, receives adequate rainfall.
- Maize and rice are grown due to high water requirements, while Rabi crops rely on rainfall, tubewells, wells and canals for irrigation.

Irrigation in South-Eastern Region

- This area comprises the districts of Gurugram and Faridabad. The rainfall is less than normal in this area.
- The major crops of this region are maize, barley, millet, oat, wheat and gram. These crops are irrigated by canals and tubewells.

Irrigation in Sandy Region

- The region including Hisar, Sirsa, Mahendragarh and Bhiwani, receives almost no rainfall.
- The main crops of this region include barley, millet, gram, maize and wheat.
- Farmers use camels for agriculture and tubewells and water sprinklers for irrigation.

> Under Micro Irrigation Scheme 'Per Drop More Crop', an area of 95.58 lakh hectare has been covered by 2024 (December) with an expenditure of ₹ 21968.75 crore.

Government Initiative for Development of Irrigation

Haryana has an agricultural economy, due to which the cultivable lands are extensively irrigated. The ground water resources are also used extensively in the state. Therefore, water management is necessary in the Haryana.

State Government's Field Water Management Programmes

Programme	Description
Atal Bhujal Yojna	• It was launched on 25th December, 2019, on Atal Bihari Vajpayee's 95th birth anniversary. • The scheme aims to improve groundwater management through sustainable resource development, with an outlay of ₹ 6000 crore over 5 years (2020-25).
On Farm Water Management	• The scheme provides financial assistance to farmers for sprinkler irrigation, drip irrigation and Underground Pipe Line Systems (UGPL), promoting water conservation in the state.
Sprinkler Irrigation System	• Sprinkler irrigation is promoted in the sandy South and South-Western parts of Haryana, where groundwater levels reach up to 200 feet. • It efficiently meets irrigation needs and benefits crops like wheat, mustard and gram. • It was introduced in districts like Rewari, Mahendragarh and Hisar from 1970. This system considers the best for irrigation in these areas.
Drip Irrigation System	• Under this scheme, Underground Pipeline System laid to provide drip irrigation. • This system is promoted for the growth of cotton and sugarcane crops.
Underground Pipe Line System	• The Underground Pipe Line (UGPL) System in Haryana is a government initiative focused on improving irrigation efficiency and water management in agriculture areas. • Laying Underground Pipe Line to transport water from good-quality sources is a key project under the **Rastriya Krishi Vikas Yojana.**
Integrated Micro Irrigation Scheme	• Under Integrated Micro Irrigation Scheme, 14 different canal outlets are selected in 13 districts where solar energy based micro irrigation schemes are implemented. • This scheme is undertaken by **HAREDA from 2018.**
PM Krishi Sinchai Yojna	• It provides 85% assistance to SC farmers and small/marginal farmers for water-conserving irrigation. • The PMKSY finalises district irrigation plans and offers end-to-end solutions, including water source creation, rainwater harvesting, on-farm application and extension services on new irrigation technologies.

Haryana Government Department for Irrigation Facilities

Department	Description
Haryana Irrigation Research and Management Institute (HIRMI)	• The institute was set up under Societies Registration Act, 1860 at Kurukshetra. • It aims to conserve and efficiently manage the water resources through research and training.
Irrigation and Water Resources Department (IWRD)	• The department is primarily responsible for construction, operation and maintenance of canals and drainage network. The head office of this department is located in Panchkula district. • It also supplies water for irrigation, drinking, pond-filling, industrial uses, etc.
Command Area Development Authority (CADA)	• CADA, Haryana has installed Pilot projects of micro irrigation in 14 villages of 13 districts. • The total cost of the project is ₹ 30.60 crore covering 2231 hectare approx.
Haryana State Drought Relief and Flood Control Board	• The board is set up to control the excess water in the rivers during monsoon. • For this, reservoirs are developed around those rivers that remain dry moist of the year but swell up in the rainy season.
Irrigation Efficiency Fund	• The fund is created to increase the efficiency of irrigation in Haryana by NABARD. • It includes 36 blocks which are identified in the state where ground water level is too low or critical. Plans are drawn to recharge the ground water. • The scheme was implemented from 2018-19.

CHECK CHAPTER KNOWLEDGE

1 Which district in Haryana has the lowest irrigational facilities?
(a) Panchkula (b) Palwal
(c) Rewari (d) Nuh

2 Which of the following is the main source of irrigation in Haryana?
(a) Tubewells (b) Canals
(c) Lift irrigation (d) Rainfall

3 What percentage of agricultural land in Haryana is irrigated by canals?
(a) 35% (b) 42%
(c) 48% (d) 52%

4 Which district has largest irrigation facility through tubewells?
(a) Kaithal (b) Panchkula
(c) Jhajjar (d) Jind

5 Which among the following districts has irrigational facilities by way of wind mills?
(a) Rohtak (b) Bhiwani
(c) Karnal (d) All of these

6 Western Yamuna Canal was started from which place lying on the banks of Yamuna river? *HSSC 2021, 19,17*
(a) Karnal (b) Jhalri
(c) Tajewala (d) Shahabad

7 Which canal is the oldest and most important in Haryana? *Accountant 2018, TGT 2016*
(a) Western Yamuna canal
(b) Gurugram canal
(c) Bhakra canal
(d) Bhalaut canal

8 This canal of Haryana was first built by Firoz Shah Tughlaq *HSSC 2024*
(a) Bhakra canal
(b) Jui canal
(c) Gurgaon canal
(d) Western Yamuna canal

9 Western Yamuna Canal do not irrigate the land areas of which district in Haryana? *HSSC 2023, 18*
(a) Ambala (b) Yamunanagar
(c) Panipat (d) Sirsa

10 Western Yamuna Canal irrigates which district of Haryana? *HSSC 2022, 17*
(a) Sonipat (b) Rohtak
(c) Karnal (d) All of these

11 Which canal in Haryana carries water to Haidarpur plant in Delhi?
(a) Barwala canal (b) Munak canal
(c) Bhalaut canal (d) Sirsa canal

12 Bhakra canal enters Haryana from which place?
(a) Barwala (b) Tajewala
(c) Tohana (d) Narwana

13 Bhakra canal irrigates which district of Haryana? *PGT 2016*
(a) Hisar (b) Sirsa
(c) Fatehabad (d) All of these

14 Bhakra canal and Western Yamuna canal are connected by which feeder project?
(a) Yamuna canal
(b) Gurugram canal
(c) Bhiwani canal
(d) Munak canal

15 Which canal takes off from the Yamuna river at Okhla? *TGT 2016*
(a) Gurugram canal
(b) Jawaharlal canal
(c) Eastern Yamuna canal
(d) Western Yamuna canal

16 Jawaharlal Canal of Haryana is taken from which main canal? *PGT 2016*
(a) Bhakra canal (b) Gurugram canal
(c) Bhiwani canal (d) Agra canal

17 Bhiwani canal is taken out from *HSSC 2023, 16*
(a) Bhakra canal (b) Okhla
(c) Yamuna canal (d) Ganga canal

18 The Agra canal irrigates which district of Haryana?
(a) Fatehabad (b) Faridabad
(c) Bhiwani (d) Jhajjar

19 Jui Canal Project was primarily designed to irrigate the semi desert areas of *HSSC 2020, 16*
(a) Bhiwani (b) Rohtak
(c) Hisar (d) Panipat

20 Which lift irrigation project is also known as Virendra Narayan Chakravarti Project?
(a) Loharu project (b) Bhiwani project
(c) Jui Canal project (d) Nangal project

21 Hathnikund Barrage is located over *TGT 2016*
(a) Yamuna river (b) Ghaggar river
(c) Hakra river (d) Ravi river

22 Masani Dam of Haryana is built on which of the following rivers? *HSSC 2023*
(a) Sahibi (b) Yamuna
(c) Krishnavati (d) Tangri

23 Which barrage was built in 1999 to replace the Tajewala barrage?
(a) Hathnikund barrage
(b) Bhakra Nangal
(c) Indira Gandhi canal
(d) Narwana project

24 The Hathnikund barrage became functional from which year?
(a) 2002 (b) 2012
(c) 1998 (d) 2000

25 Tajewala Barrage built across Yamuna river is located in *HSSC 2024*
(a) Hisar (b) Fatehabad
(c) Panchkula (d) Yamunanagar

26 Pathrala dam in Haryana is situated on which river?
(a) Ghaggar (b) Somb
(c) Saraswati (d) None of these

27 The Ottu Barrage located in the district of Sirsa in Haryana is built on the river *HSSC 2023, 20*
(a) Choutang (b) Sahibi
(c) Yamuna (d) Ghaggar

28 Chaudhary Devi Lal tourist complex is built near which dam?
(a) Ottu dam (b) Pathrala dam
(c) Anangpur dam (d) Kaushalya dam

29 Among the following, which dam is in Haryana? *HSSC 2020*
(a) Vihar (b) Ottu Barrage
(c) Tulshi (d) Asthi

30 Anangpur dam is situated in which district of Haryana?
(a) Faridabad (b) Bhiwani
(c) Karnal (d) Panipat

31 Which of the following dam is in Haryana? *HSSC 2023, 22*
(a) Kaushalya dam (b) Bilaspur dam
(c) Maithon dam (d) Indira Sagar dam

32 Which is the main source of irrigation in sandy regions of Hisar and Sirsa?
(a) Rainfall
(b) Canals
(c) Canals and Tubewells
(d) Tubewells and Sprinklers

33 Farmers of which district are given subsidies to adopt spinkler irrigation system in Haryana?
(a) Rewari (b) Mahendragarh
(c) Bhiwani (d) All of these

34 The On Farm Water Management Programmes is undertaken by Haryana Government for
(a) Land conservation
(b) Water conservation
(c) Soil conservation
(d) All of the above

35 Which district of Haryana is suffering from depletion of underground water sources?
(a) Panipat (b) Yamunanagar
(c) Kaithal (d) All of these

36 Which scheme run by Haryana Government aims to prevent water thefts?
(a) Har Khet ko Pani
(b) Har Boond Krishi ke Liye
(c) Per Drop More Crop
(d) Atal Bhujal Yojana

CORRECT ANSWERS

1. (a) **2.** (a) **3.** (c) **4.** (a) **5.** (d) **6.** (c) **7.** (a) **8.** (d) **9.** (b) **10.** (d)
11. (b) **12.** (c) **13.** (d) **14.** (a) **15.** (a) **16.** (a) **17.** (a) **18.** (b) **19.** (a) **20.** (b)
21. (a) **22.** (a) **23.** (a) **24.** (a) **25.** (d) **26.** (b) **27.** (d) **28.** (a) **29.** (b) **30.** (a)
31. (a) **32.** (d) **33.** (d) **34.** (b) **35.** (d) **36.** (a)

HARYANA

Economy

and Infrastructure

This section contains all the important topics of Haryana Economy like Agriculture, Minerals, Energy Resources, Industries, Transport, etc.

CHAPTER 21

Minerals and Energy Resources of Haryana

- A mineral is a naturally occurring substance, which has a definite chemical composition. Minerals can be identified on the basis of their physical properties, such as colour, density, hardness and chemical properties.
- Energy or power plays a very important role in human life. Power is also required for industry, agriculture, transport, communication and defense.
- Energy resources can be broadly classified into **conventional** and **non-conventional** resources.

Mineral Resources in Haryana

- The major minerals found in the state of Haryana are slate, lead, limestone, quart, China clay, manganese, mica, marble, iron-ore, copper, calcite, kyanite and asbestos, etc.
- **Mahendragarh** district of the state is known for its mineral wealth. The Aravalli hills in the Southern part of Haryana have rich mineral deposits.
- The mining and management of mineral resources in the state is done by the Mines and Geology Department. It also manages the stone quarries.

Major Minerals Found in Haryana

Iron-Ore

- Location — **Bhiwani** (small quantities and of low quality) and **Mahendragarh** district (medium quality iron-ore of magnetite variety)
- Belts — **Dhanota-Dhancholi-Mokhuta** and **Karota-Antri-Biharipur-Donkhera** located in Southern part of Narnaul (Mahendragarh district)
- Reserves — Around 40.27 lakh tonnes in Mahendragarh
- **Kaliyana** and **Tosham** hills of Bhiwani have iron-ore mines of **haematite** variety.
- Hisar is the major producer of iron pipes.
- Narnaul is famous for mining iron-ore.

Copper

- Location — Teejanwali, Ghataser, Khalra hills and Bihali ridge of Narnaul (Mahendragarh district)
- Also found in — Khudana hills, Khudana Rajawas and Khudana-Surheti hills (Bhiwani district)

Mica

- Reserves — Musnota, Panchnota, Ghataser, Bayal, Nangal Durg, Golwa and Nangal Sirohi regions (Mahendragarh district)
- Also found in — Bhondsi village (Gurugram district)
- Used in — Making of electronic and electrical equipments

Asbestos

- Location — Golva village of Narnaul region (Mahendragarh district)

- Combination — A set of six naturally occurring silicate minerals used for desirable properties.
- Used in — Nuclear plants

Manganese

- Location — Nangal Durg and Musnota villages in Narnaul (Mahenragarh distict).
- Quantity — Very low quantity in Haryana
- Used in — Industries like metal alloy, particularly in stainless steel

Graphite

- Location — Narnaul's Mundia hills, Dhani, Faizabad and Jakhani regions (Mahendragarh district)
- Also found in — Hills of Bhondsi-Ferozepur-Jhirka-Sohna-Kotla (Gurugram and Nuh district)
- Used in — Lubricants, batteries, etc.

Garnet

- Colour — Pink and translucent to opaque
- Location — Rocky areas of Ajabgarh, Khatoli, Mukundpur, Ghataser, Bayal, Islampur and Kamania in South of Narnaul (Mahendragarh district)
- Also found in — Manesar, Bhondsi and Sohna (Gurugram district)
- Used in — Abrasive, water filtration, etc.

Quartz

- Location — Musnota, Golva, Khalra and Atela (Mahendragarh district)
- Also found in — Badarpur, Manesar and Nathupur (Gurugram district), Anangpur of Faridabad
- Quantity — Mahendragarh have huge deposits of quartz of around 1,65,000 tonnes.
- Used in — Glow, ceramics and electronics

Limestone

- Location — Panchkula, Ambala, Mahendragarh, Bhiwani, Rohtak and Hisar district
- Extracted from — Malla village of Kalka tehsil (Panchkula), Barun, Khadam, Ramsar, Shola (Ambala), Jaunpur (Narayangarh tehsil), Ghani, Kyutha, Ramnathpura
- Type — Crystallised limestone is also found in Ambala and Mahendragarh.
- Used in — Cement production and Construction

China Clay

- Location — Alipur, Nathpur, Kasan, (Gurugram district), Indri and Dhosgarh villages (Nuh district)
- Also found in — Anangpur village (Faridabad)
- Used in — Ceramics, paper and cosmetics

Slate

- Location — Rewari and Mahendragarh district
- Exported to — Australia, Belgium, Neitherlands and New Zealand
- High quality slate stone is found from Kund and Bihali villages of Rewari district.

Granite

- Location — Riwasa, Dulheri and Nigana Kalan hills of Bhiwani
- Also found in — Maroli hills and Dhanota-Dhancholi areas of Mahendragarh

Tosham in Bhiwani have reserves of high quality granite.

Road Metal/Crushed Stone

- Location — Shiwalik hills of Panchkula, Aravalli hills in Mahendragarh, Bhiwani, Mewat, Faridabad, Gurugram and Yamunanagar.
- Also known as — Angular rocks or road metal stones
- Used in — Construction of roads and buildings
- Stone received from the Khanak region is of high quality.

Coarse Sand

- Location — Panchkula, Ambala and Yamunanagar districts, Yamuna and Markanda rivers
- Quality — Dadupur (Yamunanagar) has deposits of high quality sand.
- Badarpur has mines of gravel, concrete and pit sand. Pit sand is coarse sand of red and deep orange colour. Pit sand is also known as **Badarpur sand.** It is used as building material.

Badarpur sand found on the National Highway that links Delhi-Faridabad-Mathura, is world famous for its quality, courseness and **maroon** colour.

Minor Minerals Found in Haryana

Mineral	Found in
Apatite	In Dochana village of Mahendragarh and regions surrounded by Morni hills e.g. Kharag-Banolu and Sherla.
Arsanite Arsenopyrite	Hills of Sohna-Nuh-Ferozepur-Jhirka in Gurugram and Mewat districts
Brick Earth	It is found in every region of the state except the sandy regions as Mahendragarh, Hisar, Sirsa, Fatehabad and Bhiwani.
Baryte	Musnota, Bayal-Ki-Dhani in Mahendragarh and Haripur and Ser regions located in Morni hills in Panchkula district.
Calcite	Khalra, Rasulpur, Bayal, Panchnota, Musnota of Mahendragarh district
Crusher Sand	Slopes of lower Shivalik hills
Dolomite Marble	Tunda and Jaunpur in Morni hills, Dhankora, Dochana, Biharipur, Shahpur, Dhanota, Dhadcholi Khalra, Islampur, Chhapra, Bibipur, Rasulpur, Musnota, Anantri, Nangal durg villages in Mahendragarh
Feldspar	Panchnota, Musnota, Nangal Durg, Bayal, Bankri, Faizabad, Dhankora of Mahendragarh and Alipur, Kasan, Bhondsi, Ghamdoz, Ghosh Garh and Geratpur of Gurugram
Flexible Sandstone	In India, it is found in **Kaliyana village in the district of Charkhi-Dadri.** It is known by local names like **Sang-e-Tarja, dancing stone**, etc.
Gold	Narayangarh in Ambala Banks and bases of Markanda and Tangri rivers
Gravel Sand	Teka, New Mandi, Moti Mandi, Manger, Dhauj, Mohbtabad and Bandhwari of Faridabad. It is also found in the hills of Bhondasi-Ferozepur-Jhirka- Sohna of Gurugram and Nuh (Mewat) districts.
Kyanite	Mahendragarh and Nuh districts. It is light blue and yellowish in colour. Golwa village of Mahendragah, Kitla region of Nuh (Mewat)
Lead	Tosham hills of Bhiwani
Mineral Water	Shiv Kund and Shila Kund in Sohna of Gurugram district. Its temperature is 46°C to 53°C. It is believed that it cures skin diseases.
Monazite	In Mahendragarh, Bhiwani and Rewari districts. It is mostly found in the adjoining areas of Rajasthan.
Nalasand Crusher dust	The sand of the hills which comes down with water during the rain in the state is called Nalasand. Nalasand is used as crusher dust.
Salt Water	Sultanpur-Farrukhnagar in Gurugram and Nuh region of Mewat. In 1935, salt was used to manufacture by salt water in Farrukhnagar.
Saltpetre	Hisar, Sirsa, Fatehabad, Jind, Rohtak and Kurukshetra also found in Gurugram, Sonipat, Palwal, Faridabad

Energy Resources in Haryana

- Energy is a critical factor in the infrastructure of Haryana. Haryana state has limited availability of natural sources of energy. For energy, the state depends on its limited thermal generation capacity and hydro power from the jointly owned projects with other states.
- The solar intensity is relatively high in Haryana, so the state is developing its resources to harness the solar energy. **Wind** and **nuclear energy** sources are also being developed in Haryana.
- During the formation of Haryana in 1966-67, only a few villages in the state had power connections. By 29th November, 1970, all the villages in the state were electrified.

> Haryana is the first state in the country to link all its villages with electricity. This was achieved during the tenure of Chief Minister Bansilal.

- After the formation of Haryana, Haryana State Electricity Board was set up on 3rd May, 1967.
- As per Economic Survey 2024-25, total installed capacity of the state is 16015.76 MW (upto January, 2025).

Power Generation in Haryana

- To improve the financial condition of the board, an advisory committee was formed in 1993, which submitted its report in 1995 to the State Government. The committee was **Haryana Electricity Regulatory Commission.**
- As per the recommendations of the report, the State Government of Haryana reconstituted the **State Electricity Board** on 14th August, 1998, under the **Haryana Electricity Reforms Act, 1997.**
- As per the Act, State Electricity Board was bifurcated into two parts i.e. **Haryana Power Generation Corporation Limited** and **Haryana Vidyut Prasaran Nigam Limited.**
- The State Government again divided Haryana Power Generation Corporation Limited into two corporations in March 1999 to supply power smoothly in the state.
- After this, four corporations related to the production and distribution of electricity were set up in the state, which are as follows

1. **Haryana Power Generation Corporation Limited** (HPGCL)

- Date of incorporation — 17th March, 1997
- Start of operations — 14th August, 1998
- Headquarters — Panchkula
- Functions — Operation and maintenance of power generation projects
- Coverage area — Thermal power generation in Yamunanagar, Jhajjar, Faridabad and Hisar

2. **Haryana Vidyut Prasaran Nigam Limited** (HVPNL)

- Date of incorporation — 19th August, 1997
- Start of operations — 18th September, 1997
- Headquarters — Panchkula
- Functions — Transmission and distribution of electricity; later segregated into UHBVNL and DHBVNL on 1st July, 1999

3. **Uttar Haryana Bijli Vitran Nigam Limited** (UHBVNL)

- Date of incorporation — March, 1999
- Headquarters — Panchkula
- Functions — Distribution and retail supply of power
- Coverage area — **Northern districts** Ambala, Yamunanagar, Kaithal, Panchkula, Kurukshetra, Karnal, Panipat, Sonipat, Rohtak, Jind, Jhajjar

4. **Dakshin Haryana Bijli Vitran Nigam Limited** (DHBVNL)

- Date of incorporation — March, 1999
- Headquarters — **Hisar**
- Functions — Distribution and retail supply of power
- Coverage Area — Southern districts Bhiwani, Faridabad, Gurugram, Mahendragarh, Rewari, Hisar, Sirsa, Fatehabad, Dadri, Nuh, Palwal

Haryana Electricity Regulatory Commission

It is an autonomous body, formed on 17th August, 1998. The functions of this commission are

- To present recommendations to the government for development in the power sector.
- Proper determination of electricity rates in the state.
- To give favourable suggestions of time and situation to the government to maintain the balance between power generation and distribution corporations and consumers in the state.

Conventional Energy Sources

- The conventional energy sources are such sources whose reserves are limited on the Earth.
- It includes coal, petroleum and natural gas, etc.
- The energy generated from the conventional energy sources is divided into two parts
  - Thermal Electric Energy
  - Hydro Electric Energy

Thermal Power Stations in Haryana

Haryana has several thermal power plants, which contribute to the state's electricity needs. Key thermal power plants in Haryana are as follows

1. **Panipat Thermal Power Station** (PTPS)

- Location — **Panipat**
- Established on — 1st November, 1979
- Installed capacity — Total 1367.80 MW (4 units of 110 MW, 2 units of 210 MW, 2 units of 250 MW)
- Other facts — **First power station of Haryana**

▲ Panipat Thermal Power Station

2. **Rajiv Gandhi Thermal Power Station**

- Location — Khedar, Hisar
- Commissioned in the year — 2010
- Installed capacity — 1200 MW (2 units)
- Other facts — Coal-based thermal plant; constructed by Reliance Power Limited

3. Deenbandhu Chhotu Ram Thermal Power Station

- Location — Yamunanagar
- Commissioned in the year — 2008
- Installed capacity — 1200 MW (2 units of 600 MW)
- Other facts — Coal-based power plant; first power project controlled by the private sector; constructed by Reliance Energy and Shanghai Electric
- The coal is supplied by **central coalfields.**

4. Indira Gandhi Super Thermal Power Project

- Location — Jharli, Jhajjar
- Established — **First Phase** 4th March, 2011; **Second Phase** 5th November, 2011; **Third Phase** 7th November, 2012
- Installed capacity — 1500 MW (3 units of 500 MW each)
- Other facts — Joint project of NTPC, IPGCL and HPGCL; also known as **Aravalli Super Thermal Power Project.** Coal from **Mahanadi Coalfield Limited.**

5. Mahatma Gandhi Thermal Power Project

- Location — Khanpur, Jhajjar
- Established on — 19th July, 2012
- Installed capacity — 1320 MW (2 units of 660 MW each)
- Other facts — First coal-based power project set up in collaboration with **China Power Corporation.**

6. Faridabad Thermal Power Plant

- Location — Faridabad
- Installed capacity — 430 MW (originally 180 MW)
- Other facts — Only **gas-based thermal power plant** in Haryana; located 30 km from Delhi

Hydro Power Plants

There are very few rivers in Haryana and most of the land is plain so, there is little scope of hydro electricity in the state. Some of the hydro power plants are discussed below

1. Western Yamuna Canal Hydel Project

- Location — Between Hathnikund and Dadupur, Yamunanagar
- Installed capacity — 62.7 MW
- Established in — 1980
- Additional facts — Established in collaboration with Japan. **Hathnikund** is a barrage on the Yamuna river.

2. Kakroi Micro Hydel Project

- Location — Kakroi village, near Sonipat
- Installed capacity — 400 KW (4 units of 100 KW each)
- Established in — 1987-88 (work started)
- Additional facts — Under control of HPGCL, Yamunanagar from 1st June, 1999. A National Demonstration Project.

3. Dadupur Mini Hydro Electric Project

- Location — Dadupur
- Installed capacity — 4 MW
- Established in — 2009-10
- Additional facts — Established by Bhoska Power Corporation

4. Western Yamunanagar Project

- Location — Gauripur village, **Karnal**
- Installed capacity — 2 MW
- Established in — 2010-11

5. Muasapur Micro Hydel Project

- Location — Indri village, **Karnal**
- Installed capacity — 1.4 MW
- Established in — 2011-12

6. Khukni Micro Hydro Electric Project

- Location — Khukni village, **Karnal**
- Established in — 2011-12

Non-Conventional Resources of Energy

These are the energy sources which can be renewed and used for longer duration. It includes nuclear energy, solar energy, wind energy and bio-energy. These are discussed below

Nuclear Energy

Haryana has only one nuclear power plant (Gorakhpur Nuclear Power Plant) which ensures power supply in the state.

Gorakhpur Nuclear Power Plant

- The Gorakhpur Nuclear Power Plant in Haryana has been set up in village Gorakhpur of Fatehabad district on 13th January, 2014.
- The total installed capacity of this Nuclear Power Plant is 2800 MW. It consists of 4 units and each unit is capable of producing 700 MW of power.

- The first phase of the project was launched on 13th January, 2014 by the then PM Manmohan Singh.
- It was set up by Nuclear Power Corporation of India Limited (NPCIL).

▲ Gorakhpur Nuclear Power Plant

Solar Energy

- The first solar power plant in Haryana was set up at **Nandha** village in Charkhi-Dadri district.
- Solar Power Plant at **Budh Kalan** in Yamunanagar district has been set up by Haryana Power Generation Corporation Limited.
- The solar insolation level in the state is in the range of 5.5 KW to 6.5 KW per sq m of area and the state has about 320 clear sunny days in a year.
- Haryana is the only state in the country which has made it mandatory to install solar water heating systems, use of 4 star pump sets in agriculture, use of CFL in government offices and reflex bulbs, etc.

> Haryana Government has launched a training programme called **Suryamitra** to develop skilled manpower in the field of renewable energy with special focus on solar energy.

- Under the solar energy policy, 1600 MW capacity of solar power plants has been installed by year 2022.

Haryana Solar Power Policy 2023

The Government of Haryana has formulated Haryana Solar Power Policy, 2023 to promote the generation of power from solar energy.

The vision and objectives of this policy are

- To increase share of the solar power in the energy mix of the state in alignment of national policies, programmes and targets.
- To create conducive environment for the participation the private as well as public sector in setting up of solar energy projects in the state.
- To encourage adoption of the latest technologies such as battery storage and **RE**-based **EV charging**, net metering; gross metering, virtual net metering and group net metering.
- To increase income of farmers by installation of solar power plants for sale of power and also by providing solar power in day time for agricultural activities.
- Enabling solar equipment manufacturing and provision for solar waste management.
- Training and skill development R and D activities through a learning ecosystem.
- Promotion of off-grid solar applications like solar water pumps, home lighting system, etc.
- To take a holistic approach for faster and wider solar deployment, such as development of solar parks and solar power projects for sale of power to DISCOMs of Haryana and/or for captive consumption/third party sale/merchant sale by independent power producers, within and outside the state.
- Productive use of wastelands/non-agricultural lands thereby leading to socio-economic transformation and a reduction in regional disparities in development.

State Initiatives to Develop Solar Power

- Haryana state has given permission from 2014 to all institutions to install solar power plants that are capable of handling 3-5% of their power load. This is applicable to all government, private, semi-government, schools, hospitals, hotels, etc.
- Barren land areas in the state are allocated for setting up solar power plants.
- State encourages the farmers to produce electricity by installing solar power plants in their fields and even sell it.

> **ISA Headquarters**
>
> - On 25th January, 2016, the Prime Minister of India and the President of France established the headquarters of the **International Solar Alliance** (ISA) in Gurugram district of the state.
> - The International Solar Alliance's Interim Secretariat was also inaugurated idn the premises of the National Institute of Solar Energy located in the Gwal hill region of Gurugram district.
> - Government of India allotted 5 acres of land in the premises of National Institute of Solar Energy, located in Gurugram for the headquarters of ISA.
> - The ISA was established to promote the use of solar energy in the world. It is an organisation of countries in the world where solar energy is available in plenty.

Wind Energy

- In Haryana, sufficient untapped wind energy power potential is available, specifically in the **Morni hill** area of **Panchkula District** and **Aravalli hills** in Southern Haryana.
- Wind Monitoring Stations have been set up in Panchkula, Gurugram and Mahendragarh districts to assess the available wind potential for power generation in the state.
- The Haryana Renewable Energy Development Agency (HREDA) was set up as the nodal agency for managing the works related to power generated from non-conventional energy sources in the state.

Bio Energy

- Haryana has a potential to develop bio fuel due to agricultural residue, specially in the districts of Sirsa, Hisar, Bhiwani, Jind and Kaithal, where agriculture is the main activity.
- The first bio gas plant was established in 1991 at Dikadla in Panipat district.

According to the Department of Renewable Energy, Government of Haryana, the state has 112 bio gas plants.

Haryana Bio Energy Policy, 2018

The Haryana Government formulated the Bio Energy Policy, 2018 to encourage the use of biomass and to deal with the pollution problem arising due to burning of crop residues in the fields .

The main objectives of this policy are

- According to this policy, there is a target to set up biomass based power plants of 150 MW by 2022.
- To tackle the issue of straw burning and promote paddy straw based biomass power project in the state, the government has allotted 4 paddy straw based biomass power projects of 49.8 MW capacity in Kurukshetra (15 MW), Kaithal (15 MW), Jind (9.90 MW) and Fatehabad (9.90MW).
- To harness biomass based power/bio gas/bio-CNG/ bio-manure/bio fuels.
- To contribute to energy sustainability by decreasing reliance on conventional energy sources like coal and petroleum.
- To establish an efficient biomass collection, storage and transportation network for bio-energy projects.
- To support research and development, demonstration and commercialisation of new technologies.

Haryana Green Hydrogen Policy, 2024

The Government of India released the National Green Hydrogen Mission (NGHM) in January 2023.On the same line Government of Haryana on 15th February, 2024, issued the Draft Haryana Green Hydrogen Policy -2024.

Objectives

- To accelerate development and adoption of Green Hydrogen and its derivatives as alternative fuel .
- To harness the clean energy potential and enhance energy security.
- To promote manufacturing of electrolysers and other critical equipment.
- To attract investment in the Green Hydrogen and Renewable Energy sector.
- To reduce emissions from crop burning by using biomas.

Renewable Energy Department

- The department of renewable energy was established to promote the use of renewable energy such as solar, wind, biofuel, etc.
- The department constituted as nodal agency under the Energy Conservation Act, 2001 to develop the non-conventional sources of energy, known as HAREDA.

Haryana Renewable Energy Development Agency (HAREDA)

- It is the State Nodal Agency for coordinating all activities relating to renewable energy development including generation of power using non-conventional energy sources.
- HAREDA is responsible for laying down the procedure for inviting the proposals from Independent Power Producers (IPPs), DPR preparation, evaluation of project proposals, project approvals and project progress monitoring, etc.

▲ Haryana Renewable Energy Development Agency

- It functions as a single window clearing agency for all renewable energy power projects for facilitating necessary clearances and approvals on behalf of the Government of Haryana.
- HAREDA gets financial support from both, the State and the Central Government.

Renewable Energy Parks

- Renewable energy parks are established at many places of Haryana to promote the use of renewable energy and to create awareness among teachers and students.
- Energy parks are also set up to encourage technical innovation and awareness towards developing energy sources that do not create environmental degradation.
- First energy park was set up in Gurugram district with a cost of ₹ 1.87 crore named **Rajiv Gandhi Renewable Energy Park.** It was inaugurated on 12th August, 2004.
- The approval has been given for the establishment of the first district energy park at Jawahar Navodaya Vidyalaya, Nanthala in Panipat district of Haryana.

Renewable Energy Awards

- Haryana Government provides awards at district, block and Panchayat levels to encourage the use of renewable sources of energy.
- The first village to use renewable energy source at Panchayat is given ₹ 3 lakh, second village is given ₹ 2 lakh and third is awarded with ₹ 1 lakh each.
- Similarly, at the district level, the first prize winner receives ₹ 50,000 and second prize winner receives ₹ 25,000 and the first prize winner at the block level Is awarded ₹ 25,000.

- 20 renewable energy parks have been set up in 18 districts.

Renewable Energy Parks	Location
Regional Engineering College	Kurukshetra
Sir Chhotu ram State Engineering College	Sonipat
College of Agricultural and Technology	Hisar
Convent of Jesus and Mary	Ambala Cantt
Haryana Institute of Rural Development	Karnal
Hansraj Public School	Panchkula
Ahir College	Rewari
Guru Jambeshwar University	Hisar
Mini Secretariat	Karnal
Government Polytechnic	Jhajjar
Government Polytechnic	Sirsa
BKM Government Polytechnic	Narnaul, Mahendragarh
ML Institute of Technology	Rador, Yamunanagar
Model School	Nuh (Mewat)
Adarsh Mahila Mahavidyalaya	Bhiwani
College of Technology and Management	Kaithal
Navjyoti Foundation	Gurugram
YMCA Institute of Engineering and Technology	Faridabad
Vaish College of Engineering	Rohtak
Manohar Memorial College	Fatehabad

State Government Schemes

Scheme	Description
Manohar Jyoti Yojana	• The scheme Manohar Jyoti provides LED based SPV home lights to meet the lighting energy needs of the public. • The scheme was launched in 2017 by the Chief Minister of Haryana Manohar Lal Khattar. • Under the scheme, 2 LED luminary of 6 watt each, 1 LED tubelight of 9 watt, 1 DC ceiling fan of 25 watt and 1 USB port of mobile charging are provided to each household.
Mahara Gaon Jagmag Gaon Yojana	• This scheme was launched on 1st July, 2015 at Dayalpur village of Kurukshetra district. • The objectives are to provide 24 hours uninterrupted power supply, improve the electricity bill collections, reduce power thefts and line loss. • **Panchkula** is the first district to meet its objective of 24 hour uninterrupted power supply.

Scheme	Description
Ujjwal Discom Assurance Yojana (UDAY)	• This scheme was launched by Government of India in 2015. • Its objective is to make debt ridden power distribution companies free from debt. • The scheme is facilitated and monitored by Rural Electrification Corporation. • Under this scheme, the Haryana Government issued UDAY bonds from June, 2018 worth 25,950 crore. The target is to issue bonds worth 34,517.34 crore.
Bill Penalty Waiver Scheme	• The main objective of the scheme was to pay the outstanding amount of electricity so that defaultering amount can be reduced. • The scheme is introduced in rural areas in 2016. • This is a voluntary declaration scheme and consumers having payments upto 2 KW can avail the scheme. • Surcharge and penalties are waived off in this scheme.
Solar Power Plants in Gaushalas	• Haryana Government aims to install solar power plants in all the Gaushalas of the state with a grant of 80%. Rest of the cost is to be incurred by 'Gau Sewa Aayog. • Solar plants of about 2 MW capacity has been installed in 330 Gaushalas.
Suryamitra Skill Development Programme	• This programme was aimed at preparing or training individuals in the field of solar energy. In the year 2016-17, under this programme, three training programmes were conducted in Sirsa, Sonipat and Gurugram districts of the state. • 30 persons are trained in each session of this programme.
Solar Water Pumping Programme	• Department of New and Renewable Energy will provide solar pumps of 3HP to 10 HP capacity. • This programme comes under PM-KUSUM.
LED Based Solar Street Lighting Systems	• The objective is to reduce the dependence on conventional power for street lighting in rural areas. • It is a demand based scheme for which proposals are invited through respective Addl. Deputy Commissioner-cum-Chief Project Officers of the districts.
SPV Street Lighting Programme for Rural Areas	• The objective is to reduce the dependence on conventional power for street lighting in rural areas. • It is also a demand based scheme.

CHECK CHAPTER KNOWLEDGE

1 Which district has large reserves of mineral resources? *HSSC 2016*
(a) Hisar (b) Kurukshetra
(c) Mahendragarh (d) Yamunanagar

2 Gurugram and Mahendragarh are rich in *Patwari 2016*
(a) Tin (b) Dolomite
(c) Slate (d) Feldspar

3 Narnaul is famous for mining of
(a) Gypsum (b) Limestone
(c) Iron-ore (d) Slate

4 Name the district which is the major producer of iron pipes in Haryana? *HSSC 2021*
(a) Gurugram (b) Yamunanagar
(c) Hisar (d) Jind

5 Which among the following district is rich in copper?
(a) Mahendragarh (b) Karnal
(c) Hisar (d) Rewari

6 Asbestos is found in which district of Haryana? *HSSC 2023, 18*
(a) Hisar (b) Gurugram
(c) Karnal (d) Mahendragarh

7 Manganese is found in which district of Haryana? *PGT 2016*
(a) Hisar (b) Mahendragarh
(c) Karnal (d) Gurugram

8 Which of the following district is rich in limestone?
(a) Panipat (b) Sonipat
(c) Nuh (d) Ambala

9 Which of the following mineral is found in Mahendragarh?
(a) Limestone (b) Granite
(c) China clay (d) All of these

10 Which mineral is found in Rohtak? *Police Constable 2016*
(a) Limestone (b) Copper
(c) Manganese (d) Mica

11 Which place in Rewari has huge reserves of slate?
(a) Khol (b) Bayal
(c) Kund (d) Kosli

12 Which of the following districts has deposits of kyanite?
(a) Hisar (b) Ambala
(c) Rohtak (d) Mahendragarh

13 Which rivers in Haryana have traces of gold in their banks and bases?
(a) Markanda b) Tangri
(c) Both (a) and (b) (d) None of these

14 Haryana has achieved 100% *HSSC 2015*
(a) literacy (b) electrification
(c) infrastructure (d) None of these

15 In which year, Haryana state had linked all its villages with electricity?
(a) 1995 (b) 1975 (c) 1970 (d) 1995

16 Which sector in Haryana is the highest consumer of electricity?
(a) Forestry (b) Agriculture
(c) Tertiary (d) Industries

17 Haryana Electricity Reform Act was passed in the year *HSSC 2016*
(a) 1997 (b) 1998 (c) 1999 (d) 2000

18 During which year, Haryana State Electricity Board was split into two separate bodies?
(a) 1997 (b) 1999 (c) 1998 (d) 2000

19 HVPNL stands for in Haryana *HSSC 2024, 20*
(a) Haryana Voltage Purchase Nigam Ltd
(b) Haryana Voltage Prasaran Nigam Ltd
(c) Haryana Vidyut Prasaran Nigam Ltd
(d) Haryana Vidyut Purchase Nigam Ltd

20 HPPC stands for ……... in Haryana. *HSSC 2021*
(a) Haryana Prasaran Purchase Corporation
(b) Haryana Power Purchase Centre
(c) Haryana Poverty Prasaran Corporation
(d) None of the above

21 Where is the head office of HPGCL?
(a) Panchkula (b) Rohtak
(c) Gurugram (d) Mahendragarh

22 Which of the following districts is covered under Uttari Haryana Bijli Vitran Nigam Limited (UHBVNL)?
(a) Bhiwani (b) Kaithal
(c) Rewari (d) Mewat

23 Which of the following districts is covered under Dakshin Haryana Bijli Vitran Nigam Limited (DHBVNL)?
(a) Ambala (b) Faridabad
(c) Jind (d) Jhajjar

24 Which of the following is the biggest power station of Haryana? *HSSC 2022, 16*
(a) Yamunanagar Power Plant
(b) Panipat Power Plant
(c) Rajiv Gandhi Power Plant
(d) WYC Hydel Power Plant

25 In which year, Panipat Thermal Power station was commissioned?
(a) 1973 (b) 1980 (c) 1981 (d) 1979

26 Rajiv Gandhi Thermal Power Project is located in the district of
(a) Yamunanagar (b) Faridabad
(c) Hisar (d) Sirsa

27 In which year Rajiv Gandhi Power project was commissioned?
(a) 2005 (b) 2007
(c) 2009 (d) 2010

28 In which year Deenbandhu Chhotu Ram Thermal Power Plant was established?
(a) 1993 (b) 2000
(c) 2008 (d) 2009

29 Deenbandhu Chhotu Ram Power Plant is located in the district of
(a) Hisar (b) Yamunanagar
(c) Sirsa (d) Panipat

30 Indira Gandhi Super Thermal Power Project is situated at *Haryana, CET 2023*
(a) Jind (b) Hisar (c) Sirsa (d) Jhajjar

31 The Aravalli Super Thermal Power Project was founded in which year?
(a) 2001 (b) 2003 (c) 2004 (d) 2011

32 Mahatma Gandhi Thermal Power Project is situated in which district of Haryana?
(a) Panipat (b) Gurugram
(c) Sonipat (d) Jhajjar

33 In which of the following districts, Western Yamuna Canal Hydel Electricity Project is located?
(a) Sonipat (b) Yamunanagar
(c) Panipat (d) Faridabad

34 In which of the following districts Kakroi Hydel Project is located?
(a) Panipat (b) Rohtak
(c) Sonipat (d) Gurugram

35 Installed capacity of Kakroi Micro Hydel Project (per unit) is *Aganwadi 2017*
(a) 50 KW (b) 75 KW (c) 100 KW (d) 150 KW

36 In which of the following districts, Nuclear Power Plant of 2800 MW capacity is set up?
(a) Fatehabad (b) Faridabad
(c) Jhajjar (d) Panchkula

37 Which among the following non-conventional sources of energy is found abundantly in Haryana?
(a) Solar energy (b) Wind energy
(c) Nuclear energy (d) Tidal energy

38 First solar power plant in Haryana was set up in which village?
(a) Budh Kalan (b) Kakroi
(c) Khanpur (d) Nandha

39 Which programme is launched by government of Haryana for developing skilled manpower in the field of renewable energy?
(a) Samadhan Sahayak (b) Suryamitra
(c) Surya Sathi (d) Jyoti Sahayak

40 Where is the head office of International Solar Alliance situated? *HSSC 2023, 16*
(a) Gurugram (c) Karnal
(b) Panipat (d) Faridabad

41 Morni hills, which has sufficient untapped wind energy power potential is located in the district
(a) Jhajjar (b) Mewat
(c) Panchkula (d) Yamunanagar

42 Where in Haryana, the first bio-gas plant was set up? *PGT 2016*
(a) Sirsa (b) Sonipat
(c) Panipat (d) Hisar

43 Haryana Government has formulated its Renewable Energy Policy in the year
(a) 2009 (b) 2010
(c) 2005 (d) 2007

44 HAREDA is the Nodal Agency for developing energy through
(a) Coal (b) Nuclear sources
(c) Solar (d) Non-conventional

45 Where was the first energy park set up in Haryana?
(a) Kaithal (b) Karnal
(c) Gurugram (d) Kurukshetra

46 In which year, Mahara Gaon Jagmag Gaon Yojana was started?
(a) 2009 (b) 2012
(c) 2015 (d) 2017

47 Under which scheme the Haryana government issued UDAY bonds?

(a) Surya Mitra (b) Manohar Jyoti
(c) Ujjwal Discom Assurance scheme
(d) Gaushala Solar Plant Scheme

48 **Assertion (A)** Uttar Haryana Bijli Vitran Nigam Limited and Dakshin Haryana Bijli Vitran Nigam Limited are two corporate bodies of erstwhile Haryana State Electricity Board.

Reason (R) Haryana State Electricity Board was split into two separate bodies in 1999.

Codes

(a) Both A and R are true and R is the correct explanation of A.
(b) Both A and R are true but R is not the correct explanation of A.
(c) A is true but R is false.
(d) Both A and R are not true.

49 Which of the following statements is/are correct?

I. Haryana is rich in high grade iron-ore.
II. Haryana is rich in minerals, which are largely used in construction industry.

Codes

(a) Only I (b) Only II
(c) Both I and II (d) None of these

50 Which of the following statements is/are correct?

I. Haryana Electricity Regulatory Commission came into force on 17th August, 1998.
II. Haryana Electricity Reform Act, 1997 was passed by the Haryana State Legislative Assembly on 22nd July, 1997.

Select the correct answer using the codes given below.

(a) Only I
(b) Only II
(c) Both I and II
(d) Neither I nor II

51 Which of the following statements are correct?

I. The total installed capacity of Rajiv Gandhi Thermal Power Station is 1200 MW.
II. The power project is located in Hisar district.

Select the correct answer using the codes given below.

(a) Only I (b) Only II
(c) Both I and II (d) None of these

52 Wind monitoring stations has been set up in

I. Panchkula II. Gurugram
III. Kaithal IV. Mahendragarh

Codes

(a) Only I (b) I, II and III
(c) I, II and IV (d) All of these

53 Which of following statements are true?

I. Haryana was the first state in the country to achieve 100% rural electrification in 1970 itself.
II. Haryana is the sole holder of the country's rock salt resources.
III. 'Mera Pani Meri Virasat' Scheme of Haryana aims to shift farmer's focus from growing water consuming crop like paddy to other less water requiring crops.
IV. Under 'Mahara Gaon-Jagmag Gaon', more than 5,000 villages in Haryana have been provided with 24 hour power supply.

HPSC Pre 2022

(a) I, II and III (b) II, III and IV
(c) I, III and IV (d) I, II and IV

54 What is one of the main environmental benefits of using Solar Energy Technologies?

HSSC JE 2024

(a) Increased greenhouse gas emissions
(b) Reduced CO2 emissions and prevention of toxic gas emissions
(c) Depletion of natural resources
(d) Increased air pollution

CORRECT ANSWERS

1. (c)	2. (c)	3. (c)	4. (c)	5. (a)	6. (d)	7. (b)	8. (d)	9. (a)	10. (a)
11. (c)	12. (d)	13. (c)	14. (b)	15. (c)	16. (d)	17. (a)	18. (c)	19. (c)	20. (b)
21. (a)	22. (b)	23. (b)	24. (b)	25. (d)	26. (c)	27. (d)	28. (c)	29. (b)	30. (d)
31. (d)	32. (d)	33. (b)	34. (c)	35. (c)	36. (a)	37. (a)	38. (d)	39. (b)	40. (a)
41. (c)	42. (c)	43. (c)	44. (c)	45. (c)	46. (c)	47. (c)	48. (a)	49. (b)	50. (c)
51. (c)	52. (c)	53. (c)	54. (b)						

CHAPTER 22

KNOW YOUR STATE
HARYANA

Industries in Haryana

Haryana is well known for its industrial development. The state has also emerged as a base for the knowledge industry, including IT and Biotechnology. Haryana is one of the top destinations for IT/ITES facilities and the third-largest exporter of software.

The state of Haryana is a major producer of cars, two-wheelers and tractors, with significant manufacturing of auto-components.

History of Industrial Development in Haryana

- Before Independence, a few industries were concentrated in the region mainly sugar, timber and cotton mill.
- After Independence, the Central Government gave priority to industrial development from the Second Five-Year Plan. As a result, the areas of Faridabad, Sonipat, Panipat and Bahadurgarh developed as industrial units.
- The state got its share of mineral resources after its separation from Punjab in **1966**. From then, onwards the state started framing its independent industrial policy.
- The state declared 2013 as **Year of Industry and Employment**. The New Industrial Policy of 2015 stimulates further industrial growth in the state on a fast track basis.
- The policies are alligned with 'Make in India', 'Digital India' and 'Skill India' projects of Central Government.

Major Industries of Haryana

The development of industries in Haryana started after the year 1980 and industries based on local mineral resources (limestone, marble and iron) have been given priority and encouragement.

One-third of the country's sanitary goods are produced here. It is also a leader in the country in the production of tractors and cars.The following categories of industries are prominent in the state

- Food Processing Industry
- Agro Based Industry
- Automobile and Automotive Components Industry
- Petrochemical Industry
- IT Industry
- Biotech Industry and Pharmaceuticals
- Real Estate and Construction Industry
- Waste Processing and Recycling Industry

Food Processing and Allied Industries

- Haryana has the advantage of being an agrarian state. It is a major contributor to the National Foodgrains Pool.
- Apart from its own base for production of vegetables and fruits (perishable commodities), the state constitutes the route for transportation of fruit from Jammu and Kashmir and Himachal Pradesh.
- The state has a good base for production of milk and holds the potential for growth of milk and dairy based industry. Dairy industries are distributed throughout the state.

Important Food Processing Industries in Haryana

Company	Products	Foundation and Location	Key Facts
Nestle India	Infant foods, milk, chocolates, milk products, Nescafe, Kitkat, Maggi, Milkmaid, Milk bars, etc.	Founded in Switzerland by Henry Nestle in 1867. Indian branch established in 1992 at Samlakha, Panipat.	Largest food processing company in India.
Perfetti Van Melle India	Confectionery products: Happydent, Big Babol, Mentos, Alpenliebe, Centre Fresh, etc.	Established in 1994 in Manesar, Gurugram district.	Holds 25% market share in sugar confectionery, major exporter in Asia.
Yakult Danone India Pvt. Ltd.	Probiotic milk (to increase immunity)	Joint venture between Japan's Yakult and France's Danone. In India, established in 2008 at Sonipat.	Focus on promoting health through probiotics.
Glaxo Smith Kline Consumer Healthcare Ltd.	Horlicks	Founded in 1924, registered in England. Established in Khewra, Sonipat district.	One of the largest research-based pharmaceutical and health care companies.
Parle Biscuit Factory	Biscuits and snacks	Located in Bahadurgarh	Famous for Parle-G biscuits.
Madhu Ghee	Ghee	Located in Pehowa	Known for producing ghee
Lakshay Foods India Ltd.	Variety of food products	Located in Manesar, Haryana	Produces a range of food products
Haryana Cooperative Dairy Development	Vita Milk	Facilities in Jind, Ambala, Rohtak, Ballabhgarh, Sirsa, Kurukshetra, etc.	Cooperative dairy network for milk production
Sabar Dairy Milk Processing Plant	Dairy products	Located in Ambala	Milk processing and dairy products
Amul Milk Plant (IMT Rohtak)	Dairy products	Located in Rohtak	Part of the cooperative Amul brand

Cotton Textile Industries

- Cotton industry is well developed in Haryana as the state gets its raw materials from cotton producing areas of Sirsa, Fatehabad, Hisar, Bhiwani, Dadri and Jind. The first mill started in the state, in 1937, in Bhiwani.
- **Panipat** has established its place on the International map as a centre for the handloom products.
- **Gurugram-Manesar** belt has also emerged as the centre for manufacture and export of readymade garments. A number of units are engaged in the manufacturing of leather garments and other accessories.
- The Haryana State Industrial Development Corporation has developed a Textile Park at **Barhi** (Sonipat). An International Trade and Convention Centre would be set up at Panipat to promote handloom products.

Important Textile Mills in Private Sector

- **Bhiwani Textile Mills** was established by the **Aditya Birla Group** in 1937, in Bhiwani. It provides textiles to readymade cloth industry.
- **Orient Craft Limited** was established in Gurugram on 28th February, 1978. It is an export oriented company.
- **Benetton Group** The Benetton Group established its branch in **Gurugram** district. It is a multinational company and manufactures branded clothes, shoes, bags, etc. under united colours of Benetton Brand.

Paper Industries

- First paper mill started in the state in 1929 by the name of **Messers Punjab Pulp** and **Paper Mill** Limited at Jagdhri, near Yamunanagar. Many private companies have their paper manufacturing units in Sonipat, Rewari and Yamunanagar.
- Gurugram has paper mills from which paper is supplied to all over India.

Sugar Mills

- Haryana has many sugar mills as sugarcane is a commercial crop of Haryana.
- Oldest sugar mill in the region was established in Lahore, in 1933 in undivided Punjab, by the name of Saraswati Industrial Syndicate Limited (Saraswati Sugar Mill).
- A unit of this sugar mill is currently working in Yamunanagar.

Major Sugar Mills in Haryana

- Haryana State Federation of Cooperative Sugar Mills was established in 1966.
- Under the institution, 10 sugar mills are operated, rest are operated by HAFED (Haryana State Cooperative Supply and Marketing Federation).
- Important sugar mills are at Shahabad in Kurukshetra, Sonipat Sugar Mill.
- The Karnal Sugar Mill was awarded second position for its initiative for sugarcane development.

Other Sugar Mills

Main Mills	Establishment
Panipat Co-operative Sugar Mill	1956
Rohtak Co-operative Sugar Mill	1956
Karnal Co-operative Sugar Mill	1977
Shahabad Co-operative Sugar Mill	1984-85
Meham Co-operative Sugar Mill	1991
HAFED Co-operative Sugar Mill	2008

Footwear and Accessories Industries

- The state has many leather product and footwear-making industries, which are actively involved in the process of end-to-end product making.
- The major industries are at Karnal, Faridabad, Bahadurgarh, Gurugram, Manesar, Sonipat, Kundli, Ambala, etc.

Footwear Design and Development Institute (FDDI) is being set up at IMT Rohtak, in view of the demand of trained manpower of the footwear industry.

Timber Industries

- This industry is one of the main industries of Haryana in the North-East regions of the state in the districts of **Yamunanagar, Kaithal** and **Karnal.**
- **Chir, Sheesham, Keekar, Sagwan** trees are used for timber. Before 1947, the timber industry in Yamunanagar was known as **Wood Mandi** of Abdullahpur.

Automobile and Automotive Components Industries

- The automobile manufacturing sector constitutes Haryana's primary strength, due to the presence of **Maruti Suzuki, Hero, Honda, Escorts,** which have led to the development of a large number of ancillaries in this sector.
- **Gurugram-Manesar-Bawal** region has been identified as an **Auto Hub** by the Government of India. A number of auto and auto component units have already been set up in this hub.
- Haryana is the **largest producer of tractors and cars** in the country.

Major automobile industries are as follows

Escorts Limited

- Established in — 1960
- Established by — Hari Nanda and UD Nanda
- Head office — Faridabad
- Products — Heavy engineering goods like agricultural implements, railway equipments, material handling machines, auto parts, building and construction equipments, etc.

- The Faridabad Escorts unit manufactures engines, crankshafts, hydrolicks, transmission equipments and is also a tractor assembly unit.

Maruti Suzuki India

- Established in — 1982
- Location — Gurugram (around 300 acres), Manesar (around 600 acres)

- Manesar plant was established in 2007.
- It has about 50% car market share in India.
- It is a most popular brand of automobiles in India.

Sona Koyo Steering Systems

- Established in — 1985
- Established by — **The Sona Group**
- Products — Steering gears, hydraulic power steering system, propeller shift, tilt-rigid steering columns, etc.

- In 2006, Sona Koyo merged with Koyo Seiko Co. Ltd and formed JTEKT Corporation and it headquartered in Japan.
- JTEKT Corporation opened its branches in Gurugram, Bawal and Dharuhera of the state.

Talbro Automotive Components (1956)

- Branches of company Sohna, Faridabad and Gurugram
- Produces Automotive and industrial gas kits

Other Automobile Units in Haryana

Hero Motocorp	It manufactures motorcycles, established in Gurugram and Dharuhera.
Honda Motorcycle and Scooter India	Established in Manesar. It is a Japanese company.
Yamaha Motors Company Limited	It is a Japanese company, established in Faridabad.
HMT (Hindustan Machine Tools Division)	It is established in Pinjore.
Munjal Showa Limited	It was established in 2013 in Gurugram.
Omax Autos Ltd	It is established in Dharuhera (Rewari).
Jamna Auto Industries Ltd	It is a leading manufacturer of springs and parabolic springs. Its corporate office is located in Yamunanagar.
Rico Auto Industries	It is in Gurugram and produces automobile components.
Coventry Coil-O-Matic Limited	It is located in village Salhawas of Rewari district.

Petrochemical Industries

Indian Oil Corporation

- It is a public sector oil and gas company. Indian Oil Corporation was established in Panipat in 1998.
- It is the seventh refinery of IOC and one of the major refineries of South-East Asia.

DuPont India

- DuPont is a multinational company and it was started in 1802. The company produces explosive materials.
- Its Indian office is located in Gurugram. The company conducts research and development in various fields.

SRF Limited

- It was established in Gurugram in 1970 by the name of Sri Ram Fabrics (SRF) Limited. The company changed its name to SRF in 1990.
- The company produces three commodities i.e. chemicals, industrial fabrics and synthetics.
- Chemicals are further used in refrigerators and air- conditioners. Industrial fabrics produce tyres and conveyor belts. Synthetics are used in soaps, shampoos, etc.

IT Industries

- The State Government continues to accord priority to the IT and ITs sector in recognition of its potential for employment, exports, wealth generation and spin off on the growth of the services sector.
- Gurugram has emerged as the most preferred investment destination in Northern India for the IT and ITES industry.
- Apart from Gurugram, other IT centres in Haryana are **Faridabad, Ambala and Chandigarh.** Sonipat and Karnal are emerging as IT hubs.

Major IT Industries in Haryana are as follows

Tata Consultancy Services (TCS)

Established in	1968
Established by	JRD Tata and FC Kohli
Head office	Mumbai
Other office	Gurugram

National Institute of Information Technology (NIIT)

- Established in 1981
- Location Gurugram
- Objective Provide technical knowledge under Vocational Education Project

In 2004, NIIT established itself as an independent company.

Genpact

- Established in 1997
- Location Gurugram
- It is a major IT company that provides services like BPO (Business Process Outsourcing), KPO (Knowledge Process Outsourcing) financial assistance and back office for various companies, sales and marketing, supply chain, etc.
- Genpact was declared as a top company by NASSCOM for providing IT services.

IBM Daksh Limited

- Location Gurugram
- Established in 2010 (Gurugram Branch)
- Purpose Provide BPO Services

Convergys India Services Limited

- It is a major IT company established in Gurugram.
- The company provides content centre services, customer care services, technical support solutions, marketing and sales programme and other BPO services.

Other IT Industries

Other IT companies established in Haryana are Microsoft Limited, Hughes Softwares, Silicon Graphics Limited, HCL technologies Limited, Siemens India Ltd, Alkatel, GE Capital etc.

DLF Cyber City

• Established by	DLF Limited (Real Estate Company)
• Location	Udyog Vihar (Gurugram)
• Also called	**Cyber Hub**

- It is the largest IT centre of Delhi NCR. Large number of educated people from Delhi and Gurugram areas get employment here.

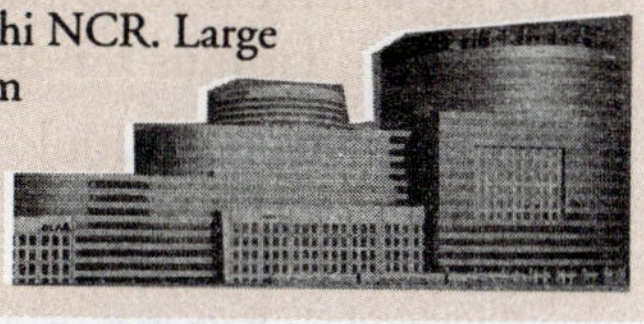

Biotech Industry and Pharmaceuticals

- The Biotech industry and pharma sector has a vast growth potential in the country and the state recognises the need for development of this sector on a sustainable basis.
- The Government of India has selected Haryana state for establishment of a **Bio-Technology Park** along with research and development facility besides promoting the establishment of a Pharma Industrial Park in the state.
- The State Government has decided to earmark and acquire about 1000 acres of land for the development of a dedicated Pharma Park in the **Kundli-Manesar-Palwal** (KMP) Expressway Global Economic Corridor.

Some Biotechnology Industries in Haryana

Ranbaxy Laboratories

• Established by	Private Company
• Established in	1961
• Location	Gurugram

- Major pharmaceutical research company focusing on R & D, infectious diseases, metabolism, pharmacology and drug development.

Eli Lilly India Pvt. Ltd.

• Established by	Eli Lilly (USA)
• Established in	1976
• Location	Gurugram

- Conducts research on biotechnology-based medicine production.

Pro-Agro Seeds Company Pvt. Ltd.

• Established by	Bayer Crop Science Group
• Established in	1977
• Location	Badshahpur, Gurugram

- Conducts research on seed technology, plant breeding, genetic marking, seed grading and hybrid crops.

Real Estate and Construction Industries

DLF Limited

- Delhi Land and Finance (DLF) Limited is a real estate company established in 1946 by Raghuvendra Singh.
- The company started its project in Gurugram in the mid of 1970. The company is involved in real estate activities and develops urban areas, makes townships and develops roads.
- In collaboration with Haryana Development Authority DLF constructed a 16 lane road of 10.5 km in Gurugram.
- It has a wide presence and developed a lot of housing societies in Gurugram.

Emaar India

- It is a real estate company established in 2005.
- It is a joint venture of Emaar Properties, Dubai and MGF Development Limited, India.
- The company is developing many residential and commercial projects in India.
- It is situated in Gurugram. The company is registered under the name Emaar MGF Land Limited.

Vipul Limited

- It is also a real estate company established in Gurugram.
- The company developed **Global Business Park** and **Millennium Plaza.** It constructs housing projects, commercial projects, etc.

Ansal Limited

- It is situated in Gurugram. It undertakes real estate development projects in urban areas.

Unitech Group

- It is India's second largest real estate investment company situated in Gurugram. It develops commercial centres and housing projects.

The Mall of India

- It is situated in Gurugram in an area of 3.6 million square feet. This company increases the retail area by opening a city centre shopping mall.

Other Industries

- Other companies that form a major construction industry of Haryana are Adani Group, Godrej Properties, Shapoorji Pallonji, Vatika, IREO, Aashiana, Mahindra, Sobha, etc. The offices of all these companies are in Gurugram district of Haryana.

- Top malls of Haryana are Ambience Mall, MGF Metropolitan, DLF City Center, MGF Megacity, Sahara Mall, Gurugram Central Plaza Mall, DT Mega Mall, Star Mall, Gold Sonk, etc.

Waste Processing and Recycling Industry

- The state encourages and promotes the industry engaged in processing of waste material e.g. urban solid waste, hazardous waste, medical waste, etc.
- As a special measure to promote this industry, the government proposes to exempt from Goods and Services Tax (GST) on any fuel manufactured by the processing of municipal solid waste.
- The recycling is set up at IMT Manesar, Rohtak, Samalkha. Solid and Liquid Waste Management Projects are being set up in three districts i.e. Yamunanagar, Kurukshetra and Kaithal.
- A waste treatment plant to convert waste to energy was set up in Karnal on Kachhwa road in February, 2018.

Key Industrial Centres in Haryana

Some of the main industrial centres in the state are as follow

Faridabad

- It is the biggest and the first industrial city of Haryana as well as of North India.
- Large and small scale industries related to production of automobiles, tractor, motorcycle, refrigerator, rubber tyres, tools, footwears, appliances of kitchen are situated here.
- First thermal power plant was established here in 1974.
- It is home to hundreds of large-scale companies like Orient Paper and Industries, JCB India Limited, Whirlpool, ABB Group, Goodyear Tyres, Knorr Bremse India Pvt. Ltd., Escorts Limited and Bata Shoes.

▲ Bata Shoes Company

- More than 1000 small industries are also located here. Adjacent to the Southern part of Delhi, the city is well-connected to the national capital and Gurugram through road and rail network.
- An exhibition cum convention centre is planned to be developed in Faridabad.

Panchkula

- Panchkula has a farm equipment industry, tractor industry, IT industry and Pharmaceutical industry.
- In 1954, Bharat Electronics was established here. Panchkula is famous for electronics products.
- Hindustan Machine Tools produces spare parts for tractors in Panchkula.

Panchkula IT Park was established in 2008 and a Nano City Project is also proposed. This Nano city will be developed on a similar line as Silicon Valley (Bengaluru) of India.

- Economic hub around Panchkula is to be developed as Information Technology (IT) Corridors.

Panipat

- Panipat is a city of textiles and carpets. It is the biggest centre for quality blankets and carpets in India and has a handloom weaving industry. The city is called **City of Weavers.**
- In addition, Panipat city is the biggest centre of **Shoddy Yarn** in the world.
- Hand-woven carpets, bed covers, etc, are exported to Australia, Canada, US, Japan, France, Spain, Britain, Switzerland, Germany and Gulf countries.

Industries in Panipat

Industry	Details
National Fertilisers Limited	A major industry run by the Central Government; also has Ammonia and Urea plant centers.
Indian Oil Refinery (Baholi)	Established in 1998; largest oil refinery in India, producing 15 million metric tonnes of oil.
Captive Electricity Machine Components	Produces 15 MW of energy.
Farm Equipment Industry (Samalkha)	Produces a large number of farm tool products.

Gurugram

- It is the most developed commercial and business centre of Haryana, located on the outskirts of Delhi. This city is also known as **Cyber City**.
- Most of the automobile and auto component manufacturers in the state have their base in the industrial areas around Gurugram. Gurugram also has a number of garment export units.
- During the last 10-12 years, Gurugram has emerged as an important location for the Information Technology (IT) and the Information Technology Enabled Services (ITES) industry in the state.
- This city is famous for the Maruti-Suzuki plant, Gems and Jewellery Industry, Electronics products, etc.
- High-tech Habitat Centre is established here.
- Gurugram is called the **City of the Millennium**. It is a hub of call centres.
- Gurugram has now emerged to become the city with the third highest Per-Capita income in India after Chandigarh and Mumbai.
- Gurugram has the presence of about 250 or 50% of the Fortune 500 companies.

Sonipat

- This city is also called the **Golden City**. Ganaur, Kundli, Rai are major industrial centres in Sonipat.
- The district is also popular for **Atlas Cycle Industries** which is one among the top three cycle manufacturers in the world but it was closed in 2018. Milton Cycle Industries Ltd. company is also located here.

> **Yakult Danone India Private Limited** in Rai and **GlaxoSmith- Kline Consumer Health Care** Limited in Khewra village are also located in Sonipat.

- Other industries in Sonipat are food processing industry, textile industry, chemical industry, bulb and tube manufacturing industry, sugar and paper industry.

Rohtak

- Industrial development has started at a rapid pace in this district due to the Single Window Clearance Facility scheme of Haryana.
- The scheme provides ease of establishing small scale industrial units. Electrical equipment, sugar, cotton textiles, threads, surgical and orthopedic instruments and spare parts industries are major industries of the district.
- **Shori Market** of Rohtak is one of the largest cloth markets of Asia.
- The district has Vita Milk Plant, Sabar Dairy Milk Plant and Research and Development Centre of Maruti Udyog.
- **Gajak and Rewari** (dry sweet made of sesame, jaggery and peanut) is very famous in Rohtak.

Bhiwani

- It is a centre for small, cottage and village industries, specially producing cotton textiles and cotton yarns.
- The first textile mill in Haryana was established in Bhiwani in 1937 by the name of **Bhiwani Textile Mills.**

> **Charkhi-Dadri** in Bhiwani has a large scale cement factory that was established in 1939 by Seth Ramkrishna Dalmia in collaboration with German engineers. It was acquired by Cement Corporation of India on 23rd June, 1981.

- The **Technological Institute of Textiles** is an industrial unit that was set up in 1943 in Bhiwani. Its textiles are exported to Bangladesh, Turkey and Belgium.
- The district is also famous for the metal industry, furniture industry, steel utensil industry, etc.

Yamunanagar

- It is one of the largest industrial centres of Haryana.
- Yamunanagar has one of the largest paper mills therefore, it is also called **Paper City**.
- The district has large number of small, medium and large industrial units producing sugar, components of machines, timber etc.
- The **timber market at Abdullahpur** spread over an area of 100 acres. It was established in 1947. It deals in the woods like Sangwan, Sheesham, Kikar, Pine, Safeda, etc.
- Goods are exported to Germany, Zimbabwe, Nepal, Dubai, Syria, UAE, Sri Lanka, Kenya, Russia, South Africa, etc.

Main Industries in Yamunanagar

Name	Estd	Location	Key Products and Facts
Ballarpur (Bilt) Paper Mills	1929	Abdullahpur	Formerly known as **Messers Punjab Pulp and Paper Mill**; produces high-quality writing and printing paper, refined oil, ghee and caustic soda.
Saraswati Sugar Mills	1993	Originally Lahore, now Yamunanagar	One of the **largest sugar mills in Asia**; a unit of Saraswati Industrial Syndicate Limited.
Bharat Starch Chemical Limited	1937	Yamunanagar	Produces starch from maize; current production capacity is 5 lakh tonnes.
Railway Carriage and Wagon Workshop	1952	**Jagadhri**	Repairs and maintains goods and coach stock units; responsible for the maintenance of **Shatabdi trains**; operates under Northern Railway Zone.
Yamuna Gases Limited	1973 (renamed in 1988)	Yamunanagar	Industrial gas production unit; renamed to **Yamuna Gases and Chemicals Limited** in 1988.
Haryana Distillery Ltd.	1969	Yamunanagar	Manufactures selector switches, rotary switches and 2-way switches; known for high-quality.

Ambala

- It is one of the largest manufacturers of scientific and surgical instruments in the country, hence called Science City.
- Ambala produces and exports around 20% of India's scientific equipments. For this purpose, large number of small scale industries are set up in Ambala.
- HMT Limited, Bhupindra Cement Factory, in Surajpur, Ambala HMT tractor factories are also situated here.
- It is also known for the production of engineering goods and textile particularly rugs which is locally known as **Durries**.
- Consumer goods like kitchen appliances, electrical appliances, gas stoves are also produced here.
- Ambala was famous for glass industry before second world war.

Kaithal

- The district has industries like rice mills, sugarcane industry, food processing, equipments for tubewells and oil refinery, wire and cables, paints, bottles, rubber rolls and plastic bag industry.
- Kaithal also has steel production and casting units.

Mahendragarh

- Mahendragarh is a district that has small amounts of mineral wealth, however there are not many industries in it.
- With the formation of Rewari as a separate district, the industrial zone of Mahendragarh got shifted to Rewari.
- Small scale units related to rubber pipes, slippers, animal dietary foods, marble, oil producing, tyre retrading and bread making industries are there.

> Some large scale units of stone crushing, cement, building material construction and cottage industries making Lac bangles are popular in Mahendragarh district.

Karnal

- Karnal has large number of rice mills that polish and pack **Basmati rice and export it to rest of the world.** Liberty Footwear industry is a famous industry of Karnal.
- Leather industry, paint industry, sugar mills, food processing and farm equipment industry are main industries of Karnal.

Rewari

- Dharuhera, Bawal and Rewari are important industrial zones of Rewari district. The region is most popular for producing brass wares.
- The brass industry began around, 1535 in the city with the help of Portuguese. During the time of Hemu, cannons were cast in Rewari for the Sher Shah Suri.

> Rewari is also known as **Brass City**. It is also popular for the making of artistic and vibrant **Tilli Juti** (Moccasin). It is specially popular in North India.

- Other industries are tile, electronics, battery etc.
- Dharuhera and Bawal have large manufacturing unit of Hero Motorcycles and Harley Davidson (assembling unit).

Hisar

- The city has a large steel industry and is also known as the **Steel City** because of the **Jindal Stainless Steel Factories.**
- It is also one of the largest producer of galvanised iron.
- This city in Haryana has small scale industries related to agro-based products like cotton ginning, spinning and yarns, leather, furniture and ropes.
- It also has mineral-based industries like iron garders, agricultural tools, PVC pipes, etc.

Sirsa

- At the time of its formation in 1975, Sirsa had only 483 small scale, 2 medium and large scale industries.
- At present, Sirsa has around 6000 small scale industries related to food processing and agricultural equipments.
- Metal industries are also located in Sirsa.

Kurukshetra

- In Kurukshetra, there are rice mills, sugar mills, cold storage, oil mills, manure producing units and milk plant.
- **Shahabad Cooperative Sugar Mill** was established in 1984-85 in Kurukshetra.

Jhajjar

- Jhajjar district has a flourishing brick industry therefore, it is sometimes known as **Bhatta King.**
- The industries in this district are sanitary wares, electronic equipments, steel industry, radio and cycle manufacturing, medical equipments and metal industry.
- **Pratapgarh Farms** is located in Jhajjar.

> Big private companies operating in Jhajjar are Parle-G, Somani Tiles, HNG Glass Limited, Surya Pipes and Lights, Panasonic India Limited (in Jharli), Reliance Industrial Estate and Yokohama Tyre Company (Bahadurgarh).

Industries and Related Places

Industry	Main Centres
Cement	Surajpur (Panchkula), Charkhi-Dadri
Sugar	Sonipat, Shahbad, Panipat, Rohtak, Jind, Karnal, Hisar, Meham, Jagadhri
Ammunition	Yamunanagar
Paper	Jagadhri (Yamunanagar), Faridabad, Sonipat, Dharuhera
Automobiles	Gurugram, Faridabad, Pinjore (Panchkula)
Bicycles	Sonipat (Atlas), Faridabad, Palwal, Jind
Petroleum	Karnal, Panipat, Bawal
Agricultural Implements	Faridabad
Engineering	Faridabad
Woollen	Hisar, Panipat
Cloth	Hisar, Bhiwani, Faridabad, Panipat, Rohtak
Leather (Shoes, Bags)	Faridabad, Jind, Karnal
Utensils (Steel and Brass)	Rewari
China Clay Potteries	Gurugram, Bahadurgarh
Sewing Machines	Ambala
Iron and Steel	Hisar, Ganaur, Panipat, Bahadurgarh
Tyre Tube	Ballabhgarh (Good Year Company), Faridabad
Electronic	Panchkula, Gurugram, Ambala, Faridabad
Plywood	Yamunanagar
Plastics	Faridabad
Sanitary	Bahadurgarh
Medicines	Gurugram, Dundahera
Hosiery	Rohtak
Scientific Instruments, Mixer	Ambala
Textile Park	Hansi
Agro Hub	Karnal, Sirsa
Maruti	Gurugram
Railway Workshop	Jagadhri (Yamunanagar)
HMT Plant	Pinjore
First Textile Mill	Bhiwani
New Wood Timber Industries	Tohana (Fatehabad)
Timber Market	Yamunanagar
Oil Refinery	Panipat

Major Private and Public Industries in Haryana

Industry	Location
Maruti Plant	Gurugram
Escorts Tractor Company	Faridabad
IOCL Oil Refinery, Urea Manufacturing Plant	Panipat
BILT Paper Mill	Yamunanagar
Indian Starch Chemicals	Yamunanagar
OSRAM, Birla Factory, Pickle Industry, Atlas Cycles, IMT	Sonipat
Railway Workshop	Jagadhri (Yamunanagar)
HMT Plant	Pinjore (Panchkula)
First Energy Bank	Panipat
First Textile Mill	Bhiwani
New Wood Timber Industries, 1st Nuclear Power Plant	Tohana (Fatehabad)
Timber Market	Yamunanagar
Good Year Tyres	Faridabad

City Titles According to Industrial Units

City	Title
Gurugram	Medicity, Cyber City, Solar City, Maruti Plant
Yamunanagar	Paper City, BILT Paper Mill, Bharat Starch Industries
Ambala	Science City, Mixie City
Rohtak	Sugar City, Education City
Hisar	Steel City
Faridabad	Industrial City
Rewari	Brass City
Sonipat	Cycle City
Panipat	Weaver City, First Energy Bank

Major Industrial Development Agencies in Haryana

Department of Industries and Commerce

- The Department of Industries and Commerce undertakes industrial development, finance management, infrastructure development and capital investment.
- It encourages private capital investment in various fields.
- It makes conducive environment for cluster development of cottage and small scale industries.
- It provides more employment opportunities and skill development through industrialisation.

Haryana Enterprises Promotion Board

- Established in 2017
- Headquarters Panchkula
- Promotional centres Delhi and Chandigarh
- Publishes 'Udyog Yug' magazine

- Haryana provides Single Roof Clearance System to facilitate prospective investors to obtain online clearances through the centre.
- This centre has also established Investment Promotion Board and Grievance cell.
- It has been constituted under the Chairmanship of Chief Minister Manohar Lal Khattar to attract domestic as well as Foreign Direct Investment in the state.
- One enterprises promotion board is set up at **Chandigarh** to provide single point contact services.
- The Board provides its online services also. There is a provision to clear the investment offers within 30 days.
- Help desk is established at **Chandigarh**.

Haryana Khadi and Village Industries Board

- Established on 19th February, 1969 by the Haryana Government
- First Chairman Chowdhary Devi Lal
- Board Structure Comprises 15 members, one meeting per month is mandatory
- Key Schemes Margin Money Scheme, Pattern Assistance Scheme, Prime Minister Employment Generation Programme, etc.

- The industry thrives on producing village products through cottage industries like Khadi handlooms, honey, soaps, aggarbattis, candles, bags, carpets, mats, etc.
- This industry encourages the youth to involve in Khadi Industry and gives them training which can generate scope for employment.
- Khadi centres are opened in every district headquarter of Haryana.

> Haryana Khadi and Village Industries Board started its selling counters at **Panchkula** on 1st November, 2018 and in **Jhajjar** on 1st October, 2019.

- It provides credit facilities from banks to set up cottage industries in the production of Khadi products.

Haryana State Industrial and Infrastructural Development Corporation (HSIIDC)

Established on	8th March, 1967 under the Companies Act, 1956
Purpose	Promotion of medium and large-scale industries for balanced regional development
Headquarter	Panchkula
Ownership	100% equity held by the Haryana State Government
Function	Acts as an institutional entrepreneur and financial institution
Financial Assistance	Provides loans, equipment re-finance/ leasing and working capital

- The corporation has established Industrial parks and industrial modern township.
- It provides electricity, water, transport, communication, fuel and banking facilities for the development of industries and industrial estates.

Industrial Townships Developed by HSIIDC

- The HSIIDC has developed an Industrial Model Township (IMT) at **Manesar.** More and more IMTs are being developed at Rohtak (3,800 acres), Faridabad (1,800 acres), Roz-ka-Meo (1,500 acres) and Kharkhoda (3,000 acres).
- Some regions of Haryana that lie within the Delhi-Mumbai Industrial Corridor (DMIC) are also developed as industrial townships. They are **Faridabad-Palwal, Rewari, Hisar, Kundli-Sonipat** and **Manesar-Bawal.**
- The HSIIDC has also developed skill development centres for youth. These are as under
  - National Institute of Design (Umri) Kurukshetra
  - Indian Institute of Corporate Affairs, IMT Manesar
  - National Automotive Testing Infrastructure Project, IMT Manesar
  - Footwear Design and Development Centre IMT Rohtak

Haryana Enterprise Promotion Centre (HEPC)

- **Established on** 2nd February, 2017 under Haryana Enterprises Promotion Act, 2016
- **Objective** To act as single point of contact between Investors and the State Government.
- **Function** Provides secretarial services to Haryana Export Promotion Board (HEPB)

Haryana State Small Industries and Export Corporation

- **Established on** 19th July, 1967
- **Objective** Assists small and medium-scale industries in Haryana
- **Function** Provides raw materials at subsidised rates to small-scale industries
- **Export promotion** Encourages small industries to produce high-quality products for export

Haryana Agro Industries Corporation Limited

- **Location** Murthal, Sonipat
- **Function** Provides research and development facilities for agro-based industries
- **Focused area** Cost reduction and value enhancement in agro-processing.
- The corporation also employs rural youth for apiculture (rearing of honey bees for honey and wax), mushroom production and compost production.

State Government Initiatives for Industrial Development

Inland Container Depot and Storage Centres

- The State Government has set up Inland Container Depot for providing the storage and warehouse facilities to businesses.
- It is set up at Faridabad, Rewari and Panipat.
- The Container Corporation of India (CONCOR) is setting up a cold chain complex at **Rai (Sonipat).**
- In Bawal, warehousing facilities are developed with Public Private Partnership (PPP) Model.

Industrial Development Centres

- Centre for Industrial Development is set up in Bawal, Rewari district to initiate industrialisation.
- Another centre for Industrial Development is set up in Saha, Ambala district.
- The centres are developed to provide world class facilities to encourage big companies to invest there. Nerolac, Exide, Becton etc, have been operating their units here.

Special Economic Zone (SEZ)

- Haryana has 8 notified Special Economic Zones (SEZs), 29 formally approved SEZs and 28 SEZs having in principle approval.
- It is appreciated widely for being the state with highest number of SEZs in the country.
- DLF SEZ at Gurugram and United SEZ at Rai (Sonipat) are notable.
- Reliance Haryana **SEZ at Jhajjar** is India's largest SEZs project with a capital outlay of US $ 10 billion.
- **Panchkula** is developed as Nano City and IT corridor. The state has come out with Haryana Special Economic Zones Act, 2006, for facilitating development of SEZs in the state and framed rules under it.

Hi-Tech Habitat Centre

- It is located at Gurugram.
- Its parent agency is Haryana State Electronics Development Corporation (Harton).

- Haryana Shehri Vikas Pradhikaran (HSVP) has set up a Haryana International Habitat Centre at Panchkula in 2023.

Industrial Parks in Haryana

To encourage private investment, industrial parks are set up in Haryana. These are as follow

Gems and Jewellery Parks

- These parks have been identified as an industry having good potential for development in the state.
- The government has set up a Gems and Jewellery Park Complex at **Udyog Vihar** (Gurugram) to promote this sector.
- It will be endeavour of the government to seek SEZ status for this park.
- One Software Technology Park of India is already set up at Gurugram district.
- The state provides 6.8% employment in IT sector.

Mega Food Parks

- These are established by **Ministry of Food Processing** to provide a direct linkage from farms to processing industries and then to consumers.
- In Haryana, 2 fully developed food parks are operational in **Rai** of Sonipat district and **Saha** at Ambala district.
- Third park is developing at **Barhi** in Sonipat. All the parks are developed by HSIIDC.

Export Promotion Industrial Park

- The park is situated in the district of **Sonipat in Kundli.**
- The park is being developed by **Haryana State Industrial Development Corporation Limited.**
- The park promotes the production and export of processed food items, readymade garments, auto spare parts, electronics, sports goods and handlooms.

Information Technology Park

- Information technology park is at Panchkula district. The park is set up by **HSIIDC.**
- The park has business establishments, training institutes, media and information technology companies.

> In line with Digital India's Mission, the Haryana Government will set up three Software Technology Parks along with Electronics and ICT academy.

- These parks are to be set up in Panchkula, Rai (Sonipat) and Rohtak.

▲ Information Technology Park

Other Parks

Name	Place
Readymade Garments Park	Gurugram
Leather Garments Park	Bahadurgarh
Readymade Apparel Park	Barhi (Sonipat)
Pharmaceutical Park	Karnal (Proposed)
Footwear Park	Karnal
Information Technology Park	Panchkula
Information Technology Park	Manesar
Biotechnology Park	Manesar
Leather Park	Kharkhoda (Sonipat) (Proposed)

Industrial Estates

- Haryana has established 103 industrial estates through its development agencies. The industrial estates in the state are developed by Haryana State Industrial Development Corporation (HSIDC), Haryana Urban Development Authority (HUDA) and private players.
- The important industrial estates are Kundli (Sonipat), Samalkha (Panipat), Tohana (Fatehabad) and Roz-ka-Meo (Gurugram).

Industrial Clusters

- The State Government has earmarked various regions for setting up production units of one kind. **Panipat** is developed as textile cluster, **Gurugram** as auto parts and **Faridabad** as light engineering.
- Rural areas are also developed as industrial clusters such as **Ismailabad** in Kurukshetra for Jute manufacturing, **Farrukhnagar** in Gurugram for Jute and cane furniture, **Odhi** in Rewari for leather footwear, frame manufacturing in Mahendragarh etc.
- A petrochemical complex is established at Panipat that caters to the production of petrochemical products. The state also plans to set up Nuclear plant at Faridabad.

Haryana Industrial Policy, 2015

This policy is also called **Enterprises Promotion Policy, 2015**. It came into effect from 11th August, 2015.

The main features of this policy are as follow

- The Haryana State Government aims to create 4 lakh jobs with this policy by attracting an investment of ₹ 1 lakh crore. The state will open 20 new SEZ.
- The industrial policy promotes the **Makes in India, Digital India** and **Skill India Projects** run by Central Government.

It aims to increase industrial investment by 87%.

The four foundation pillars of this policy are

- Ease of doing business (NIRBAADH).
- Enhancing competitiveness of industry.
- Balanced regional growth.
- Supporting the MSME and revising implementation structures.

NIRBAADH

New Industrial Regulation by Automatic Approval and Delegation in Haryana (NIRBAADH).

To promote ease of doing business following steps are taken

- **Two tier system of project clearances** will be done-one for projects with investment of more than ₹ 10 crore and other for less than ₹ 10 crore.
- System of online clearances by creating **e-biz** portal starting from 1st October, 2015.
- No need to obtain CLU (Change of Land Use) permission in 31 blocks will ease out the procedures.
- Simplified mechanism for industrial licensing to promote private sector investment.

Enhancing Productivity and Competitiveness

- Skill development centres with 70% placement guarantee. Innovation campus at a cost of ₹ 4 crore, 7 incubation centres and 7 universities.
- Set up mobile application development centres.
- Rural BPOs to be set up in Rohtak, Hisar, Sonipat, Kurukshetra and Sirsa.
- Connect 6,000 villages with broadband speed.

Balanced Regional Growth

- Manufacturing and industrial corridor-AKIC and DMIC for industrial development with Japanese collaboration.
- Mega projects to be developed in Gurugram, Manesar and Barwaa with investment of ₹ 20,000 crore.

Supporting MSME

- ₹ 1000 crore investment for developing MSME, providing collateral free loans, technology development centres and rural functional clusters.
- 2 per unit of tariff on Electricity for Micro and Small Enterprises in C and D category blocks for 3 years.

Structures for Implementation

- The State Government has developed 4 institutions for the implementation of the industrial policy. These are Economic Advisory Council, Policy Monitoring Mechanism, Grievance Redressal Committees and Creation of Bureau of Industrial Promotion.
- The target areas of policy 2015 are auto, education and skill, energy, electronics, cloth, defense, logistics, food processing, ITE, pharmaceuticals and medical products.
- The policy aims to increase the competitiveness of MSME, through cluster development and adoption of **Zero Defect Zero Effect** manufacturing practices.

Haryana Enterprises and Employment Policy, 2020

- The vision of this policy is to promote Haryana as a favoured destination for investments, regional development and export diversification.
- The objective is to attract investments of INR 1 lakh crores and generate 5 lakh jobs in the state.
- The policy aims to develop world class infrastructure with lower operating costs.
- The policy supports MSME for enhancing productivity, quality and market access.
- Three tier grievances redressal committees are constituted to resolve industrial disputes.
- Based upon indepth analysis of geographic situation, skill base, available resources and manufacturing capabilities, seven thrust areas are identified.
- The state aims to provide greater investment opportunities in the seven areas.

  They are
  - Auto, auto component and light engineering
  - Agro based, food processing and allied industry
  - Textile and apparel
  - Electronic system design and manufacturing
  - Defense and aerospace manufacturing
  - Pharmaceutical and medical devices
  - Chemical and petrochemicals
  - Large scale energy and data storage

Haryana Electronic System Design and Manufacturing (ESDM) Policy, 2024 (Draft)

- The policy draft is issued by Department of Industries and Commerce, Government of Haryana.
- It envisions to leverage Haryana's strategic location, strong industrial base and skilled workforce to establish a conducive ESDM ecosystem.
- It comprises a comprehensive framework encompassing various dimensions such as financial support, research and development, global linkages, infrastructure, etc

Objectives of this policy

- To attract investments of INR 15,000 crore in electronic manufacturing.
- To create 75,000 employment opportunities.
- To promote exports from Haryana and achieve contribution of 5% to national export.
- To develop industrial network through the establishment of manufacturing clusters, centre of excellence and industrial parks.
- To encourage Research and Development (R&D).

Industrial Awards in Haryana

The scheme of state awards is implemented in Haryana to promote entrepreneurs and workers. So that more industrial development takes place. The awards in this category are as follows

- **State award** of ₹ 3 lakh for **outstanding entrepreneurship** in micro, small and medium enterprises in agro and food processing, automobiles, auto parts, textiles, engineering, pharmaceuticals, IT and electronics, footwear and defense.
- **State Export Award** of ₹ 5 lakh each is given in 18 export categories, including one outstanding women exporter award. 19 consolation prizes of ₹ 51,000 each are also given.
  The industries in which the awards are given are engineering, agro based, glass, scientific instruments, handlooms, Readymade garments, pharmaceuticals and IT.
- **State Labour Welfare Board,** awards the industrial labours for their all round effort skill and efficiency. A sum of ₹ 1 lakh is awarded under Mukhya Mantri Shram Ratan Award, ₹ 50,000 under Haryana Shram Bhushan Award, ₹ 20,000 for Haryana Shram Veer Award and 20,000 for Haryana Shram Veerangna Award.

CHECK CHAPTER KNOWLEDGE

1 The biggest industrial city of Haryana as well as in North India is *HSSC 2022, 20*

(a) Gurugram (b) Panipat
(c) Faridabad (d) Kurukshetra

2 Haryana Government had declared which among the following years as 'the Year of Industry and Employment'? *HSSC 2016*

(a) 2013 (b) 2012 (c) 2014 (d) 2011

3 Which city has a textile and carpet industry and is also known as city of weavers? *HSSC 2021, 20, 15*

(a) Ambala (b) Panipat (c) Karnal (d) Bhiwani

4 Shori Bazar in Rohtak, Asia's largest market is for *HSSC 2024, 17*

(a) Grain (b) Auto spare parts
(c) Cloth (d) Wood

5 Which district of Haryana is known as Wood Mandi of Abdullahpur? *Patwari 2016*

(a) Kaithal (b) Karnal
(c) Yamunanagar (d) Sirsa

6 First paper mill was started in the state in which year? *TGT 2016*

(a) 1929 (b) 1935 (c) 1940 (d) 1944

7 Haryana State Federation of Cooperative Sugar Mills established in

(a) 1956 (b) 1966
(c) 1977 (d) 1984

8 Sugar mills are concentrated where in Haryana? *HSSC 2023, 16*

(a) Shahabad (b) Pehowa
(c) Ladwa (d) Thanesar

9 Which place in Haryana has a flourishing industry of a special kind of footwear 'Tilla Jutti'? *PGT 2016*
(a) Rewari (b) Jagadhri
(c) Hisar (d) Fatehabad

10 Which automobile company is established in Gurugram? *HSSC 2017*
(a) Maruti (b) Hundei
(c) Volkswagon (d) Fiat

11 Maruti Suzuki established its first automobile factory at which place in Haryana? *HSSC 2020, 15*
(a) Bahadurgarh (b) Gurugram
(c) Rohtak (d) Bhiwani

12 Hindustan Machine Tools is situated where in Haryana? *HSSC 2016*
(a) Faridabad (b) Ambala
(c) Gurugram (d) Pinjore

13 The city of Sonipat is popular for which industry? *HSSC 2019, 17, PGT 2016*
(a) Sugar industry (b) Stationery
(c) Bicycle industry (d) Steel industry

14 Which factory is situated in Baholi in Panipat? *HSSC 2019, 16*
(a) Cement (b) Sugar
(c) Fertiliser (d) Oil refinery

15 Due to production of scientific equipments, which city in Haryana is nicknamed as Science city? *HSSC 2022, 19*
(a) Panipat (b) Gurugram
(c) Faridabad (d) Ambala

16 Which city in Haryana is also referred as Hub of IT industry? *HSSC 2020, Group D 2018*
(a) Panipat (b) Gurugram
(c) Sonipat (d) Jind

17 DLF SEZ is at
(a) Faridabad (b) Rohtak
(c) Jhajjar (d) Gurugram

18 In which of the following districts, Reliance has set up its SEZ? *PGT 2015*
(a) Jhajjar (b) Ambala
(c) Panchkula (d) Faridabad

19 In which place Economic SEZ was established? *Group D 2018*
(a) Rohtak (b) Ambala
(c) Mahendragarh (d) Gurugram

20 Which is known as 'Brass city' of Haryana? *HSSC 2019*
(a) Rewari (b)Narnaul
(c) Kaithal (d) Kundli

21 Which district of Haryana has Hero Motorcycle Factory? *HSSC 2016*
(a) Faridabad (b) Rewari
(c) Palwai (d) Mahendragarh

22 Which district of Haryana is one of the largest Producer of iron pipes? *HSSC 2019, 16*
(a) Ambala (b) Panchkula
(c) Hisar (d) Kurukshetra

23 Which city is called as steel city of Haryana? *HSSC 2020, 18*
(a) Gurugram (b) Hisar
(c) Bhiwani (d) Kaithal

24 Sanitary wards production are clustered where in Haryana? *TGT 2016*
(a) Bahadurgarh (b) Kundli
(c) Samalakha (d) Hodal

25 Pratapgarh farms situated in *HSSC 2019*
(a) Jhajjar (b) Hisar
(c) Karnal (d) Fatehabad

26 Identify the wrong match. *HSSC 2018*
(a) Bata Shoe-Faridabad
(b) Rajdoot Motors-Faridabad
(c) HMT-Faridabad
(d) Atlas-Sonipat

27 Liberty Shoe factory is situated where in Haryana? *HSSC 2017, 16*
(a) Ambala (b) Panipat
(c) Dharuhera (d) Karnal

28 In which year Railway Carriage and Wagon Workshop was established in Yamunanagar? *HSSC 2020, 19*
(a) 1952 (b) 1972
(c) 1962 (d) 1942

29 Mahendragarh in Haryana is famous for what? *HSSC 2019, 18*
(a) Lac bangles
(b) Metal works
(c) Leather works
(d) Stationary

30 The Benton group has its production unit in which city of Haryana? *HSSC 2019*
(a) Bhiwani (b) Gurugram
(c) Faridabad (d) Panipat

31 Saraswati Sugar Mills is located where in Haryana? *PGT 2016*
(a) Rohtak
(b) Yamunanagar
(c) Faridabad
(d) Panipat

32 The two major and significant industrial corridors that pass-through Haryana are DMIC and AKIC. While DMIC stands for Delhi Mumbai Industrial Corridor, AKIC stands for *HSSC 2020*

(a) Ahmedabad Kanyakumari Industrial Corridor
(b) Ambala Kanyakumari Industrial Corridor
(c) Amritsar Kolkata Industrial Corridor
(d) Aurangabad Kohima Industrial Corridor

33 Which institution helps in developing Khadi industries in Haryana? *PGT 2016*

(a) Haryana Khadi Board
(b) Haryana Khadi and Village Industries Board
(c) Haryana Industrial Board
(d) Haryana Village Development Board

34 In which year Haryana Khadi and Village Industries board was formed? *HSSC 2018*

(a) 1969
(c) 1968
(b) 1970
(d) None of the above

35 In which of the following years, HSIIDC came into existence? *HSSC 2024, PGT 2015*

(a) 1965 (b) 1967
(c) 1969 (d) 1971

36 Which of the following organisation is responsible for making industrial model township in Manesar? *HSSC 2020*

(a) Haryana State Urban Development Corporation
(b) Haryana Enterprises Promotion Board
(c) Haryana State Industrial and Infrastructure Development Corporation
(d) The Government of India

37 On which date the New Enterprises Promotion Policy came into effect? *HSSC 2016*

(a) 11th August, 2015
(b) 11th September, 2015
(c) 11th March, 2015
(d) 11th April, 2015

38 National Institute of Design in Kurukshetra is developed by which government institution?

(a) HAICL (b) HSIIDC
(c) HEPB (d) HKVIB

39 Match the following.

Industrial Estate	District
A. Kundli	1. Fatehabad
B. Samalkha	2. Sonipat
C. Tohana	3. Gurugram
D. Roz-ka-Meo	4. Panipat

Codes

	A	B	C	D		A	B	C	D
(a)	2	4	1	3	(b)	1	2	3	4
(c)	4	1	2	3	(d)	3	2	1	4

40 Match the following.

Industry	District
A. Cement	1. Ambala
B. Sugar	2. Gurugram
C. Automobiles	3. Sonipat
D. Scientific Instruments	4. Surajpur

Codes

	A	B	C	D		A	B	C	D
(a)	1	3	2	4	(b)	2	1	4	3
(c)	3	4	2	1	(d)	4	3	2	1

CORRECT ANSWERS

1. (c)	**2.** (a)	**3.** (b)	**4.** (c)	**5.** (c)	**6.** (a)	**7.** (b)	**8.** (a)	**9.** (a)	**10.** (a)
11. (b)	**12.** (d)	**13.** (c)	**14.** (d)	**15.** (d)	**16.** (b)	**17.** (d)	**18.** (a)	**19.** (d)	**20.** (a)
21. (b)	**22.** (c)	**23.** (b)	**24.** (a)	**25.** (a)	**26.** (a)	**27.** (d)	**28.** (a)	**29.** (a)	**30.** (b)
31. (b)	**32.** (c)	**33.** (b)	**34.** (a)	**35.** (b)	**36.** (c)	**37.** (a)	**38.** (b)	**39.** (a)	**40.** (d)

CHAPTER 23

Transport and Communication in Haryana

- Individuals use means of transport and mass communication to transport various goods, services and ideas from one place to another.
- The Transport Department of Haryana provides adequate, well coordinated, safe and efficient transport services.

Transport System in Haryana

- Haryana has a fully developed transport infrastructure. Haryana's 14 districts are located in the National Capital Region (NCR) and its surrounding areas, which has led to the state's highly developed transportation infrastructure.
- Most popular and commercially important road of Haryana is **Grand Trunk Road**. It is NH-1 and passes through the North-East of Haryana. This road is also called **Sher Shah Suri Road** and has great historical importance.
- The transport system of Haryana is divided into 3 main categories
  - Road transport
  - Rail transport
  - Air transport

Road Transport in Haryana

- In Haryana, all villages, towns and districts are connected with all weather metalled roads.
- At the time of its formation, the total roadway in the state was 5100 km.
- As per Economic Survey 2024-25, the total road length in Haryana is 33,543 km (upto 30th November, 2024).
- The **Haryana State Agricultural Marketing Board** has constructed village roads to link them to the districts.

• Road density	104.69 km per sq km
• Highest road density	**Ambala**
• Lowest road density	**Jind**
• Largest road length	Hisar (2108 km)
• Smallest road length	Faridabad (522 km)
• Award received	ARSTU Trophy for maximum improvement in vehicles (2008-09)
• PPP model for bus-stands	Pipli (Kurukshetra) and Rajiv Chowk (Gurugram)
• District with longest village road	Sirsa (1642 km)

- District with highest national highway length — Bhiwani (313 km)
- District with shortest national highway length — Fatehabad
- Road availability per lakh population — 182.58 km
- District with maximum road length per lakh population — Bhiwani
- District with minimum road length per lakh population — Faridabad
- Driving training centres — Bahadurgarh (Maruti Udyog), Kaithal (Ashok Leyland), Bhiwani (Central Govt.), Mewat

The roads of Haryana are divided into 3 categories which are as follows

Roads Category in Haryana

- National Highways
- State Highways
- Major District Roads

National Highways

- National Highways are constructed and maintained by the National Highways Authority of India (NHAI). It connects every major city of India.
- As per the NHAI, the total length of National Highways in Haryana is 3395 km (Dec, 2024), which is about 2.0% of the total National Highways in India.
- According to NHAI, the longest NH in the state is **NH-9** (285.9 km) and shortest is **NH-148 A** (6 km).
- NH-1 passes through the districts of Sonipat, Panipat, Karnal, Kurukshetra and Ambala in North Haryana and after passing from Delhi, it enters Faridabad on way to Agra.
- NH-9 passes through 6 districts of Haryana.
- NH-10 passes through Haryana and connects Delhi-Punjab through Fazilka.

Some Major National Highways in Haryana

NH No.	Length (km)	Routes Covered
44	257.8	Ambala-Pipli-Karnal-Delhi-Mathura
48	83.215	Delhi-Gurugram - Jaipur
9	285.850	Delhi - Hisar - Sirsa - Dabwali
5	28.300	Ambala - Kalka
709	73.290	Rohtak - Panipat
344	71.060	Yamunanagar - Shahzadpur
7	37.385	Shahzadpur - Panchkula
152	116.375	Ambala - Narwana
52	143.2	Punjab Border (Khanauri) - Narwana
352	187.675	Narwana - Rohtak - Bawal
105	17.500	Pinjore - Baddi
54	33.546	Bhatinda - Dabwali - Hanumangarh
344	21.425	Ambala - Shahzadpur
907	45.880	Jagadhari - Ponta Sahib
334-B	176.090	Meerut - Sonipat - Jhajjar - Charkhi Dadri - Loharu
11	78.540	Jhunjhunu - Chirawa - Narnaul - Rewari
703	18.920	Sardulgarh - Sirsa
709A	164.975	Bhiwani - Jind - Karnal - Meerut
444A	32.415	Ambala - Saha - Shahabad
248A	22.090	Sahpura - Alwar - Nuh - Gurgaon
148B	96.87	Kotputli - Charkhi Dadri - Bhiwani - Barwala - Tohana
248BB	18.00	Kherki Daula - Dwarka Expressway - Delhi
152A	32.00	Khanauri - Kaithal
907G	15.00	Jagadhari - Bilaspur
148N	80.00	Vadodara - Kota - Sohna
152D	230.00	Gangheri - Kalanaur - Charkhi Dadri - Narnaul
148NA	46.50	KMP Expressway (Western Peripheral Expressway) - Ballabgarh - Delhi
344N	0.50	Dichaon Kalan - Bahadurgarh
148A	6.00	Delhi - Gurugram (MG Road)
NE2	44.00	Eastern Peripheral Expressway

State Highways

- The State Highways are roads that links important cities, towns and district headquarters in the state. Its maintenance is done by the State Public Work Department (PWD).
- As per Economic Survey 2024-25, the total length of State Highways in Haryana is 1,638 km.
- The shortest State Highway in Haryana is SH-6(A), with the length of 3.70 km and longest is SH-12 with the length of 192.32 km.

Some Major State Highways in Haryana

NH No.	Route	Length (km)
SH-1	Jagadhri - Bilaspur - Sadhaura - Narayangarh - Raipur Rani Road	63.90
SH-2	Surewala Chowk - Fatehabad	75.50
SH-4	Kala Amb - Sadhaura - Shahbad	50.01
SH-5	Saharanpur - Ambala	15.14
SH-6	Saharanpur - Radaur - Pipli - Pehowa	103.64
SH-6(A)	Jagadhri - Paonta	3.70
SH-7	Karnal - Ladwa - Shahbad	59.25
SH-8	Kunjpura - Karnal - Kaithal - Khanauri	95.85
SH-9	Kaithal - Pehowa - Patiala	60.25
SH-10	Gohana - Jind - Barwala - Agroha - Adampur - Bhadra	134.78
SH-11	Meerut - Sonipat - Gohana - Assandh - Kaithal - Patiala	166.81
SH-12	Karnal - Assandh - Jind - Hansi - Tosham	192.32
SH-14	Panipat - Safidon - Jind - Bhiwani - Loharu	129.78
SH-22	Bahadurgarh - Jhajjar - Kosli	77.60
SH-24	Rewari - Kanina - Mahendragarh - Loharu	92.45
SH-32	Sirsa - Rania - Jeevannagar	70.43
SH-33	Nilokheri - Dandrodhi	28.64

Major and Other District Roads

- These roads connect the villages and blocks to the districts.
- There roads are constructed and maintained by Municipalities and Village Panchayats.
- As per Economic Survey 2024-25, the length of major and other roads in Haryana is 28,514 km.

Transport Department of Haryana

- Haryana transport department has two wings- **Commercial wing** and **Regulatory wing**. The commercial wing operates the Haryana roadways buses.
- At the time of formation of state, Haryana Transport Corporation limited was a public sector undertaking and had two regional transport authorities. In 1987, the State Government appointed three new regional transport authorities.
- At present, the state has regional transport offices in every district that is run entirely by Haryana roadways.
- Before 1972, there was 50% partnership of private sector in roadways buses. Now it is entirely owned by State Government.

State Government/Initiatives for Road Transport

Sarthi

- Operation of air-conditioned bus services started.
- Provides world-class bus services in tie-up with Volvo.
- Operated on several routes in the state Volvo AC bus service started on Delhi-Chandigarh-Gurugram road.

Haryana Gaurav

- Regular buses at nominal fares connecting various places in Haryana.
- Known as 'Aam Aadmi Ki Khas Bus'.
- Deluxe facilities at ordinary fares. Facilities include FM radio, phone charger and machine-operated doors/ windows.

Haryana Uday

- CNG bus service to promote pollution free transport.
- Aims to reduce pollution levels in the state.
- Low-floor CNG buses run on Delhi- Gurugram and Delhi-Faridabad routes.
- Being extended to Panchkula, Rohtak, Gurugram and Faridabad.
- Proper arrangements for clean water and cleanliness at bus stations being made for the passengers.
- State Government is constructing eco-friendly bus terminals.

Swachh Bharat Abhiyan

- Proper arrangements for clean water and cleanliness at bus stations being made for the passengers.
- State Government is constructing eco-friendly bus terminals.

Harpath

- It is a mobile application developed with the objective of providing pothole free roads.
- It uses **Geospatial technologies** to help people in reporting their grievances about damaged roads, accident black spots and online tracking of complaint.
- The app is developed by State Government in collaboration with **National Remote Sensing Centre** and **National Information Centre**.
- GPS based vehicle tracking system has been introduced in 400 buses of Haryana roadways.
- The state has 16 training centres for light vehicle driving and a training centre for driving of heavy vehicles at **Murthal** (Sonipat).
- Three Institutes of Driving Training and Research (IDTR) are located at **Bahadurgarh, Kaithal** and **Rohtak**.
- A fourth IDTR is being set up in Kaluwas village of Bhiwani district.

Haryana State Road Agencies

Agency	Description
Haryana Roadways Engineering Corporation (HREC), Gurugram	• It was incorporated in November, 1987 and is registered under Companies Act, 1956. • The main **objectives** of the HREC are as follows – To promote, establish, administer and manage Bus Body Building Workshop. – To manufacture bus bodies according to design and specifications approved by the company and to import and export buses.
Haryana State Roads and Bridges Development Corporation Limited	• It is engaged in the construction, repair and activities related to the maintenance and making of bridges, pavements, tunnels, bye passes, etc. • It works under Haryana Public Works Department on Public-Private-Partnership (PPP) basis.

Major Expressways in Haryana

Panipat Elevated Expressway

- Located in Panipat, built to ease NH-1 traffic between Delhi and Panipat. 10 km long; main 6-lane section in Panipat city is 3.6 km.Longest 6-lane flyover in India. Built under Build Operate Transfer (BOT) by L & T T Panipat Elevated Corridor Limited (PECL).

***KMP Expressway** (Western Peripheral Expressway)*

- 135.6 km long, 6-lane expressway started in 2006. Acts as a Delhi bypass for traffic from NH-1, NH-2, NH-8 and NH-10.
- Connects **Sonipat** (Kundli) to Palwal via Gurugram, Mewat and Manesar. Passes through Bahadurgarh, Nuh, Sohna, Hathin, etc.

***KGP Expressway** (Eastern Peripheral Expressway)*

- 135 km long, 6-lane expressway linking Kundli and Palwal via Ghaziabad.
  Passes through Sonipat, Baghpat, Ghaziabad, Noida and Faridabad.

***Dwarka Expressway** (NH-248BB)*

- 29 km long, 8-lane expressway (18.9 km in Haryana, 10.1 km in Delhi).
- Alternate road link to decongest Delhi-Gurugram Expressway.
- Part of the **Golden Quadrilateral Project** under NHDP.
- Enhances connectivity between Delhi, Mumbai, Chennai and Kolkata.
- India's largest and Asia's second largest toll gate consisting of 32 lanes is situated on this expressway.

Transport Policy of Haryana Government, 2017

The State Government had changed the Transport Policy, 2016 and approved the Stage Carriage Scheme in the year 2017. The main **functions** of this policy are as follows

- The Transport Department will allow the firms which operate private bus services to run buses on 452 routes in the state. Any private company can apply to operate a private bus service.
- According to this policy, permits granted under 'City Bus Service Scheme' in the year 2004 will also be valid.
- Under this policy, the right to determine the terms and conditions for private bus service provider companies was concentrated by the State Government.
- To use any vehicle in the state as a 'traffic vehicle', it is necessary to take approval under Section 66 of the Motor

Vehicles Act, 1988. All private buses operating in the state are allowed under this act only.

Modified Stage Carriage Scheme

- It is modified on 7th March, 2024.
- This scheme revises the operational framework for stage carriage services in Haryana, aiming to enhance efficiency and service quality.

Road Safety and Awakening

- Road Safety Clubs' have been constructed in all Government colleges of the state, which aim to make students aware of the subject of road safety.
- The State Government also announced a Safe School Vehicle Policy to ensure the safety of students.
  The major functions of this policy are as follows
  - It has been made mandatory to instal CCTV cameras and GPS in all school buses.
  - It is mandatory to have a female attendant in school buses.
- The State Government has formed a committee under the chairmanship of **K.S. Radhakrishnan** in order to take up the analysis of road safety related measures.
- The State Government announced the State Road Safety Policy in the year 2016. Under this policy, the State Transport Department was entrusted with the task of lead agency to ensure road safety.
- The State Transport Department will function under the Secretariat of the State Road Safety Council.

Haryana Electric Vehicle Policy, 2022

- Effective from 10th July 2022 (for 5 years)
- Aligns with FAME I & II under National Electric Mobility Mission Plan (NEMMP)
- **Key objectives**
  - To promote clean transportation and EV adoption
  - To establish affordable and accessible charging stations
  - To make Haryana a global EV manufacturing hub
  - To generate employment opportunities
  - To encourage R&D in electric mobility
  - It covers new and existing units in specified industrial areas
- It provides incentives for EV manufacturers (BEV, FCEV, PHEV, SHEV), component and battery makers as well as units expanding/converting to EV sector ($\geq$ 50% of FCI investment).
- **Net SGST Reimbursement** is also available in following ways
  - 50% reimbursement for 10 years or until FCI realisation.
  - 5% investment subsidy for low Net SGST units (Max ₹ 5 Cr/year for mega units).

Haryana Antyodaya Parivar Parivahan Yojana (HAPPY)

- It has been implemented by State Government in 2025.
- Under implementation of this scheme, poor families having annual income of upto ₹ 1 lakh can avail free travel upto 1,000 km every year in Haryana Roadways.

Railway Transport in Haryana

- At the time of formation of the state, 3245.11 km railway line was available, out of which the length of the meter gauge line was 2985.55 km and that of narrow guage was 259.56 km.
- At present, the state has about 4439.16 km of railway track of which meter gauge lines are 4178.31 km and narrow gauge lines are 260.85 km.
- The oldest railway station of Haryana is **Rewari Railway Station.**
- First Private Sector Rail Project was initiated in the **Gurugram** district.
- Rail Network in Haryana falls under three Railway Zones and five Railway Divisions.
- The zones are **North Western Railway** Zone (Bikaner and Jaipur divisions); **Northern Railway** Zone (Delhi and Ambala divisions) and **North Central Railway** Zone (Agra division).
- Ambala Division of Indian Railways is the headquarters of Northern Railway Zone. It consists of 1118.53 km of railway line. It also consists of narrow gauge line of 96.54 km.
- The Delhi Division covering 1470.68 km of railway line runs through various parts of Haryana.
- Ferozepur Division has 1849.95 km railway line and 164.31 km narrow gauge line.
- The state also has a narrow guage track starting from Kalka of Panchkula district running upto Shimla.
- The State has the record to run the first CNG train from Rewari to Rohtak on 15th January, 2015.
- There is no railway line and railway station in Nuh town of Mewat district.

Main Railway Routes in Haryana

- Haryana is connected to all parts of India by broad gauge railway line. The main railway station of Haryana is **Chandigarh.**
- The major railway stations in Haryana are – Ambala Cantonment, Ambala City, Bahadurgarh, Ballabhgarh, Bawal, Bhiwani, Bhiwani City, Faridabad, Gurugram, Hisar, Jagadhri, Jakhal Junction, Karnal, Kurukshetra, Loharu, Mahendragarh, Palwal, Sirsa, Sonipat and Kalka.

There are three important rail routes in Haryana

1. Delhi-Rewari-Alwar Rail Route

- This is the **oldest rail route** in Haryana and passes through Southern part of the state.
- The **first railway line** was built in Haryana between Delhi and Rewari in 1873. This was first meter guage commercial line.
- This rail route is a part of Jaipur division of North-West Railway Zone. **The Rewari Junction (established in 1873) lies on Delhi-Jaipur-Ahmedabad rail line.** It is the biggest and oldest railway junction in Haryana.
- At present, the Delhi-Rewari rail route works under the Delhi Division of Northern Railway. However, Rewari Junction is still part of the Jaipur division of the North-Western Railway zone.
- One branch of the Rewari-Bhatinda railway line connects Bhiwani with Rohtak via Kalanaur and another branch Hisar with Jakhal *via* Barwala. Another rail route from Hisar connects Hisar to Bhiwani via Churu (Rajasthan).
- This rail route connects Rewari to different places. They are
  - Rewari-Delhi rail route
  - Rewari-Bawal-Alwar rail route
  - Rewari-Narnaul-Ringas Rajasthan rail route
  - Rewari-Kanina-Mahendragarh-Satnali -Loharu rail route
  - Rewari-Dadri-Bhiwani- Hansi-Hisar-Sirsa -Bhatinda rail route
  - Rewari-Rohtak rail route

2. Delhi-Ambala-Amritsar Route

- This rail route passes from Eastern part of the state and goes to North connecting Delhi to the places of Sonipat, Panipat, Karnal, Kurukshetra and Ambala, reaching upto Amritsar in Punjab.
- Another line from Ambala connects Delhi to Chandigarh.
- The **last station** of this line is **Kalka** in Panchkula district from which a narrow gauge line connects to Shimla passing through Yamunanagar.

> **Delhi-Ambala-Amritsar route is the first line in the state that runs on electricity.** The Delhi-Ambala sector was electrified in 1998, Ambala-Chandigarh line in 1998-99 and Chandigarh-Kalka line in 1999-2000. Now, this line is electrified upto Kalka.

- **Ambala Cantonment area** is the main junction of this route and 5th busiest route of India. The Delhi-Kalka route, Ambala-Atari route and Ambala-Moradabad route passes through this junction.
- The **headquarters** of the Northern Railway zone is located in **Ambala.** The headquarters regulates rail transport in more than half of Haryana and Punjab.

3. Delhi-Jind-Firozpur Route

- This rail route connects Delhi to **Central** and **Western parts** of the state *viz.* Bahadurgarh, Rohtak, Jind, Narwana, Tohana and Jakhal upto Firozpur in Punjab.
- Major railway junctions on this route are Rohtak, Jind and Jakhal.
- The Rewari-Jhajjar-Rohtak line connects this route with Delhi-Rewari route.

Major Link Railway Routes of Haryana

Link Railway Route	Connecting Points
Rohtak-Gohana-Panipat Rail Route	Connects Delhi-Jind-Ferozepur rail route with Delhi- Ambala- Amritsar rail route at Panipat Junction.
Jind-Safidon-Panipat Link Rail Route	Connects Jind to Panipat Junction *via* Safidon.
Narwana-Kaithal-Kurukshetra Link Rail Route	Connects Narwana Junction to Kurukshetra Junction *via* Kaithal.

Routes to Other States

The main railway routes passing through Haryana are

- Amritsar-Delhi
- Bhiwani-Rohtak-Delhi
- Delhi-Ferozepur
- Kalka-Howrah
- Delhi-Shimla
- Rewari-Ahmedabad
- Ambala-Ferozepur
- Kalka-Jodhpur
- Amritsar-Howrah

New Railway Projects in Haryana

- Indian Railways is constructing a new Rohtak- Meham-Hansi railway line with an estimated cost of ₹ 680 crore.
- Rohtak-Panipat railway line in Rohtak is to be elevated to decongest the city with an estimated cost of ₹ 315 crore.

Railway Heritage Museum, Haryana

- It is located in Rewari district of Haryana. Initially, steam locomotives were built here, but in the year 2002, when steam locomotives went out of circulation, it was made a heritage museum.

- It is the only steam locomotive museum in the country. Steam engines were taken from here to shoot the famous films 'Gadar' and 'Bhaag Milkha Bhaag'.

Metro Railway Network in Haryana

Various places of Haryana are connected to Delhi via Delhi Metro Rail Network. Delhi Metro provides quick services in these areas. They are as follows

Delhi-Gurugram Metro Rail

- First Metro Rail Network in Haryana started in Gurugram in the year 2010.
- The yellow line of Delhi metro rail connected Southern part of Delhi, i.e. Qutub Minar to HUDA city centre in Gurugram.
- Delhi Metro has received approval to provide metro services from Cyber city Gurugram to Dwarka Sector-21 in Delhi.
- Metro plans are laid to develop the line to link IFFCO Chowk to Sohna road and Gurugram to Dwarka Sector 21 directly.

> At present, HUDA city centre metro service is a 49.02 km long stretch that is connected to Samaypur Badli of North Delhi. It is the second largest metro line of Delhi Metro.

Mundka-Bahadurgarh Metro Rail Route

- The work of this line started in 2013 and was completed by June 2018.
- The route links Delhi to the border of Bahadurgarh and provides western connectivity of Haryana. It is the green line of Delhi Metro rail.
- There are total 7 **metro stations** on this railway out of which 4 are in Delhi and 3 in Haryana.

Delhi-Faridabad Metro Rail Route

- Faridabad is a major industrial town of Haryana. It was connected to Delhi in **three phases**.
- In the **first phase**, Central Secretariat was linked to Sarita Vihar on 3rd October, 2010.
- In **second phase**, this line was extended to Badarpur of Faridabad in 2011.
- In **third phase**, the line was further extended to Mujesar in 2015. It is the violet line of the Delhi metro rail service.
- This metro line connects Kashmiri Gate in Delhi to Mujesar in Faridabad via Central Secretariat.
- The line will be further extended to connect Ballabhgarh to YMCA Chowk in Faridabad.

Rapid Metro Rail, Gurugram

- Rapid Metro is a fully elevated metro rail system serving the city of Gurugram, Haryana since 2013.
- It is linked with Delhi Metro's Yellow Line at Sikandarpur and connects commercial areas of Gurugram.
- The line is being operated by Rapid Metro Rail Gurugram (RMGL), linking the major satellite towns like Faridabad, Gurugram, Bahadurgarh, Kundli, etc.
- Rapid metro has a total length of 11.7 km serving 11 stations.

▲ Rapid Metro Rail, Gurugram

Narela-Kundli Metro Rail Route

- This link will provide connectivity to Narela in North of Delhi to Kundli in Sonipat.
- Under this project, it is estimated to spend ₹ 968.2 crore.

National Freight Corridor

- To facilitate transportation of heavy Cargo and to provide a strong infrastructural base to the economy, the Central Government has initiated the projects for high speed rail network.

- These are Diamond quadrilateral high speed rail network, Eastern dedicated freight corridor and Western dedicated freight corridor.
- The Eastern dedicated freight corridor will pass through **Ambala and Yamunanagar** while Western dedicated freight corridor will pass through **Rewari** in Haryana.

> Haryana is the first Indian state to achieve 100% electrification of its railway network. This milestone was achieved in March 2023.

Air Transport in Haryana

- It is an important means of transport in Haryana for movement of people and cargo. Perishable goods and agro products are sent to different parts of the country from Haryana through air transport.
- The Civil Aviation Wing of Haryana Government was formed on **1st November, 1966.** The aviation department has set up domestic as well as international airports in Haryana.
- As per Economic Survey 2024-25, the state has 5 civil aviation airstrips in **Hisar, Bhiwani, Karnal, Narnaul** and **Pinjore.**
- The state has 2 flying training centres in **Karnal** and **Pinjore.**
- The state has 6 airports that cater to national and international traffic for both passengers and cargo. They are **Karnal, Hisar, Pinjore, Narnaul, Bhiwani and Jind.**
- **Ambala, Bhilwara, Bhiwani, Hisar, Kalka** and **Sirsa** are air force stations that are highly secure and cater to defence needs of the entire Northern region of India.
- India's First Aero Sports Centre was established on 31st January, 2010 in the Narnaul city near Bachhod Airstrip. It is known as **Rajiv Gandhi Aero Sports Centre.**
- The state has Ambala Air Force Base in Ambala, Hisar Flying Club in Hisar, Karnal Flying Club in Karnal and Pinjore Flying Club in Pinjore.

Important Airports in Haryana

Some important airports in Haryana are as follows

Chandigarh International Airport

• Location	Union Territorty of Chandigarh
• Type	International Airport
• Accessibility	It has been connected to Punjab by the Greater Mohali Area
• Features	Modern infrastructure, primarily made of glass and steel

Chandigarh International Airport

- This airport caters to 6 domestic airlines and connects Chandigarh to 2 international and 15 domestic destinations. In 2014, aviation companies were allowed to open their services here.
- On 11th September, 2015, a new terminal at this airport was inaugurated by PM Narendra Modi. Chandigarh Airport is one of the most important airports in the North India.
- It serves the states of Punjab, Haryana and Himachal Pradesh. More than 28 takeoffs and landings per day took place in this airport.

> Chandigarh International Airport has been renamed as Shaheed Bhagat Singh International Airport in September 2022.

Hisar Airport

- Hisar Airport is spread over 4194 acres of land. It has been renamed of **Maharaja Agrasen International Airport.**
- This airport is 165 km from Indira Gandhi International Airport and 280 km from Chandigarh International Airport.
- The development of this airport is planned to be completed in the following three phases

First Phase
The airport was upgraded for domestic flights in technical collaboration with the Airport Authority of India which completed by December, 2018.

↓

Second Phase
In this phase, the process of construction of aero-city hub has been completed. This airport is served by 6 or 7 seater aircraft.

↓

Third Phase
In this phase, the international airport is expected to be completed by the year 2030.

Karnal Airport

• Location	3 km East Karnal
• Also known as	Karnal Flying Club
• Used for	General aviation and pilot training since 1967
• Expansion	In 1999, by merging with Hisar and Pinjore aviation clubs

- The Haryana State Government approved the plans to develop the airport to operate domestic passenger services under the UDAN scheme.

Cargo Airport

- The government intends to set up an international Cargo Airport in the National Capital Region (NCR).
- The site for the project has been identified at Bhaini Maharajpur and Bhaini Bhairon villages in the state, which are in the NCR.

> **Ambala Air Force Station**
> - It is an air base East of the urban Ambala area.
> - This air base was first built in 1948, following the Independence of India.
> - It is used for military and government flights. It is also used to fly in politicians and other key people.
> - The Indian Air Force base at Ambala was attacked by the Pakistani Air Force in both the 1965 and 1971 wars.

Gurugram Airstrip

- It is also called **Bhondsi airstrip** or **Silokhera airstrip**. It is located 10 km South of Gurugram city centre. It is a small airstrip and has just 1 runway.
- It has been included in the UDAN-Regional Connectivity scheme for operation of domestic flights.

Narnaul Airstrip

This airstrip is mainly used by Rajiv Gandhi National Centre for Aero Sports and it was inaugurated in 2010.

Haryana Civil Aviation Training Institute

- This is the state's highest civil aviation training institute. It was established on 1st November, 1966 for the purpose of providing aviation training to pilots. The training centres are located in Karnal and Pinjore.
- In 2008-09 and in 2012-13, Haryana Civil Aviation Training Institute received the Runners up trophy for Best Flying Training Institution.
- The main **functions** of Haryana Civil Aviation Training Institute are
  - The institute undertakes development of airstrips, helipads and also provides training to the pilots.
  - Management of materials required for training and to arrange air transport for the main persons of the state.
  - To coordinate with training centres.

▲ Haryana Civil Aviation Training Institute

Communication in Haryana

- Mass communication refers to the study and analysis of resources that connect large parts of the population, such as radio, television, newspapers, magazines, etc.
- The first Post Office Passport Seva Kendra of the state was opened in Karnal on 25th March, 2017 and the 45th Post Office Passport Seva Kendra of India was opened in Faridabad on 27th April, 2017.

Some popular communication systems of the state are as follows

Print Media

It consists of newspapers and magazines. They remain important means of mass communication in the state even after the advent of internet and digital technology.

Newspaper

- The first newspaper printed in Haryana was **Hariyana Tilak** which was published from Jhajjar. **Pandit Deen Dayal Sharma** was its editor.
- **Hariyana Tilak** first published in 1923 was a weekly newspaper published in Urdu and Hindi language from Rohtak. Since then many newspapers have come up in the state.
- **Refah-e-Aam** was the second newspaper edited by him which also circulated in Haryana in pre-Independence period.
- Another important newspaper from Haryana was **Jaat Samachar** first published in 1889. Its editor was Babu Kanhiya Lal.
- In 1916, **Jat Gazette** was published from Rohtak. Chaudhary Chotu Ram was its editor.
- **Jyotish Martand** was started from Gurugram in 1925.
- **Brahmin Samachar** started from Jagadhri, **Sawdhan** from Bhiwani, **Audichya Brahmin** newspaper was published from Karnal in the same year i.e. 1925.

- The newspapers started in 1926 were **Bhakti** Editor Surdevi, **Medh Prabhakar** edited by Nanu Verma and **Ahir Hiteshi** edited by Rao Ganeshi Lal.
- Pandit Prahlad Verma published **Jyotish Samachar** from Rewari in 1928.
- Sri Sharma started **Haryana Tilak** in Urdu from 1929.
- **Sandesh** was started by Pandit Neki Ram Sharma in 1930. Kirti Prasad Jain initiated **Aatmanand** in the same year.
- **Gram Sewak** was started by Hardev Sahay in 1936 and **Sewak** in 1941.

First newspaper from Hisar was 'Gyanodaya Patra' published in 1948 whose editor was Brahmanand.

- Monthly newspaper **Vijayanand** was published from Ambala in 1956 whose editor was Aatmaram Jain.
- Weekly newspaper **Chetna** was published in 1957 whose editor was Rabindra Nath Vashisth.
- **Haryana Kesari** was started in 1958 from Bhiwani under Banarasi Das Gupt and K.B. Dutta.
- **Dainik Haribhoomi** is the first National Newspaper published on 5th September, 1996 from Rohtak.
- Haryana's first Hindi newspaper **Jain Prakash** was published by Editor and Journalist Ziyalal Jain in the year 1985.

Other Newspapers and their Editors

Newspaper	Editor
Haryana Sandesh	Mahesh Chandra
Rangeela Musafir	Pyarelal Sharma
Amar Jyoti	Ramcharikh
Sudharak	Acharya Bhagwan Dev
Hindi Mewat	Gumani Rai Arya
Haryana Kesari	Mushi Ram
Anand Bhoomi	Rajkumar Gupta
Chetna	Devavrat Vashisht
Haryana Samachar	Ramdhari Gaud
Bhola Insan	Bharatham Sijgh Pawar
Vijay Anand	Prithviraj Jain
Gautam Vani	Jitendra Kumar
Paigam-A-Watan	Rooplal Mehta
Nari Kalyan	Chandraprabhu Sharma
Harijan Pukar	Kartar Devi
Narnaul Magazine	Bholaram Sharma
Gram Sahyogi	Dinanath Siddhantalankar
Vishleshan	Jayanath Nalin
Haryana Magazine	Manuhari Pathak
Munch	Rakesh Vats
Sunahri Bharat	Purushottam Lal Agarwal and VP Agarwal

Magazines

Magazines are an important medium of transferring the information to target groups. It is an important medium that showcases the culture of a society.

Some of the famous magazines are as follows

- **Haryana Samvad** It is a monthly magazine published up by Public Relations and Cultural Affairs Department, Haryana. It is published in Hindi language. It started publishing in 2008. It also started publishing in Punjabi language from 2010.
- **Krishi Samvad** It started its publication from 2008.
- **Haryana Review** It was started in 2008 in English.
- **Tameer-e-Haryana** It is an Urdu magazine published from Haryana from 2008.
- **Ubharta Haryana** It is a trendy magazine in Haryana that discusses latest issues related to economy, society and polity.
- **Harigandha** It is a magazine published by Sahitya Akademi of Haryana. It was started in 2011. It encourages new talent by publishing their works. The magazine also has an electronic version.
- **Haryana Kheti** It is a magazine published by Haryana Agricultural University.
- **Shiksha Saarthi** It is a magazine published by Department of Haryana Agricultural University.

Radio

- It is an extremely popular means of mass communication in urban and rural areas of Haryana.
- **Akashvani Rohtak** (AIR Rohtak) was the first radio station to be set up in Haryana on 8th May, 1976.
- Several other radio stations were also established in the state namely **Akashvani Kurukshetra** on 24th June, 1991 and **Akashvani Hisar** on 26th January, 1999.
- Other radio stations are – Radio Sirsa, Radio Mewat, Radio Karnal, Radio Ambala and Radio Gurugram.

- **Alfaz-e-Mewat** is a community radio station established in 2012 to facilitate local programmes.
- **Radio Manav Rachna** is a community radio station catering the student needs in the Aravalli Campus and Manav Rachna educational institutions.
- Hisar also has a radio station catering exclusively to agricultural universities and was launched in 26th January, 1999.

Television

- On **1st November, 2012** the Television Studio Centre alongwith Satellite Earth Station and DD-2 transmitter was commissioned at Hisar. Narrowcasting from LPT, Hisar was also started simultaneously.
- **Hisar Doordarshan Kendra** is the only Programme Production Centre in Haryana, located in Sector-13, Hisar. It is operated by Prasar Bharati.
- At present, many satellite television channels operate in Haryana along with Doordarshan.
- The state also has well equipped television studios in Gurugram, Hisar, Sirsa, etc.

Theatre, Television and Radio Artists from Haryana

Name	Description
Pandit Harderam	First music composer and singer of Aakashvani, Delhi
Duliram	Theatre personality of Aakashvani, Delhi
Ranbir Dahiya	Stage artist and television actor
Krishna Sharma	Artist in Aakashvani and television
Ram Niwas	Famous theatre artist
Seema Dhankar	Theatre, Aakashvani and television artist
Narendra Balhara	Doordarshan and Aakashvani artist
Karambir Saini	Theatre and television actor
Rajbala Phogat	Doordarshan, theatre and Aakashvani artist
Rajneesh Kaur	Famous theatre artist
Mahavir Guddu	Stage director, radio and television actor
Yash Tonk	Stage and television actor
Manish Joshi	Stage and television actor
Jaswant Singh Tohnavi	Stage and television actor
Ram Mehar	Aakashvani Delhi artist
Nathu	Dramatist in Aakashvani Delhi
Dr. Sudhir Sharma	Theatre artist
Dr. R.S. Waldia	National level theatre artist
Mahesh Vashist	Famous theatre artist
Dr. Surendra Sharma	Dramatist of national level
Dr. Vinod Sangwan	State-level artist of radio and television
Jagbir Rathi	Theatre, radio, TV artist, dancer, comic poet and stage director
Angrez Kaur	Theatre, TV and radio artist
Pinki Chaudhary	Theatre, TV and radio artist
Sumer Chand Sharma	National level theatre personality
Gajendra Phogat	Theatre, Aakashvani, Doordarshan artist
Praveen Kumari	Singer in theatre, radio and television
Mahipal	Theatre personality
Dharmpal	Famous comedian and national level dramatist
Narsi	Famous theatre personality

Mobile Communication

- Proper communication and good network system is the decisive feature of an emerging state like Haryana. Haryana offers a statewide network for extremely effective telecommunication facilities.
- Various private sector players such as Reliance, Jio, Tata Teleservices, Bharti Telecom, Vi are operating in the state for smooth and efficient communication.
- BSNL has its operations in the state. Gurugram, Faridabad, Bahadurgarh, Kundli and Chandigarh are major cities that use telecom services widely.

Information Technology in Haryana

- The State Government recognises the importance of IT in catalysing economic activity, in efficient governance and in developing human resource.
- It has a prominent and progressive role in improving efficiency and effectiveness in organisations.
- Haryana government encourages replacement of traditional delivery system of public services by IT driven system of governance that works better, costs less and is capable of serving the citizens' needs with ease.
- The Haryana Government implemented its **Information Technology** (IT) **Policy** in 2002. The policy was subsequently revised in 2017.
- Under this policy, there is a provision to encourage technology, ITES/BPO industry.

- This policy seeks to facilitate private domain initiative in e-transition of Haryana by providing critical infrastructure, systems framework and enabling environment.
- The government has also announced a policy for technology Parks and IT corridors have been established.
- To promote the IT sector, **Information Technology Park** was established in 2008 in Panchkula.
- Cyber City was started in Gurugram to promote this sector.

Projects Run by Haryana Electronics & IT Department

Project	Details
State Data Centre	Established in 2012 to provide backend digital services to government departments. Connects 62 applications of state boards, corporations and district headquarters.
State Wide Area Network (SWAN)	Launched in 2007 to provide internet and intra-connectivity across government departments. Supports data transfer, video conferencing, etc. at district HQs, Civil Secretariat, blocks, and townships.
Harsamadhan Portal	Public grievance portal developed by NIC and Haryana State Centre. Enables users to lodge complaints online and track their status, enhancing transparency.
E-Disha (Electronic Delivery of Integrated Services of Haryana)	E-Disha Kendras at district and sub-division levels provide services like birth/death/marriage certificates, land records, pensions, insurance, passport, driving license, vehicle registration, etc.
HALRIS & HRIS	Haryana Land Record Information System (HALRIS) and Haryana Registration Information System (HRIS) for computerised land records management.
Biswas	Software for billing water and sewerage services by the Public Health Engineering Department.
HaPPIS	Online pension disbursal system by the Haryana government.
Jansahayak	E-delivery system for 36 time-bound citizen services in Haryana.

Haryanvi Cinema

- The Haryana film industry is nicknamed as **Hariwood**.
- The **first film of Haryana was Harphool Singh Jat Julani** directed by Anand. It was released in 1970. **Beera Shera** was a popular film that came up in 1974 whose director was Anup Singh. It was followed by **Vir Ghatothkach** in 1974. Its actor was Chandgiram.

> Haryana's first commercially successful film **Bahurani** was released in the year 1982. **Chandrawal**, the best film of the state, was released in the year 1984. It was the first commercial super hit film in the state. The lyrics of this film are very popular.

- In the year 1984, the film named **Bhabhi Ka Aashirwad** was also released and in 1985, two films named **Chail Galllyaan Jangi** and **Lado Basanti** were relased.
- In 2000, Aswini Chaudhary and Kumud Chaudhary won the Indira Gandhi Award for 47th Best First Film of a Director at the National Film Awards for the Haryanvi film **Lado Basanti**. The producer of this film was Kumud Chaudhary.
- **Pagadi The Honour** was released in 2015. It is the first Haryanvi film which has received two national awards. It received the title of Best Haryanvi Film and its actress Baljinder Kaur won Best Supporting Actor (Female) award at 62nd National Film Awards.
- Haryanvi movie **Satrangi** released in 2016 received the Best Film Award in 63rd National Film Awards. The actor was Yashpal Sharma.
- **Devi Shankar Prabhakar** is a successful producer of Haryana film industry known to make many successful films.
- **Jayant Prabhakar** has directed most number of Haryanvi films.
- **Jagat Jakhar** is a popular and the best actor in Haryana.
- Haryana has developed some districts as ideal shooting locations which includes historical places, ancient locations, beautiful gardens, modern city and farm lands. They are in Kurukshetra, Hisar, Faridabad, Gurugram, Ambala, Karnal, Panipat and Panchkula.

List of Famous Haryanvi Films

Year	Title	Year	Title
1968	Dharti	1987	Chhora Jaat Ka
1973	Beera Shera	1987	Gulaabo
1982	Bahurani (First commercially successful Haryanvi movie)	1991	Jatani, Phool Badan, Mhara Peehar Sansra
1984	Chandrawal (First commercial superhit Haryanvi movie), Sapne Ka Jikr	1991	Panghat, Muklava, Lambardar, Ke Supne Ka Jikr
1985	Laado Basanti, Bhanwar Chameli	1991	Phaagan Aaya Re
1986	Mhari Dharti Mhari Maa	2000	Laado
1987	Jhanakdar Kangana	2011	Muthbhed-A Planned Encounter
1987	Bataeu	2012	Chandrawal-A
1987	Chabilee	2012	Tera Mera Vaada
1987	Chail Gabru	2015	**Pagdi** The Honour (Best Haryanvi Film at 62nd National Film Awards)
1987	Chhora Haryane Ka, Chhori Sapele Ki	2001	Chand Chakori Chandro
1988	Bairee (Bhaal Singh, Shoshi Ranjan)	2004	Dhakad Chhora
1993	Jaat	2014	Kunba, Maati Kare Pukaar
2014	Dear vs. Ber	2016	Satrangi, Mati Kare Pukaar
2019	Sadgi	2020	Mudda
2021	Malaal	2022	Dada Lakhmi

Haryana Film and Entertainment Policy, 2022

- It was introduced to promote Haryanvi cinema, artists, and culture. The policy also aims to make Haryana a top destination for film production.
- The Filmmakers can receive a subsidy of up to ₹ 2 crore to promote Haryanvi films.
- The Haryana Film Promotion Board (HFPB) will implement the policy.
- The policy provides a single-window mechanism for all permits and clearances for film, web-series or serials.
- The State Government will support the setting up of film and TV studios in Haryana.
- The State Government will strive to set up a Film City in Haryana.
- The governing council oversees the implementation of the policy.
- The council includes the Administrative Secretary of the Tourism Department, the Administrative Secretary of the Art and Cultural Affairs Department and others.
- Actress **Meeta Vashisth** is the chairperson of the governing council.

Famous Cinema Personalities from Haryana

Deep Chand

- Born in: 1884 in Sihri Khanda, Sonipat
- Disciple of: Folk singer Sangi Chajju Ram
- Popularised: Folk singing with instruments like Sarangi, Nagada and Dholak

Usha Sharma

- Career: Renowned dancer trained under Birju Maharaj
- Noteworthy: First Haryanvi woman to perform on Doordarshan
- Lead actress: In Chandrawal (1984), Haryana's highest-grossing film
- President of: Haryana Arts Council

Sunil Dutt

- Born on: 6th June, 1929 inKhurd (Pakistan), resettled in Yamunanagar after Partition
- Career: Actor, director, producer and politician
- Notable films: Mother India, Waqt, Mujhe Jeene Do
- Noteworthy: Cabinet Minister for Youth Affairs & Sports (2004-05)
- Awarded: Padma Shri in 1968
- Died on: 25th May, 2005

Khwaja Ahmed Abbas

- Born on: 7th June, 1914 in Panipat
- Career: Film director, screenwriter, novelist and journalist
- Directed acclaimed films: Jaat Hindustani, Do Boond Pani, Dharti Ke Lal
- Screen writing: Scripts for Raj Kapoor's films (Awara, Shree 420, Bobby, Mere Naam Joker)
- Awarded: Palme D award at Cannes Festival (For Neecha Sagar, 1946 Film) Padma Shri in 1969
- Died on: 1st June, 1987 in Bombay

Om Puri

- Born on: 18th October, 1950 in Ambala
- Career: Acclaimed actor in Indian and international films

- Notable films: Ghashiram Kotwal, Ardh Satya, Mirch Masala, Sadgati
- Awarded: Padma Shri in 1990
- Died on: 6th January, 2017

Surendra Sharma

- Born in: 1945 in Nangal, Mahendragarh
- Career: Comic poet known for Marwari dialect poetry
- Awarded: Padma Shri in 2013

Satish Kaushik

- Born on: 13th April, 1956 in Mahendragarh
- Career: Actor, producer and director
- Noteworthy: Assisted Shekhar Kapoor in Masoom (1983)
- Awards: Won Filmfare Best Comedian Award twice (1990, 1997)
- Died on: 9th March, 2023

Naseeb Singh Kundu

- Born on: 27th November, 1961 in Titoli, Rohtak
- Career: Acted in Haryanvi films like Chandrawal, Lado Basanti, Jar, Jameen, Joru

Sonu Nigam

- Born on: 30th July, 1973 in Faridabad
- Career: Renowned playback singer
- Films: Won National Film Award (2004) and Filmfare Best Male Playback Award (2003, 2005)

Yashpal Sharma

- Born on: 1st January, 1967 in Hisar
- Career: Graduated from NSD in 1994
- Films: Hazaar Chaurasi Ki Maa, Gangajal, Hazaron Khwahishein Aisi

Mallika Sherawat

- Born on: 24th October, 1976 in Hisar as Reema Lamba
- Career: Known for bold roles in Murder, Khwaish, Pyaar Ke Side Effects

Madhu Sharma

- Born on: 8th January, 1976 in Pehowa, Kurukshetra
- Career: Famous Ragni and Saang singer
- Notable compositions: Main Suraj Tu Meri Kiran Bagdo, Ankhiyan Mein Ghalya Kajal

Randeep Hooda

- Born on: 20th August, 1976 in Jassia, Rohtak
- Career: Debuted in Monsoon Wedding (2001)
- Films: Once Upon a Time in Mumbai, Kick, Sarbjit

Parineeti Chopra

- Born on: 22nd October, 1988 in Ambala
- Career: Started as PR advisor for Yash Raj Films, later turned actress
- Films: Ishaqzaade, Kesari, Daawat-e-Ishq, Namaste England

Juhi Chawla

- Born on: 13th November, 1967 in Sonipat
- Noteworthy: Won Miss India 1984, became a leading Bollywood actress
- Notable films: Qayamat Se Qayamat Tak, Darr, Hum Hain Rahi Pyaar Ke

Popular Film Artists from Haryana

Name	Place	Field	Name	Place	Field
Manushi Chhillar	Rohtak	Actress and Model	Jaideep Ahlawat	Rohtak	Actor
Ashwini Chaudhary	Rohtak	Producer, Director	Satyen Kappu	Panipat	Actor
T.P. Agarwal	Sonipat	Producer, Director	Mohit Ahlawat	Panipat	Actor
Ashok Ghai	Rohtak	Producer, Director	Manoj Kumar	Yamunanagar	Actor
Subhash Ghai	Rohtak	Producer, Director	Sonu Nigam	Faridabad	Singer
Pankaj Butalia	Ambala	Producer, Director	Satish Kaushik	Mahendragarh	Writer, Actor, Director
J.P. Kaushik	Rohtak	Music Director	Richa Sharma	Faridabad	Singer (Female)
Sunil Dutt	Yamunanagar	Actor	Sara Gurpal	Fatehabad	Actress and Model
Juhi Chawla	Sonipat	Actress	Sitaram Panchal	Jind	Actor
Randeep Hooda	Rohtak	Actor	Rupinder Handa	Sirsa	Singer (Female)
Pooja Batra	Rohtak	Actress	Ritu Jalgan	Jind	Actress
Raj Tilak	Panipat	Actor	Sapna Chaudhary	Rohtak	Singer, Actress, Dancer
Mallika Sehrawat	Hisar	Actress	Himanshu Mallik	Sonipat	Actor

CHECK CHAPTER KNOWLEDGE

1 The Grand Trunk Road does not pass through which of the following districts?
(a) Sonipat (b) Panipat
(c) Kurukshetra (d) Bhiwani

2 Grand Trunk Road is the part of
(a) NH-1 (b) NH-2
(c) NH-8 (d) NH-10

3 Which district of Haryana has the highest road density of metalled roads?
(a) Ambala (b) Panchkula
(c) Kaithal (d) Jhajjar

4 ....district has the largest length of metalled roads in the state. *PGT 2016*
(a) Hisar (b) Kaithal
(c) Bhiwani (d) Panipat

5 The longest National Highway in Haryana is *PGT 2016*
(a) NH-71 (b) NH-9
(c) NH-65 (d) NH-73

6 The shortest National Highway of Haryana is
(a) NH-148A (b) NH-22
(c) NH-8 (d) NH-71

7 World's shortest and widest National Highway will be built in which place of Haryana? *Haryana Police Constable 2018*
(a) Yamunanagar (b) Gurugram
(c) Kaithal (d) None of these

8 Which NH passes through Haryana that connects Delhi-Punjab and Fazilka? *HSSC 2023, 21*
(a) NH-65 (b) NH-8
(c) NH-2 (d) NH-10

9 Dharuhera industrial area is located on which National Highway? *Mandi Supervisor 2017*
(a) Delhi-Rohtak (b) Delhi-Agra
(c) Delhi-Jaipur (d) Delhi-Ambala

10 Delhi-Faridabad Skyway is a part of which National Highway?
(a) NH-1 (b) NH-71
(c) NH-10 (d) NH-2

11 Panipat Expressway is a part of which National Highway? *PGT 2016*
(a) NH-1 (b) NH- 71
(c) NH-3 (d) NH-4

12 KMP stands for *HSSC 2022, 16*
(a) Kundli-Manesar-Palwal
(b) Kundli-Meerut-Palwal
(c) Kundli-Madhya-Palwal
(d) None of the above

13 The total length of Kundli-Manesar-Palwal Expressway is *Haryana Police Sub-Inspector 2018*
(a) 140 km (b) 135 km (c) 125 km (d) 150 km

14 Which scheme is known as 'Aam Aadmi Ki Khas Bus'?
(a) Sarthi (b) Haryana Gaurav
(c) Haryana Uday (d) Harpath

15 The main objective of the Haryana Uday scheme is
(a) to provide air-conditioned bus services
(b) to promote pollution free transport through CNG buses
(c) to provide free transport for women
(d) to construct eco-friendly bus terminals

16 Primary function of the Harpath mobile application is *HSSC 2024*
(a) to provide real-time bus tracking
(b) to report road damages and accident black spots
(c) to book online bus tickets
(d) to monitor air pollution levels

17 Which organisation collaborated with the Haryana Government to develop the Harpath mobile application?
(a) ISRO and DRDO
(b) National Remote Sensing Centre and National Informatics Centre
(c) NITI Aayog and Ministry of Transport
(d) Haryana Transport Department and Volvo

18 The correct statements about KMP Expressway is/are
1. Sonipat and Gurugram are major cities on it.
2. It acts as a Delhi bypass for traffic coming from North of Delhi on NH-1.

Select the correct answer using the codes given below.
(a) Only 1 (b) Only 2
(c) Both 1 and 2 (d) None of these

19 Where did the first train run in Haryana? *Mandi Supervisor 2018*

(a) Narwana-Kaithal (b) Delhi-Rewari
(c) Hisar-Sirsa (d) Delhi-Ambala

20 Where is the oldest railway and biggest Station Junction of Haryana located, which was established in 1873? *HSSC 2020, PGT 2016*

(a) Ambala (b) Rewari
(c) Sirsa (d) Hansi

21 In which city of Haryana the headquarter of Northern Railway Zone located?

(a) Panchkula (b) Kurukshetra
(c) Gurugram (d) Ambala

22 In which year a railway carriage and wagon workshop was established in Jagadhri of Yamunanagar district of Haryana? *HSSC 2022, 19*

(a) 1952 (b) 1972
(c) 1962 (d) 1942

23 First CNG demo train was started between which two stations of Haryana? *Haryana Tabla Virtuoso 2018*

(a) Jhajjar to Rewari
(b) Rohtak to Rewari
(c) Rohtak to Chandigarh
(d) Chandigarh to Hisar

24 Which district of Haryana has no railway line? *HSSC Shift Attendant 2016*

(a) Mahendragarh (b) Mewat
(c) Kaithal (d) Sirsa

25 Which city in Haryana had the first metro rail? *PGT 2016*

(a) Bhiwani (b) Hisar
(c) Gurugram (d) Karnal

26 Eastern Dedicated Freight Corridor will pass through which district of Haryana?

(a) Ambala (b) Yamunanagar
(c) Rewari (d) Both (a) and (b)

27 ....became the first state where all railways track has been electrified. *HSSC 2023*

(a) Punjab (b) Tamil Nadu
(c) Haryana (d) Gujarat

28 Which of the following is an airport in Haryana? *HSSC 2020*

(a) Indira Gandhi airport
(b) Hisar airport
(c) Shivaji airport
(d) Begumpet airport

29 Hisar Airport in Haryana is formally known as .... International Airport. *HSSC 2023*

(a) Daya Ram (b) Maharaja Agrasen
(c) Bhagat Singh (d) Pandit Nekiram

30 Which airstrip in Haryana is also called Silokhera Airstrip?

(a) Narnaul (b) Gurugram
(c) Karnal (d) Hisar

31 Ambala Air Force Station was built in.......

(a) 1948 (b) 1950
(c) 1957 (d) 1960

32 Haryana's first Hindi Newspaper 'Jain Prakash' was published by the first Editor and Journalist, Ziyalal Jain in the year .... *HSSC 2023, 16*

(a) 1980 (b) 1985 (c) 1975 (d) 1970

33 'Sandesh' weekly Magazine was launched by.......in Haryana. *HSSC 2020*

(a) Kirti Sharma (b) Nekiram Sharma
(c) Mohan Bhagvat (d) Baje Bhagat

34 Which among the following is a magazine by Sahitya Akademi Haryana?

(a) Haryana Samvad (b) Jat Gazette
(c) Kayakalp (d) Harigandha

35 The oldest radio station of Haryana is

(a) All India Radio, Hisar
(b) All India Radio, Rohtak
(c) All India Radio, Gurugram
(d) All India Radio, Kurukshetra

36 In which year, Television Studio Centre alongwith Statellite Earth Centre and DD-2 transmitter was commissioned in Haryana?

(a) 2001 (b) 2002 (c) 2003 (d) 2004

37 Doordarshan Kendra, the only programme producing centre in Haryana is located at

(a) Faridabad (b) Gurugram
(c) Ambala (d) Hisar

38 First Post Office Passport Seva Kendra of Haryana opened in

(a) 5th January, 2015 (b) 25th March, 2017
(c) 15th August, 2018 (d) 27th April, 2017

39 Which newspaper was started in 1923 and published in Urdu and Hindi?

(a) Haryana Tilak (b) Jyotish Samachar
(c) Ahir Hiteshi (d) Sudharak

40 The magazine published by the Public Relations and Cultural Affairs Department, Haryana is

(a) Harigandha (b) Haryana Review
(c) Haryana Samvad (d) Ubharta Haryana

41 Which magazine focuses on agricultural advancements in Haryana?

(a) Haryana Kheti (b) Haryana Review
(c) Krishi Samvad (d) Krishi Saarthi

42 Which community radio station was established in 2012 to facilitate local programmes?
(a) Radio Manav Rachna
(b) Alfaz-e-Mewat
(c) Radio Karnal
(d) Radio Ambala

43 All India Radio, Rohtak is the oldest radio station of Haryana which was established in *HSSC CET 2024*
(a) 1947 (b) 1976
(c) 1987 (d) 1966

44 Panchkula IT Park was established in which year? *HSSC 2019*
(a) 2008 (b) 2006
(c) 2005 (d) 2004

45 The main purpose of the Harsamadhan Portal is
(a) provide employment to youth
(b) register land records
(c) lodge public grievances online
(d) conduct digital surveys

46 What is the purpose of E-Disha Kendras?
(a) Provide IT training to students
(b) Offer financial loans to startups
(c) Deliver integrated public services
(d) Promote digital literacy in rural areas

47 HALRIS stands for
(a) Haryana Agriculture Land Reform Information System
(b) Haryana Land Record Information System
(c) Haryana Automated Legal Record and Information System
(d) Haryana Artificial Land Registration Information System

48 Biswas software system is used for
(a) Online billing of water and sewerage
(b) Management of pension records
(c) Online property tax payment
(d) Digital banking transactions

49 Which was the first Haryanvi film to receive two National Awards?
(a) Satrangi
(b) Lado Basanti
(c) Pagdi The Honour
(d) Beera Shera

50 Which feature film of Haryana is a superhit film of 1984 whose songs are still very famous? *HSSC 2019*
(a) Dhan Paraya
(b) Lambardar
(c) Chandrawal
(d) Lado Basanti

51 Singer Sonu Nigam belong to which district of Haryana?
(a) Panipat (b) Faridabad
(c) Mahendragarh (d) Rohtak

52 Match the following.

List I (National Highway)	List II (Passing Point)
A. NH-71	1. Roorkee
B. NH-71A	2. Ambala
C. NH-73	3. Rewari
D. NH-72	4. Rohtak

Codes

	A	B	C	D		A	B	C	D
(a)	3	1	4	2	(b)	1	2	3	4
(c)	3	4	1	2	(d)	2	4	1	3

CORRECT ANSWERS

1. (d)	**2.** (a)	**3.** (a)	**4.** (a)	**5.** (b)	**6.** (a)	**7.** (b)	**8.** (d)	**9.** (c)	**10.** (d)
11. (a)	**12.** (a)	**13.** (b)	**14.** (b)	**15.** (b)	**16.** (b)	**17.** (b)	**18.** (c)	**19.** (b)	**20.** (b)
21. (d)	**22.** (a)	**23.** (b)	**24.** (b)	**25.** (c)	**26.** (d)	**27.** (c)	**28.** (b)	**29.** (b)	**30.** (b)
31. (a)	**32.** (b)	**33.** (b)	**34.** (d)	**35.** (b)	**36.** (b)	**37.** (d)	**38.** (b)	**39.** (a)	**40.** (c)
41. (c)	**42.** (b)	**43.** (b)	**44.** (a)	**45.** (c)	**46.** (c)	**47.** (b)	**48.** (a)	**49.** (c)	**50.** (c)
51. (b)	**52.** (c)								

HARYANA

Political Administration

This section contains all the important topics of Haryana Political Administration like Administrative structure, Judiciary, Panchayati Raj, etc.

CHAPTER 24

Haryana Administrative Structure

The State Governments in India are established under **Part VI**, Articles-**152** to **237** of the Indian Constitution. These provisions define the structure and functioning of the Legislature, Executive and Judiciary at the state level.

The State Government of Haryana is also organised in accordance with these constitutional provisions. Its administrative structure includes

- Executive — Tasked with implementing laws and policies effectively.
- Legislature — Responsible for creating laws and framing policies for the state.

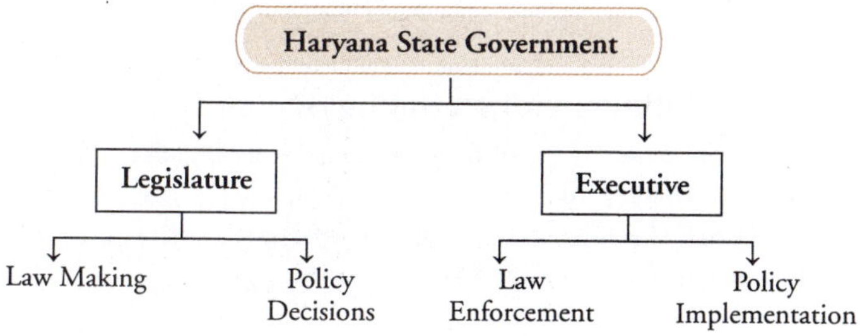

Legislature

The state of Haryana has **unicameral legislature** which is known as 'Legislative Assembly'. Unicameral legislature is legislature which consists of one house.

Legislative Assembly of Haryana

- Exclusive powers — Listed under Seventh Schedule of Indian Constitution
- Term — 5 years **(Article 172)**, unless dissolved earlier by the Governor on the Chief Minister's request
- Eligibility — Members must be Indian citizens, over 25 years old (Article 173) and not declared insane or insolvent by any court
- Elected by — Universal Adult Franchise and direct election
- Voting age — 18 years
- District with least seats — Panchkula (2), Charkhi Dadri (2)
- Districts with highest seats — Hisar (7)
- Unreserved districts — Mahendragarh, Nuh, Faridabad

Organs of Legislative Assembly

- Speaker
- Deputy Speaker
- Members of Assembly

Speaker

- Elected by — Members of the Legislative Assembly
- Appointed by — President
- Term — 5 years
- Voting — Doesn't vote but can cast a deciding vote
- Bill classification — Decides whether a bill is a money bill or not
- If the proposal to relieve a Speaker from his office is under consideration, then he does not preside over that house.
- For the meeting of the house in the Legislative Assembly, 1/10th members of the house should be present.

> - **Shanno Devi** was the **first Speaker of Haryana Legislative Assembly**. She was also the first woman Speaker of India.
> - The first male speaker of Haryana was **Rao Virendra Singh**.
> - **Harmahendra Singh Chadda** was elected Speaker of Vidhan Sabha for three terms 1987-91, 2005-06 and 2009-11.

Deputy Speaker

- Elected by — Members of the Legislative Assembly
- Voting — Vote as a member and can also cast a deciding vote in Speaker's absence
- Term — 5 years
- He presides over the house in the absence of the Speaker and ensures smooth functioning.
- He also presides when a resolution for the removal of the speaker is being considered.

Members of the Assembly

- Elected by — People of their constituency and represents their interests and concerns
- Term — 5 years
- They participate in debates, discussions and voting on bills and resolutions.
- They contribute to the law-making process.
- They engage in local development and addresses the needs of their constituency.

Delimitation Commission

- The Delimitation Commission of India is established under the Delimitation Commission Act to redraw the boundaries of Legislative Assembly and Lok Sabha constituencies based on the latest census.
- When Haryana state was formed on 1st November, 1966, the **First Delimitation Commission** allocated 54 seats in the Legislative Assembly, with 10 seats reserved for Scheduled Castes.
- In March, 1967, the Second Delimitation Commission increased the seats to 81.
- In March, 1977, the Third Delimitation Commission further increased the seats to 90.
- Till date, no member has been nominated by the Governor in the Legislative Assembly of Haryana.
- As per Article 332, seats shall be reserved for Scheduled Castes and Scheduled Tribes.

Haryana Reserved 17 Seats for the Scheduled Castes

1. Pataudi	2. Bawani Khera
3. Jhajjar	4. Kharkhauda
5. Shahabad	6. Narwana
7. Hodal	8. Kalanaur
9. Issrana	10. Guhla
11. Mulana	12. Ratia
13. Uklana	14. Kalanwali
15. Sadhaura	16. Bawal
	17. Nilokheri

Haryana Vidhan Sabha Secretariat

Haryana Secretariat is one of the most magnificent buildings situated at Chandigarh.

It was designed by French architect **Le Corbusier** and its ceremonial gate was presented to India by the French Government.

Before the formation of Haryana state, the part of Vidhan Sabha Secretariat that was used by Punjab Legislative Council is presently used by Haryana Legislative Assembly.

Various Legislative Assemblies of Haryana

First State Assembly

Tenure 1-11-1966 to 28-02-1967

- The inaugural session of the assembly was held on 6th December, 1966.
- It was the smallest assembly in the state, consisting of only 54 members.
- **Bhagwat Dayal Sharma** served as the Chief Minister, while **Shanno Devi** was the Speaker.

Second State Assembly

Tenure 17-03-1967 to 21-11-1967

- The assembly consisted of 81 members.
- The first session of this assembly took place on 17th March, 1967.
- **Rao Virendra Singh** served as the Chief Minister, with **Shri Chand** and later **Manphool Singh** as Speakers.
- This assembly marked the first Non-Congress Legislative Assembly in Haryana and for the first time, President's rule was imposed in the state on 21st November, 1967.

Third State Assembly

Tenure 15-07-1968 to 21-01-1972

- The assembly comprised 81 members, with the first session held on 15th July, 1968.
- **Chaudhary Bansi Lal** served as the Chief Minister and **Ran Singh** was the Speaker.
- The first census in Haryana was conducted during this assembly.
- **On 29th November, 1970,** Haryana became the first state to electrify all its villages.

Fourth State Assembly

Tenure 03-04-1972 to 30-04-1977

- The first session of this assembly took place on 3rd April, 1972.
- There were two Chief Ministers during this period: **Chaudhary Bansi Lal** initially, followed by **Banarasi Das Gupta** and two Speakers **Banarasi Das Gupta** followed by **Swaroop Singh**.
- **President's Rule** was imposed for the second time on 30th April, 1977.
- It was the first assembly to complete its tenure.

Fifth State Assembly

Tenure 04-07-1977 to 19-04-1982

- The assembly consisted of 90 members.
- The first session was held on 4th July, 1977.
- Two Chief Ministers served during this assembly **Chaudhary Bhajan Lal** initially, followed by **Chaudhary Bansi Lal** and two Speakers **Ran Singh** and **Col Ram Singh**.
- **Sushma Swaraj**, a renowned politician, became the youngest Cabinet Minister at the age of 25 during this assembly.

Sixth State Assembly

Tenure 24-06-1982 to 23-06-1987

- The first session took place on 24th June, 1982.
- Two Chief Ministers served during this assembly **Chaudhary Bhajan Lal** and **Chaudhary Bansi Lal**.
- The Speaker of the assembly was **Sardar Tara Singh**.

Seventh State Assembly

Tenure 09-07-1987 to 06-04-1991

- The first session was held on 9th July, 1987, with **Harmohendra Singh Chaddha** serving as the Speaker.
- Four Chief Ministers took office a total of six times during this assembly Chaudhary Devi Lal, Om Prakash Chautala (three times), Banarasi Das Gupta and Hukum Singh.

Eighth State Assembly

Tenure 09-07-1991 to 10-05-1996

- The first sitting was held on 9th July, 1991.
- **Chaudhary Bhajan Lal** served as the Chief Minister, while Ishwar Singh was the Speaker.
- The Panipat event took place on 1st January, 1992 during this assembly.

Ninth State Assembly

Tenure 22-05-1996 to 14-12-1999

- The first sitting took place on 22nd May, 1996.
- **Chaudhary Bansi Lal** served as the Chief Minister and Chatar Singh Chauhan was the Speaker.
- A ban on alcohol was implemented from 1st July, 1996 to 1st April, 1998 during this assembly.

Tenth State Assembly

Tenure 09-03-2000 to 08-03-2005

- **Om Prakash Chautala** served as the Chief Minister and Satbir Singh was the Speaker.
- The first sitting of this assembly took place on 9th March, 2000.

Eleventh State Assembly

Tenure 21-03-2005 to 21-08-2009

- The first sitting took place on 21st March, 2005.
- **Bhupinder Singh Hooda** was Chief Minister of this assembly and there were two Speakers ; First Harmohender Singh Chaddha and later Dr. Raghuvir Kadiyan.

Twelfth State Assembly

Tenure 28-10-2009 to 20-10-2014

- The first sitting took place on 28th October, 2009.
- **Bhupinder Singh Hooda** served as the Chief Minister, while Harmohender Singh Chaddha and Kuldeep Sharma were the Speakers.

Thirteenth State Assembly

Tenure 20-10-2014 to 28-10-2019

- **Manohar Lal Khattar** served as the Chief Minister and Kanwar Pal Gurjar was the Speaker.
- This assembly saw the highest number of women MLAs (13) elected.

Fourteenth State Assembly

Tenure 28-10-2019 to 08-10-2024

- The Speaker of this assembly is **Gyan Chand Gupta** and Deputy Speaker is **Ranbir Singh Gangwa**.
- Chief Minister of this assembly is **Manohar Lal Khattar** and Deputy Chief Minister is **Dushyant Chautala**.

Fifteenth State Assembly

Tenure 08-10-2024 to Present

- **Nayab Singh Saini** is the Chief Minister of Haryana.
- **Harvinder Kalyan** serves as the Speaker of the Haryana Legislative Assembly.
- Krishan Lal Middha holds the position of Deputy Speaker of the Haryana Legislative Assembly.

- **Chandrawati** was the first woman member of the Haryana Legislative Assembly and the first woman Governor of Puducherry.
- **Prasanna Devi** was elected as the member of Legislative Assembly 6 times, the most by any woman.
- **Kurukshetra** is the only district in Haryana with no constituency.
- **Jhajjar** is the only district headquarter with reserved seats for SCs.

List of Speakers

Name	From	To
Shanno Devi	6th December,1966	17th March, 1967
Rao Birendra Singh (shortest term)	17th March, 1967	23rd March, 1967
Shri Chand	30th March, 1967	19th July, 1967
Manphool Singh	20th July, 1967	21st November, 1967
Ran Singh	15th July, 1968	3rd April, 1972
Banarsi Das Gupta	3rd April, 1972	15th November, 1973
Sarup Singh	16th November, 1973	4th July, 1977
Ran Singh	04th July, 1977	8th May, 1978
Col. Ram Singh	15th May, 1978	24th June, 1982
Sardar Tara Singh (longest term)	24th June, 1982	9th July, 1987
Harmohender Singh Chaddha	09th July, 1987	9th July, 1991
Ishwar Singh	09th July, 1991	22nd May, 1996
Chhatar Singh Chauhan	22nd May, 1996	27th July, 1999
Ashok Kumar Arora	28th July, 1999	1st March, 2000
Satbeer Singh Kadian	9th March, 2000	21st March, 2005
Harmohender Singh Chaddha	21st March, 2005	12th January, 2006
Raghubir Singh Kadyaan	13th January, 2006	27th October, 2009
Harmohender Singh Chaddha	28th October, 2009	28th January, 2011
Kuldeep Sharma	04th March, 2011	2nd November, 2014
Kanwar Pal Gurjjar	3rd November, 2014	2nd November, 2019
Gian Chand Gupta	04th November, 2019	24th October, 2024
Harvinder Kalyan	25th October, 2024	Incumbent

** As on January, 2026*

Representation of Haryana in Parliament

- The number of seats of Haryana in Rajya Sabha is 5, while number of seats in Lok Sabha is 10.
- The largest constituency in terms of area is **Bhiwani-Mahendragarh** while in terms of population, the largest Lok Sabha constituency is **Faridabad**.
- According to the report of Delimitation Commission of India, 1971, the seats of Sirsa and Ambala Lok Sabha constituency are reserved for Scheduled Castes.

Haryana Executive

- The Executive is the branch of government responsible for the day-to-day administration and implementation of state policies.
- The Executive at the state level comprises of the **Governor, Chief Minister, Council of Ministers** and the **Advocate General.**

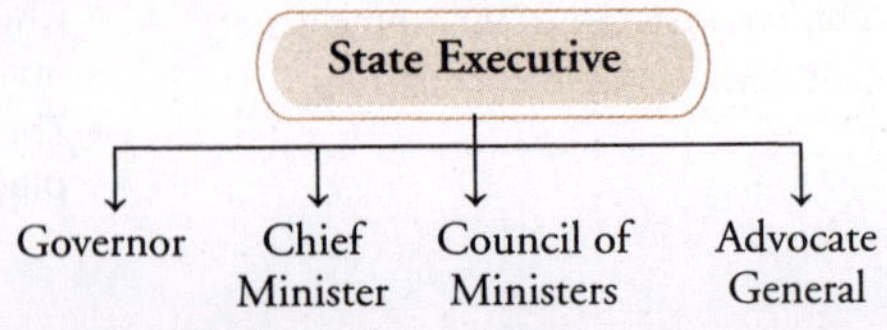

Governor

- The **Governor** is the Constitutional head of the state's Executive, as outlined in Article 153 of the Indian Constitution.
- The **President of India** appoints the Governor for a term of five years, as per Article 155, based on the advice of the Prime Minister.
- The Chief Justice of the Punjab and Haryana High Court administers the oath of office to the Governor under **Article 159**.
- The Haryana **Raj Bhawan** serves as the official residence of the Governor of Haryana.

Qualifications

To be eligible for appointment as a Governor, a person must meet the following criteria

- Be a citizen of India and at least 35 years of age.
- Not be a member of Parliament or any State Legislature.
- Not hold any office of profit under the Central or State Government.

Powers and Functions

- All executive actions of the state are carried out in the name of the Governor.
- The Governor appoints key officials, including the Chief Minister, **Council of Ministers**, Advocate General and the Chairman and members of the State Public Service Commission.
- The Governor serves as the Chancellor of state universities, appointing Vice-Chancellors, presiding over the Senate and overseeing the functioning of universities and affiliated colleges.
- At the start of each newly formed Legislative Assembly's term and the first session of every year, the Governor addresses the assembly.
- A bill passed by the State Legislature becomes law only after receiving the Governor's assent.

> The Governor can also issue an ordinance under Article 213 when the assembly is not in session.

- The **Governor** has the power to **pardon**, commute or **postpone** the punishment of individuals convicted by a court under Article 161.

List of Haryana Governors

Name	From	To
Dharma Vira	1st November, 1966	14th September, 1967
B.N. Chakraborty (*longest tenure*)	15th September, 1967	26th March, 1976
R.S. Narula	27th March, 1976	13th August, 1976
Jaisukh Lal Hathi	14th August, 1976	23rd September, 1977
Harcharan Singh Barar	24th September, 1977	9th December, 1979
S.S. Sandhawalia	10th December, 1979	27th February, 1980
G.D. Tapase	28th February, 1980	13th June, 1984
SMH Barni	14th June,1984	21st February, 1988
H.A. Barari	22nd February, 1988	6th February, 1990
Dhanik Lal Mandal	7th February, 1990	13th June, 1995
Mahabir Prasad	14th June, 1995	18th June, 2000
Babu Parmanand	19th June, 2000	1st July, 2004
Om Prakash Verma (Shortest tenure)	2nd July, 2004	7th July, 2004
A.R. Kidwai	7th July, 2004	27th July, 2009
Jagannath Pahadia	27th July, 2009	26th July, 2014
Kaptan Singh Solanki	27th July, 2014	24th August, 2018
Satyadev Narayan Arya	25th August, 2018	July, 2025
Bandaru Dattatreya	15th July, 2021	20th July, 2025
Ashim Kumar Ghosh	21st July, 2025	Incumbent

** As on January, 2026*

Dharma Vira　B.N. Chakraborty　Bandaru Dattatreya　Ashim Kumar Ghosh

Chief Minister

- According to Article 163 of the Indian Constitution, a Council of Ministers, headed by the Chief Minister, assists the State Executive in the functioning of the State Government.
- The Chief Minister serves as the head of government at the state level. While the Governor is the formal head of the state, executive powers are vested in the Chief Minister.
- The Chief Minister is elected for a term of five years, with the possibility of re-election and is appointed by the **Governor** of the state.
- **Pandit Bhagwat Dayal Sharma** was the first Chief Minister of Haryana.
- In Haryana, Om Prakash Chautala served as Chief Minister for a maximum of five times, Bansi Lal 4 times, Bhajan Lal 3 times and Banarsi Das Gupta, Devi Lal, Bhupinder Singh Hooda each served two terms.

Chief Ministers of Haryana

Chaudhary Devi Lal

- Born 25th September, 1915
- Place Teja Khera (Chautala village), Sirsa district, Haryana
- Death 6th April, 2001

- A prominent farmer leader, he played an active role in the formation of Haryana state.
- In 1987, he initiated the Nyaya Yudh (Battle for Justice) movement and introduced the old-age pension scheme in the state.
- His mausoleum, known as **Sangharsh Sthal**, is located on the banks of the Yamuna river in Delhi.
- He was widely recognised by titles such as **Tau, King-maker, Jan-Nayak** and **Sher-e-Haryana**.
- He became a Member of Parliament in 1980, a Rajya Sabha member in 1998 and served as Deputy Prime Minister from 1989 to 1991 in the non-Congress governments of Prime Ministers V.P. Singh and Chandra Shekhar.

Banarsi Das Gupta

- Born 5th November, 1917
- Place Bhiwani district
- Death 29th August, 2007

- He was the editor of **Apna Desh** and **Haryana Kesri** newspapers.
- He authored the book **Panchayati Raj Kyu Aur Kaise**.
- He actively participated in the Bhoodan Movement and distributed thousands of acres of land among the landless.
- He was imprisoned multiple times during British rule.
- He served as Speaker, Deputy Chief Minister and Chief Minister of Haryana.
- He was elected as a member of Rajya Sabha in April, 1996.
- He fought against the dowry system, untouchability and child marriage.

Pandit Bhagwat Dayal Sharma

- Born 26th January, 1918
- Place Beri town, Jhajjar district
- Death 22nd February, 1993

- His tenure as Chief Minister of Haryana was the shortest, lasting only 143 days.
- He was the **first and only nominated** Chief Minister of Haryana.
- He was popularly known as **Pandit Ji** and mentored politicians like Bansi Lal and Bhajan Lal.

- He served as the Governor of Odisha in 1977 and Madhya Pradesh from 1980 to 1984.
- The University of Health and Sciences, Rohtak and the Post Graduate Institute of Medical Sciences are named after him.

Rao Birendra Singh

- Born 20th February, 1921
- Place Nangal Pathani village, Rewari district.
- Death 30th September, 2009

- He became the first elected and non-Congress Chief Minister of Haryana.
- His tenure as Speaker was the shortest, lasting only 16 days.

- He founded the **Vishal Haryana Party** in 1967, the first regional party of Haryana.
- He played a significant role in separating Rewari from Mahendragarh to create a new district in 1989.
- He served as the first male Speaker of the Haryana Legislative Assembly.

Hukam Singh

- Born 18 February, 1926
- Place Charkhi-Dadri, Bhiwani district
- Death 26th February, 2015

- He served as the 8th Chief Minister of Haryana.

Chaudhary Bansi Lal

- Born 26th August, 1927
- Place Golagarh village, Bhiwani district
- Passed away 28th March, 2006

- He was known as the **Architect of Modern Haryana** and the **Iron Man of Haryana**.
- At the age of 41, he became the youngest Chief Minister of Haryana and the first **Jat Chief Minister**.
- During his tenure, Haryana achieved 100% electrification in 1970.
- In 1996, he founded the **Haryana Vikas Party** after separating from the Indian National Congress.
- He implemented a ban on alcohol in 1996, which was later lifted in 1998 .
- He introduced the **Lift and Fountain** irrigation systems for agricultural development in Haryana.
- He was an Indian independence activist.

- He served as the **Defence Minister** from 1975 to 1977 and as the **Railway Minister** from 1984 to 1986.
- He served as a Rajya Sabha member twice (1960-66, 1976-80) and a Lok Sabha member three times (1980-84, 1985-86, 1989-91).
- He was part of the famous **Lal trio of Haryana** along with **Devi Lal** and **Bhajan Lal**.

Bhajan Lal

- Born 6th October, 1930
- Place Koranwali village, Bahawalpur district (now in Pakistan)
- Death 3rd June, 2011

- He served as the Chief Minister of Haryana for a total of 12 years, the longest tenure in the state's history (non-consecutive).

- He founded the **Haryana Janhit Congress** on 2nd December, 2007, which later merged with the Indian National Congress in 2016.
- He served as the Chief Minister of Haryana twice, from 1979 to 1986 and from 1991 to 1996.
- He held positions as a Union Cabinet Minister, including Union Agricultural Minister and Minister of Forests and Environment.

Om Prakash Chautala

- Born 1st January, 1935
- Place Sirsa district
- Death 20th December, 2024

- He was the leader of the Indian National Lok Dal (INLD)
- He was the son of Chaudhary Devi Lal.
- He served as the Chief Minister of Haryana five times.
- He once held the shortest tenure as Chief Minister, serving for only 5 days.

Bhupinder Singh Hooda

- **Born** 15th September, 1947
- **Place** Sanghi village, Rohtak district.

- He was the first **Chief Minister of Haryana born in independent India**.
- His key contributions include establishing seven state universities, one central university and IIM Rohtak.

- He also formulated the New Industrial Policy and Sports Policy for Haryana.
- He was the leader of the Indian National Congress.
- He served as the 9th Chief Minister of Haryana, holding the longest tenure from 5th March, 2005 to 26th October, 2014.
- He was elected as a member of Parliament from Rohtak in 1991, 1996, 1998 and 2004.

Manohar Lal Khattar

- Born 5th May, 1954
- Place Nindana village, Rohtak district.

- Key initiatives include announcing all-woman police stations in each district and taking steps to implement the 'Beti Bachao Beti Padhao' scheme.
- He is also known as the **4th Lal of Haryana**.
- He is a member of the **Rashtriya Swayamsevak Sangh** (RSS) and Bharatiya Janata Party (BJP).
- He served as the 10th Chief Minister of Haryana.

Nayab Singh Saini

- Born 25th January, 1970
- Place Mizapur Majra

- He launched the One Time Settlement Scheme-2025 to ease financial stress on small shopkeepers, traders and entrepreneurs by helping then clear old tax dues and make a fresh financial start.
- He won the election from the Ladwa constituency in Kurukshetra district.
- In July, 2024, the Saini government increased the expenditure limit for **Gram Panchayats.**The limit was raised from ₹ 5 lakh to ₹ 21 lakh.
- This change allowed panchayats to access sufficient funds without the need for e-tenders.

List of Chief Ministers of Haryana

Name	Tenure From	Tenure Upto
Pandit Bhagwat Dayal Sharma	1st November, 1966	23rd March, 1967
Rao Birender Singh	24th March, 1967	20th November, 1967
President's Rule	21st November, 1967	21st May, 1968
Bansi Lal	22nd May, 1968	30th November, 1975
Banarsi Das Gupta	1st December, 1975	30th April, 1977
President's Rule	30th April, 1977	20th June, 1977
Chaudhary Devi Lal	21st June, 1977	28th June, 1979
Bhajan Lal	29th June, 1979	5th June, 1986
Bansi Lal	5th June, 1986	20th June, 1987
Chaudhary Devi Lal	20th June, 1987	2nd December, 1989
Om Prakash Chautala	2nd December, 1989	22nd May, 1990
Banarsi Das Gupta	22nd May, 1990	12th July, 1990
Om Prakash Chautala (*shortest tenure*)	12th July, 1990	17th July, 1990
Hukum Singh	17th July, 1990	22nd March, 1991
Om Prakash Chautala	22nd March, 1991	6th April, 1991
President's Rule	6th April, 1991	22nd June, 1991
Bhajan Lal	23rd June, 1991	10th May, 1996
Bansi Lal	11th May, 1996	23rd July, 1999
Om Prakash Chautala	24th July, 1999	4th March, 2005
Bhupinder Singh Hooda	5th March, 2005	24th October, 2014
Manohar Lal Khattar	26th October, 2014	12th March, 2024
Nayab Singh Saini	12th March, 2024	Incumbent

** As on January, 2026*

President's Rule in Haryana

Article 356 allows the President to take over the executive functions of the state. In Haryana, President's Rule has been imposed three times

President's Rule in Haryana

↓

First President's Rule

Imposed from 21st November, 1967 to 21st May, 1968. The President was Zakir Hussain, the Prime Minister was Indira Gandhi and the Governor was B.N. Chakraborty.

↓

Second President's Rule

Imposed from 30th April, 1977 to 20th June, 1977. The President was B.D. Jatti, the Prime Minister was Morarji Desai and the Governor was Jaisukh Lal Hathi.

↓

Third President's Rule

Imposed from 6th April, 1991 to 22nd June, 1991. The President was R. Venkataraman, the Prime Minister was P.V. Narasimha Rao and the Governor was Dhanik Lal Mandal.

Council of Ministers

- **Article 163** of the Indian Constitution states that there should be a Council of Ministers with the Chief Minister at the head to assist the State Government.
- The Council of Ministers is appointed by the Governor on the advice of the Chief Minister.
- A person must be a member of either the Legislative Assembly or Legislative Council to be appointed in Council of Ministers.
- The Executive Authority of the state lies with the Council of Ministers, led by the Chief Minister.
- The Council of Ministers (also known as **Cabinet Ministers**) is jointly responsible for the work done by the government.
- The tenure is five years, but they must resign if a no-confidence motion is passed against the ruling party in the Legislative Assembly.

The Council of Ministers includes Cabinet Ministers, Ministers of State, Ministers of State (Independent charge), Deputy Ministers and Secretaries of the House.

State Secretariat

- The State Secretariat is also known as Chief Secretary office. It is the law executing body of the State Government.
- There are separate department of different ministeries in the Secretariat. Decision making, policy formulation, policy execution and administration are carried out from the State Secretariat.
- In Haryana, the State Secretariat is situated in its capital, i.e. **Chandigarh**. The State Secretariat is headed by Chief Secretary who is the senior most IAS officer in the state.
- Chief secretary is assisted by Secretaries of other departments including Joint Secretaries, Deputy Secretaries and Under Secretaries.

Major Political Parties of Haryana

In each state, there are political parties that operate solely within that state, known as local parties. The local political parties of Haryana are as follows

Bharatiya Lok Dal

- It was founded in 1974.
- Chaudhary Devi Lal was an important leader of this party.
- The party's election symbol was a farmer ploughing the land. In 1987, Chaudhary Devi Lal became the Chief Minister of Haryana after winning the elections under this party. However, in 1990, the party split.

Janata Dal

- This party was established on 11th October, 1988 following the merger of the Janata Party, Lok Dal (B) and Jan Morcha. In 1989, with support from other parties, Janata Dal formed the government at the centre.
- The party's election symbol was Wheel. Currently, the party has split into several factions.

Indian National Lok Dal

- It was founded in October, 1996 by Om Prakash Chautala and Chaudhary Devi Lal as Haryana Lok Dal (Rashtriya). The party's symbol is eyeglasses.
- Om Prakash Chautala serves as the Chairperson, while Ajay Singh Chautala is the General Secretary.
- In 2019 Assembly Elections, the party won 1 seat and in 2024 Assembly Elections, it won 2 seats.

Haryana Vikas Party

- Established in 1996 by former Chief Minister Chaudhary Bansi Lal, the party formed a government in Haryana through an alliance with the BJP.
- In 2004, the party merged with the Indian National Congress.

Jannayak Janta Party

- It was founded on 9th December, 2018 and is based on Devi Lal's ideology of socialism. Its symbol is key.
- It was founded by Dushyant Chautala the great grandson of Chaudhary Devi Lal who is also the Chairman of this party.
- It was formed in Jind and is very popular in many parts of Haryana. In 2019 Assembly Elections, the party secured 19 seats and in the recent 2024 assembly elections, if didn't secure even a single seat.

CHECK CHAPTER KNOWLEDGE

1 Haryana Legislative Assembly is ...... in nature.
(a) unicameral (b) bicameral
(c) Both (a) and (b) (d) None of these

2 The term of the State Legislative assembly is
(a) two years (b) eight years
(c) five years (d) one year

3 On 31st November, 1966, after the formation of Haryana, how many seats were determined by the First Delimitation Commission? *HSSC 2023, 21*
(a) 35 (b) 43
(c) 54 (d) 56

4 In which year the number of members of Haryana Vidhan Sabha reached to 90?
(a) 1966 (b) 2008
(c) 1977 (d) 2001

5 How many seats are there in the current Haryana Legislative assembly? *HSSC 2021, 20*
(a) 150 (b) 90
(c) 105 (d) 95

6 Who was the first Speaker of Haryana Vidhan Sabha? *HSSC 2016*
(a) Manphool Singh (b) Ishwar Singh
(c) Shanno Devi (d) Kuldeep Sharma

7 Haryana Vidhan Sabha is situated at *Junior Engineer 2018*
(a) Rohtak (b) Panipat
(c) Ambala (d) Chandigarh

8 The first Legislative assembly elections were held in Haryana in the year *TGT 2016*
(a) 1972 (b) 1966
(c) 1960 (d) 1968

9 When was the President rule imposed in Haryana for the first time?
(a) 21st December, 1970
(b) 20th March, 1965
(c) 21st November, 1967
(d) 10th April, 1969

10 The first census in Haryana was held during which period? *HSSC 2022, 20*
(a) Second assembly (b) Tenth assembly
(c) Third assembly (d) Eighth assembly

11 When was President Rule imposed on Haryana for the second time? *HSSC Junior Engineering 2021*
(a) 1971 (b) 1987
(c) 1977 (d) 1969

12 Which politician became the youngest Cabinet Minister in fifth state assembly?
(a) Sushma Swaraj
(b) Chaudhary Devi Lal
(c) Om Prakash Chautala
(d) Arvind Kejriwal

13 The current assembly of Haryana is the
(a) Eleventh legislative assembly
(b) Thirteenth legislative assembly
(c) Twelfth legislative assembly
(d) Fifteenth legislative assembly

14 Who has been elected as the Deputy speaker of the 14th Haryana assembly?
(a) Gyan Chand Gupta
(b) Ranbir Singh Gangwa
(c) Ramesh Kaushik
(d) Rahul Chaudhary

15 .... is the present (as on December 2024) Chief Minister of Haryana. *HSSC 2024*
(a) Kumar Swami (b) Nayab Singh Saini
(c) Manohar Parikas (d) None of these

16 As on 1st December, 2019, who is Deputy Chief Minister of Haryana? *HSSC Field Cadre 2020*
(a) Mahipal Dhanda
(b) J.P. Nadda
(c) Dushyant Chautala
(d) Kanwar Pal

17 How many members from Haryana are elected for Rajya Sabha? *HSSC 2023, 20*
(a) 1 (b) 5
(c) 3 (d) 7

18 How many seats come under Haryana Lok Sabha? *SSC Accountant 2021*
(a) 12 (b) 10
(c) 5 (d) None of these

19 Which is the largest Lok Sabha Constituency in terms of population? *Haryana Accountant 2018*
(a) Karnal (b) Hisar
(c) Gurugram (d) Faridabad

20 Which of the following Lok Sabha constituency is reserved for Schedule caste in Haryana?
(a) Bhiwani-Mahendragarh *HSSC 2023*
(b) Ambala
(c) Gurugram
(d) Sonipat

21 What is the residential place of the Governor of Haryana? *Haryana Tehsil Welfare Officer 2018*
(a) Panch Mahal (b) Haryana Raj Bhawan
(c) Vidhan Parishad (d)Vidhan Sabha

22 Who was the first Governor of Haryana?
(a) B.N. Chakraborty *PGT 2016*
(b) Dharma Vira
(c) R.S. Narula
(d) G.D. Tapase

23 What was the tenure of the first Governor of Haryana, Dharma Vira? *HSSC 2020, Haryana Tehsil Welfare Officer 2018,*
(a) Around 5 months
(b) Around 7 months
(c) Around 10 months
(d) None of the above

24 Who among the following served as Governor for the longest term? *Haryana Group D 2018, Haryana Patwari Exam 2015*
(a) Dharma Vira
(b) Birendra Narayan Chakraborty
(c) Ranjeet Singh Narula
(d) Jaysukh Lal Hathi

25 As on 1st January, 2020, who was the Governor of Haryana? *HSSC Field Cadre 2020*
(a) Shri Satyadev Narayan Arya
(b) Prof Kaptan Singh Solanki
(c) Shri Om Prakash Verma
(d) Shri Jagannath Pahadia

26 Who was the Constitutional head (Governor) of Haryana in 2019?
(a) Manohar Lal Khattar
(b) Dushyant Chautala
(c) Satyadev Narayan Arya
(d) Ranbir Singh Gangwa

27 Haryana faced President's Rule for how many times?
(a) Once (b) Twice
(c) Thrice (d) None of these

28 Who amongst the following has all the executive powers of the State Government?
(a) Chairman of Legislative Assembly
(b) Governor of the State
(c) Chief Minister of State
(d) Deputy Chief Minister of State

29 Who was the first Chief Minister of Haryana?
(a) Bhagwat Dayal Sharma *HSSC 2023, 20*
(b) Rao Virender Singh
(c) Devi Lal
(d) Bansi Lal

30 The mausoleum of which of the following Chief Minister of Haryana is in Delhi?
(a) Devi Lal (b) Bansi Lal
(c) Banarasi Das Gupta (d) Bhajan Lal

31 Bhagwat Dayal Sharma, the first CM of Haryana, represented which constituency? *Haryana Police Sub-inspector 2018*
(a) Bhiwani (b) Tosham
(c) Pataudi (d) Jhajjar

32 Who was the first Non-Congress Chief Minister of Haryana who took oath on 24th March, 1967?
(a) Chaudhary Bhajan Lal
(b) Devi lal
(c) Bansi lal
(d) Rao Birendra Singh

33 Haryana's longest serving Chief Minister, Bansi Lal, was holding which office in Central Government in 1975-77? *Haryana Police Constable 2018*
(a) Home Ministry (b) Finance
(c) Defence (d) Parliamentary affairs

34 Who formed Haryana Vikas party? *Haryana Agriculture Inspector 2017*
(a) Hukum Singh
(b) Chaudhary Bansi Lal
(c) Bhupendra Singh Hudda
(d) Chaudhary Devi Lal

35 Which freedom fighter later became CM of Haryana? *HSSC FE 2022, 20*
(a) Shri Rao Birendra Singh
(b) Chaudhary Bansi Lal
(c) Chaudhary Devi Lal
(d) Shri Manohar Lal Khattar

36 Which Chief Minister of Haryana banned the consumption of alcohol in the state on July, 1996? *Haryana Lab Attendant 2018*
(a) Bansi Lal (b) Devi Lal
(c) B.D. Sharma (d) Bhajan Lal

37 Which among the following served as Chief Minister for the longest term? *HSSC 2020*
(a) Hukum Singh (b) Pt. Bhagwan Dayal
(c) Bansi Lal (d) Rao Birender Singh

38 Who among the following was never the Chief Minister of Haryana? *Mandi Supervisor 2017*
(a) Banarasi Das Gupta (b) G.D. Tapse
(c) Hukum Singh (d) Rao Birender Singh

39 By whom, the Council of Ministers of the state is appointed?
(a) Governor (b) Chief minister
(c) Prime minister (d) Speaker

40 The Council of Ministers are elected for how many years?
(a) 6 (b) 5
(c) 2 (d) 4

41 Where is State Secretariat situated in Haryana?
(a) Rohtak (b) Chandigarh
(c) Bhiwani (d) Gurugram

42 Who is the head of State Secretariat?
(a) Joint secretary (b) Deputy secretary
(c) Chief secretary (d) Under secretary

43 Who founded the Indian National Lok Dal?
(a) Devi Lal
(b) Bhajan Lal
(c) Bansi Lal
(d) Manohar Lal

44 In which year Jannayak Janta party was formed?
(a) 2001 (b) 2018
(c) 1985 (d) 1996

45 Consider the following statements.
I. Shanno Devi was the first Speaker of Haryana Vidhan sabha.
II. She is the only female Speaker of Haryana Vidhan sabha.

Which of the statements given above is/are correct?
(a) I Only
(b) II Only
(c) Both I and II
(d) None of the above

CORRECT ANSWERS

1. (a)	2. (c)	3. (c)	4. (c)	5. (b)	6. (c)	7. (d)	8. (b)	9. (c)	10. (c)
11. (c)	12. (a)	13. (d)	14. (b)	15. (b)	16. (c)	17. (b)	18. (b)	19. (d)	20. (b)
21. (b)	22. (b)	23. (c)	24. (b)	25. (a)	26. (c)	27. (c)	28. (c)	29. (a)	30. (a)
31. (d)	32. (d)	33. (c)	34. (b)	35. (b)	36. (a)	37. (c)	38. (b)	39. (a)	40. (b)
41. (b)	42. (c)	43. (a)	44. (b)	45. (c)					

CHAPTER

25

KNOW YOUR STATE
HARYANA

Haryana Judiciary

- The judiciary is the third pillar of governance, alongside the legislative and executive branches.
- Articles 214 to 237 of the Indian Constitution define the judicial structure.
- India has a unified justice system, headed by the Supreme Court and supported by High Courts.
- High Courts oversee District Courts, with Subordinate Courts functioning under their supervision.
- The Hierarchical Structure of Indian Courts
  - Supreme Court
  - High Court
  - District and Sessions Court
- The Punjab and Haryana High Court, located in Chandigarh, serves as the common institution for Haryana, Punjab and UT of Chandigarh.

High Court

- Article 214 of the Indian Constitution provides for a High Court in every state.
- The 7th Constitutional Amendment (1956) introduced Article 231, allowing a single High Court to serve two or more states or Union Territories.

Historical Background of High Court of Punjab and Haryana

- The Punjab and Haryana High Court originated as the **Lahore High Court**, established under the India Act of 1915 on 20th-21st March, **1919** in Lahore. After the 1947 partition, it became part of Pakistan.
- **Sir Shadilal** of Rewari was the first Indian judge of the Lahore High Court, took oath in 1920. He was honoured with the title **Rai Bahadur.**
- The East Punjab High Court was established at **Shimla on 15th August, 1947** by Governor-General Lord Mountbatten under the Indian Independence Act, inheriting the work of the Lahore High Court.
- On 26th January, 1950, the East Punjab High Court was renamed the **Punjab High Court.**
- A bench of the Punjab High Court was set-up in **Delhi,** in 1952.

> The Punjab High Court was relocated to **Chandigarh** on 17th January, 1955 under the leadership of Prime Minister Jawaharlal Nehru.

- In 1956, following the merger of the Patiala and East Punjab States Union (PEPSU) into Punjab, jurisdiction passed to the Chandigarh High Court.
- The Delhi High Court was established separately in 1966.

Creation of High Court of Punjab and Haryana

- Following the re-organisation of Punjab in 1966, two new states, (Punjab and Haryana) and the Union Territory of Chandigarh were formed.
- On **1st November, 1966**, the Punjab High Court was renamed the High Court of Punjab and Haryana, with jurisdiction over Punjab, Haryana and Chandigarh. The building was designed by the French architect **Le Corbusier.**

- The first Chief Justice of the Punjab and Haryana High Court was **Justice Ram Lal**.
- The first Chief Justice, after the re-organisation of the High Court in 1966, was **Justice Mehar Singh**.
- **Justice Donald Falshaw** was the **first Chief Justice to resign** from the High Court of Punjab and Haryana. Justices **Ranjit Singh Narula** and **Jitendra Vir Gupta** also resigned in 1977 and 1991, respectively.
- **Justice Veerswamy Ramaswamy** (1987-89) was the first and only Chief Justice to face impeachment, though the trial process was not completed.
- Justices Ranjit Singh Narula and Surjit Singh Sanghawalia later became Governors of Haryana.

▲ High Court of Punjab and Haryana

List of Chief Justices of High Court of Punjab and Haryana

Chief Justice	From	To
Justice Ram Lall (first)	15th August, 1947	18th January, 1949
Justice Sudhi Ranjan Das	19th January, 1949	21st January, 1950
Justice Eric Weston	21st January, 1950	8th December, 1952
Justice Amar Nath Bhandari (longest tenure)	9th December, 1952	18th November, 1959
Justice Gopal Das Khosla	19th November, 1959	14th December, 1961
Justice Donald Falshaw	15th December, 1961	29th May, 1966 (Resigned)
Justice Mehar Singh	9th May, 1966	14th August, 1970
Justice Harbans Singh	15th August, 1970	8th April, 1974
Justice Daya Krishan Mahajan	10th April, 1974	11th May, 1974
Justice Ranjit Singh Narula	11th May, 1974	31st October, 1977 (Resigned)
Justice Anand Dev Koshal	1st November, 1977	17th July, 1978
Justice Surjit Singh Sandhawalia	17th July, 1978	28th November, 1983
Justice Prem Chand Jain (ACJ)	28th November, 1983	31st July, 1985
Justice Prem Chand Jain	1st August, 1985	18th August, 1986
Justice Hariday Nath Seth	18th August, 1986	14th October, 1987
Justice Debi Singh Tewatia (shortest tenure)	15th October, 1987	29th October, 1987
Justice R.N. Mittal (ACJ)	30th October, 1987	11th November, 1987
Justice Veeraswami Ramaswami	12th November, 1987	6th October, 1989
Justice Shanti Sarup Dewan (ACJ)	6th October, 1989	23rd October, 1989
Justice Shanti Sarup Dewan	24th October, 1989	31st December, 1989
Justice Jitendra Vir Gupta (ACJ)	1st January, 1990	8th July, 1990
Justice Jitendra Vir Gupta	9th July, 1990	1st May, 1991 (Resigned)
Justice Gokal Chand Mittal (ACJ)	19th March, 1991	4th August, 1991
Justice Iqbal Singh Tiwana (ACJ)	5th August, 1991	18th September, 1991
Justice Bipin Chandra Verma	19th September, 1991	2nd May, 1992
Justice Mandagadde Rama Jois	3rd May, 1992	31st August, 1992
Justice S.S. Sodhi (ACJ)	1 September, 1992	12th November, 1992

Chief Justice	From	To
Justice Sudarshan Dayal Agarwala	13rd November, 1992	14th January, 1994
Justice Sudhakar Pandit Rao Kurdukar	16th January, 1994	27th March, 1996
Justice M.S. Liberhan (ACJ)	27th June, 1996	30th July, 1996
Justice R.P. Sethi (ACJ)	16th August, 1994 27th March, 1996	10 September, 1994 27 June, 1996
Justice K. Sreedharan	30th July, 1996	18th October, 1997
Justice Amarjeet Chowdhary (ACJ)	18th October, 1997	7th November, 1997
Justice A.B. Saharya	7th November, 1997	14th September, 2002
Justice G.S. Singhvi (ACJ)	14th September, 2002	14th October, 2002
Justice Binod Kumar Roy	14th October, 2002	21st February, 2005
Justice G.S. Singhvi (ACJ)	21st February, 2005	25th February, 2005
Justice H.S. Bedi (ACJ)	26th February, 2005	11th March, 2005
Justice D.K. Jain	11th March, 2005	9th April, 2006
Justice H.S. Bedi (ACJ)	10th April, 2006	2nd October, 2006
Justice S.S. Nijjar (ACJ)	3rd October, 2006	28th November, 2006
Justice Vijender Jain	28th November, 2006	1st August, 2008
Justice J.S. Khebar (ACJ)	2nd August, 2008	11th August, 2008
Justice Tirath Singh Thakur (Also became Chief Justice of Supreme Court)	11th August, 2008	16th November, 2009
Justice J.S. Khebar (ACJ)	17th November, 2009	29th November, 2009
Justice Mehtab S. Gill (ACJ)	29th November, 2009	5th December, 2009
Justice Mukul Mudgal	5th December, 2009	3rd January, 2011
Justice Ranjan Gogoi (ACJ)	4th January, 2011	11th February, 2011
Justice Ranjan Gogoi	12th February, 2011	22nd April, 2012
Justice M.M. Kumar (ACJ)	23rd April, 2012	8th June, 2012
Justice Jasbir Singh (ACJ)	8th June, 2012	23rd September, 2012
Justice Arjan Kumar Sikri	23rd September, 2012	11th April, 2013
Justice Jajbir Singh (ACJ)	12th April, 2013	31st May, 2013
Justice Sanjay Kishan Kaul	1st June, 2013	25th July, 2014
Justice Ashutosh Mohunta (ACJ)	26th July, 2014	15th December, 2014
Justice S.J. Vazifdar (ACJ)	15th December, 2014	6th August, 2016
Justice Shiavax Jal Vazifdar	7th August, 2016	3rd May, 2018
Justice Ajay Kumar Mittal (ACJ)	4th May, 2018	2nd June, 2018
Justice Krishna Murari	2nd June, 2018	22nd September, 2019
Justice Ravi Shankar Jha	6th October, 2019	13th October, 2023
Justice Ritu Bahri (ACJ)	15th October, 2023	3rd February, 2024
Justice Gurmeet Singh Sandhawalia	4th February, 2024	8th July, 2024
Justice Sheel Nagu	9th July, 2024	Incumbent

As on April, 2025

Other Courts of Haryana

The other courts of Haryana are discussed below

District and Sessions Court

- **Every district has two types of courts** District Courts for civil cases and Sessions Courts for criminal cases, as per the Code of Criminal Procedure.
- Courts are established by the State Government and are presided over by a judge appointed by the Governor, in consultation with the High Court.
- **The Haryana Judicial Service is divided into two categories** Haryana Civil Judicial Service and Higher Judicial Service.
- All District and Sessions Courts in Haryana are under the control of the High Court of Punjab and Haryana.

Revenue Court

- The Revenue Court handles cases related to land revenue and associated disputes in the state.
- Each district has a Revenue Court, with the Board of Revenue being the highest Revenue Court in the district.
- The Revenue Court system includes the Court of Commissioners, Collectors, Tehsildars and Sub-Tehsildars.

Family Court

- The Family Court is established in every state under the Family Courts Act, 1984.
- It hears cases related to family matters, domestic relationships, marriage and other related proceedings.
- Appeals against judgements given by the Family Court can only be made in the High Court.

State Administrative Tribunal

- The Administrative Tribunal is a **quasi-judicial** institution established to address the backlog of cases in various courts.
- It aims to reduce workload, expedite decisions and handle disputes related to taxes and administrative matters.

> The Haryana Administrative Tribunal Rules, 2017, were approved by the Haryana Cabinet in 2018 for the establishment of the Haryana Administrative Tribunal.

State Legal Services Authority

- The State Legal Services Authority (SLSA) is established in every state under the Legal Services Authority Act, 1987, which was enforced from **9th November**, 1995.
- In Haryana, the SLSA operates from **Chandigarh**, under the Legal Services Authority Rules, 1996.
- The SLSA is headed by the Chief Justice of the High Court of Punjab and Haryana, with a senior judge serving as the Executive Chairman.
- Prominent members of the SLSA include the Secretary of the State Women Commission, Welfare Board, Commission for Scheduled Castes and Scheduled Tribes and the State Advocate General.

> In Haryana, the SLSA operates at the High Court level (with the Chairman being a High Court Judge), at the district level (with the Chairman being a District and Sessions Court Judge) and at the sub-division level.

Lok Adalats

- Article 39(A) was added to the Directive Principles of State Policy through the 42nd Amendment of the Indian Constitution in 1976, providing for free legal aid to weaker sections of society.
- Lok Adalats were given statutory status under the **Legal Services Authorities Act, 1987**.
- Lok Adalats handle long-pending civil cases and criminal cases where settlement is not possible.
- Lok Adalats function as Civil Courts and their judgements are final, with no possibility of appeal.

> The **First Permanent Lok Adalat** in Haryana was set-up on 7th August, 1998 in **Chandigarh**.

- Haryana has 15 Permanent Lok Adalats, located in Ambala, Panchkula, Rohtak, Hisar, Gurugram, Bhiwani, Sirsa, Sonipat, Rewari, Karnal, Faridabad, Kaithal, Kurukshetra, Yamunanagar and Panipat.
- Lok Adalats are functional in all districts of Haryana, consisting of one judge, one advocate and one social worker.
- The State Legal Services Authority has established intermediary centres in Haryana to provide legal advice and aid to the public.

Free Legal Aid

- The State Legal Services Authority also provide legal aid to the needy citizens in the state.
- With the cooperation of the State Government, it also runs various schemes to provide legal aid to the citizens of the state.

Alternative Dispute Resolution (ADR) Mechanisms

- The State Legal Services Authority provides relief to the citizens from unwanted disputes and cumbersome legal procedures through mediation centres.
- Disputes are resolved by legal experts in these centres.

Commercial Courts

- The Commercial Courts, Commercial Division and Commercial Appellate Division of High Courts Act, 2015, provides for the establishment of Commercial Courts in states.
- Haryana set-up its **Special Commercial Court in Gurugram** on 27th October, 2017 with jurisdiction covering the entire state of Haryana.

Environmental Courts

- Environmental Courts specifically handle cases related to violations of environmental laws.
- The Haryana State Government has established two Environmental Courts, located in **Faridabad** and **Kurukshetra.**
- The **Faridabad Environmental Court** has jurisdiction over Faridabad, Palwal, Mewat, Gurugram, Mahendragarh, Jind, Rohtak, Jhajjar, Dadri, Bhiwani and Rewari.
- The **Kurukshetra Environmental Court** has jurisdiction over Ambala, Panchkula, Yamunanagar, Karnal, Kaithal, Sirsa, Fatehabad, Hisar, Sonipat and Panipat.

District Consumer Courts

- The **Consumer Protection Act** came into force on 24th December, 1986, outlining consumer rights and providing for their protection.
- It establishes a 3-tier District Consumer Court system at the National, State and District levels.
- In Haryana, Consumer Redressal Cells and Consumer Forums have been set-up in every district except Charkhi-Dadri.
- Under the 1986 Act, Consumer Courts in Haryana handled cases involving amount up to ₹ 20 lakh. However, with the enactment of the Consumer Protection (Jurisdiction of District Commission, State Commission and National Commission) Rules, 2021, these courts can now handle cases involving amounts up to ₹ 50 lakh.

Institutions and Commissions in Haryana

Lokayukta

- Lokayukta is a **quasi-judicial** institution in Haryana.
- The Haryana Lokayukta Act was initially passed in 1997, but was canceled by the then Governor Mahavir Prasad on 19th September, 1999.
- The Haryana **Lokayukta Act, 2002**, came into force on 27th January, 2003.
- The tenure of the Lokayukta is **5 years** and the appointment is made by the Governor.

Pritam Pal Singh was appointed as the first Lokayukta of Haryana in 2011.

- The Haryana Lokayukta has the authority to hear and investigate complaints against the Chief Minister, members of the State Legislative Assembly, Heads and Deputy Heads of Municipal Councils and Committees, Mayors and Deputy Mayors of Municipal Corporations, Officers of Panchayati Raj Institutions and Chancellors and Vice-Chancellors of universities.

State Vigilance Bureau

- The Special Inquiry Agency was established in Haryana in June, 1967 and was renamed the State Vigilance Bureau in 1978.
- Again in February 2023, it was renamed as the Anti-corruption Bureau.
- The State Vigilance Bureau is headed by the State Vigilance Officer at the state level and by Divisional and District Vigilance Officers at the division and district levels, respectively.
- The office of the Haryana State Vigilance Bureau is located in **Panchkula.**

Advocate General

- As per Article 165 of the Indian Constitution, the **Governor of the state** appoints the Advocate General.
- A person to be appoint as an Advocate General should be a citizen of India, should be practicing law for 10 years or more, or should be a judge in High Court for minimum 10 years.
- **Babu Anand Swarup** was the first Advocate General of Haryana.
- Advocate General is the first Legal Officer of the state, who advises the State Government from time to time. He also attends the meeting of the State Legislative Assembly but do not have voting rights in the assembly.

District Vigilance Committee

- The District Vigilance Committee in Haryana was established through an amendment to the Lokayukta Act.
- The committee consists of three members, chosen by the Haryana Lokayukta.

> One member of District Vigilance Committee must be a retired **Legal Officer** who previously served as a Civil Judge, while the other two members do not have specific requirements.

State Information Commission

- The Haryana State Information Commission was established under Right to Information Act, 2005.
- The headquarters of the Commission is located in **Chandigarh.**
- Members of the Commission are appointed by the Governor for a term of **6 years** or until they reach the **age of 62**, whichever comes first.
- The Commission is headed by the **Chief Information Commissioner.**

State Election Commission

- The Commission is responsible for the direction, control and supervision of all elections for Panchayati Raj Institutions and Municipal Boards in Haryana.
- It was constituted on 18th November 1993, under the provisions of **Articles 243K** and **243ZA** of the Indian Constitution.
- The headquarters of the Commission is located in **Panchkula** district.
- The first Commissioner of the Commission was **J.K. Duggal.**
- The Commissioner is appointed by the Governor.

▲ State Election Commission, Haryana

Haryana Staff Selection Commission

- The Haryana Staff Selection Commission was established on 28th January, 1970.
- It was formerly known as the **Subordinate Services Selection Board.**
- The Commission is responsible for recruiting staff for various Group C and D posts in Zila Parishads, Panchayat Samities, Municipal Corporations, trusts, etc.
- The Commission consists of 6 members, apart from the Chairman, who are appointed by the Governor on the advice of the Chief Minister and Council of Ministers.
- The tenure of the Chairman is **3 years** or until reaching **68 years** of age, whichever is earlier, while the tenure of other members is up to 65 years of age.
- The headquarters of the Commission is located in **Panchkula** district.

Haryana Public Service Commission

- The Punjab Public Service Commission was established in 1937 under the Government of India Act, 1935, which provided for independent Public Service Commissions for each province.
- According to **Article 315** of the Indian Constitution, a Union Public Service Commission is established at the center and State Public Service Commissions are established in each state.

▲ Haryana Public Service Commission

- The **Haryana Public Service Commission** was established in November, 1966 under Sub-section 2 of Section 85 of the Punjab Re-organisation Act of 1966.
- The headquarters of the Haryana Public Service Commission is located in **Panchkula** district.

- The Secretary and members of the Commission are appointed by the Governor for a term of **6 years** or until reaching **62 years** of age, whichever comes first.
- The Commission is responsible for recruiting staff for various Group A and B posts.

Haryana Human Rights Commission

- The Protection of Human Rights Act was enacted in Parliament in 1993.
- The **Haryana** Human Rights Commission (HHRC) was established under Section 21 of the 1993 Act.
- The first Chairman of the Commission was **Bijendra Jain**, a retired Chief Justice of the High Court of Punjab and Haryana.
- The Commission's headquarters is located in **Chandigarh**.
- All members of the Commission are appointed by the Governor for a term of **5 years** or until reaching **70 years** of age, whichever is earlier.
- The Chairman is appointed by the Governor based on recommendations from a committee consisting of the Chief Minister, Speaker, Leader of the Legislative Assembly and Home Minister.
- The Chairman must be a retired or working judge of the State High Court. Other members must have at least 7 years of experience as a District or Sessions Court judge.
- One member of the Commission must have a distinguished record in human rights activities.

> In 2015, a branch of the HHRC was established in **Haryana Bhawan**, **New Delhi**, to hear cases related to Southern Haryana and surrounding areas.

- The salaries of the Chairman and members are paid from the State Consolidated Fund.

Haryana State Commission for Women

- The Haryana State Commission for Women was constituted under the Haryana State Commission for Women Act, 2012.
- The Commission comprises a Chairman, Vice-Chairman and four members from non-governmental organisations, all appointed by the Governor for a term of 3 years.
- Its headquarters is located in **Panchkula**.
- The Chairperson and more than half of the members of the Commission should be women.
- The Joint Commissioner of Women and Child Development Department and the Commissioner of the Haryana Women Crime Cell are ex-officio members.
- The Commission aims to achieve gender equality, enforce laws strictly and address issues of discrimination, atrocities and exploitation against women.

Haryana Law Enforcement

Haryana Law Enforcement
- Police Administration
- Police Ranges and Districts in Haryana
- Police Commissionerates
- Haryana Police Officers
- Police Training Centres

Police Administration

- The **Haryana Police Department** is the law enforcement agency for the state.
- The **State Crime Record Bureau** was established on 1st April, 1987 to collect and analyse crime-related data, with its headquarters in **Panchkula**.
- The State Police Headquarters is also located in **Panchkula**.
- The Police Intelligence Branch and CID (Crime Investigation Department) are established to control crimes in the state.

Police Ranges and Districts in Haryana

- Haryana is divided into 5 **Police Ranges** to ensure smooth law and order management.
- There are 6 Revenue Ranges and 3 Police Commissionerates Panchkula, Gurugram and Faridabad. Gurugram Police Commissionerate is the largest.
- Hansi is considered a police district and is the **largest Police Range** in the state.
- Ambala was separated from Panchkula Commissionerate and made into a new Police Range.
- Kaithal and Kurukshetra were moved from Ambala and included in the Karnal Range.
- Panipat was separated from Rohtak and added to the Karnal Range.
- Bhiwani was separated from Hisar and added to the Rohtak Range.

> Nuh and Palwal were separated from Gurugram and included in the Faridabad Range.

Police Commissionerates

- Police commissionerates of Haryana, total 3 in number, are as follows

Commissionerate	Urban Area
Faridabad commissionerate	Faridabad
Gurugram commissionerate	Gurugram
Panchkula commissionerate	Panchkula

Police Ranges in Haryana

Police Range	Districts	Headquarters
Ambala	Ambala, Yamunanagar and Kurukshetra	Ambala
Hisar	Hisar, Hansi, Fatehabad, Sirsa and Jind	Hisar
Karnal	Karnal, Panipat and Kaithal	Karnal
Rohtak	Rohtak, Jhajjar, Sonipat, Bhiwani and Charkhi- Dadri	Rohtak
Rewari	Rewari, Palwal, Mahendragarh and Nuh	Rewari

Revenue Ranges in Haryana

Revenue Range	Districts
Ambala	Ambala, Yamunanagar, Panchkula and Kurukshetra
Karnal	Karnal, Panipat and Kaithal
Rohtak	Rohtak, Jhajjar, Sonipat, Bhiwani and Charkhi-Dadri
Hisar	Hisar, Fatehabad, Jind and Sirsa
Gurugram	Gurugram, Rewari and Mahendragarh
Faridabad	Faridabad, Palwal and Nuh

Haryana Police Officers

- The highest post in Haryana Police is the **Director General of Police** (DGP).
- Each Police Range is headed by an officer not below the rank of Additional Director General (ADG) of Police.
- Each Police Range is subdivided and headed by a **Sub-Divisional Officer**.
- Each district is headed by a **District Superintendent of Police or Deputy Commissioner of Police**.
- Each district is divided into district circles, headed by a **Circle Inspector**.
- Each district circle is further subdivided into police stations.
- Police stations are headed by a **Police Station Officer**, the lowest-ranking police officer in the hierarchy.

Police Training Centres

- Police training centres in Haryana are located in Bhondsi (Gurugram) and Sunaria (Rohtak).
- The Commando Training Complex is situated in Newal, Karnal district.
- Haryana Police Academy is located in Madhuban, Karnal, offering world-class facilities for training police officers, as well as judicial and administrative officers.
- In-service training and 'In-service Courses' are also provided at the Haryana Police Academy.
- The **State Forensic Science Laboratory** was established in Rohtak in 1973 and later shifted to Madhuban, Karnal in 1976.

CHECK CHAPTER KNOWLEDGE

1 In which year was the High Court of Judicature at Lahore established? *HSSC 2019*
(a) 1909 (b) 1919 (c) 1929 (d) 1939

2 Before independence, the High Court of Punjab and Haryana was situated at which place? *Haryana Accountant 2019, PGT 2016*
(a) Lahore (b) Islamabad
(c) Peshawar (d) Rawalpindi

3 After partition, where was the East Punjab High Court established?
(a) Delhi (b) Chandigarh
(c) Shimla (d) Lahore

4 In which year was the seat of Punjab High Court shifted to Chandigarh?
(a) 1947 (b) 1950 (c) 1951 (d) 1955

5 Who designed the High Court building of Chandigarh? *HSSC 2023*
(a) Edwin Lutyens (b) Le Corbusier
(c) Laurie Baker (d) Both (a) and (b)

6 What is the number of permanent judges in the Punjab and Haryana High Court?
(a) 68 (b) 58 (c) 39 (d) 48

7 Who was the first Chief Justice of Punjab and Haryana High Court? *Haryana Lab Attendant 2021, 18, 16*
(a) Sodhi Ranjan Das (b) Eric Weston
(c) Amar Nath Bhandari (d) Ram Lal

8 Which Chief Justice of Haryana High Court also served as a Governor?
(a) Ranjit Singh Narula (b) Harbans Singh
(c) Mukul Mudgal (d) A.K. Sikri

9 As of 1st February, 2020, who was the Chief Justice of the High Court of Haryana? *HSSC-Field Cadre 2020*
(a) Justice Ravi Shankar Jha
(b) Justice Ajay Tiwari
(c) Justice N.V. Ramana
(d) Justice Alok Sood

10 Haryana Judicial Service is divided into how many categories?
(a) Haryana Civil Judicial Service
(b) Haryana Higher Judicial Service
(c) Both (a) and (b)
(d) None of the above

11 Which of the following is a quasi-judicial institution in Haryana? *HSSC 2022*
(a) Family Court
(b) Administrative Tribunal
(c) Environmental Court
(d) Revenue Court

12 Where is the Haryana State Legal Services Authority set up?
(a) Ambala (b) Rohtak
(c) Chandigarh (d) Panchkula

13 When was the first permanent Lok Adalat set up in Haryana?
(a) 7th August, 1998 (b) 17th January, 1955
(c) 10th May, 2005 (d) 1st November, 1966

14 Which statement holds true for Lok Adalats?
(a) It is a Civil Court.
(b) It is a platform for peaceful resolution of conflicts.
(c) Appeal against judgement is not possible.
(d) All of the above

15 Where is the Special Commercial Court of Haryana located? *HSSC 2024*
(a) Chandigarh (b) Panipat
(c) Faridabad (d) Gurugram

16 Where in Haryana is the Environmental Court held?
(a) Faridabad (b) Kurukshetra
(c) Both (a) and (b) (d) None of these

17 How many Environmental Courts have been established by the State Government of Haryana?
(a) 1 (b) 2 (c) 3 (d) 4

18 Which place in Haryana does not have a District Consumer Court?
(a) Hisar (b) Mahendragarh
(c) Bhiwani (d) Charkhi-Dadri

19 Who was the first Advocate General of Haryana? *Haryana Panchayat Officer 2017*
(a) Krishna Murari (b) D.K. Jain
(c) Babu Anand Swarup (d) Premchand Jain

20 Who was the first Lokayukta of Haryana?
(a) Naval Kishore Aggarwal
(b) Pritam Pal Singh
(c) Babu Parmanand
(d) Ranjeet Kumar

21 What is the tenure of Lokayuktas in Haryana? *HSSC 2023*

(a) 6 years (b) 2 years
(c) 5 years (d) 4 years

22 Where is the office of the State Vigilance Bureau situated?

(a) Panchkula (b) Hisar
(c) Sonipat (d) Gurgaon

23 In which year was the name of the Special Inquiry Agency changed to the State Vigilance Bureau?

(a) 1980 (b) 1990 (c) 1972 (d) 1978

24 How many members of the District Vigilance Commission are selected by the Haryana Lokayukta?

(a) 3 (b) 5 (c) 7 (d) 2

25 Who appoints the members of the State Information Commission? *HSSC 2024*

(a) Chief Justice of High Court
(b) Governor
(c) President
(d) Prime Minister

26 Where is the Haryana State Information Commission situated?

(a) Panchkula (b) Chandigarh
(c) Gurugram (d) Ambala

27 Who was the first Commissioner of the State Election Commission of Haryana?

(a) Mehar Singh (b) Pritam Pal Singh
(c) J.K. Duggal (d) Donald Falshaw

28 Who appoints the Commissioner of the Haryana State Election Commission? *HSSC 2022*

(a) Chief Minister (b) President
(c) Chief Justice (d) Governor

29 When was the Haryana Staff Selection Commission (HSSC) formed? *Haryana Accountant 2018*

(a) 26th January, 1960
(b) 2nd October, 1975
(c) 10th December, 1965
(d) 28th January, 1970

30 Where is the Haryana Public Service Commission (HPSC) situated? *HSSC 2020, 19*

(a) Sonipat (b) Panipat
(c) Gurugram (d) Panchkula

31 Who appoints the Chairman of the Haryana Public Service Commission? *Haryana Fire Station Officer 2019*

(a) President (b) Governor
(c) Chief Minister (d) None of these

32 Where is the Haryana Human Rights Commission located?

(a) Chandigarh (b) Gurgaon
(c) Rohtak (d) Bhiwani

33 Who was the first Chairman of the Haryana Human Rights Commission?

(a) Bijendra Jain (b) Premchand Jain
(c) Anand Dev Kaushal (d) Darbari Lal Gupta

34 What is the tenure of the Chairman of the Haryana State Commission for Women?

(a) 2 years (b) 5 years
(c) 3 years (d) 1 year

35 Where is the State Police Headquarters of Haryana situated? *HSSC 2021, 19*

(a) Kurukshetra (b) Panchkula
(c) Karnal (d) Ambala

36 Which of the following is a police district but not a state district of Haryana? *Haryana Junior Engineer 2019*

(a) Palwal (b) Hansi
(c) Manesar (d) None of these

37 How many revenue divisions are there in Haryana? *HSSC 2020*

(a) 7 (b) 6 (c) 5 (d) 3

38 Jhajjar district of Haryana falls under which Police Range?

(a) Karnal (b) Hisar
(c) Ambala (d) Rohtak

39 The district of Nuh in Haryana comes under the administrative division of .... *HSSC 2020*

(a) Rohtak (b) Karnal
(c) Faridabad (d) Ambala

40 Rewari district of Haryana falls under which of the following Revenue Range?

(a) Karnal (b) Gurugram
(c) Hisar (d) Rohtak

CORRECT ANSWERS

1. (b)	**2.** (a)	**3.** (c)	**4.** (d)	**5.** (b)	**6.** (c)	**7.** (d)	**8.** (a)	**9.** (a)	**10.** (c)
11. (b)	**12.** (c)	**13.** (a)	**14.** (d)	**15.** (d)	**16.** (c)	**17.** (b)	**18.** (d)	**19.** (c)	**20.** (b)
21. (c)	**22.** (a)	**23.** (d)	**24.** (a)	**25.** (c)	**26.** (b)	**27.** (c)	**28.** (d)	**29.** (d)	**30.** (d)
31. (b)	**32.** (a)	**33.** (a)	**34.** (c)	**35.** (b)	**36.** (b)	**37.** (b)	**38.** (d)	**39.** (c)	**40.** (b)

CHAPTER 26

KNOW YOUR STATE
HARYANA

Local Self Government in Haryana

- Modern local self-government in India is structured into two tiers **Rural local self-government** and **Urban local self-government.**
- The key developments in its evolution include

1957	The **Balwant Rai Mehta Committee** was established to review and strengthen the Community Development Programme (CDP) and the National Extension Service (NES). It recommended **Democratic Decentralisation,** with **three-tier** Panchayati Raj System.
1959	Based on the Balwant Rai Mehta committee's recommendations, the **Three-Tier Panchayati Raj** System was first introduced in Nagaur district of Rajasthan.
1992	The 73rd and 74th **Constitutional Amendment** Acts were enacted, granting constitutional status to the Panchayati Raj System and Municipalities, respectively.

- These amendments added Part IX and Part IXA to the Constitution, introducing several new provisions and incorporating Schedules 11 and 12, which detail the powers, authority, and responsibilities of rural and urban local bodies.

- The local self government in Haryana is structured through both urban and rural bodies. Urban areas are governed by Municipal Corporations, Municipal Councils and Municipal Committees, while rural areas have Panchayati Raj Institutions like Gram Panchayats, Panchayat Samiti and Zila Parishad.

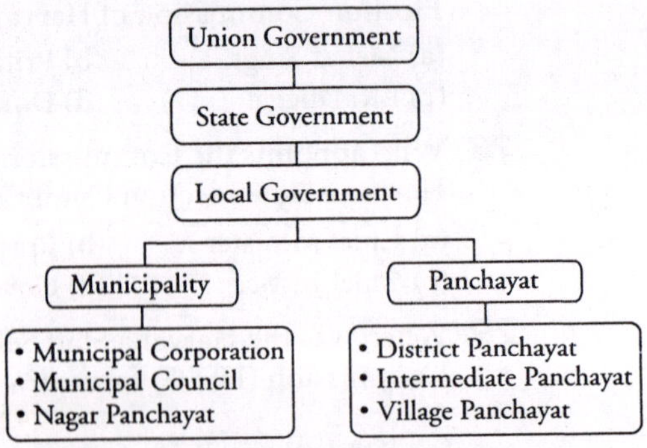

▲ Panchayti Raj System in India

Panchayati Raj in Haryana

- **Haryana** adopted the **Three-Tier Panchayati Raj System in 1966,** following its establishment as a separate state.
- **In 1972,** the Haryana Government formed a committee under the chairmanship of **Mandu Singh Malik** to review and improve the Panchayati Raj System.

- Based on the **Mandu Singh Malik Committee's** recommendations, the Zila Parishad was dissolved in 1973.
- The Panchayati Raj Institutions in Haryana are elected by the Haryana State Election Commission, with its headquarters at **Haryana Panchayat Bhawan, Chandigarh.**

Three-Tier Panchayati Raj System in Haryana

It includes the following bodies

1. Gram Panchayat

- The Gram Panchayat is the lowest level of the Three-Tier Panchayati Raj System.
- It is a powerful body headed by a **Sarpanch.** No scheme or work can be implemented without consent of the Gram Panchayat.
- Gram Panchayats have various sources of income/finance such as grants-in-aid from the Consolidated Fund of State, taxes, duties, tolls fees etc.
- Each Gram Panchayat has three integral bodies, namely - Gram Sabha, Panchayat and Nyaya Panchayat.

Gram Panchayat

↓

Gram Sabha
- Gram Sabhas are formed by one or two villages.
- Each and every villager whose name is included in the voter's list and who has attained 18 years of age, is the member of Gram Sabha.
- At least two Gram Sabha meetings in an year i.e. on **13th April** and **2nd October** is mandatory in Haryana.

↓

Panchayat
- Panchayat consists of 1 Sarpanch and other members.
- The members of the Gram Sabha form the Panchayat.

↓

Nyaya Panchayat
- Each village has a Nyaya Panchayat to address local problems. It constituted by the elected members of the Panchayat.
- Nyaya Panchayat cannot assign jail term as a form of punishment.

2. Panchayat Samiti

- The Panchayat Samiti is the intermediate or second tier of the Panchayati Raj System, also referred to as the **Block Samiti, Kshetra Samiti** or **Zonal Council.**
- It primarily comprises the heads of Gram Panchayats, women representatives and members from Scheduled Castes (SCs) and Scheduled Tribes (STs).
- The Samiti includes a Chairperson, Vice-Chairperson, directly elected members from territorial constituencies (as defined under Section 58 of the Act) and members of the Haryana Legislative Assembly representing constituencies wholly or partially within the Panchayat Samiti area.

Block Development Officer

- The Block Development Officer (BDO) serves as the nodal officer for the Panchayat Samiti.
- As the administrator, the BDO oversees all activities and ensures proper utilisation of funds across the Gram Panchayats within their jurisdiction.

3. Zila Parishad

- The Zila Parishad is the **highest tier of local governance in rural areas.**
- It comprises the members directly elected from district wards, Chairpersons of all Panchayat Samitis in the district, Members of Parliament and Members of the Haryana Legislative Assembly whose constituencies fall within the district.
- The **Directorate of Development and Panchayat** serves as the key institution for managing the Panchayati Raj System in the state.
- The Zila Parishad is headed by a President, supported by **District Development and Panchayat Officers** (DDPOs) at the district level and **Block Development and Panchayat Officers** (BDPOs) at the block level.

Haryana Panchayati Raj Act

- Before 1994, the Punjab Gram Panchayat Act, 1952 and Punjab Panchayati Raj Act, 1952 governed the Panchayati Raj system in Haryana.
- Under the **Punjab Gram Panchayat Act, 1952,** Gram Panchayats had a tenure of 3 years and the Sarpanch was elected by the Panchas. There was no reservation for women, but one seat was reserved for Scheduled Caste (SC) candidates.
- In 1963, the Act was amended to allow direct election of Panchayat members by voters and the tenure was extended to 5 years.

> - In 1971, under Chief Minister **Bansi Lal**, the power to elect the Sarpanch was restored to the Panchas.
> - In 1978, **Chaudhary Devi Lal** amended the law, granting voters the right to elect the Sarpanch directly.

- In 1991, under Chief Minister **Bhajan Lal**, the tenure of Panchayats was reduced back to 3 years.

Haryana Panchayati Raj Act, 1994

- The Haryana Panchayati Raj Act was enacted on **22nd April, 1994**, in line with the 73rd Constitutional Amendment Act. At that time, **Chaudhary Bhajan Lal** was the Chief Minister of Haryana.
- **The Haryana Panchayati Raj Election Rules** were established on 24th August, 1994, followed by the **Haryana Panchayati Rules** on 16th February, 1995.
- On 14th August, 1996, the rules related to finance, budget, audit, taxation and works for Panchayats were formulated.
- The Haryana Panchayati Raj Act, 1994 applies to the entire state of Haryana and under it, Panchayati Raj Institutions (PRIs) are entrusted with responsibilities related to all 29 subjects listed in the Eleventh Schedule of the Constitution.

> These 29 prominent subjects include key areas such as fuel, bridges, roads, electricity, family welfare, primary education, health services, poverty eradication programme, land reforms, drinking water, animal husbandry, irrigation, tree plantation, public distribution services, markets and fairs, Khadi and Gramodyog, among others.

- According to **Chapter X of the Haryana Panchayati Raj Act, 1994**, each Panchayat Samiti is required to establish the following committees
  - General Committee
  - Finance, Audit and Planning Committee
  - Social Justice Committee
- **Section 164 of Part** V of the Act states that the State Election Commission, in consultation with the government, is responsible for preparing the voter list for each electoral division concerning Gram Panchayat, Panchayat Samiti and Zila Parishad elections.
- As per **Section 128 of Chapter XIV**, the quorum for Zila Parishad meetings is as follows
  - One-third of the members for an ordinary meeting
  - One-half of the serving members for a special meeting

Reservation in Panchayat

- The Haryana Panchayati Raj Act, 1994 mandates the reservation of seats for Scheduled Castes and women in proportion to their population across all three tiers of Panchayati Raj Institutions (PRIs).
- **Provision** 9(2) of Schedule 1 reserves one-third of seats for women at all levels, including those reserved for Scheduled Castes women.
- **Article** 9, Schedule 1 ensures that seats for Scheduled Castes are reserved in every Gram Panchayat, in proportion to their population in that area.
- The allotment of reserved seats is done either on a **rotational basis** or **through lottery**.
- The post of Sarpanch is reserved for Scheduled Castes and women based on their population.

> In a Gram Panchayat, if **Backward Classes** population is 2% or more of the total population, there will be a dedicated post for them in the Panchayat and the area will be divided into wards accordingly.

Haryana Panchayati Raj Amendment Act, 2015

The **Haryana Panchayati Raj Amendment Act, 2015** was passed to empower **Gram Panchayats.**
The key provisions of the Act include

- Candidates for **Panchayati Raj Institutions** (PRIs) must have completed at least 10th grade education.
- Women and Scheduled Castes candidates must have completed at least 8th grade, while women from Scheduled Castes must have completed at least 5th grade to be eligible for election.
- Haryana became the **Second State in India**, after Rajasthan, to require minimum educational qualifications for candidates in PRIs, effective from 7th September, 2015.
- The Act **prohibits** individuals from contesting elections if they
  - are charged with a criminal offense punishable by over 10 years of imprisonment
  - have defaulted on agricultural loans
  - have unpaid electricity bills
  - do not have a functional toilet at home
  - Do not meet the minimum educational qualifications

> Haryana is the **first state in India to use Electronic Voting Machines** (EVMs) in Panchayat elections.

New Developments in Panchayati Raj

- The Sarpanch cannot hold more than the prescribed amount of cash in reserve. If the amount exceeds the limit, a 21% interest will be charged on the excess.
- A no-confidence motion cannot be raised against the Sarpanch in the Panchayat.
- The role of the Up-Sarpanch (Deputy Chief) has been diluted.
- Sarpanchs and Panchas can be suspended for 6 years if they fail to fulfill judicial duties or neglect their responsibilities.
- In Haryana, elected representatives must resign within 7 days of the announcement of Panchayati Raj elections.

Haryana Panchayat Raj (Amendment) Bill, 2024

The bill was passed in November, 2024 to amend the Haryana Panchayati Raj Act, 1994.

The salient **features** of the bill are given below

- Panch seats are reserved for Backward Classes (B) in every **Gram Panchayat.**
- Number of reserved wards are proportional to half the percentage of Backward Classes (B) in the Gram Sabha population.
- Reserved wards are allocated by lottery, excluding those already reserved for Scheduled Castes and Backward Classes (A).
- Reservation follows a rotational system in subsequent elections.
- At least one panch from Backward classes (B), if their population is 2% or more of the total.
- Member seats are reserved for Backward Classes (B) in every **Panchayat Samiti.**

> Number of reserved wards are proportional to half the percentage of **Backward Classes** (B) in the block population.

- Reserved wards are allotted by lottery, excluding those already reserved for Scheduled Castes and Backward Classes (A). Reservation follows a rotational system in subsequent elections.
- If total reserved wards (SC, BC-A and BC-B) exceed 50% of total wards, BC-B reservations are adjusted to maintain the 50% limit.

Powers and Responsibilities of Panchayats in Haryana

- All Anganwadi centres and state-run primary schools will be managed under the supervision of Panchayats.
- The representatives of PRIs will be part of the Selection Committee for Anganwadi assistants and workers.
- Women members nominated by Zila Parishads and Panchayat Committees can take the **Child Development Project Officer** (CDPO) along for inspecting Anganwadi centers.
- Gram Panchayats recommend eligible individuals for old age pensions, widow pensions, disability pensions, etc.

> Gram Panchayats supervise the Public Distribution System (PDS) in villages and handle the distribution of Ration Cards. They also report any issues to the Controller of Gram Panchayat Food and Supplies.

- Based on the recommendations of Panchayati Samiti, non-conventional fuel sources like biogas plants as well as improved chulhas are provided to people.
- Gram Panchayats prepare Annual Development Plans and Budget Plans and organise sports competitions at the district and block levels.
- If any person from a village is taken into custody by the police, the Police Station Officer must inform the Sarpanch.
- Based on the recommendations of the State Finance Commission, Panchayati Raj Institutions receive 3% of the stamp duty and registration fees as revenue, as well as 20% of the income earned from animal fares in the district.
- Haryana State Roadways buses serving rural areas set their schedules based on the advice of Panchayat Samiti and Zila Parishad. For new routes, their consultation is prioritised.
- Zila Parishads can undertake projects worth up to ₹ 5 lakh, Panchayat Samitis up to ₹ 3 lakh and Gram Panchayats up to ₹ 1.25 lakh.

Gram Vikas Samiti

- Gram Vikas Samitis were formed by Haryana Government in 1992 and registered under the **Societies Registration Act.** Its Members include Sarpanch, a Women Panch, a Panch of SC and Backward Class respectively, one retired defense personnel and two members of Gram Sabhas.
- The objective of Gram Vikas Samiti is to speed up the rural development and bring transparency and quality in the system. The **Sarpanch is the head** of the Gram Vikas Samiti.
- The Samiti undertakes various developmental works in villages such as running Adult Education Programmes, Drought Management, Crop Diversification, Community Development Programmes, etc.
- The funds that the Central and State Governments send for the Gram Panchayats are deposited in the village Development Fund and the Sarpanch and two Members of the Village Development Committee manage this fund.

State Finance Commission for Panchayats

The State Finance Commission is established every five years under **Article 243 (I)** and **243 (Y)** of the Constitution. The key points are

- Haryana State Finance Commission is constituted for five years by the State Governor as per Section 213 of **Haryana Panchayati Raj Act, 1994.**
- The **First Haryana State Finance Commission** was formed on 31st May, 1994.
- The **Sixth Haryana State Finance Commission** was formed on 22nd September, 2020 under **P. Raghavendra Rao** as the Chairman and Vikas Gupta (IAS), as the Member Secretary of the Commission.

New Projects Related to Panchayati Raj System

- Under the **Swachh Bharat Mission**, the financial assistance for constructing toilets has been increased from ₹ 9,100 to ₹ 12,000.
- The Haryana Government launched **e-Panchayat services** on 26th April, 2015 in Rohtak to promote e-governance. **Panchayat Diwas** is celebrated on 24th April and the e-portal run by the Haryana Government is called **Mahari Panchayat**.
- **Sui village in Bhiwani** district was declared the **first Swa-Prerit Gram** under the **Swa-Prerit Adarsh Gram Yojana** (Self-Driven Ideal Village Scheme).
- 12 villages in Palwal and Faridabad districts, with more than 50% SC population, were provided ₹10 lakh each as development funds under the **Pradhan Mantri Adarsh Gram Yojana** (Prime Minister's Model Village Scheme).
- The **Women Farmer Empowerment Scheme** was launched in Bhiwani, Jhajjar and Hisar districts to empower women farmers, promoting community-managed sustainable agriculture and the use of locally available resources.
- The Haryana Government launched the **Garvit Grameen Yojana**, also known as **Gramin Vikas ke Liye Tarun Yojana**, on the birth anniversary of Swami Vivekananda in 2015. This scheme aims to provide self-employment opportunities to educated youth by offering free skill development training, with a certificate awarded upon successful completion.
- In 2016-17, the **Water Conservation and Water Harvesting Scheme** was initiated in the state to promote water conservation and harvesting in blocks with overflowing groundwater.
- During the year 2023-24, an amount of ₹20 crore has been approved under the **Haryana Swaran Jayanti Mahagram Yojana** (SMAGY) for laying sewerage system in villages having population 10,000 or more than 10,000.

> Under the **Haryana Gramin Vikas Yojana** (HGVY), an amount of ₹ 400.02 crore has been approved for the year 2024-25.

- An amount of ₹ 100 crore has been approved for the year 2024-25 for implementation of **Grey Water Management Projects under Swachh Bharat Mission-Grameen** (SBM-G).

Awards given to Gram Panchayats in Haryana

Award	Description
Best Performing Panchayat Award	Given to the best-performing village in each district of Haryana, with a prize of ₹5 lakh.
Best Performing Gram Panchayat Award	Awarded to the top Gram Panchayat in the state, with a prize of ₹10 lakh. This award is also known as the **Chaudhary Devi Lal Award**.
Best Zila Parishads Award	Three Zila Parishads are recognised for their outstanding performance, with the first prize receiving ₹8 lakh, the second ₹5 lakh and the third ₹3 lakh.
Cleanest Village Award	A ₹5 lakh prize is given to the cleanest village, which has no open defecation. Additionally, Gram Panchayats receive financial aid ranging from ₹ 2,400 to ₹ 8,400, depending on the population, for maintaining environmental cleanliness.
Deen Dayal Upadhyay Panchayat Sashaktikaran Puraskar	Five Panchayats were awarded on 24th April, 2015, National panchayat Day, including Doharka (Gurugram), Dabodha (Gurugram), Nissing (Karnal), Dubri (Karnal) and Zila Parishad of Kurukshetra.
Rashtriya Gaurav Gram Sabha Award	Awarded to Gram Panchayats that have made outstanding contributions to socio-economic development by involving Gram Sabhas in their decision-making processes.

Local Self Government in Urban Areas

- The Twelfth Schedule, which was added to the Indian Constitution through the 74th Amendment Act, focuses on the functions of urban local self-governments.
- This schedule includes 18 subjects related to the responsibilities of urban local bodies.
- Urban areas are divided into multiple wards, each forming an urban local body.
- Haryana enacted the **Haryana Municipal Corporation (Amendment) Act, 1994** to implement the 74th Amendment Act.

- The election process, tenure, reservation and other aspects of urban local self-government are similar to those in the Gram Panchayat system.
- In 2016, the Haryana Government also introduced educational and character qualifications for representatives in urban local self-governments, similar to those in PRIs.

> In Haryana, there are currently 87 municipalities under the Urban Local Bodies Department, including 10 municipal corporations, 19 municipal councils and 58 municipal committees.

According to **Section 2** of the **Haryana Municipality Act, 1973,** the urban local self-government in Haryana is divided into three parts, as outlined below

Local Self Government in Urban Areas

- Municipal Committee
- Municipal Council
- Municipal Corporation

1. Municipal Committee

- Small urban areas with a population ranging from **20,000 to 3,00,000** are managed by Municipal Committees in Haryana.
- The number of elected members in these municipalities varies between 10 to 24, with 2 to 3 nominated members.
- The Municipal Committees consist of a **Chairperson,** a Deputy Chairperson and three types of members which are elected members, nominated members and ex-officio members (such as Members of Parliament, Members of the Legislative Assembly and Rajya Sabha members representing the area).

2. Municipal Council

- A Municipal Council is an urban local body that governs a city with a population ranging from **3 lakh to 10 lakh.**
- The members of the Municipal Council include a **Chairperson,** a Deputy Chairperson and three types of members elected, nominated and ex-officio.

> The number of elected members ranges from 25 to 55, while the number of nominated members is between 3 to 5.

- In Haryana, 50% of the seats in the Municipal Council are reserved for women.
- The Municipal Council can form a maximum of 5 committees.

3. Municipal Corporation

- A Municipal Corporation governs urban areas in Haryana with a population **exceeding 10 lakh.**
- The members include the **Mayor** (head of the Municipal Corporation), **Deputy Mayor** and three types of members — Elected, Nominated and Ex-officio.
- Elections are held every 5 years, with the Mayor's **tenure** lasting for 5 years.
- A **no-confidence motion** can be brought against the Mayor after two years in office.
- The number of elected members in Municipal Corporations ranges from 60 to 110 and the number of nominated members is between 5 to 10.
- Haryana has 11 **Municipal Corporations** which include Faridabad, Gurugram, Ambala, Panchkula, Sirsa, Yamunanagar, Rohtak, Hisar, Panipat, Karnal, Sonipat.
- **Faridabad is the largest** and oldest (formed in May 1994) and **Sonipat is the smallest** (formed on 1st June, 2015) Municipal Corporation of the State.

> Seven districts of Haryana received the status of Municipal Corporation in 2010. These are Hisar, Rohtak, Panchkula, Yamunanagar, Karnal, Ambala and Panipat.

- In Haryana, initially one Mayor and one Deputy Mayor were elected from among the councillors of each ward. However, from 5th September, 2018, the Mayors are directly elected through elections. These elections are also known as **Mayoral elections.**

> **Some Important Articles and their Provisions**
>
> Article 243 I — Establishment of State Finance Commission
>
> Article 243 K — Establishment of State Election Commission
>
> Article 243 Z (D) — Establishment of District Planning Committes
>
> Article 243 Z (E) — Establishment of Metropolitan Planning Committees

Haryana Municipal (Amendment) Bill, 2016

- The Haryana Municipal Amendment Bill was passed by the Haryana Legislative Assembly on 31st March, 2016 to enhance the Three-Tier System of urban local self-government.
- It amends Section 13(A) of the Haryana Municipal Act, 1973 and Section 8 of the Haryana Municipal Corporation Act, 1994.

- **Educational qualifications** for candidates
  - Male candidates must have at least a matriculation (Class X) certificate.
  - Women candidates and SC candidates must have passed at least Class 8.
  - SC women candidates must be at least Class 5.
- All candidates must file a self-declaration confirming they have a functional toilet at home.
- The Bill **prohibits** people from contesting elections if
  - They are charged in a criminal case punishable with more than 10 years of imprisonment.
  - They are defaulters of co-operative loans, government loans or electricity bills.
  - They do not have a functional toilet at home.

Haryana Municipal (Amendment) Bill, 2017

- This act was enacted by the Haryana Legislative Assembly in 2017.
- Modifications have been made to the Haryana Municipal Corporation Act, 1994.
- As per the amendment, Municipal Committees can now be formed in cities with a population of over 3 lakh.

Haryana Municipal (Amendment) Bill, 2018

- The Punjab and Haryana High Court upholds the constitutionality of **Haryana Municipal** (Amendment) Bill, 2018 whereby the State Election Commission (SEC) was empowered to remove municipal presidents and members on grounds of statutory disqualification under Section 13 A of the Act.

The Haryana Municipal Corporation (Amendment) Bill, 2022

- It has been passed to amend the Haryana Municipal Corporation Act, 1994.
- The salient features of the bill are
  - Seats will be reserved for Backward Class (B) in each corporation.
  - Reservation will be proportional to half the percentage of BC-B population in the total corporation population.
  - It excludes seats already reserved for Scheduled Castes and Backward Class (A).
  - Selection will be based on wards with the highest BC-B population percentage.

Haryana Municipal (Amendment) Bill, 2024

- It has been passed to amend the Haryana Municipal Act, 1973.
- The salient features of the bill are
  - Seats will be reserved for Backward Classes (B) in every Municipal Council/Committee.
  - Reservation will be proportional to half the percentage of BC-B population in the total Municipal population.
  - Reserved seats will be allotted by lottery from the proposed reserved seats, excluding those already reserved for SC and BC-A.
  - Selection will be based on wards with the highest BC-B population percentage.

This reservation policy aligns with **Article 243-T(6)** of the Indian Constitution. The Supreme Court upheld the validity of this provision in **Dr. K. Krishna Murthy & Ors. V/s. Union of India & Anr. (2010).**

CHECK CHAPTER KNOWLEDGE

1 Which is the lowest level of the Haryana Panchayati Raj system? *HSSC 2020, Haryana Clerk 2019*

(a) Nyaya panchayat (b) Zila panchayat
(c) Gram panchayat (d) Block panchayat

2 How many meetings should be held by Gram Sabha mandatorily in Haryana in a year?

(a) 2 (b) 4
(c) 5 (d) 3

3 Which is the middle level of the Panchayati Raj System in Haryana? *HSSC 2021*

(a) Gram sabha (b) Zila parishad
(c) Panchayat samiti (d) None of these

4 Which amongst the following is the second Tier of Panchayati Raj in Haryana? *HSSC 2023, 20*

(a) Gram panchayat (b) Panchayat samiti
(c) District panchayat (d) Zila parishad

5 Block development and Panchayat officer is selected for which of the tier of Panchayat?

(a) District level (b) Block level
(c) Village level (d) Both (a) and (b)

6 Which is the highest level of governance in rural Haryana?

(a) Panchayat samiti (b) Taluka samiti
(c) Block panchayat (d) Zila parishad

7 Before the enactment of Haryana Panchayati Raj Act, the panchayats in Haryana were formed under which Act? *HSSC 2022*

(a) Panchayati Raj Act, 1994
(b) Punjab Gram Panchayat Act, 1952
(c) Panchayati Raj Act, 1971
(d)All of the above

8 Which Chief Minister of Haryana amended the Panchayati Raj Act and gave back the right to choose Sarpanch to the voters?

(a) Chaudhary Devi Lal
(b) Bhajan Lal
(c) Bansi Lal
(d) Manohar Lal Khattar

9 In which year, Chaudhary Devi Lal amended the Panchayat Act?

(a) 1970 (b) 1994
(c) 1978 (d) 1964

10 Who reduced the tenure of Panchayats from 5 to 3 years?

(a) Bansi Lal
(b) Bhajan Lal
(c) Om Prakash Chautala
(d) Banarasi Das

11 On which date Haryana Panchayati Raj Act came into force? *Haryana Clerk 2019*

(a) 1st April, 1994 (b) 22nd April, 1994
(c) 1st April, 1993 (d) 23rd April, 1994

12 Who was the Chief Minister of Haryana at the time of Haryana Panchayati Raj Act, 1994?

(a) Chaudhary Devi Lal
(b) Chaudhary Bhajan Lal
(c) Chaudhary Bansi Lal
(d) None of the above

13 After 73rd Constitutional Amendment, functions related to how many subjects have been entrusted to PRIs?

(a) 29 subjects (b) 11 subjects
(c) 23 subjects (d) None of these

14 Which of the following committees is not approved by the Panchayat Samiti according to Haryana Panchayati Raj Act, 1994? *HSSC 2020*

(a) Health and Welfare committee
(b) Finance, Audit and Planning committee
(c) Social Justice committee
(d) General committee

15 In Section 164 of Haryana Panchayati Raj Act, 1994 which of the following provision is accepted? *Haryana Clerkship 2021*

(a) Preparing the list of voters
(b) Declaring the holidays
(c) Mentioning the duties of members
(d) None of the above

16 According to Haryana Panchayati Raj Act, 1994, at a special meeting of Zila Parishad, the quorum shall be *HSSC 2024*

(a) One-third of total members
(b) One-half of the member of members actually serving for the time being
(c) Half of total members
(d) One-third of the present members

17 The Panchayati Raj Act 1994, reserves .... seats for women in all the three tiers of local government.
(a) one-tenth (b) one-third
(c) one-fourth (d) one-sixth

18 Which of the following statements regarding Haryana Panchayati Raj Act, 1994 is incorrect?
(a) It provides for a Three-Tier Panchayati Raj System
(b) It provides for reservation of seats for Scheduled Tribes
(c) It provides for reservation of seats for Scheduled Castes
(d) None of the above

19 What is the minimum educational qualification fixed by Haryana Government for people to contest elections under Panchayati Raj Amendment Act, 2015? *Haryana Group D 2018*
(a) Graduate (b) Higher Secondary
(c) Secondary (d) Primary

20 What is the minimum qualification needed to contest in Panchayat elections by women of Scheduled Castes in Haryana? *HSSC 2023, Haryana Group D 2018*
(a) Class X pass (b) Class VIII pass
(c) Class XII pass (d) None of these

21 Haryana Government has fixed .... qualification for those contesting in Panchayati Raj institutions. *Haryana Group D 2015*
(a) post graduate (b) educational
(c) primary (d) various

22 From which date, the mandate to fix minimum qualifications for Panchayats adopted in Haryana?
(a) 7th December, 2017 (b) 10th January, 2000
(c) 7th September, 2015 (d) 10th April, 2008

23 In which state, EVM were used for the first time in Panchayat elections? *Haryana Clerk Exam 2019*
(a) Rajasthan (b) Haryana
(c) Himachal Pradesh (d) Gujarat

24 For how many years, a Sarpanch can be suspended if found reluctant to undertake his duties properly in Haryana? *HSSC 2022*
(a) 6 (b) 4
(c) 2 (d) 5

25 Which form of local government in rural Haryana should also have one defense personnel as its member?
(a) Gram Vikas Samiti (b) Gram Sabha
(c) Gram Panchayat (d) Zila Parishad

26 What is the tenure for the working of the Finance Commission?
(a) 6 years (b) 3 years
(c) 4 years (d) 5 years

27 When was the first State Finance Commission formed in Haryana? *HSSC 2020*
(a) 26th April, 1994 (b) 31st May, 1994
(c) 15th October, 1994 (d) 2nd June, 1994

28 What is the e-portal of local governance of rural areas of Haryana called? *HSSC 2024*
(a) Apna Panchayat (b) Haryana Panchayat
(c) Mahari Panchayat (d) Panchayat Mission

29 Villages of Palwal and Faridabad were chosen for initiating which scheme by the Central Government?
(a) Swachh Bharat Abhiyan
(b) Gramin Vikas Ke Liye Yojana
(c) Prime Minister Model Village Scheme
(d) Women Farmer Empowerment Scheme

30 In which year the Garvit Grameen Yojana started by Haryana Government?
(a) 2015 (b) 2008
(c) 2010 (d) 2016

31 What is the prize money given to the cleanest village in Haryana?
(a) ₹ 2 lakh (b) ₹ 5 lakh
(c) ₹ 8 lakh (d) ₹ 1 lakh

32 Which of the following award given in Haryana is also called Chaudhary Devi Lal Award?
(a) Best Performing Gram Panchayat
(b) Cleanest Village Award
(c) Best Performing Zila Parishad
(d) Best Village Award

33 Which among the following panchayat of Haryana received the Panchayat Sashaktikaran Puruskar in 2015?
(a) Doharka (b) Dabodha
(c) Dubri (d) All of these

34 Which panchayat of Haryana received Rashtriya Gaurav Gram Sabha Puruskar?
(a) Nissing (b) Jagadhri
(c) Dubri (d) Naraingarh

35 Under which Amendment Act, local bodies are given constitutional status?
(a) 78th (b) 75th
(c) 74th (d) 92nd

36 How many tiers of local governance is fixed by the Haryana Municipal Act?
(a) Three (b) Four
(c) Two (d) None of these

37 What is the percentage of women reservation in Municipal Council of Haryana?
(a) 30 (b) 50 (c) 10 (d) 65

38 How many Municipal Corporations are there in Haryana? *HSSC 2021, 16*
(a) 21 (b) 5 (c) 16 (d) 10

39 Which among the following cities in Haryana has a Municipal Corporation?
(a) Kurukshetra (b) Sirsa
(c) Bhiwani (d) Ambala

40 Which is the smallest Municipal Corporation of Haryana? *HSSC 2021*
(a) Sonipat (b) Faridabad
(c) Karnal (d) Rohtak

41 When was the Haryana Municipal Amendment Bill passed by Legislative Assembly? *Haryana Lab Attendant 2018*
(a) 7th August, 2014
(b) 28th February, 2017
(c) 19th December, 2015
(d) 31st March, 2016

42 What is the minimum qualification of malecandidates contesting in urban local bodies of Haryana? *Haryana Clerk Exam 2016*
(a) MBBS (b) LLB
(c) 12th (d) 10th

43 Haryana Municipal Corporation Amendment Bill was enacted in which year by Haryana Legislature? *Haryana Tabla Player 2018*
(a) 2015 (b) 2014
(c) 2012 (d) 2017

44 Consider the following statements.
I. Haryana Panchayati Raj Act was passed in the year 1994.
II. It adopted Two-Tier Panchayati Raj System.

Which of the statements given above is/are incorrect?
(a) Only I
(b) Only II
(c) Both I and II
(d) None of the above

45 Consider the following statements
I. There is no reservation for women in Panchayats of Haryana.
II. There is no reservation for SCs and STs in Panchayats of Haryana.

Which of the statements given above is/are correct?
(a) I Only
(b) II Only
(c) Both I and II
(d) None of the above

46 Match List-I with List-II. *HPSC HCS (Prelims) 2023*

List I (Article)	List II (Provision)
A. 243 (K)	1. State Finance Commission
B. 243 (I)	2. State Election Commission
C. 243 Z (D)	3. Committee for District Planning
D. 243 Z (E)	4. Committee for Metropolitan Planning

Choose the correct answer from the options given below.

	A	B	C	D
(a)	1	2	3	4
(b)	4	3	2	1
(c)	3	2	1	4
(d)	2	1	3	4

CORRECT ANSWERS

1. (c)	2. (a)	3. (c)	4. (b)	5. (b)	6. (d)	7. (b)	8. (a)	9. (c)	10. (b)
11. (b)	12. (b)	13. (a)	14. (a)	15. (a)	16. (b)	17. (b)	18. (b)	19. (c)	20. (b)
21. (b)	22. (c)	23. (b)	24. (a)	25. (a)	26. (b)	27. (c)	28. (c)	29. (c)	30. (a)
31. (b)	32. (a)	33. (d)	34. (a)	35. (c)	36. (a)	37. (b)	38. (d)	39. (d)	40. (a)
41. (d)	42. (d)	43. (d)	44. (a)	45. (d)	46. (d)				

CHAPTER 27

District Profile of Haryana

- Haryana was established as a separate state on 1st November, 1966, initially comprising seven districts, i.e. Ambala, Jind, Karnal, Hisar, Rohtak, Gurugram (Gurgaon) and Mahendragarh.
- Over time, the state has expanded its administrative structure through the re-organisation of existing districts, adding fifteen new districts.
- The creation of these additional districts occurred as follows

Year	Districts	Date
1972	Bhiwani, Sonipat	22nd December
1973	Kurukshetra	23rd January
1975	Sirsa	26th August
1979	Faridabad	15th August
1989	Kaithal, Panipat, Rewari, Yamunanagar	1st November
1995	Panchkula	15th August
1997	Fatehabad, Jhajjar	15th July
2005	Nuh (Mewat)	4th April
2008	Palwal	15th August
2016	Charkhi-Dadri	1st December

- Currently, Haryana is organised into 6 administrative divisions and **23 districts**, with each district further divided into tehsils, sub-divisions and blocks.

Administrative Divisions of Haryana

Division	Districts
Ambala Division	Ambala, Kurukshetra, Yamunanagar and Panchkula
Faridabad Division	Faridabad, Mewat (Nuh) and Palwal
Gurugram Division	Gurugram, Mahendragarh and Rewari
Hisar Division	Hisar, Jind, Sirsa, Fatehabad and Hansi
Rohtak Division	Rohtak, Sonipat, Bhiwani, Jhajjar and Charkhi-Dadri
Karnal Division	Karnal, Panipat and Kaithal

1. Ambala Division

Ambala (Mixi City)

- Ambala is located in the Northern part of Haryana state.
- The district is surrounded by **Yamunanagar** to the East, **Panchkula** to the North, districts **Mohali** and **Patiala** (Punjab) to the West and district **Kurukshetra** to the South.

Brief Information

Establishment	1st November, 1966
Area	Around 1,569 sq km
Headquarters	Ambala City
Population	11,28,350 (Male-5,98,703, Female-5,29,647)
Decadal Growth Rate	19.83% (2001-11)
Sex-Ratio	885
Literacy Rate	81.75%
Population Density	717 person/sq km
Soil	Yellow
Crops	Wheat, paddy, maize, sugarcane

Rivers	Ghaggar, Markanda, Tangri
Main Mineral	Limestone
Industries	Cement, Sugar, Sewing Machine, and Electrical Equipment, Handloom, Agricultural Machine and Grinder Mixer
Fairs	Bawan Dwadashi, Teej Mela, Guga Navami Fair

Important Facts

Origin and Early History

- The origin of the name of Ambala is believed to be in the name of **Ambalika**, a character in Mahabharata.
- According to some beliefs, it is called Ambala due to the large number of **mango orchards** in Ambala, but according to District Gazetteer, Ambala was founded by Amba Rajput in the 14th century.
- Another belief is that it was named Ambala after **Amba Devi** (Bhavani Devi), whose temple is also presently located in Ambala.

> Ambala is a major and historical district of Haryana. According to historical evidence, Aryans resided in Ambala and made Ambala their capital.

British Era and Development

- British ruled over Ambala in 1823 and made it the headquarters of the political agent for the states near the Satluj river.
- In 1842, Ambala was subjugated to Shimla.
- The cantonment was established in 1843 AD from Karnal to Ambala and it received the status of district in 1847 AD.
- At the time of its formation, its tehsils were Ambala, Ropar Kharar, Jagadhri, Naraingarh and Nalagarh.
- In 1859, Ambala became the headquarter of the district which was under the administration of Punjab.
- The **Revolt of 1857** was first started in Ambala in Haryana.
- Viceroy Lord Canning introduced the **postal facility** in Ambala in **1860 AD.**
- Ambala was connected to the **railway line in 1880 AD.**
- The Simon Commission, set up on 8th November, 1927, was opposed in Ambala.

Post-Independence and Modern Ambala

- Nathuram Godse was hanged in Ambala jail on 15th November, 1949.
- The Regional Archives at Ambala was established on 1st April, 1986. Ambala is a **major military city** of India.
- Ambala is also known as **Scientific City** because about 35% of scientific instruments are manufactured here.
- Mixi industry, metal casting, submarine motor pump, gas-stove, engineering related equipments etc. are the major industries in Ambala.
- The **glass industry** of Ambala is famous since World War II.
- The headquarter of the Northern Railway Zone is located in Ambala. The Frozen Tier Martyr Memorial is also located at Ambala Airfield.
- Ambala is also famous for its **carpet industry** called Dari in the common language.
- Railway garages, wagon workshops and food processing centres are located in Ambala.

Tourist Places

- Mahaveer Udyan
- Indira Udyan
- Badshahi Bagh Gurdwara
- Sis Ganj Gurdwara
- Manji Sahib Gurdwara
- Sangeet Sahib Gurdwara
- Ambika Devi Temple
- Sharda Temple
- Radha-Kishan Temple
- Bhawani Amba Temple
- Lakhi Shah Dargah
- Taqwal Shah's Dargah
- St. Paul's Church
- Kingfisher
- Naugaja Peer
- Morni Hills
- Gurdwara Lakhnore Sahib Shaheed Memorial

Kurukshetra (Dharma Nagari)

- It is located in the **Northern part** of the state.
- Kurukshetra district is surrounded by Ambala in the North, Patiala district of Punjab in the North-West, Yamunanagar in the North-East, Kaithal in the West and South-West and Karnal district in the South.

Brief Information

Establishment	23rd January, 1973
Area	1,530 sq km
Headquarters	Kurukshetra
Population	9,64,655 (Males-5,10,976 Females-4,53,679)
Decadal Growth Rate	16.8% (2001-11)
Sex Ratio	888
Literacy Rate	76.3%
Population Density	630 person/sq km
Soil	Yellow
Crops	Wheat, paddy, sugarcane
Rivers	Markanda, Ghaggar, Apaga

Important Facts

Ancient and Historical Significance

- Kurukshetra is situated between the Saraswati and the Drishadvati rivers.
- The region was named Kurukshetra after the name of **King Kuru**.
- **Maharishi Ved Vyas** composed the Mahabharata while sitting on the banks of the river Saraswati.
- There was a battle between 10 kings in Kurukshetra even before Mahabharata period.
- Description about Kurukshetra is also found in **Rigveda** and **Yajurveda** of Vedic period. The Saraswati river of this region is considered sacred.
- Kurukshetra is also known as the **cradle of the Vedic Civilisation**. It is the main centre of Aryan culture.
- Kurukshetra is famous for the **Mahabharata War** and the preaching of **Srimad Bhagavad Gita** by Shri Krishna.
- It was the **capital** of Hastinapur in ancient times.
- Since ancient times, Kurukshetra is considered as the starting point of great Hindu pilgrimage.

Religious Importance

- It is the main religious place of the state. It is also called **Dharmanagri**. Here on the occasion of solar eclipse, devotees from all over the country come to bathe and worship. There are about 360 religious places here.
- **Bhadrakali Shaktipeeth** is one of the famous 51 Shaktipeeths of India which is located in Kurukshetra.
- **Sankaracharya** of Kamakoti Peeth built the temple of Krishna-Arjuna Rath and Sankaracharya temple near Jyotisar Sarovar. It was at **Jyotisar** that Sri Krishna preached the Gita to Arjuna.

> Kurukshetra Mahotsav is organised in the district every year in the month of December.

Thanesar's Legacy

- Thanesar is an ancient city located in Kurukshetra. It was the capital of **Srikanth Janapada district** in ancient India. The emergence of Vardhana clan took place in Thanesar.
- In Buddhist and Jain literature, Thanesar is mentioned in the name of **Thun** or **Thuna** village.

Economic and Agricultural Facts

- This region is famous for rice cultivation; mainly basmati rice is produced here. **Asia's second largest grain market** is located at **Ladwa** in Kurukshetra.
- Kurukshetra is called the **rice bowl** of India along with Karnal and Kaithal.
- Co-operative Sugar Mill is located at Shahabad in Kurukshetra.

Parks and Education

- Purushottam park, Harshvardhan park and Tapovan park are located here. Hence, Kurukshetra is also known as **City of Park**.
- In the year 1911, Swami Shraddhanand laid the foundation of Gurukul in Kurukshetra.
- **Kurukshetra University** was established in the year 1956.
- P. Sthanu Dutt Sharma played an important role in the establishment of a Manuscript museum located in Kurukshetra University.
- **Kalpana Chawla Planetarium** is built in the memory of Kalpana Chawla, the first Indian woman astronaut in Kurukshetra.

Tourist Places

- Narayan Temple
- Sarveshwar Temple
- Bhadrakali Shaktipeeth
- Neel Kranti Dam
- Brahmasarovar
- Valmiki Ashram
- Kamali Wale Baba ka Dera
- Dukh Bhanjan Mahadev temple
- Sthaneshwar Mahadev Temple
- Lakshmi Narayan Temple
- Birla Mandir
- Sri Krishna Museum
- Parakeet
- Jyotisar
- Kamal Nath Teerth
- Narkatari Teerth

Yamunanagar

- It is located in the **North-East** of the state.
- The Yamunanagar district, situated at the foothills of the Shivalik hills, is a rich natural area.
- The Northern region of the district is a piedmont plain.

- It is bounded by **Himachal Pradesh** in the North, **Uttar Pradesh** in the East, **Ambala** in the West and **Kurukshetra** district in the South.

Brief Information

Establishment	1st November, 1989
Area	1,768 sq km
Headquarters	Yamunanagar
Population	12,14,205 (Male-6,46,718, Female-5,67,487)
Decadal Growth Rate	16.6% (2001-11)
Sex Ratio	877
Literacy Rate	78.9%
Population Density	687 person/sq km
Soils	Red, loam
Crops	Wheat, sugarcane, gram, maize, paddy, sunflower
Rivers	Yamuna, Somb, Boli, Saraswati, Chautang and Rakshi river
Industries	Sugar, Paper and Ammunition Industry

Important Facts

Ancient Names and Early History

- In the Mahabharata period, Jagadhri of Yamunanagar was also called **Yogendra** or **Yogendri.** Yogendra was called a warrior, a kingdom, a place or a mountain.
- The ancient name of Yamunanagar was **Abdullapur.**

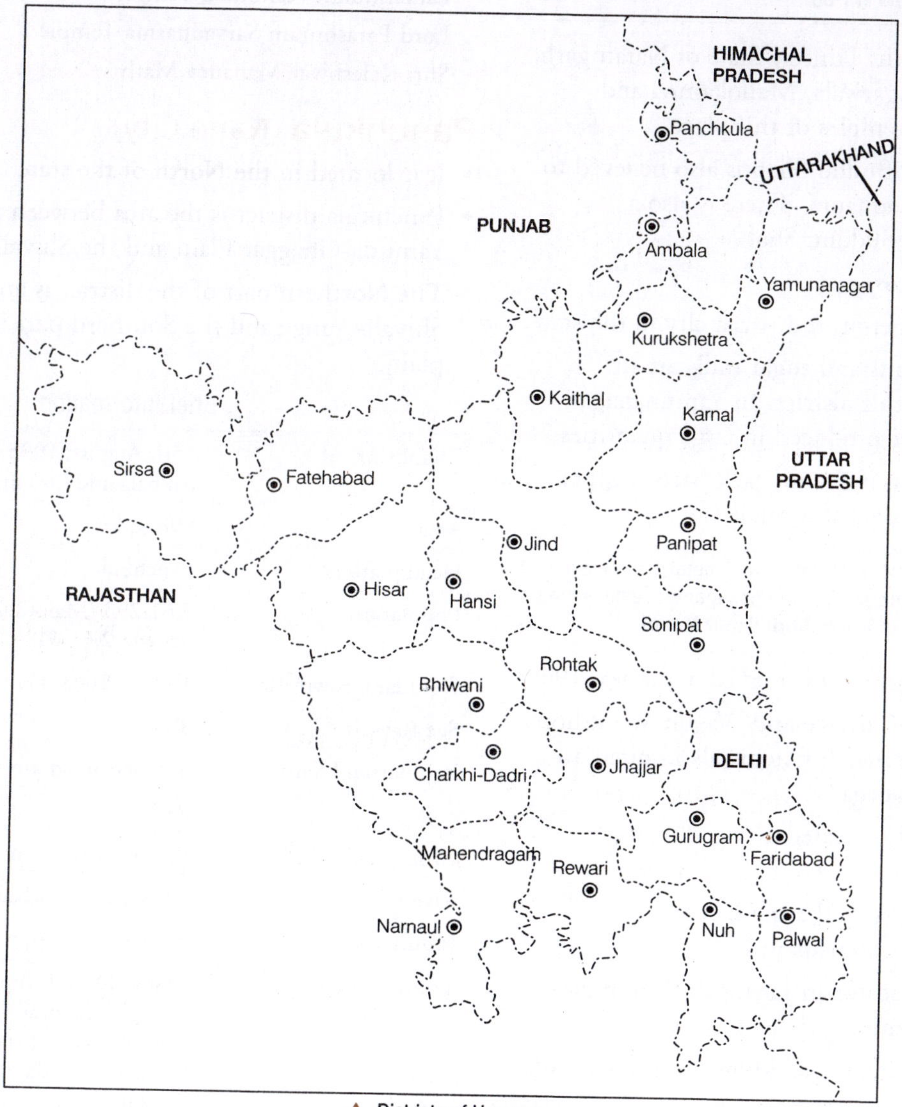

▲ Districts of Haryana

- Some old coins of the Samudragupta and Chauhans and Tomars of Delhi have been found from Jagadhri in Yamunanagar.
- Adibadri in Yamunanagar has a confluence of Saraswati and Somb rivers which is called **Saraswati-Somb Prayag.**
- It is also known as **Jagadhri Yamunanagar** due to having Jagadhri Railway Station in the district.
- **Buriya** town is located on the banks of river Yamuna in Jagadhri. In the 18th century it was the headquarters of the Princely State of Kaswa Buriya.
  The Princely State of Buriya was founded by Sardar Nanhu Singh of Bhangi Misal.
- A 500-year-old Digambar Jain temple is also located in this town.

> The Mustafabad principality of Yamunanagar was founded by **Jat Desu Singh Dallewala** in 1763.

- **Sadhaura** was a part of the Princely State of Naraingarh in the 19th century. Gagarwala, Manokamna and Torawala are the main temples of this place.
- The association of Peer Budhu Shah is also believed to be from the village of Sadhaura. There is also a Gurdwara named after Buddhu Shah.

Industrial and Economic Aspects

- Yamunanagar is a prosperous industrial city in the state.
- Clusters of plywood units and sugar mills are in abundance amount in this district. In Yamunanagar, fruits and vegetables are produced in large quantities.
- In Yamunanagar, liquor, hydraulic jack parts, copper and aluminium utensils are also made.

> Yamunanagar city is famous for timber and metal market since ancient times. **Timber market** in Yamunanagar was established in the year 1947. It was known as **Abdullapur Mandi**.

- Distillery at Yamunanagar was established in the year 1969.
- The Mumbai Railway Carriage and Wagon Workshop and factories of Bharat Starch Chemicals Limited are also located in Yamunanagar.
- The railway office is also located at Jagadhri in Yamunanagar district.
- **Jagadhri** of Yamunanagar is the main centre of manufacturing of **brass utensils** in India.
- Saraswati Sugar Mill located in Jagadhri, Yamunanagar is **Asia's largest sugar mill.**
- Yamunanagar in Haryana is also known as the **City of Paper.**

Research and Development

- The Saraswati River Research Institute is located at Adibadri in Yamunanagar.
- Saraswati Heritage Development Board has been established for research and restoration of Saraswati river in the state.
- It is being developed as an international pilgrimage site due to the excavation of Saraswati river at Mughalavali in Yamunanagar.

Tourist Places

- Gurdwara Lakhan Majra
- Birbal's Rangmahal
- Tajewala Complex
- Chitta Temple
- Kalesar Wildlife Sanctuary
- Panchmukhi Hanuman Temple
- Lord Parashuram Sarvadharma Temple
- Shri Kaleshwar Mahadev Math
- Gurdwara Kapal Mochan
- Hathni Kund Barrage
- Kalesar
- Adi Badrinath Temple
- Chaneti Stupa

Panchkula (Nano City)

- It is located in the **North** of the state.
- Panchkula district is the area between the Yamuna-Ghaggar Plain and the Shivalik Range.
- The Northern part of the district is an extension of the Shivalik range and the Southern part is a piedmont plain.

Brief Information

Establishment	15th August, 1995, separated from Ambala and become the 17th district
Area	898 sq km
Headquarters	Panchkula
Population	5,61,293 (Male-2,99,679, Female-2,61,614)
Decadal Growth Rate	19.8% (2001-11)
Sex Ratio	873
Population Density	625 person/sq km
Soil	Red
Crops	Rice, wheat, gram
Rivers	Ghaggar, Sirsa, Kaushalya
Industries	Electronic Equipments, HMT
Tourist Places	Mansa Devi Temple, Bhima Devi Temple, Chandi Temple, Kalka Devi Temple, Mata Samlotha Temple, Gurdwara Nada Sahib, Budhiya Palace, Tikkar Tal Lake

Important Facts

Formation and Basic Facts

- Panchkula district was formed by combining the Kalka and Panchkula tehsils of Ambala district.
- It is the **second smallest** district in the state by area.

> The origin of the name Panchkula is believed to be from the local word **Panch** (five) and **Kul** (canals), hence, Panchkula is also called the **City of Five Irrigation Canals.**

- These canals of the state receive water from **Ghaggar** river. They extend from Nada Sahib to Mansa Devi.

Geographic and Climatic Aspects

- Mohali, Chandigarh and Panchkula are also called **Tricity.**
- Ghaggar is the main river of Panchkula district, it was earlier known as Saraswati.
- Panchkula district is a hilly region. Many places in this district are connected with the Pandavas.
- The climate of Panchkula district is **tropical** continental. The climate of the district is favourable for vegetative growth.
- Morni hills are situated in Panchkula which have **Karoh Peak** (1514 m), the highest point of the state.
- Tropical and dry deciduous forests are found in Panchkula district.

Economic and Industrial Features

- Bhupendra Cement Manufacturing Factory and Bharat Electricals, etc. are located in Panchkula.
- Spare parts of tractor are manufactured by **Hindustan Machine Tools Limited** in Panchkula.
- Panchkula is highly affected by the earthquake due to being located in the **Himalayan boundary fault zone.**
- An IT park was also established in Panchkula in the year 2008.
- Panchkula is highly famous for electronic goods.

Cultural and Tourists Aspects

- **Yadavindra Gardens** located in Pinjore of Panchkula. It is called the Nandan forest of Northern India. A mango fair is held every year in this garden.
- Panchkula is home to **Asia's largest cactus garden** Panchkula is a **satellite city** of the Union Territory of Chandigarh.
- The **Chandi Mandir Cantonment** is also located here, which is the headquarters of the Western Command of the Indian Army. The headquarters of Haryana Public Service Commission is located in Panchkula.

2. Faridabad Division

Faridabad

- It is located in the **Southern part** of the state.
- It is bordered by Gurugram in the West, Palwal in the South, Uttar Pradesh in the East and the national capital Delhi in the North.

Brief Information

Establishment	15th August, 1979
Area	741 sq km (lowest area)
Headquarter	Faridabad
Population	18,09,733 (Male 9,66,110, Female 8,43,623)
Sex-Ratio	873
Population Density	2442 person/sq km
Soil	Yellow
Canal/River	Gurugram Canal and Yamuna River
Crops	Wheat, millet, mustard
Major Mineral	Gravel

Industries	Paper, Cotton Textile, Agricultural Machinery, Leather, Plastic, Tire-Tube Motorcycles, Tractors and Electronic Industries
Fairs	Samadhi Fair of Baba Udasnath ji
Tourist Places	Barkhal Lake, Raja Nahar Singh Palace, Shine Temple, Surya Mandir, Megapai Aravalli Golf Ground, Place of Sati (Hodal)

Important Facts

Historical Context and Formation

- This district was formed as the 12th district of Haryana.
- After independence, Faridabad was built to rehabilitate the migrants from Pakistan.
- According to religious beliefs, the city of Faridabad was founded in 1607 by **Sheikh Farid.**
- Faridabad is known for its significant **Henna** production.

Industrial and Economic Significance

- Faridabad is a leading industrial city of Haryana.
- Cera Sanitary Ware Limited, Escort Limited, Eicher Limited, JCB India Limited, Kelvinator Refrigerator, Bata India Limited, etc. industries are located in Faridabad.
- The village of Faridabad, **Tigaon** is called the **village of the immortal martyrs.**

Environmental and Military Aspects

- The Environmental Court has also been established in Faridabad.
- **Raja Nahar Singh Base** of Indian Air Force is located in Faridabad.

Sports and Infrastructure

- **Nahar Singh Stadium** was established in 1981 in Faridabad. It is an international level cricket stadium.
- The first international level match was held here on 19th January, 1988 (India/West Indies).
- Regional Centre for Biotechnology is also located in Faridabad.

Demographic Profile

- Faridabad is the densely populated district with highest population and highest urban population and also has the highest number of females in the state.
- Faridabad has the highest population growth rate and it also has the highest slum population.
- Faridabad is also the first city of the state with 20 lakh population.

Mewat (Nuh)

- It is located in the **South** of the state.
- It is surrounded by Gurugram in the North, Palwal in the East, Rewari in the West, Rajasthan (Alwar) in the South, Rajasthan (Bharatpur) in the South-West and Uttar Pradesh (Mathura) in the South-East.

Brief Information

Establishment	4th April, 2005
Area	1,507 sq km
Headquarter	Nuh
Population	10,89,263 (Male-5,71,162, Female-5,18,101)
Decadal Growth Rate	37.93% (2001-11)
Sex-Ratio	907
Literacy Rate	54.08%
Population Density	723 person/sq km
Soil	Yellow
Crops	Wheat, mustard, bajra
Main Mineral	Slate Stone
Fair	Shivji Fair
Tourist Places	Chuhimal Ka Talab, Kotla Lake, Kotla Hill, Jhulti Minar (Shaking Minaret), Classic Golf Resort, Gandhi Park, Tawadu Fort, Sheikh Musa Mosque

Important Facts

- The district was carved out on 4th April, 2005, by separating some parts of Gurugram and Faridabad districts.
- It is the 20th district of Haryana. At the time of formation, this district was named **Satyamevapuram.**
- The **first mobile court** of the country was established in Mewat (Nuh) district.
- Most of part is a plain area in the district. It is the highest sex-ratio district within the state.
- **The first Country Club of the Country** is also located in Mewat district. It is on Delhi-Jaipur Highway near Manesar. The club is spread over an area of 30 acres.
- A 300-acre **Classic Golf Resort** in the Aravalli mountain range is located in Mewat.

Chuhimal Pond

- This pond was constructed by Seth Chuhimal in an area of 10 acres below the black mountain.
- This pond was made strong by Hukamchand, son of Chuhimal.
- The artistic Chatri near this pond attracts tourists a lot.

Palwal (City of Cotton)

- It is located in the **Southern part** of the state.
- The district borders **Mewat (Nuh)** in the South, **Gurugram** in the North-West, **Faridabad** in the North and **Uttar Pradesh** in the East.

Brief Information

Establishment	15th August, 2008
Area	1,359 sq km
Headquarter	Palwal
Population	10,42,708 (Male-5,54,497, Female-4,88,211)
Sex-Ratio	880
Literacy Rate	69.3%
Population Density	767 person/sq km
Soil	Yellow

Crops	Wheat, sugarcane, millet
River	Yamuna
Fair	Baldav Chhath Fair
Tourist Places	Panchavati Temple, Balram (Dauji) Temple, Sati ka Sthan, Radha - Krishna Temple, Pandava Forest, Dabchick

Important Facts

Historical and Cultural Context

- According to beliefs, this region was named Palwal after the name of the **Hindu Pandit Palwal** related to the Pandavas kingdom of Mahabharata period.
- There is also a belief that Palwal is named after the **demon Palavasur.**
- According to some scholars, Pandavas stayed in Palwal during the period of Agyatvas.
- Palwal's Hodal belongs to the Odo caste of Mahabharata period. The name of this region is **Aplava** in **Ain-e-Akbari.**
- Netaji Subhash Chandra Bose laid the foundation of Mahatma Gandhi Ashram here in the year 1938. Gandhiji was first arrested on 8th April, 1919 at Palwal station.

Archaeological and Economic Features

- Remanants of elephants and artistic objects have been found in excavations at a place called Autha near Hathin region in Palwal district.
- Skill Development University in the state is proposed in Dudhola village of Palwal district.
- Palwal is famous for sugar and cycle industry.

3. Gurugram Division

Gurugram

Brief Information

Establishment	1st November, 1966
Area	1,258 sq km
Headquarter	Gurugram
Population	15,14,432 (Male-8,16,690, Female-6,97,742)
Decadal Growth Rate	73.9% (2001-11)
Sex Ratio	854
Literacy Rate	84.7%
Population Density	1,204 person / sq km
Soil	Yellow
Crops	Millets, jowar, wheat, barley, gram
River/Canal	Gurugram Canal
Main Minerals	Potassium nitrate (Shora), ceramic, kharia clay, mica, quartz
Industries	Maruti Car, Utensils, Electronics, Drugs and Pharmaceuticals
Fairs	Gugga Navami, Shah Chokha Khori Fair, Sheetla Mata Fair, Budho Mata Fair, Ramnavami Fair, Mahadev Fair
Tourist Places	Mata Sheetla Devi Temple, Shama, Sultanpur National Bird Sanctuary, Damdama Lake, Sohana Fort, Pataudi Palace, Sarai Allawardi Village's Masjid

- It is located in the **South** of the state.
- In its North lies the **National Capital Delhi, Faridabad** lies in the East, **Rewari** in the West, **Jhajjar** in the North-West and **Alwar (Rajasthan)** in the South.

Important Facts

Historical Context

- The name of Gurugram is related to the name of Guru Dronacharya. It is believed that Guru Dronacharya imparted spiritual education of Kaurava and Pandavas at this place.
- According to District Gazetteer, its name is **Guru Gaon** or **village of spiritual teacher.**

Economic and Industrial Aspects

- Haryana receives the highest revenue from Gurugram.
- **Maruti Udyog** was established in Gurugram in the year 1983. In 14th December, 1983, the company launched its first car.
- **Hero Honda Company's** main unit was established in the year 1984 in Gurugram. In January 2011, Hero Honda Company split into Hero Motor Corp. and Honda Motors (Japan). The Gurugram plant was renamed as **Hero Motocorp.**
- Special Economic Zone (SEZ) is being established in Manesar, Gurugram.
- Gurugram is also known as **Mall Capital of India** and **Financial capital of Haryana.**

- Biotech Technology Park, Hi-tech Technology Park and Ratna Jewellery Park are also located in Gurugram.
- Gurugram is also called the **World's Call Centre Capital**.
- Asia's **largest Private City Scheme** has been launched by DLF in Gurugram.
- **Software Technology Park** has been jointly set-up by Hartron and Haryana Urban Development Authority in the district.
- **Industrial Model Township** is being developed at Manesar in Gurugram district.
- The Aravalli hills are located in Gurugram.

Modern Development and Infrastructure

- Gurugram was declared a Municipal Corporation on 24th December, 2007.
- Gurugram is one of the four major satellite cities of Delhi and is a part of the National Capital Region.
- Gurugram has the **largest toll gate in Asia** and the third largest in the world on National Highway 32.
- The first metro train in Haryana started in Gurugram in the year 2010.
- The first Green Road and Harimandir Sanskrit School of Haryana are located in Gurugram.

> Haryana Government announced plans to develop Gurugram as a smart city with its own resources on 22nd September, 2015.

- Gurugram is also known as **Cyber City** and **Solar City**.
- The first police station of the State Cybercrime Branch has been opened in Gurugram itself.
- Metrino pod, the country's first-pod taxi service, has been started in Gurugram.

Education, Cultural and Research Hub

- First Defence University of the country is being set-up in Binola village of Gurugram.
- Asia's first Photographic Art Centre has opened in Gurugram.
- Haryana Public Administration Institute is also located in Gurugram.
- **The first food bank of the state** was established on 10th November, 2013 in Gurugram.
- **Rahi day** is celebrated every Sunday in Gurugram. It is the first city in India to do so.
- **The Kingdom of Dreams**, India's first live entertainment theatre and holiday destination, is located in Gurugram.
- The country's first Model Carrier Centre, **Solar Energy Institute** and **White Palace** are located in Gurugram.

▲ The Kingdom of Dreams Performing Art

- A **National Brain Research Institute,** dedicated to neuroscience, is located in Manesar, Gurugram.
- The headquarters of the Indian Corporate Affairs Institute is located in Manesar, Gurugram.
- The tallest steel idol of the state is in Gurugram.

Pataudi Palace

- Architect Robert Tor Russel and Heinz built a palace for Nawab Ibrahim Ali Khan in the town of Pataudi, Gurugram in the year 1935. It is known as Pataudi Palace.
- The palace is currently run by the Neemrana group as a heritage hotel.

Mahendragarh

Brief Information

Establishment	1st November, 1966
Area	1,899 sq km
Headquarter	Narnaul
Population	9,22,088 (Male-4,86,665, Female-4,35,423)
Decadal Growth Rate	13.4% (2001-11)
Sex-Ratio	895
Literacy Rate	78.9%
Population Density	486 person/sq km
Soil	Red
Crops	Wheat, mustard, gram, millet, sunflower
Main Minerals	Iron, limestone, slate stone, marble, asbestos, barite, mica, quartz
River	Dohan
Fairs	Gugga Navami Utsav, Baba Bhilai Nath Smriti Mela, Baba Kesaria Smriti Mela, Bhura Bhawani Mela

- This district is the **Southernmost** district in the state.
- It is bordered by **Bhiwani** in the North-West, **Dadri** in the North, **Jhajjar** in the North-East and **Rewari** district in the East.

Important Facts

Historical and Cultural Aspects

- According to some beliefs, Mahendragarh and its surrounding areas were developed by King **Anangpal** who was the grandfather of Prithviraj Chauhan.
- The region was ruled by **King Anangpal** through his cousin, **King Naun Karan**, whose jurisdiction was Dhosi hills.
- In the medieval period, Mahendragarh was also known as **Nandigram, Naharnoul** and **Sinhon Ka Dahar,** due to which it was named as Narnaul.
- The region was named as Mahendragarh after Mohinder Singh, the son of the ruler of Patiala.
- It is also believed that Mahendragarh was inhabited by **Malik Mahmud Khan** (Babur's servant).
- Narnaul town of Mahendragarh was a part of Jaipur state during the 15th century and it was a part of Hisar district during British rule.
- Narnaul in Mahendragarh had factory at the time of Akbar. Jalali coins were minted here.
- A fort was built here in the 17th century by the Maratha ruler **Tatya Tope.**

▲ Jal Mahal: A Place in Middle of Man Sagar Lake

- Mahendragarh was earlier known as **Kanoud** due to being inhabited by Kanauadia Brahmins.
- Narnaul of Mahendragarh is considered to be the **Tapasthali of Maharishi Chayavan.**
- **Satnami Sect** was founded by **Virbhan** in 1543 AD in Narnaul.
- The Shaheedi Memorial of 1857 revolutionaries is located in Nasibpur of Mahendragarh.

Geographical and Natural Resources

- The highest part of the Aravalli plain in Haryana is in Kultajpur village, South-West of Narnaul town, which is 652 m high and is called the Dhosi hills.
- Narnaul is also called the **City of Ponds and Baoli.**
- This district **ranks first** in mustard production in Haryana.

> Mahendragarh holds an important position from the point of view of mineral resources. It is also called the **City of Minerals**.

- Due to abundance of **slate stone**, slate is supplied to the country and abroad.
- This district is particularly famous for **lac bangles.**

Administrative and Infrastructure

- It is the only district in the state whose district headquarters is located in Narnaul city and not in Mahendragarh city.
- No highway passes through this district of the state.
- Mahendragarh has the only **Central University** of Haryana, which was established in the year 2009 in Jant pali village.
- There is a **semen bank** in Narnaul where a liquid nitrogen plant is installed.
- North India's largest logistics park is located in Narnaul.
- It has the minimum population growth rate and the urban population of Haryana.

Ateli

- It is located 20 km from Narnaul in the North-East direction. The Ateli region of Narnaul is famous for slate stone hills and grain mandis.
- Due to the abundance of slate stone in this area, the slate industry is developing rapidly here.

Tourist Places

- Shiv Mandir
- Jalmahal
- Birbal ka Chhatta
- Ibrahim Khan's Tomb
- Madhogad Fort
- Narnaul's Bawadia
- Chamunda Devi Temple
- Chor Gumbad
- Shah Vilayat's Tomb
- Dhosi Hill
- Hamza Peer

Kanina Village

- It is located about 15 km North-East of Mahendragarh.
- Kanina village in Narnaul is a historical site which was inhibited by Ahira Kanharam in the 13th century.
- Rao Harsevak, (decendant of Rao Harjimal) of Kanina village, defeated the Khanzadas of Mewat in battle. Harsevak's brother Gumairam had assisted Wazir Rao Mitrasen of Rewari in the Battle of Mandan between 1770-1785.
- This region was incorporated into the Princely State called **Kanina Nabha** after 1857. In the year 1938-39, the Raja of Bikaner did the work of connecting this area with the railroad.
- The subedar of this region, Chhajjuram, Budhram, Jamadar Bhairon Singh, Major Bhavani Singh and Prabhati Singh, brought glory to the name of this region in the First and Second World Wars.
- From this area, Ganeshilal, Gangaram, Netram, Rao Kirodimal, Bhup Singh and Ranjit Singh were freedom fighters of the Azad Hind Fauj. The Pargana Multipurpose Society in this region was established in the year 1939.

Rewari (Brass City)

Brief Information

Establishment	1st November, 1989
Area	1,594 sq km
Headquarter	Rewari
Population	9,00,332 (Male-4,74,335, Female-4,25,997)
Decadal Growth Rate	17.64% (2001-11)
Sex-Ratio	898
Literacy Rate	80.99%
Population Density	565 person/sq km
Soil	Yellow
Crops	Wheat, gram, sugarcane
River	Sahibi
Fairs	Baba Surajgiri Fair, Gugga Navami Fair, Basant Panchami Fair, Syed Baba Samadhi Fair
Tourist Places	Bagh Wala Talab, Rao Tej Singh Talab, Ghanteshwar Temple, Hanuman Temple, Lal Masjid, Sandpiper, Jungle Babbler, Rampura Fort

- It is located in the **Southern part** of the state.
- It is surrounded by Mahendragarh in the West, Dadri in the North-West, Jhajjar in the North, Gurugram and Nuh in the East and Rajasthan (Alwar) in the South.

Important Facts

Historical Context

- According to religious beliefs, the city of Rewari was founded by **King Rawat** of Mahabharata period named after his daughter Revathi.
- According to modern historians, the city of Rewari was founded by King **Karampal**, nephew of Prithviraj Chauhan.

Industrial and Economic Aspects

- Rewari is famous for the **brass metal ware industry**, tiledar jhuti industry and Hero Motocorp motorcycle industry.
- Hero Honda Motors Limited was established in the year 1986-87 in Malpura village of Dharuhera, Rewari. In 2011, it was renamed as Hero Motocrop.
- Rewari is also known as **Brass City** and **Veer Nagari**.
- Slate-stone mine is situated in Kund village of Rewari.

Transport and Heritage

- Rewari Railway Station is the largest and oldest railway station in Haryana. It was founded in 1873.
- The Regional Research Centre of the State Agricultural University is located at Bawal in Rewari.
- Along with this, Industrial Development Centre is also being established at Bawal.
- The Bangwala pond near Rewari was built by Nandram Ahir.

Rezang La Memorial in Rewari has been constructed for the valour of the Ahir Regiment soldiers of Rewari in the India-China war of 1962.

- The first cancer institute of the state is being established in Mirpur area of Rewari.
- **Lal Masjid** in Rewari was built during the reign of **Akbar**.
- **Swami Dayanand** built a cow-shed in the district.

4. Hisar Division

Hisar (Steel City)

- It is located in the **West** of the state. It is the second largest district in the state in terms of area.
- This district is surrounded by Rajasthan to the West, Bhiwani to the South, Rohtak in the South-East, Jind in the East and Fatehabad district in the North.

Brief Information

Establishment	1st November, 1966
Area	3,983 sq km
Headquarter	Hisar city
Population	17,43,931 (Male-9,31,562, Female-8,12,369)
Decadal Growth Rate	13.4% (2001-11)
Sex-Ratio	872
Literacy Rate	72.89%
Population Density	438 person/sq km
Soil	Loam
Canal	Western Yamuna Canal
Crops	Wheat, paddy, cotton, gram, mustard, oilseeds and pulses
Main Mineral	Potassium nitrate (Shora), limestone
Industries	Sugar, wool textiles and iron and steel industries
Fairs	Janmashtami Fair, Dussehra Fair, Gugga Peer Smriti Mela, Kali Devi Temple Fair, Agrasen Jayanti Fair
Tourist Places	Vishnoi Temple, Jain Temple, Gujari Mahal, Sheikh Junaid's Mazar, Jahaz Kothi, St. Thomas Church, Baba Laldas Dham, Amti Talab

Important Facts

Historical and Ancient Context

- At the time of creation of the Haryana on 1st November, 1966, Hisar was so large that the complete Hisar division was included in it except Jind district.
- Hisar's ancient name was **Isuyar.** The Siswal Civilisation developed along the Chautang river in Hisar.
- **Feroz Shah Tughlaq** founded the city of Hisar in 1354 AD. Hisar in Persian language means fort.
- Four gates of Hisar Fort built by Feroz Shah are famous as Nagauri Gate, Mori Gate, Delhi Gate and Talaki Gate.
- The Hansi city of Hisar has 5 entry gates-Delhi Gate (East), Hisar Gate (West), Gosain Gate (North-West), Barasi Gate (South) and Umra Gate (South-West).
- **Rakhigarhi**, the biggest site of the Harappan civilisation, is located in Hisar district.
- Hisar was part of the Delhi Sultanate under Lodhis.
- The origin of the Aggrawal society is believed to be from a place called **Agarwah** of Hisar.

Economic and Research Aspects

- Due to the semi-arid climate and bright sunshine, cotton is cultivated in Hisar and nearby areas.
- Hisar Textile Mill has contributed significantly to the development of the city of Hisar.

> The **Central Buffalo Research Institute** was established here in the year 1985. The only **National Research Centre on Equines** (NRCE) of India is also located here.

- Research work on paddy was started in 1970 at Haryana Agricultural University, Hisar.
- Cotton is mainly produced in Hisar.
- Haryana National Institute of Industrial Research, Hisar was established in the year 1986.

Industry and Infrastructure

- Jindal Pipe Factory with modern machines is world famous in Hisar.
- Hisar is also known as **Steel City** and **Magnet City.** Iron pipes are mostly manufactured here.
- The state's first model Employment Guide and Counselling Centre has been built in Hisar.
- **Asia's largest animal farm** is located in Hisar. Hisar is called the **Duke of Wellington** of the Mughal Era.
- Railway shipping yard is also located in Hisar.
- Hansi city is famous for **Peda** sweets in the state.

Jind (Jayanti Devi Nagar)

- It is located in the **West** of the state.
- It is surrounded by **Kaithal** to the North, **Karnal** to the North-East, **Panipat** to the East, **Sonipat** to the South-East, **Rohtak** to the South, **Hisar** to the South-West, **Fatehabad** to the West, and **Patiala** and **Sangrur** of Punjab to the North-West.

Brief Information

Establishment	1st November, 1966
Area	2,702 sq km
Headquarter	Jind city
Population	13,34,152 (Male-7,13,006, Female-6,21,146)
Decadal Growth Rate	12.13% (2001-11)
Sex-Ratio	871
Population Density	494 person/sq km
Soil	Loam
Crops	Paddy, wheat, millet, sugarcane, oilseeds, Jowar, cotton
Canal	Western Yamuna Canal
Industries	Sugar, Leather and Cycle Industry
Fairs	Hatkeshwar Fair, Bilsar Fair, Sacha Sauda Fair, Dhamtan Sahib Fair, Baba Bholunath Fair, Jamna Ka Mala.
Tourist Places	Joyanti Devi Temple, Jeetagiri Temple, Kakdaur (Jind), Bhuteshwar Temple, Parshuram Temple, Bulbul, Hariyal, Pandu-Pindara, Rani ka Talab, Prachi Tirtha, Barah Herbal Park, Pushkar Tirtha, Hatakeshwar Tirtha, Hazrat Gabi Sahib Dargah, Kirsoli Tila and Jayanti Archaeological Museum

Important Facts

Historical Context

- During the Mahabharata period, the temple of Vijaya Devi Jayanti Devi was built by Pandavas here. Later, the area around the Jayanti Devi Temple was called Jayantipuri, which was later called Jind.

> Jind nagar was established by **Raja Gajpat Singh** in the 18th century. Raja Gajpat Singh had a war with Rahim Dad Khan in 1775. King Gajpat Singh won the battle in 1763 with Afghan Governor Jean Khan.

- In 1775, Gajpat Singh sacked the region from the Afghans and made it the capital of his kingdom in 1776.
- Gajpat Singh, Rani Shobha Rai, Bhag Singh, Sangat Singh and Swarup Singh were the principal rulers in Jind.
- Jind Fort was built by Gajpat Singh.
- Jind and Dadri districts were merged with Patiala and Pepsu on 15th July, 1948. After independence, Jind was made a sub-division of Sangrur district.
- The **Jind Prajamandal** was established in Sangrur by Hansraj Rahbar in the year 1938.

Geographical and Economic Context

- Jind is the district, which rears largest number of buffaloes in Haryana.
- Leather cleaning is mainly done in Jind.
- Cooperative milk plant is also located in Jind.

> **Uchana**
>
> Raja Dahir Singh Shyokand of Nangloi region of Delhi along with Atri Gotriya Brahman, Rana Valmiki and Kataria Nai, established a township in a high place near Sarsana village of Hisar which was known as Uchana village in the past.

Sirsa (City of Saints)

- It is located in the far **West** of the state.
- It is surrounded by **Fatehabad** to the East, **Bhatinda** district of Punjab to the North, **Muktsar** district of Punjab to the North-East, **Hanumangarh** district of Rajasthan in the West and South.

Brief Information

Establishment	26th August, 1975
Area	4,277 sq km
Headquarter	Sirsa City
Population	12,95,189 (Male-6,82,582, Female-6,12,607)
Decadal Growth Rate	16.0% (2001-11)
Sex-Ratio	897
Population Density	303 person/sq km
Soil	Red
Crops	Wheat, paddy, chana, mustard, cotton
River	Ghaghara
Main Mineral	Potassium nitrate (Shora)
Fairs	Gangaur Cultural Fair, Bhuman Shah Fair, Sarsai Nath Fair, Baba Bhumgatah Fair, Radha Swami Fair
Tourist Places	Dadi Sati Temple, Baba Taraji's hut, Gurudwara Chormar Shaheedan, Dera Sacha Sauda

Important Facts

Historical and Ancient Context

- In Sirsa, Maharaja Prithviraj Chauhan defeated Muhammad Ghori twice. Iltutmish ruler of Delhi Sultanate appointed **Hemal Bhatti** as a Governor here in 1212 AD. Later, Bhatti descendants established the Bhatner city here.

- In the medieval period, the city used to come under the Princely State of **Rania.**
- The British built **Bhatiana** district in 1837 and converted Sirsa as its headquarters. In 1857, the British were defeated here.
- Bhatiana district was divided and Sirsa tehsil was formed in 1884 which was later merged with Hisar district.
- Sirsa district was carved out of Hisar on 26th August, 1975. Sirsa is also mentioned in the Mahabharata.
- It is believed that Nakula headed to Sirsa after conquering Rohtak.

> Sirsa's ancient name was **Shirishka**. This name is mentioned in Mahabharata, Ashtadhyayi and Divyavadan.

- Some historians believe that the name Sirsa of this district was named after Shirishvan. In ancient times, there were dense forests, which were cleaned and established this city.
- The **war of Chormar** was fought here.
- Saraswati river flowed through this region in ancient times.

Geographical and Economic Context

- It is the **largest district in terms of area** of the state.
- This district is famous for cotton and citrus fruits.
- Here, the **Mangiana project** related to horticulture has been started in collaboration with the country of Israel.
- Sirsa occupies the **first place** in **bovine rearing.** The district has maximum number of cow sheds in the state.
- Sirsa has the highest world record for blood donation.

Education and Modern Identity

- Chaudhary Devi Lal University, the fifth university in the state, is located in Sirsa.
- Sirsa is also known as the **City of Saints** and the **City of Literature** and the **City of Forest.**
- The Indian Air Force Base is located in Sirsa.

Fatehabad

- The district of Fatehabad is located in the **western** region of the state.
- To its North lies the **Mansa** district of Punjab, **Jind** is located in the East, **Hisar** in the South and **Sirsa** district in the West.

Brief Information

Establishment	15th July, 1997
Area	2,538 sq km
Headquarter	Fatehabad
Population	9,42,011 (Male-4,95,360, Female-4,46,651)
Decadal Growth Rate	16.8% (2001-11)
Sex-Ratio	902
Population Density	371 person/sq km
Soil	Loam
Crops	Wheat, gram, rice
Canal	Bhakra Canal
Main Mineral	Potassium nitrate (Shora)
Fair	Dussehra
Tourist Places	Lat Masjid, Humayun's Masjid, Tohana Fort, Mir Shah Mazar, Fatehabad Fort

Important Facts

Historical and Archeological Context

- Fatehabad was established by separating it from Hisar.
- The existence of Fatehabad is believed to be from the time of Emperor Ashoka.
- In ancient times, the region was inhabited by the Bhil caste and this area was known as **Udayanagari.**

> Fatehabad city was founded in 1352 by Feroz Shah Tughlaq. He named the city as Fatehabad after his son **Fateh Khan.**

- It was a part of Rania Princely State. But after 1784 AD, Khan Bahadur Bhatti made Fatehabad the headquarters of a new Princely State.
- **Kunal mound** and **Banawali mound** archaeological sites are located at Fatehabad.
- Remnants of Siswal culture have been found from Kunal and that of Harappan culture from Banawali.

Industrial and Modern Aspect

- In Fatehabad, the leather foils, scales, water drawer from wells, Mashk, etc. made by Muslims were in great demand all over the Northern India.
- The **first cotton mill** was established here in the year 1963. Fatehabad is also famous for **cotton threads.**
- The first nuclear power plant of the state is located in village Gorakhpur in Fatehabad. Around **2,800 MW** of power is generated from this nuclear plant.

- **Jakhal** is an important railway junction of Fatehabad.

> **Tohana**
>
> Fort of Tohana at Fatehabad is historically significant. In view of the importance of this fort, foreign invaders attacked it about 38 times. Tohana was also a developed city under Indus valley, civilisation. **Panini** has also discussed this city in his book **Ashtadhyayi.** Due to having origin place of five canals in Tohana, it is also called the **City of Rivers.**

Hansi

- Hansi district is newest district in Haryana carved out from Hisar district.
- It is located at a distance of 26 kilometres (16 mi) east of Hisar on NH-9. Geographically, it is semi-arid with around 46 cm of annual rainfall.

Important Facts

- The name Hansi is believed to have evolved from ancient names such as 'Asi' or 'Asikare', which are mentioned in Panini's Ashtadhyayi.
- The city was also historically known as 'Asigarh', a name derived from its renowned sword-making industry and fort, Asigarh Fort.
- According to another tradition, Hansi was founded by the **Tomar king Anangpal** in honor of his guru, Hansakar.
- The district comprise of two blocks-**Hansi** and **Narnaund.** It has **3 tehsils** (Hansi, Narnaund and Bass, Hansi) and 1 sub-tehsil (Kheri Chopta).

Brief Information

Establishment	December 2025
Area	1,289 km2 (498 sq mi)
Headquarter	Hansi
Population	527,670
Population Density	409/km2 (1,060/sq mi)
Tourist Places	Asigarh Fort, Barsi gate, Baba Jaggannathpuri Samadha temple

5. Rohtak Division

Rohtak (Education Hub)

- It is located in the South-East of the state.
- The district is surrounded by **Jind** to the North, **Hisar** to the North-West, **Bhiwani** to the West, **Dadri** to the South-West and **Jhajjar** to the South-East and **Sonipat** district to the North-East.

Brief Information

Establishment	1st November, 1966
Area	1,745 sq km
Headquarter	Rohtak City
Population	10,61,204 (Male-5,68,479, Female-4,92,725)
Sex Ratio	867
Literacy Rate	80.4%
Population Density	608 person/sq km
Soil	Clayey
Crops	Millets, jowar, sugarcane, wheat, cotton, barley, gram
Main Mineral	Limestone
Rivers	Saraswati, Markanda
Industry	Cotton Textile Industry
Fairs	Fair of Baba Mastanath, Mela Shyamji
Tourist Places	Shiva Temple, Tiliyar Lake, Gau Karna Talab, Lal Masjid, Glass Masjid, Dini Masjid, Qazi's Masjid, Manji Sahib's Gurdwara, Sai Mandir (Kharavad), Maham.

Important Facts

Historical and Archaeological Context

- Rohtak district was a part of Hisar division from the middle of 1858 to 1884 and it remained a part of Delhi from 1884 to 1910. Later it was merged with Ambala division in the year 1912.
- Rohtak is related to Mahabharata period **Rohtika.**
- According to mythological beliefs, the city of Rohtak was founded by **King Rohtas.**
- During the Mahabharata, Duryodhana's army stopped here.
- The discovery of archaeological objects found from here reveals the remains of Indus Valley Civilisation.

Economic and Geographical Aspects

- This city has been famous for **timber and agricultural production since** ancient times.
- The Simon Commission, formed on 8th November, 1927, was strongly opposed in Rohtak district. A meeting was held in Rohtak in the year 1929, whose chief guest was Motilal Nehru.

> Rohtak is not bordered by any other State or Union Territory.
> Rohtak is also called the **education city** and **political capital** of Haryana.

- **Hosiery industry** in the state is mainly located in this district.

- Electrical goods, sugar, surgical instruments, cotton yarn, cotton clothes and bicycle parts, etc. are made in Rohtak.
- **Asia's largest wholesale clothing Shorie market** is located in Rohtak.
- Rohtak's **Rewri** and **Gajjak** are very famous.

Educational and Memorial Sites

- **Maharishi Dayanand University** was established in Rohtak in the year 1976.
- A state level war memorial was established in this university in the year 2004.
- A district-level war memorial is located in Mansarovar park, Rohtak, on which the names of the martyrs of the entire district have been inscribed on marble rocks.

Sonipat (Education City)

- It is located in the **South-East** of the state.
- It is bordered by **Panipat** in the North, **Jind** in the North-West, **Rohtak** in the West, **Jhajjar** and **Delhi** in the South. Its Eastern boundary determines the river Yamuna.

Brief Information

Establishment	22nd December, 1972
Area	2,122 sq km
Headquarter	Sonipat
Population	14,50,001 (Male-7,81,299, Female-6,68,702)
Decadal Growth Rate	13.35% (2001-11)
Sex-Ratio	856
Soil	Yellow
Crops	Wheat, paddy, sugarcane, jowar, millet, pulses, sunflower, mushroom
River	Yamuna
Industries	Sugar, Cycle and Paper Industry
Fairs	Mela Baba Shamakshah, Dera Nagn Balaknath Satkumbha Fair
Tourist Places	Khwaja Khizr Khan Tomb, Pir Jamal ka Mazar, Mama - Bhanja Dargah, Akbarpur Barota, Shani Temple, Digambar Jain Temple, Baba Dham Temple, Murthal, Ancient Temple of Guru Gorakhnath

Important Facts

Historical Context

- Sonipat district was formed by separating the two tehsils of Rohtak district, Sonipat and Gohana.
- In ancient times, its name was **Sonprastha**, which means City of Gold or Golden City.
- One concept is that Sonipat is named after Shravan Kumar. Shravan Kumar stopped at seeing the atmosphere of the place while offering the pilgrimage to his parents.
- In the Mahabharata, Yudhishthira asked Duryodhana for five provinces or states, Sonipat was one of those.

According to a legend, it was the capital of the **Chakravarti King Chakavain** in the Mahabharata and Puran period.

Archaeological Context

- Statues of Surya, Yaksha-Yakshini and Adishiva and their vehicle Nandi have been found through the excavations done near Sonipat.

▲ Jurasik Park Inn, a Water Amusement Park Located in Sonipat District

- The coins and copper stamps of Yaudheya Clan have also been obtained from Sonipat district.
- Earthen pots have been found during excavation at Khedi Gujjar place of Sonipat.
- Sonipat was invaded by Najib-ad-Dawlah in 1765 AD.
- During the excavation in 1871, 1200 Greek Bactrian half dirhams and seals of Harshavardhana have been found here.

Economic and Agricultural Context

- The railroad was started here in about 1880 AD.
- The **Northern region** of Sonipat is called the **Rice Bowl**.
- Sonipat ranks first in the country in the production of mushroom, sunflower and citrus crops.
- International fruit and vegetable market is located in Ganaur of Sonipat.

- The first agricultural and exploration processing Institutes of Northern India has been established in the villages of Bhigan and Kurad in Sonipat district.
- Beer is produced by Beverages Limited Company at Murthal in Sonipat.
- Sonipat is world renowned for **bicycle industry**.
- The state's first rail coach factory is proposed in Sonipat.

Educational and Modern Aspect

- State Protection Home has been set up by the State Government under the Juvenile Justice Act in Sonipat.
- Sonipat is also known as **Education Capital**.
- The country's first state-of-the-art Anganwadi center has been established in Hasanpur village of Sonipat district.
- The first Ethanol Plant of Haryana is in Sonipat.
- A statue of Vishnu lying on Shesh Shaiya is located at Fazilpur in Sonipat.
- The first women's university of Northern India is Bhagat Phool Singh Mahila Vishwavidyalaya at Khanpur Kalana in Sonipat. **India's First Tourism University** is located at Rai in Sonipat.

> The first Government Engineering College of Haryana, Deenbandhu Chhotu Ram University of Science and Technology is located in Murthal of Sonipat.

Bhiwani

- This district is located in the **Western** region of the state.
- The district is bordered by **Hisar** in the North, **Rohtak** in the East, **Mahendragarh** in the South and **Charkhi-Dadri** district in the South-East.

Brief Information

Establishment	22nd December, 1972
Area	4,778 sq km (including Dadri)
Headquarter	Bhiwani
Population	16,34,445 (Male-8,66,672, Female-7,67,773)
Decadal Growth Rate	14.7% (2001-11)
Sex-Ratio	886
Population Density	342 person/sq km
Soil	Loam
River	Dohan
Crops	Wheat, millet, cotton, gram, mustard
Main Mineral	Potassium nitrate (Shora)
Industry	Textile Industry
Fairs	Baba Kherewala Fair, Dussehra Fair, Sati Smriti Fair, Sheetla Mata Fair
Tourist Places	Gauri Shankar Temple, Shri Harihar Temple, Baba Mungipa Temple, Red Robin, Derongo, Tosham ke Panchtirth, Peer Mubarakshah, Dargah, Panchmukhi Hanuman Temple

Important Facts

Historical and Geographical Context

- Bhiwani district was formed by separating it from Mahendragarh and Hisar districts, which had four tehsils namely Dadri, Loharu, Bhiwani and Bawani Khera.
- According to beliefs, this city was established by Rajput **Ruler Neem** on the basis of his queen Bhani, which later changed into different names such as **Bhiani**, **Bhiyani** and finally known as Bhiwani.
- Bhiwani district is also described in **Ain-i-Akbari**.
- Bhiwani was the largest city in terms of area of the state before carving out Dadri district.
- The archaeological discoveries at Mitathal in Bhiwani district suggest that this region was a part of the Harappan civilisation.
- A mint of the Princely State of Jaipur was discovered in Loharu of Bhiwani district.

> Radhaswami Satsang Bhawan Complex in Dinod town of Bhiwani has a hexagonal pyramid and a star shaped like star building. This building is made **without pillars**.

- In the Northern part of Bhiwani lie the Piedmont plains and the Aravalli mountain range in the South.
- The railway line construction was started in Bhiwani in 1881 and in 1883 rail transport was started in the district.
- The first canal was built at Bhiwani in 1893.
- Bhiwani has been described as a well known centre of trade since ancient times in the Gazettee of Hisar district.

Economic and Industrial Aspects

- Bhiwani Central Cooperative Bank was established in Bhiwani in the year 1992.
- This district is also called **Kashi of Haryana**, the city of temples and the **city of charitable trusts**.

- Bhiwani Textile Mill was established in the year 1937. It occupies an important place in the manufacture of cloth and yarn.
- The yarn made in this mill is exported to countries like Bangladesh, Turkey, and Belgium, etc.

Education and Cultural Aspects

- **Board of School Education of Haryana** is located in Bhiwani.
- This district is being developed into a **boxing center,** due to which it is also known as **Mini Cuba of India.**
- Birla Group's Technology Institute of Textile and Science is located in Bhiwani, which is the first of its kind in North India.
- The famous **Shyamsar lake** is located in Bhiwani.

Well in Rohnat

The village of Rohnat is known as Martyrs village of Bhiwani. In this village, the Jats of Bura gotra revolted against the British in 1857. In this rebellion, the village was attacked with cannons by the British, due to which some of the women here jumped into the well with children. This well reminds the freedom struggle even today.

Jhajjar (City of the Martyrs)

Brief Information

Establishment	15th July, 1997
Area	1,834 sq km
Headquarter	Jhajjar
Population	9,58,405 (Male-5,14,667 Female-4,43,738)
Decadal Growth Rate	8.90% (2001-11)
Sex-Ratio	862
Literacy Rate	80.8%
Population Density	523 person/sq km
Soil	Clayey
Crops	Gram, wheat
River	Sahibi
Industries	Sanitary Industry, Iron and Steel Industry, Utensils and Sugar Industry
Fairs	Festival of Saloni
Tourist Places	Thakurdwar, Dighal Village Shivalaya, Bhimeshwari Devi Temple, Kazi Masjid, Rudmal Temple, Bua Dome, Bhindawas Bird Sanctuary, Sparrow Tourism Site

- It is located in the **South-East** of the state.
- It is bordered by **Rohtak** to the North, **Sonipat** to the North-East, Gurugram to the South-East, Union Territory of **Delhi** to the East, **Charkhi-Dadri** to the West and **Rewari** district to the South.

Important Facts

Historical Context

- This district was formed by separating it from Rohtak district.
- In ancient times, it was named **Chhajju Nagar,** which was founded by a Jat named **Chhajju.**
- Jhajjar is also known as the **City of Martyrs.**
- Ghori settled Jhajjar at the request of Jhoj Gehlavat or Jhajjhu.

Major Cities and Economic Aspect

- The two major cities of Jhajjar district are **Bahadurgarh** and **Beri.** Bahadurgarh was founded by Rathi Jats. Bahadurgarh was earlier known as **Saraffabad.** A large number of industrial units have been set up in Bahadurgarh town of Jhajjar.
- The largest cattle fair of the state is held at Jahazgarh village in Jhajjar district.
- **Jhajjari** (Pitcher pots) is highly famous in Jhajjar.
- Beri town of Jhajjar is called the **City of Wealthy People.**

Political and Educational Legacy

- The first Chief Minister of Haryana, Pandit Bhagwat Dayal Sharma, belongs to Jhajjar district itself.
- Archaeological Museum of Jhajjar is the largest and important museum of Haryana. It was founded in the year 1959 by Omanand Saraswati.
- Hindi medium branch in Haryana was opened in Jhajjar in the year 1914.
- The first court in Jhajjar was opened in the year 1919.

The **first nuclear university** of the state is proposed to be built in Jhajjar.

Cultural Sites and Other Aspect

- Niracha Dham located in Jhajjar has religious significance. This Dham is also known as Baba Bhagwandas Ashram.
- The **Dome of Bua** is one of the major tourist places in Jhajjar, built by Bua, the daughter of Mustafa Kalol.
- The **largest bus stand of the state** is the bus stand of Jhajjar.

- **Saraffabad** was the old name of Bahadurgarh. Lala Bhagwandas built a pond in Bahadurgarh in 1865.

Charkhi-Dadri

Brief Information

Establishment	1st December, 2016
Area	1,370 sq km
Population Density	334 Person/sq km
Headquarter	Charkhi-Dadri
Population	4,48,920 (Male-54%, Female-46%)
Sex-Ratio	881
Literacy Rate	70%
Soil	Loam
Crops	Wheat, jowar, millet, mustard
Fair	Hanuman Fair
Tourist Places	Rest House Temple, Hanuman Temple, Rangila Hanuman Temple, Devidham, Sri Guru Nanak Satsang Sabha, Bala Wala Johar, Shyamsar Sarovar, Kapuri Hill

- Charkhi-Dadri district is located in the **Western** part of Haryana state.
- It is surrounded by **Bhiwani** in the North-West, **Rohtak** in the North-East, **Jhajjar** in the East, **Rewari** in the South-East and **Mahendragarh** district in the South.
- Rohtak and Charkhi-Dadri districts of the state do not share a border with any other state.

Important Facts

- This town was founded by **Bilvaraj Chauhan**, the younger son of Prithviraj Chauhan.
- The name of this city originated from the Sanskrit word **Dadur** which means **Frog**.
- Later it was named as Dadri. The village named Charkhi was located near this area; hence, the name of this district changed as Charkhi- Dadri.
- A cement factory was established by Seth Ramakrishna Dalmia in 1939 in Charkhi-Dadri. In 1982, it was acquired by Cement Corporation of India.
- Charkhi-Dadri is the second land-covered district of Haryana after Rohtak. **Kaliyana village** of Charkhi-Dadri is the only place in India where flexible sandstone (Hilna stones) is found.

Note Adequate statistics are not available after the formation of district.

6. Karnal Division

Karnal (Rice Bowl)

- This district is located in the **Eastern** part of the state.
- The district is bordered by Uttar Pradesh in the East, Jind and Panipat in the South, Kaithal in the West, Kurukshetra in the North and Yamunanagar in the North-East.

Brief Information

Establishment	1st November, 1966
Area	2,520 sq km
Headquarter	Karnal
Population	15,05,324 (Male-7,97,712, Female-7,07,612)
Decadal Growth Rate	18.2% (2001-11)
Sex-Ratio	887
Literacy Rate	74.7%
Population Density	597 person/sq km
Soil	Yellow
Crops	Paddy, sugarcane, sunflower
Main Mineral	Potassium nitrate (Shora)
River	Yamuna
Industries	Sugar Industry, Liberty Shoe Industry, Vanaspati Industry
Fairs	Gugga Peer Fair, Parasara Fair, Pandu Fair, Chadi Fair
Tourist Places	Sita Mai Temple, Karna Lake, Oasis (Uchana), Punda Pul, Karna Talab, Devi Temple, Gandhi Memorial Hall, Aditi Ka Mandir, St. James Church Tower

Important Facts

Historical Context

- The city of Karnal was founded by **King Karna.** In ancient times, the name of this city was **Karnalaya.**
- This region is believed to be associated with the Mahabharata period. It is believed that King Karna used to donate gold daily at the modern **Karnatal** (Karna lake) place in Karnal city.
- King Karna donated his armour and kundal on the banks of Karna lake to Lord Indra.
- There is a beautiful bell house of Karna and Lord Surya near Karna lake.

- Before the formation of the state of Haryana, this city used to come under Punjab province.
- In 1739, Nadir Shah defeated the Mughal Emperor Mohammad Shah (Rangeela) in Karnal.
- In 1763, Karnal was taken over by the King of Jind and in 1797; George Thomas took control over it.

Economic and Agricultural Context

- Karnal is also called the **Rice Bowl** and **Paris** of **Haryana.**
- Processing of milk products is studied at the **National Dairy Research Institute** located in Karnal. Through this, the work of research, teaching and training is also done.
- Liberty shoes manufactured in Karnal are exported abroad.

Educational Development

- In 1947, the first institution for Education and Training of Overseas was established in Nilokheri in Karnal.
- Forensic Science Laboratory was established in Madhuban, Karnal in 1976.
- The first NCC Academy of the state will also be established in Gharaunda, Karnal.
- Kalpana Chawla Medical University is located in Karnal. On 28th November, 2016, the first Horticulture University of the state has been established in Karnal which is named as **Maharana Pratap Horticulture University.**

Indri

It is the main tourist destination of the state. Baba Simran Das Kachchi Samadhi is located at this place. This Kachchi Samadhi has religious significance in the state.

Panipat (Weaver Town)

- It is located in the **Middle-East** of the state.
- It is surrounded by **Uttar Pradesh** in the East, **Karnal** in the North, **Jind** in the West and **Sonipat** district in the South.
- The Eastern boundary of the district is determined by the Yamuna river.

Brief Information

Establishment	1st November, 1989
Area	1,268 sq km
Headquarters	Panipat
Population	12,05,437 (Male-6,46,857, Female-5,58,580)
Decadal Growth Rate	24.33% (2001-11)
Sex-Ratio	864
Literacy Rate	77.5%
Population Density	951 person/sq km
Soil	Yellow
Crops	Wheat, paddy, sugarcane
Major Mineral	Limestone
River	Yamuna
Industries	Sugar, Woollen, Handloom and Iron and Steel Industry
Fairs	Durga Ashtami Fair, The Fair of the Tomb of Kalandar, Papari Mata Fair
Tourist Places	Devi Talab Shiva Temple, Ibrahim Lodi's Tomb, Salarganj Gate, Kala Amb, Jama Masjid, Kabulibagh Masjid, Blue – Jay, Spiritual Museum, Syed Roshan Ali Shah Dargah, Skylark

Important Facts

Historical and Ancient Context

- Panipat was formed as a new district by separating the Panipat and Assandh tehsils of Karnal district.
- It was merged with Karnal again on 24th July, 1991 and it was again made a separate district in January 1992.
- The ancient name of Panipat was **Panduprastha** or **Panaprastha.**
- This city is also historically important. This city was the center of politics in the Muslim period.
- Three main battles were fought here, which are known as First War, Second War and Third War of Panipat.
- During the Mahabharata period this place was known as **Vanaprastha.**
- It is a very ancient city of the time of Mahabharata. It was one of the five provinces sought by the Pandavas from the Kauravas.
- The revolutionary **Maulvi Kalandar** of Panipat revolted against the British in 1857, due to which he was hanged by the British.

Industrical and Economic Hub

- Production of oil started in 2002 in oil refinery at Panipat.
- Under the handloom industry in Panipat, blanket, bed cover, carpets and tapestry are manufactured which are exported abroad.

Excellent and artistic woollen carpets and handloom items are also manufactured in Panipat, hence it is also known as the **City of Weavers** (Handloom town). Blankets for the Indian Army are manufactured in Panipat itself.

- Panipat is the largest centre for the production of old cotton clothes and low price blankets in the country.
- An ammonia plant is also located at Panipat.
- Saalkha division of Panipat district has industries of iron casting and agricultural machinery.
- Textile machinery is also manufactured in Panipat.
- India's first carding machine was manufactured in Panipat itself.

> National Fertilisers Limited was established on 23rd August, 1974 in Panipat. This plant manufactures urea and manure.

- The **country's first Artificial Rubber Plant** has also been established in Panipat.
- Pachrang pickles, canned dry vegetables and basmati rice are exported to many countries from Panipat.
- A Captive Power Plant is located at Panipat.

Social and Development Initiatives

- **Beti Bachao Beti Padhao** programme was started on 22nd January, 2015 from Panipat.
- Haryana's first **Annapurna Textile and Grain Bank** is located in Raghunath Dham Temple of Panipat, supporting local communities.
- Residential school for the physically challenged is also situated in Panipat.

▲ Panipat Museum (Spread Information and Create Awareness about Archaeology, History, Art and Crafts of Haryana)

Kaithal (City of Kapil Muni)

- It is located in the **North-West** of Haryana.
- It is surrounded by **Kurukshetra** in the North, **Jind** in the South, **Karnal** in the East and **Patiala** district of Punjab in the North-West.

Brief Information

Establishment	1st November, 1989 carved out of Kurukshetra
Area	2,317 sq km
Headquarter	Kaithal
Population	10,74,304 (Male 5,71,003, Female 5,03,301)
Decadal Growth Rate	13.55% (2001-11)
Sex-Ratio	881
Literacy Rate	69.15%
Population Density	464 person/sq km
Soil	Yellow
Crops	Wheat, paddy
Rivers	Saraswati, Markanda
Fairs	Pundark Fair, Vamana Dwadashi Fair, Phalgu Fair
Tourist Places	Hanuman Temple, Ambkeshwar Temple, Gyarah Rudari Shiva Temple, Vikra Temple, Geeta Temple, Anjani Tila, Kutti Shiva Temple, Devji Temple, Navagrah Kund, Ento ki Bawli, Kalam Mausoleum, Gurdwara Neem Sahib, Gurdwara Manji Sahib, Tomb of Razia Sultan

Important Facts

Historical Context

- This district was earlier a tehsil of Karnal district.
- It has two tehsils called Kaithal and Guhla and Kaithal, Pudri, Chika and Kalaya are towns.
- It has also been a sub-division of Karnal and Kurukshetra districts.
- In the year 1973, when Kurukshetra district was made a separate district, Kaithal region came under Kurukshetra.
- The cultured name of Kaithal is **Kapisthal** which means a dwelling place of apes. This place is considered to be the birth place of the monkey God Hanuman Ji.
- According to mythological beliefs, Kaithal was founded by **Emperor Yudhishthira.**
- Jats of Kaithal opposed Timur Lung in 1398.
- A fort was built by the Mughal Emperor **Akbar** in Kaithal.

Economic and Cultural Aspect

- Kaithal district is an agricultural region. The economy here is based on agriculture.
- Kaithal district is also famous for **Lav-Kush Mahateerth** in Mundri village situated on Karnal road.
- Kaithal, Pundri, Siwan and Kalayat show that the soil of Kaithal is religious and cultural. Kaithal is also called the **City of Gurudwaras.**
- It is also called **Chhoti Kashi** due to the Navagraha Kunda located in Kaithal.
- Agriculture is a major contributor to Kaithal's economy. **Basmati rice** produced here is also exported abroad.
- Kaithal manufactures machineries which are installed in the foundry factories.
- The Guru Recitation of both Granth Sahib and Ramayana is done in **Topiyo Wala Gurudwara** in Kaithal.

Educational Aspect

- The oldest college of Kaithal is **Radha Krishna Sanatan Dharma College**, which was established in the year 1954.
- In 1970, the **Indira Gandhi Girls' College** was established by the Rashtriya Vidya Samiti.

CHECK CHAPTER KNOWLEDGE

1 When the state of Haryana was formed in 1966, the state had .... number of districts. *HSSC 2020*
(a) ten (b) eleven (c) six (d) seven

2 Which district has been declared as the 22nd district of Haryana? *HSSC 2021*
(a) Nuh (b) Charkhi-Dadri
(c) Palwal (d) None of these

3 Manji Sahib Gurdwara is located at which place of Haryana? *Haryana Conductor 2017*
(a) Panipat (b) Jind (c) Rohtak (d) Ambala

4 Ambala is famous for *HSSC Group D 2018*
(a) watermelon (b) mango
(c) jackfruit (d) apple

5 When was Ambala established as a military cantonment? *HSSC 2022, 20*
(a) 1811 (b) 1843
(c) 1856 (d) 1901

6 Which district of Haryana is famous for its scientific equipments? *Conductor 2017*
(a) Ambala (b) Gurugram
(c) Panipat (d) Hisar

7 This city of Haryana is called as Nano city *HSSC CET 2024*
(a) Jhajjar (b) Palwal
(c) Gurugram (d) Panchkula

8 .... is famous by the name 'Battle ground' and 'Dharmanagri'. *HSSC 2018*
(a) Panipat (b) Kurukshetra
(c) Mewat (d) Kargil

9 Bhadrakali Shaktipeeth, one of the 51 Shaktipeeths, is located in which district? *HSSC 2016*
(a) Jind (b) Narnaul (c) Kurukshetra (d) Panchkula

10 Which of the district of Uttar Pradesh shares boundary with the Sonipat district of Haryana? *HSSC CET 2024*
(a) Gorakhpur (b) Baghpat
(c) Ghaziabad (d) Auraiya

11 Which district is known as 'City of Park' in Haryana?
(a) Hisar (b) Palwal
(c) Rewari (d) Kurukshetra

12 Hathni Kund Barrage Project is associated with which district of Haryana? *HSSC 2019*
(a) Sonipat (b) Panipat
(c) Yamunanagar (d) Fatehabad

13 Jhajjar district of Haryana was earlier part of this district
(a) Hisar (b) Rohtak
(c) Sirsa (d) Rewari

14 Saraswati Sugar Mill is located at *PGT 2016*
(a) Rohtak (b) Panipat
(c) Yamunanagar (d) Faridabad

15 Yamunanagar is also known by which other name in Haryana? *HSSC 2023, 19*
(a) City of clothes (b) Steel city
(c) City of copper (d) City of paper

16 Panchkula is famous for *PGT 2016*
(a) watches
(b) utensils
(c) electronic goods/items
(d) sunglasses

17 Bhiwani district of Haryana was formed in the year
(a) 1996 (b) 1972 (c) 1976 (d) 1982

18 The highest peak of Haryana is located at which place?
(a) Palwal (b) Sirsa
(c) Bhiwani (d) Panchkula

19 Which factory is located in Faridabad? *Haryana Conductor 2017*
(a) Rubber (b) Tractor
(c) Refrigerator (d) All of these

20 Who founded Faridabad in Haryana? *HSSC 2020*
(a) Jahangir
(b) Malik Mohmud Khan
(c) Sheikh Farid
(d) Raja Mahar Singh

21 Faridabad is famous for which production?
(a) Cotton (b) Sugarcane
(c) Henna (d) Furniture

22 Which district is known as 'Cotton city' in Haryana?
(a) Hisar (b) Rewari (c) Jhajjar (d) Palwal

23 Gurugram district came into existence in which year? *HSSC 2018*
(a) 1955 (b) 1966 (c) 1977 (d) 1988

24 The first Defense University of India is located in which district of Haryana? *HSSC 2019*
(a) Faridabad (b) Ambala
(c) Gurugram (d) Mahendragarh

25 The National Brain Research Institute is located in which place of Haryana? *HSSC 2022, 19*
(a) Bhiwani (b) Hisar
(c) Kurukshetra (d) Gurugram

26 Haryana Government has announced to develop .... as a smart city in the year 2015. *HSSC 2020*
(a) Thari (b) Panipat (c) Ambala (d) Gurugram

27 Which district is known as 'Solar City' of Haryana? *Anganwadi 2016*
(a) Gurugram (b) Karnal
(c) Hisar (d) Panipat

28 Mahendragarh district ranks first in Haryana in the production of *PGT 2016*
(a) Rice (b) Utensils
(c) Mustard (d) Cycles

29 Fatehabad district of Haryana is famous for which among the following industries? *HSSC CET 2024*
(a) Cotton thread (b) Steel
(c) Silk (d) Tractor

30 Rewari district is famous for which of the following Industries? *HSSC 2019, PGT 2016*
(a) Brass metalware (b) Tiledar Jutti
(c) Hero Motocorp (d) All of these

31 Which district of Haryana is also known as 'Steel City' and 'Magnet City' in the state? *HSSC 2021, 19*
(a) Hisar (b) Palwal
(c) Mewat (d) Kurukshetra

32 Which district of Haryana is the largest producer of Iron pipes? *Shift Attendant 2016*
(a) Sonipat (b) Gurugram
(c) Faridabad (d) Hisar

33 Haryana National Institute of Industrial Research was established in which year? *HSSC 2019*
(a) 1982 (b) 1985 (c) 1986 (d) 1988

34 Which district is known as 'Heart of Haryana'?
(a) Jind (b) Karnal (c) Panipat (d) Sonipat

35 Which is the largest district of Haryana in terms of area? *HSSC 2021*
(a) Bhiwani (b) Faridabad
(c) Sirsa (d) Hisar

36 Gorakhpur Nuclear Power Plant is located in which district of Haryana? *Haryana Police 2018*
(a) Bhiwani (b) Kaithal (c) Fatehabad (d) Rewari

37 Rohtak was formed in which year?
(a) January, 1960 (b) November, 1966
(c) October, 1990 (d) December, 2000

38 Which district is known as 'Educational City' of Haryana?
(a) Kaithal (b) Panipat (c) Rohtak (d) Jind

39 Hosiery industry is mainly found in which district of Haryana? *Anganwadi 2016*
(a) Rohtak (b) Bhiwani
(c) Ambala (d) Gurugram

40 'Golden city' of Haryana is *HSSC 2023, 19*
(a) Panipat (b) Ambala (c) Rewari (d) Sonipat

41 In which district of Haryana is Atlas cycle industry located? *PGT 2016*
(a) Hisar (b) Sonipat
(c) Fatehabad (d) Sirsa

42 Bhiwani Textile Mill was established in which year?
(a) 1924 (b) 1934 (c) 1937 (d) 1939

43 .... is known as 'Mini Cuba in India' because a large number of boxers come from this region. *Haryana Police 2018*
(a) Bhiwani (b) Ambala (c) Karnal (d) Palwal

44 Charkhi-Dadri district came into existence in the year *HSSC 2019*
(a) December, 2014 (b) December, 2016
(c) December, 2013 (d) December, 2015

45 Which city was settled by Bilvaraj Chauhan, the younger son of Prithviraj Chauhan? *Haryana Clerk 2016*
(a) Charkhi-Dadri (b) Sirsa
(c) Hisar (d) Jind

46 Which is the important industry of Charkhi-Dadri and Surajpur? *Haryana Clerk 2016*
(a) Cement (b) Paper
(c) Sugar (d) None of these

47 National Dairy Research Institute is located in which place? *HSSC 2019*
(a) Karnal (b) Sirsa (c) Panipat (d) Bhiwani

48 Which of the following manufactured goods of Karnal is exported abroad? *Haryana Clerk 2016*
(a) Liberty shoes (b) Paints
(c) Wooden furniture (d) Steel

49 After whose name the Medical college of Karnal was established in Haryana? *Haryana Clerk 2016*
(a) Chaudhary Devi Lal (b) APJ Abdul Kalam
(c) Kalpana Chawla (d) Karnal

50 Which district is known as 'City of Gurudwaras'?
(a) Sonipat (b) Kaithal
(c) Sirsa (d) Hisar

51 Which district is known as 'City of Weavers'? *HSSC 2020,19,16*
(a) Karnal (b) Panipat
(c) Sirsa (d) Hisar

52 Urea plant is located in which district of Haryana? *HSSC Clerk 2016*
(a) Sonipat (b) Mahendragarh
(c) Panipat (d) None of these

53 Given below are the Administrative Divisions of Haryana alongwith the districts it includes. *HCS Prelims 2023*

Administrative Division	Districts Included
A. Hisar	Hisar, Fatehabad, Jind, Bhiwani, Sirsa
B. Rohtak	Jhajjar, Sonipat, Bhiwani, Charkhi-Dadri, Rohtak
C. Karnal	Panipat, Karnal, Kurukshetra, Kaithal
D. Ambala	Ambala, Kurukshetra, Panchkula, Yamunanagar

Which of the above Administrative Divisions are correctly matched?
(a) A and B (b) B and C
(c) C and D (d) B and D

54 Match the following as per popular beliefs. *HCS Prelims 2023*

A.	City of five canals	1.	Kaithal
B.	City named after wife of Neem Singh	2.	Panchkula
C.	City in Arabic meaning Fort	3.	Bhiwani
D.	City named after a place of monkeys	4.	Hisar

Codes

	A	B	C	D		A	B	C	D
(a)	1	2	3	4	(b)	2	3	4	1
(c)	3	4	1	2	(d)	4	1	2	3

55 Given below is a list of districts along with district's touching its boundaries is given below *HCS Prelims 2023*

1.	Jind	Hisar, Kaithal, Panipat, Karnal
2.	Rohtak	Jind, Charkhi, Dadri, Hisar, Rewari
3.	Rewari	Mahendragarh, Gurugram, Nuh, Jhajjar
4.	Hisar	Bhiwani, Rohtak, Sirsa, Fatehabad

Which of the above is/are correctly matched?
(a) 1, 2 and 3 (b) 2, 3 and 4
(c) 2 and 4 (d) 1 and 3

CORRECT ANSWERS

1. (d)	2. (b)	3. (d)	4. (b)	5. (b)	6. (a)	7. (d)	8. (b)	9. (c)	10. (b)
11. (d)	12. (c)	13. (b)	14. (c)	15. (d)	16. (c)	17. (b)	18. (d)	19. (d)	20. (c)
21. (c)	22. (d)	23. (b)	24. (c)	25. (d)	26. (d)	27. (a)	28. (c)	29. (a)	30. (d)
31. (a)	32. (d)	33. (c)	34. (a)	35. (c)	36. (c)	37. (b)	38. (c)	39. (a)	40. (d)
41. (b)	42. (c)	43. (a)	44. (b)	45. (a)	46. (a)	47. (a)	48. (a)	49. (c)	50. (b)
51. (b)	52. (c)	53. (d)	54. (b)	55. (d)					

HARYANA

Miscellaneous

This section contains Miscellaneous topics like Demography, Education, Sports, Social welfare schemes, etc.

CHAPTER 28

Demographic Profile of Haryana

- The **first census** of the state of Haryana was done in the year 1971. The Census 2011, was the **fifth** census for the state.
- According to the Census 2011, the total population of the state is 2,53,51,462 in which the number of **males** is 1,34,94,734 and the number of **females** is 1,18,56,728.
- Haryana is at the **18th rank in India in terms of population**. The state is home to 2.09% of the total population of the country.
- According to the Census 2001, Haryana's population was only 2.06% of the total population of the country.
- According to Census 1981, Haryana had 12 districts.
- **Faridabad** has the highest population and **Panchkula** has the lowest population in the state.

Five Districts with Maximum and Minimum Population of the State

Maximum (in descending order)		Minimum (in ascending order)	
District	Population	District	Population
Faridabad	18,09,733	Charkhi-Dadri	5,02,276
Hisar	17,43,931	Panchkula	5,61,293
Bhiwani	16,34,445	Rewari	9,00,332
Gurugram	15,14,432	Mahendragarh	9,22,088
Karnal	15,05,324	Fatehabad	9,42,011

Five Districts with Maximum and Minimum Male Population of Haryana

Maximum (in descending order)		Minimum (in ascending order)	
District	Male Population	District	Male Population
Faridabad	9,66,110	Charkhi-Dadri	2,65,949
Hisar	9,31,562	Panchkula	2,99,679
Bhiwani	8,66,672	Rewari	4,74,335
Gurugram	8,16,690	Mahendragarh	4,86,665
Karnal	7,97,712	Fatehabad	4,95,360

Five Districts with Maximum and Minimum Female Population of Haryana

Maximum (in descending order)		Minimum (in ascending order)	
District	Female Population	District	Female Population
Faridabad	8,43,623	Charkhi-Dadri	2,36,327
Hisar	8,12,369	Panchkula	2,61,614
Bhiwani	7,67,773	Rewari	4,25,997
Karnal	7,07,612	Mahendragarh	4,35,423
Gurugram	6,97,742	Jhajjar	4,43,738

Decadal Growth Rate of Haryana

The change in the number of people in a region in ten years is called 'Decadal Growth'.

As per the 2011 Census

- Decadal growth rate — 19.90%, (down from 28.06% in 2001)
- National average growth rate — 17.7% (2.2% lower than Haryana)
- Female growth rate — 21.23%
- Male growth rate — 18.75%
- Rank of Haryana in growth rate — 16th in India
- The population growth rate has decreased by 8.16% in the year 2011 as compared to the population of 2001.
- Haryana recorded its lowest decadal growth in 2011 (19.90%) and the highest in 1971 (32.22%).

Five Districts with Maximum and Minimum Decadal Growth Rate of Haryana

Maximum (in descending order)		Minimum (in ascending order)	
District	Growth Rate (in %)	District	Growth Rate (in %)
Gurugram	73.96	Jhajjar	8.90
Nuh	37.93	Ambala	11.23
Faridabad	32.54	Jind	12.13
Palwal	25.76	Rohtak	12.88
Panipat	24.60	Sonipat	13.35

Population Density of Haryana

Population density refers to the number of people living in per square kilometre.

As per Census 2011

- Haryana's population density — 573 persons per sq km (478 in 2001)
- Rank in population density — 11th
- The largest decrease (44 points) in population density of Haryana was recorded in 1951-61.
- The highest increase (106 points) in population density of Haryana was recorded in 1991-2001.
- The lowest increase in population density of Haryana was recorded in 1901-1911.

Five Districts with Maximum and Minimum Population Density of the State

Maximum (in descending order)		Minimum (in ascending order)	
District	Density (Person/sq km)	District	Density (Person/sq km)
Faridabad	2,442	Sirsa	303
Gurugram	1,204	Charkhi-Dadri	334
Panipat	951	Bhiwani	342
Palwal	767	Fatehabad	371
Nuh	723	Hisar	438

Sex-Ratio in Haryana

Sex-ratio refers to the number of females per thousand males.

As per the Census 2011

- Haryana's sex-ratio — 879 (861 in 2001)
- Sex-ratio in urban areas — 873/1000
- Sex-ratio in rural areas — 882/100
- After independence Haryana recorded minimum growth in sex-ratio (-5) in the year 1991, while it recorded maximum increase in sex-ratio (+18) in 2011.

Five Districts with Maximum and Minimum Sex-ratio in the State

Maximum (in descending order)		Minimum (in ascending order)	
District	Sex-Ratio	District	Sex-Ratio
Nuh (Mewat)	907	Gurugram	854
Fatehabad	902	Sonipat	856
Rewari	898	Jhajjar	862
Sirsa	897	Panipat	864
Mahendragarh	895	Rohtak	867

Literacy Rate in Haryana

A person aged 7 or above who can read or write with understanding any language is considered literate.

As per the Census 2011

- Haryana's literacy rate — 75.55%
- Haryana's male literacy rate — 84.06% (increased by 5.6%)
- Haryana's female literacy rate — 65.94 (increased by 10.2%)

- After the independence, the lowest increase in the average literacy rate of the state has been recorded in the year 2011 (7.7%) and the highest increase (18.72%) in the year 1991.

Five Districts with Maximum and Minimum Literacy Rate of the State

Maximum (in descending order)		Minimum (in ascending order)	
District	Literacy Rate (%)	District	Literacy Rate (%)
Gurugram	84.70	Nuh (Mewat)	54.08
Panchkula	81.88	Charkhi-Dadri	67.04
Ambala	81.75	Fatehabad	67.92
Faridabad	81.70	Sirsa	68.82
Rewari	80.99	Kaithal	69.15

Five Districts with Maximum and Minimum Male Literacy Rate of the State

Maximum (in descending order)		Minimum (in ascending order)	
District	Male Literacy Rate (in %)	District	Male Literacy Rate (in %)
Rewari	91.44	Nuh (Mewat)	69.94
Gurugram	90.46	Fatehabad	76.14
Mahendragarh	89.72	Sirsa	76.43
Jhajjar	89.31	Kaithal	77.98
Faridabad	88.61	Jind	80.81

Five Districts with Maximum and Minimum Female Literacy Rate

Maximum (in descending order)		Minimum (in ascending order)	
District	Female Literacy Rate	District	Female Literacy Rate
Gurugram	77.98	Nuh (Mewat)	36.60
Panchkula	75.99	Palwal	54.23
Ambala	75.75	Fatehabad	58.87
Faridabad	73.84	Kaithal	59.24
Rohtak	71.72	Sirsa	60.40

Haryana Population (Census 2011)

District	Male Population	Female Population	Total Population	Population Density	Sex-Ratio
Ambala	5,98,703	5,29,647	11,28,350	717	885
Panchkula	2,99,679	2,61,614	5,61,293	625	873
Yamunanagar	6,46,718	5,67,487	12,14,205	687	877
Kurukshetra	5,10,976	4,53,679	9,64,655	630	888
Kaithal	5,71,003	5,03,301	10,74,304	464	881
Karnal	7,97,712	7,07,612	15,05,324	597	887
Panipat	6,46,857	5,58,580	12,05,437	951	864
Sonipat	7,81,299	6,68,702	14,50,001	683	856
Rohtak	5,68,479	4,92,725	10,61,204	608	867
Jhajjar	5,14,667	4,43,738	9,58,405	523	862
Faridabad	9,66,110	8,43,623	18,09,733	2442	873
Palwal	5,54,497	4,88,211	10,42,708	767	880
Gurugram	8,16,690	6,97,742	15,14,432	1204	854
Nuh (Mewat)	5,71,162	5,18,101	10,89,263	723	907
Rewari	4,74,335	4,25,997	9,00,332	565	898
Mahendragarh	4,86,665	4,35,423	9,22,088	486	895
Bhiwani	8,66,672	7,67,773	16,34,445	342	886
Jind	7,13,006	6,21,146	13,34,152	494	871
Hisar	9,31,562	8,12,369	17,43,931	438	872
Fatehabad	4,95,360	4,46,651	9,42,011	371	902
Sirsa	6,82,582	6,12,607	12,95,189	303	897
Charkhi-Dadri	2,65,949	2,36,327	5,02,276	334	881
Total (2011)	1,37,60,683	1,20,93,055	2,58,53,738	573	879

Child Population and Sex-Ratio in Haryana

As per the Census 2011

• Haryana's total child population (age 0-6 years)	3,380,721 (Boys are 1,843,109 and Girls are 1,537,612)
• Percentage of children (in the total population)	13.3% (15.8% in 2001)
• The total child population in state	In urban areas is 1,095,609 and rural areas is 2,285,112
• Highest number of children in state	Nuh
• Lowest percentage of this age group in state	Ambala
• Child sex-ratio (age 0-6)	834 (819 in 2001)

- Child sex-ratio of Haryana in rural areas — 835
- Child sex-ratio of Haryana in urban areas — 832
- Thus, the proportion of 0-6 years age group population has decreased by 2.5% between the years 2001-11. The main reason for this is the decrease in fertility rate.
- According to Census 2011, the proportion of population in the age group 0-6 in the state (13.3%) is 0.3% less than the national average (13.6%).

Five Districts with Maximum and Minimum Child Sex-ratio of the State

Maximum (in descending order)		Minimum (in ascending order)	
District	Child Sex-Ratio	District	Child Sex-Ratio
Nuh	906	Mahendragarh	775
Palwal	866	Jhajjar	782
Panchkula	863	Rewari	787
Sirsa	862	Sonipat	798
Fatehabad	854	Ambala	810

Rural and Urban Population in Haryana

As per the Census 2011

- Haryana's rural population — 16,509,359 (65.12% of state's total Population)
- Haryana's urban population — 8,842,103 (34.88% of state's total Population)
- Ranking of Haryana in India — 16th based on rural-urban population, 17th in rural population, 14th in urban population
- National(average) rural growth rate — 12.2% (2.35% more than Haryana's growth rate)
- Rural growth rate of Haryana — 9.85%
- Urban growth rate of Haryana — 44.59%
- Highest population growth in district — Gurugram (236.53%)
- Lowest population growth in district — Sirsa (8.79%)
- Sex-ratio in urban areas — 873 (847 in 2001)
- Sex-ratio in rural areas — 882 (868 in 2001)
- Average literacy rate — Urban 83.1% and Rural 71.4%
- Male literacy rate — Urban 88.6% and Rural 81.6%
- Female literacy rate — Urban 76.9% and Rural 60%
- District with highest rural population — Bhiwani (1,313,123)
- District with lowest rural population — Panchkula (248,063)
- District with highest population growth rate — Nuh (32.89%)
- District with lowest population growth rate — Gurugram (16.43%)
- District with highest rural population percentage — Nuh (88.61%)
- District with lowest rural population percentage — Faridabad (20.49%)
- Towns with population (1-10 Lakh) — 19 towns
- Towns with population (More than 10 lakh) — 1 town (Faridabad)

Five Districts with Maximum and Minimum Rural Population of the State

Maximum (in descending order)		Minimum (in ascending order)	
District	Rural Population	District	Rural Population
Bhiwani	13,13,123	Panchkula	2,48,063
Hisar	11,90,443	Faridabad	3,70,878
Karnal	10,50,514	Gurugram	4,72,179
Jind	10,28,569	Rohtak	6,15,040
Sonipat	9,96,637	Ambala	6,27,576

Five Districts with Maximum and Minimum Urban Population of the State

Maximum (in descending order)		Minimum (in ascending order)	
District	Urban Population	District	Urban Population
Faridabad	14,38,855	Nuh	1,24,106
Gurugram	10,42,253	Mahendragarh	1,32,855
Panipat	5,55,085	Fatehabad	1,79,588
Hisar	5,53,488	Rewari	2,33,430
Ambala	5,00,774	Kaithal	2,36,011

Demographic Profile of Haryana

Birth and Death Rate in Haryana

Birth rate in Haryana	20.5 per thousand
Urban birth rate in Haryana	18.2 per thousand
Rural birth rate in Haryana	21.9 per thousand
Death rate in Haryana	5.8 per thousand
Urban death rate in Haryana	5.0 per thousand
Rural death rate in Haryana	6.3 per thousand
Child mortality rate in Haryana	30 per thousand
Urban child mortality rate in Haryana	25 per thousand
Rural child mortality rate in Haryana	32 per thousand

Haryana Religion Based Census

Population of Haryana follows Hinduism	87.46%
Buddhists population in Haryana	0.02% (lowest)
Increase in Muslim population in Haryana	1.25%
Decrease in Hindu population in Haryana	0.77%
Highest Hindu population district	Mahendragarh (99.04%)
Highest Muslim population district	Nuh (79.20%)
Highest Christian population district	Gurugram (0.64%)
Highest Buddhist population district	Panchkula (0.18%)
Highest Jain population district	Gurugram (0.49%)
Highest Sikhs population district	Sirsa (26.17%)
Lowest Christian population district	Mahendragarh (0.03%)
Lowest Sikhs population district	Nuh (0.05%)
Lowest Buddhist population district	Yamunanagar
Lowest Jain population district	Kaithal (0.03%)
Community having the highest sex-ratio	Christian (918)
Community having highest literacy rate	Jain (94.2%)
Community having the lowest literacy rate	Muslim (40%)

Haryana: Religion Based Census Statistics 2011

Religion	Total	Persons (%)	Total	Male (%)	Total	Female (%)
Hinduism	2,21,71,128	87.46	1,18,21,082	53.32	1,03,50,046	46.68
Islam	17,81,342	7.03	9,40,027	52.77	8,41,315	47.23
Sikhism	12,43,752	4.91	6,53,468	52.54	5,90,284	47.46
Jainism	52,613	0.21	27,358	52.00	25,255	48
Christianity	50,353	0.20	26,165	51.96	24,188	48.04
Buddhism	7,514	0.02	4,099	54.55	3,415	45.45
Others	44,760	0.18	22,535	50.35	22,225	49.65
Total Population	**2,53,51,462**	**100**	**1,34,94,734**	**100**	**1,18,56,728**	**100**

Occupational Structure in Haryana

Haryana's average workforce participation rate	35.17% (36.36% in rural areas and 32.95% in urban areas)
Working group in Haryana	35.17% of total population of State
Dependent group in Haryana	64.83% of total population of State
Male workforce in Haryana	76.34%
Female workforce in Haryana	23.66%
Workforce living in rural areas	67.33%
Workforce living in urban areas	32.67%
Worker classification	76.68% are workers and 21.32% are marginal workers
Workforce related to agriculture	44.96%
Workforce employed in domestic industries	2.94%
Workforce employed in other sectors	52.10%

Population of Scheduled Castes (SC) in Haryana As per the Census 2011

- Total SC population — 51,13,615 (20.17%)
- Share in India's SC population — 2.54%
- Total SC Males — 27,09,656
- Total SC Females — 24,03,959
- Literacy Rate — 66.85% (75.92% male ; 56.64% female)
- District with highest SC literacy rate — Rewari
- District with lowest SC literacy rate — Sirsa
- State's overall SC sex ratio — 887
- State's SC Child-Sex Ratio (0-6 yrs) — 876

Districts with Highest and Lowest SC Population

Maximum (in descending order)		Minimum (in ascending order)	
Districts	SC Population	Districts	SC Population
Hisar	4,08,785	Nuh (Mewat)	75,251
Sirsa	3,87,381	Panchkula	1,01,830
Bhiwani	3,41,162	Mahendragarh	1,56,314
Karnal	3,39,604	Jhajjar	1,70,448

Note *There are no Scheduled Tribes (STs) in Haryana.*

CHECK CHAPTER KNOWLEDGE

1 The Census of 2011 was the .... census of Haryana.
(a) 1st (b) 3rd
(c) 5th (d) 7th

2 What is the total population of Haryana as per Census 2011? *PGT 2016*
(a) 2,63,72,462 (b) 2,53,51,462
(c) 2,72,63,462 (d) 2,51,53,462

3 What is the rank of Haryana in India in terms of total population of the state? *PGT 2016*
(a) 14th (b) 15th
(c) 16th (d) 18th

4 As per Census 2011, what is the percentage of total population of Haryana to the total population of the country? *Haryana Police 2018*
(a) 2.09% (b) 4.08%
(c) 6.70% (d) 10.10%

5 Which district of Haryana is the most populous district of the state?
(a) Faridabad (b) Gurugram
(c) Hisar (d) Panchkula

6 As per Census 2011 and prediction of 2020, which city of Haryana has the highest population? *HSSC 2023, 21*
(a) Ambala (b) Faridabad
(c) Panipat (d) Gurugram

7 Which district of Haryana has the lowest population in the state?
(a) Panchkula (b) Fatehabad
(c) Faridabad (d) Rewari

8 Which district of Haryana has the highest female population as per Census 2011? *HSSC Auction Recorder 2016*
(a) Gurugram (b) Bhiwani
(c) Karnal (d) Faridabad

9 Which district of Haryana has the lowest female population?
(a) Bhiwani (b) Panchkula
(c) Hisar (d) None of these

10 What is the population growth rate of Haryana, as per Census 2011?
(a) 15.69% (b) 17.49%
(c) 18.5% (d) 19.90%

11 What is the rank of Haryana in India in terms of population growth in the state? *HSSC 2022, 20*
(a) 15th (b) 16th
(c) 17th (d) 14th

12 As per Census 2011, which district of Haryana has the highest population growth rate in the state? *PGT 2016*
(a) Gurugram (b) Mewat
(c) Faridabad (d) Palwal

13 As per Census 2011, which district of Haryana has the lowest population growth rate in the state?
(a) Ambala (b) Jind
(c) Jhajjar (d) Gurugram

14 The crude density of population is known as *Haryana Tehsildar 2019*
(a) Mathematical density
(b) Agricultural density
(c) Nutritional density
(d) None of the above

15 What is the Population density of Haryana as per Census 2011? *HSSC CET 2024*
(a) 573 (b) 666 (c) 733 (d) 855

16 Which district of Haryana has the highest population density, as per Census 2011? *HSSC 2020, PGT 2016*
(a) Panipat (b) Rohtak
(c) Panchkula (d) Faridabad

17 Which district of Haryana has the lowest population density, as per census 2011? *PGT 2016*
(a) Sirsa (b) Jhajjar
(c) Karnal (d) Rewari

18 What is the sex-ratio of Haryana, as per census 2011? *HSSC 2024, 20*
(a) 844 (b) 879 (c) 911 (d) 958

19 Which district of Haryana has the highest sex-ratio in the state as per Census 2011?
(a) Fatehabad (b) Sirsa
(c) Mewat (Nuh) (d) Rewari

20 Which district of Haryana has the lowest sex-ratio in the state as per Census 2011?
(a) Rohtak (b) Gurugram
(c) Jind (d) Sonipat

21 What is the literacy rate of Haryana, as per Census 2011? *HSSC CET 2024, 15, PGT 2016*

(a) 65.94% (b) 75.60%
(c) 84.06% (d) 91.11%

22 Which district of Haryana has the highest literacy in the state as per Census 2011?

(a) Faridabad (b) Ambala
(c) Gurugram (d) Panchkula

23 Which district of Haryana has the lowest literacy rate in the state as per Census 2011? *Anganwadi 2016*

(a) Mewat (Nuh) (b) Sirsa
(c) Kaithal (d) Fatehabad

24 Which district of Haryana has recorded highest female literacy rate as per Census 2011? *HSSC 2021, HSSC Clerk 2017,*

(a) Faridabad (b) Ambala
(c) Karnal (d) Gurugram

25 Which district of Haryana has recorded lowest female literacy rate as per Census 2011? *HSSC Supervisor 2017*

(a) Mewat (Nuh) (b) Mahendragarh
(c) Rewari (d) Bhiwani

26 As per the Census 2011 what is the percentage of population of children (0-6 years) in Haryana?

(a) 12.3% (b) 13.3%
(c) 13.6% (d) 13.9%

27 The child sex-ratio of Haryana, as per Census 2011 is

(a) 840 (b) 845
(c) 859 (d) 834

28 As per Census 2011, what is the percentage of rural population of Haryana? *HSSC 2023, PGT 2016*

(a) 65.12% (b) 62.5%
(c) 72.5% (d) 75.12%

29 As per Census 2011, which district of Haryana has the highest urban population in the state?

(a) Gurugram (b) Hisar
(c) Panipat (d) Faridabad

30 As per Census 2011, which district of Haryana has the lowest urban population in the state?

(a) Mahendragarh (b) Fatehabad
(c) Nuh (d) Rewari

31 What is the child mortality rate of Haryana as per Census 2011?

(a) 39 per thousand (b) 40 per thousand
(c) 30 per thousand (d) 50 per thousand

32 Population of which religious group is highest in Haryana? *HSSC Supervisor 2017*

(a) Hindusim (c) Buddhist
(b) Muslim (Islam) (d) Jewish

33 As per Census 2011, how much percentage of working population is engaged in agricultural practices? *HSSC 2022*

(a) 44.96% (b) 45.90%
(c) 50.22% (d) 60.26%

34 As per Census 2011, what is the percentage of the total Scheduled Caste (SC) population of Haryana to the total SC population of the country? *PGT 2016*

(a) 1.0% (b) 2.54%
(c) 3.51% (d) 4.61%

35 As per Census 2011, which district of Haryana has the highest SC literacy rate in the state?

(a) Sirsa (b) Gurugram
(c) Rewari (d) Mewat

36 As per Census 2011, which district of Haryana has the highest SC population in the state?

(a) Jhajjar (b) Mewat
(c) Panchkula (d) Hisar

37 Which district of Haryana has the lowest SC population in the state as per Census 2011?

(a) Sirsa (b) Mewat
(c) Bhiwani (d) Hisar

38 Which state of India does not have any Scheduled Tribe population?

(a) Jammu and Kashmir (b) West Bengal
(c) Haryana (d) Bihar

39 As per 1981 Census, Haryana had......... districts. *HSSC CET, 2024*

(a) 9 (b) 11
(c) 12 (d) 10

CORRECT ANSWERS

1. (c)	2. (b)	3. (d)	4. (a)	5. (a)	6. (b)	7. (a)	8. (d)	9. (b)	10. (d)
11. (b)	12. (a)	13. (c)	14. (a)	15. (a)	16. (d)	17. (a)	18. (b)	19. (c)	20. (b)
21. (b)	22. (c)	23. (a)	24. (d)	25. (a)	26. (b)	27. (d)	28. (a)	29. (d)	30. (c)
31. (c)	32. (a)	33. (a)	34. (b)	35. (c)	36. (d)	37. (b)	38. (c)	39. (c)	

CHAPTER 29

KNOW YOUR STATE
HARYANA

Education and Health Sector in Haryana

- The efforts to develop education in Haryana began even before the country gained independence.
- Prior to becoming a full-fledged state, only 20% of Haryana's population was literate. However, according to the Census 2011, the state's literacy rate has risen to 75.6%, with male literacy at 84.1% and female literacy at 65.9%.
- Haryana ranks 22nd in the country in terms of literacy rate. Among its districts, **Gurugram** has the highest literacy rate at 84.7%, while **Mewat** has the lowest at 54.1%.

Beginning of Integrated Education in Haryana

- Haryana focused more on organised education after the revenue settlement of 1830-40.
- A district school was opened in Delhi in 1858, followed by similar schools in Jhajjar, Rohtak, Karnal and Rewari, all linked to the University of Calcutta.
- By 1860, only Hisar and Bhiwani had one **Anglo-Middle School** each. Until 1877, the only college for people from Haryana was in Lahore.
- **Gurukuls** were introduced in Haryana after Swami Dayanand Saraswati established Arya Samaj in 1875 AD.

> In 1882 AD, the Education Commission made recommendation for setting-up of model schools in each district and by 1907, these schools were established to improve primary and secondary education.

Education in Haryana

- On 3rd June, 2011, the Haryana State Government notified the Right to Free and Compulsory Education Rules, 2011 under the Right to Education Act.
- This ensured that every child in Haryana receives free study materials.

Primary and Secondary Education

- Primary education means elementary or basic education. Primary education is considered to be the basis of the entire education system due to its completion at the elementary level.

Education System and Growth

- The **Directorate of Education** in **Panchkula** district oversees the management of primary and secondary education.
- Senior IAS officers serve as Directors of the **Department of Secondary Education.**
- **Primary Schools** (Classes 1-5) Increased from 4,447 to 8,743 schools.
- **Secondary Schools** (Classes 6-8) Increased to 1,287 schools.
- **Higher Secondary Schools** (Classes 9-12) Increased to 1,960 schools.

Central Schemes for Primary and Secondary Education

Following are Central Government's schemes related to primary and secondary education

Beti Bachao Beti Padhao Programme

- Launched on — 22nd January, 2015 in Panipat (By PM Narendra Modi)
- Run by — Joint initiative of three central ministries, namely Ministry of Women and Child Development, Ministry of Health and Family Welfare and Ministry of Human Resource Development.
- Objective — Eliminate sex discrimination and promote education for girls.
- The scheme was initially launched with a budget of ₹100 crore.
- The renowned wrestler **Sakshi Malik** has been appointed as the Brand Ambassador for the scheme in Haryana.

Aarohi Model School

- Launched by — Central Government in 2011-12.
- Objective — Improve level of education in backward blocks of Haryana from Classes 6th to 12th.
- Location — 36 Educationally Backward Blocks of Haryana, with one school in each block.
- Implementation — Part of the State Education Policy since 2015-16.
- Impact — Gained recognition from other states for its school infrastructure and education reform.

Operational Areas for Schemes

The scheme is active in 10 districts of Haryana

- Panipat
- Fatehabad
- Jind
- Sirsa
- Palwal
- Mahendragarh
- Hisar
- Mewat
- Kaithal
- Bhiwani

Rashtriya Madhyamik Shiksha Abhiyan (RMSA)

- Launched in — 2009
- Implemented in Haryana — 2009-11

Its main objectives are as follows

- To improve the quality of secondary education by freeing children from social and gender based barriers in the education sector.
- Provide universal access to secondary level education to every child by the year 2017 and to ensure universal retention for every child by the year 2020.

Sarva Shiksha Abhiyan

- Implementation — 2001 (By Central Government), 2002 (in Haryana)
- Conducted by — Haryana School Education Project Council
- Headquarters of Haryana council — Panchkula
- Head of Haryana council — Chief Minister of Haryana
- Its objective is to remove gender and social inequality in the field of education.
- The main goal of this programme is to build new schools, provide alternative education facilities, build rooms and toilets in schools and provide modern training to teachers.
- The 86th Constitutional Amendment further strengthened the objectives of the Sarva Shiksha Abhiyan.

Mid-Day Meal Scheme

- Launched by — Central Government on 15th August, 1995
- Implemented in — Government primary schools, local bodies, state-aided primary and minor secondary schools
- Under this scheme, nutritious food is provided to all children daily. The main objective of this scheme is to increase enrollment and attendance of children in schools.

PM Schools for Rising India (PM SHRI)

- Launched by — Central Government on 7th September, 2022
- Objective — Setting up more than 14,500 PM SHRI Schools
- These schools showcase the implementation of the National Education Policy, 2020.

NIPUN Bharat Mission

- Launched by — Central Government on 5th July, 2021
- Objective — It is an umbrella scheme under which various programmes have been launched to achieve universal acquisition of foundational literacy and numeracy skills at primary level by 2025.

State Government's Schemes for Primary and Secondary Education

The State Government's schemes related to Primary and Secondary Education are as follows

Heritage Corner Scheme

- Announced by — Haryana CM Manohar Lal Khattar
- Launch date — 30th December, 2020
- Objective — Introduce students to India's rich history, culture and national heroes.
- In the first phase, heritage corners will be built in 100 schools. Later, these corners will be established in all schools of the state.

> Information about the major historical monuments of every district and archives of the Department of Archaeology will be available in every school in the district.

Reading Mission 2022

- Launched by — Haryana State Government
- Objective — Promote reading habits among young students
- Under this mission, state's monthly book review sessions and mass book reading are to be organised by students in educational institutions.
- Besides, a 45-minute mass reading programme should be held on the fourth Saturday of the month.

Samagra Shiksha

- The vision of Samagra Shiksha scheme is to ensure inclusive and equitable quality education from pre-nursery (pre-school) to senior secondary stage by 2030 in accordance with Sustainable Development Goals (SDGs) for education.
- The aim of the scheme is to universalise quality school education.
- The main **objectives** of Samagra Shiksha are
  - to make provision equality education and enhancing learning out comes of students
  - bridge social and gender gaps in school education
  - ensuring minimum standards in schooling provision
  - support in implementation of Right of Children to Free and Compulsory Education (RTE) Act, 2009
  - to promote vocationalisation of education

Right to Education

- The State Government has notified the **Free and Compulsory Education Rules-2011** for every child of Haryana under the Right to Education Act on 3rd June, 2011.
- Under this, the government provides free textbooks, practice books and costumes to the children.

Chief Minister School Beautification Scheme

- Launched in — 2011-12
- Objective — Promote hygiene awareness among students in state schools
- Schools are selected at block, district and state levels for beautification funding.
- Funding allocation
  - **Block level** ₹ 50,000 per selected high school and secondary school.
  - **District level** ₹ 1 lakh per selected high school and secondary school.
  - **State level** ₹ 5 lakh per selected high school and secondary school.

Haryana CHEERAG Scheme

- CHEERAG stands for **Chief Minister Equal Education Relief Assistance and Grant Scheme.**
- It is also known by the names – Haryana Cheerag Yojana or Mukhyamantri Haryana Saman Shiksha, Rahat Evam Anudan Yojana.

- It was launched by Department of Elementary Education on 1st July, 2022.

> CHEERAG Scheme's objective is to provide quality education to poor students by securing their admission in private school.

- Eligible students can take free of cost education from Class 3rd to 12th in listed private schools.

Punjabi Language Incentive Scheme

- Haryana Government conferred the status of second state language to Punjabi language in the year 2010.
- Under this scheme, the scholarships are given to those students who continue to study Punjabi language in 9th and 11th grades on the basis of marks obtained in Punjabi language in 8th and 10th grade board examinations.
- The scholarships are awarded as ₹ 50 per month for students of 9th and 10th and ₹ 75 per month for students of 11th and 12th.

Cash Reward Scheme

- It was launched by the Government of Haryana in the year 2008-09.
- Under this scheme, the lumpsum amount is provided by the Government to the scheduled caste students (both boys and girls) from the 5th to the 8th grades for the purchasing of school bags, school dress and stationery items.

Free Text Book Scheme

- The Free Text Book Scheme was started by the Government of Haryana in the year 2008-09.
- Under this scheme, free textbooks are provided to all scheduled caste students studying in Classes from 9th to 12th.

Free Education for Girls

- Under this scheme, free education has been provided to all girls upto graduation.
- Transport facility has also been provided by the State Government for the girls of **Mewat** and **Morni** areas.

Residential and Childhood Schools

- To promote girls education, residential schools for girls are being opened in every educationally backward block under **Kasturba Gandhi Balika Vidyalaya Scheme.**
- Residential schools have been established in Panipat for physically challenged students.
- Many Bachpan pre-schools have been opened by the voluntary organisations in the state for the working laboures children near their workplace.

Schemes for SCs and STs Students in Haryana

- Dalits and backward class students are provided **free coaching** by the State Government for the preparation of government jobs.
- **Pre-metric Scholarship** is provided to scheduled castes students of Classes 9th and 10th in the state.
- **Post-metric scholarship** scheme has also been started for the scheduled castes students of the state.
- **Babu Jagjivan Ram Hostel Scheme** has been started keeping in view the educational housing requirement of the students of scheduled castes and backward classes of the state.
- **Monthly Incentive Scheme** for scheduled caste students has been launched in the state.
- **Free Bicycle** to SC student scheme was launched in the year 2008-09. The main objective of this scheme is to provide educational avenues to students of SC families.

Dr. Ambedkar Medhavi Chhatar Sansodhit Yojana

- **Dr. Ambedkar Medhavi Chhatar Sansodhit Yojana** was launched in the state in the year 2005-06.
- This scheme was started to provide scholarships to students belonging to scheduled castes and backward classes.
- Under this scheme, there is a provision to give ₹ 8,000 to ₹ 12,000 annual scholarship to students from Class 9 to postgraduate level of scheduled castes based on the percentage.

> Under this scheme, students of other backward classes are given the benefit of this scholarship in Class 11th on the basis of Class 10th marks.

Haryana School Education Board

- It was established in the year 1969 in Chandigarh, which was shifted to **Bhiwani** district in the year 1981.

Key Milestones

Year/Key Point	Description
1970	Conducted the 10th Class examinations for the first time.
1976	Conducted the 8th standard examination for the first time (middle school leaving exam.)
1985-86	Introduced the 10 + 2 + 3 system by the State Government.
1987	Conducted the 12th examination under the 10+2 system for the first time.
1990	Conducted the 10+2 (Professional) examination.
1994	Established the Haryana Open School.
2006-07	Implemented the semester system for the first time.
2006-07	Haryana became the first state to implement the CCE (Continuous and Comprehensive Evaluation) system at the school level.

State Council of Educational Research and Training

- The State Council of Educational Research and Training (SCERT) was established in April, 1979 in Gurugram by merging the 'State Institute of Education' and 'State Science Institute' with the main objective of improving the quality of education and training and skill development of teachers.
- This council organises seminars from time-to-time for the development of creative and scientific approach of teachers. This council surveys schools in the state and determines the syllabus.

Sainik School in Haryana

- The Sainik Schools are located in Karnal and Rewari districts of Haryana.
- The first Sainik School in Haryana, Sainik Vidyalaya, was established in Kunjpura village in Karnal, in 1961.

Sainik School, Kunjpura

- The Sainik School located in Rewari district was established on 20th August, 2008.
- A new Sainik School is being set-up in Matanhail village of Jhajjar district.
- The new Sainik School in Jhajjar is being set-up on 312 acres of land.

Kendriya Vidyalaya in Haryana

- Kendriya Vidyalaya is a primary and secondary education institute in India, established in 1963.
- It is affiliated with the Central Board of Secondary Education (CBSE) in India.

- In Haryana, 23 Kendriya Vidyalayas are functioning.
- There are no Kendriya Vidyalayas located in Kaithal and Mewat.
- Two Kendriya Vidyalayas are located in districts like Panipat, Rewari, Jhajjar, Gurugram, etc.

Jawahar Navodaya Vidyalaya in Haryana

- Jawahar Navodaya Vidyalaya was launched in 1986 as an experimental initiative.
- It is managed by the **Navodaya Vidyalaya Samiti**, an autonomous body under the Ministry of Human Resource Development, Department of Higher Education and Government of India.

- The scheme aims to establish Sarvodaya Schools at the rural level across state.
- Jawahar Navodaya Vidyalayas have been established in all districts of Haryana except Palwal and Charkhi-Dadri.

Jawahar Navodaya Vidyalaya in Haryana

District	Location	District	Location
Ambala	Po Kaulan	Rewari	Naichana
Yamunanagar	Gulabgarh	Nuh	Nagina
Panchkula	Mouli	Hisar	Pabra
Kurukshetra	Nivarsi	Sirsa	Odhan, Dabwali (Shergarh)
Karnal	Sagga	Fatehabad	Khera Kheri
Panipat	Naultha	Jind	Khunga Kothi
Kaithal	Titram	Bhiwani	Devarala
Sonipat	Butana	Mahendragarh	Karira
Rohtak	Ghuskani	Gurugram	Farrukhnagar
Jhajjar	Kaloi	Faridabad	Mothuka
Palwal	Garhpuri	–	–

Higher Education in Haryana
(Colleges and Universities)

- Higher education plays a significant role in the development of a state.
- The **first university of the state** was established in the year 1927 at Rohtak, which is currently named as **Pandit Nekiram College.**
- Initially, this college was imparted education upto 12th standard only. In the year 1944, it was recognised for graduation.
- The **first degree college of the state** is the **SA Jain College**, which was established in the year 1938.
- In the year 1944, All India Jat Heroes Memorial Colleges was established in Rohtak and Vaishya College in Bhiwani.
- **Ahir University** was established in the year 1945 in Rewari district of the state. After this, in the year 1946, Vaishya College was established in Rohtak.
- There were only 6 universities (1 government and 5 non-government) in the state of Haryana at the time of independence to India.
- At the time of formation of the state (1966), Haryana had only 1 university (Kurukshetra University) and 45 colleges.
- Special provision for higher education for girls has been made in the state.
- There are 97 government-aided private colleges in the state out of which 35 are for girls.

> According to the Economic Survey 2023-24, out of the total 182 Govt. colleges, 63 Govt. colleges schools are exclusively for girls.

Major State Universities

University	Description
Kurukshetra University 	• This university was established on 11th January, 1956 as a residential university on the banks of Brahma Sarovar in Kurukshetra. • Its foundation was laid by **Dr. Rajendra Prasad**, the first President of India. It is spread over about 400 acres of land. • It is located on the holy land where the Mahabharata War took place and the message of Bhagavad Gita was given. • This university was started with Sanskrit department only. • The Post Graduate Regional Centre of this university is located in Jind. • The Manuscript Museum at Kurukshetra University was established by **Pt. Sthanu Dutt Sharma.**
Chaudhary Charan Singh Agricultural University 	• This university was established on 2nd February, 1970 in Hisar. It is one of the largest universities in Asia. It is named after the seventh Prime Minister of the country. • Earlier it was under **Punjab Agricultural University**. After the establishment of the state, it was made an independent body. • It was awarded as the best institute in 1997 and also won the Sardar Patel Outstanding Institute Award, in 2016 by the Indian Institute of Agricultural Research.

University	Description
Maharishi Dayanand University 	• This university was established in the year 1976 in Rohtak. It provides education related to many fields including undergraduate and postgraduate. • This institute has 36 departments related to education and research. There are affiliated colleges in the districts of Bhiwani, Faridabad, Gurugram, Jhajjar, Hisar, Panipat, Rohtak, Sonipat, etc. • Two satellite campuses of this university are located in Rewari and Gurugram.
Chaudhary Devi Lal University 	• This university was established on 2nd April, 2003 in the name of former Deputy Prime Minister of India, Chaudhary Devi Lal. The university is located in Sirsa district. The university is spread over about 6 acres of land. It has 16 academic departments. • There is proper arrangement of library, laboratory and hostels here.
Bhagat Phool Singh Mahila Vishwavidyalaya 	• This university is located in Khanpur Kalan, Sonipat. It was established in the year 2006. This university, established by the Government of Haryana, is the **first women's university** in North India. • This university also provides education in Micro Financial Management and Integrated Energy Resources Management by CSUIR (Center for Society University Interface and Research). An India-Asian Study Center has also been established under the UGC in this university.

Central University

- The Central University of Haryana was established in the year 2009 in **Janta-Pali village** (Mahendragarh).
- This university was established by the Government of India under the Central Universities Act, 2009. The university is spread over 488 acres of land. The university is temporarily being run in **Narnaul Government College**.
- There are 30 departments in the University under which graduation, post-graduation, M-Phil and Ph.D courses are offered.

Other Universities of Haryana

University	Establishment
Pandit BD Sharma University of Health Sciences, Rohtak	2008
Lala Lajpat Rai University of Veterinary and Animal Science, Hisar	2010
Dr. Bhimrao Ambedkar National Law University, Sonipat	2012
Indira Gandhi University, Rewari	2013
Chaudhary Bansilal University, Bhiwani	2014
Chaudhary Ranbir Singh University, Jind	2014
Haryana Vishwakarma Skill University, Palwal	2016
Maharana Pratap Horticulture University, Karnal	2016
Gurugram University, Gurugram	2017

Private Universities of Haryana

- 25 private universities have been established in Haryana to enhance the quality and accessibility of higher education.
- The **first World University of Design in the country** was set-up in 2018 in Sonipat, under the Haryana Private University Act, 2006.

Private Universities of Haryana

University	Location	Establishment Year
Maharishi Markandeshwar University	Ambala	1993
PDM University	Bahadurgarh	1995
North Camp University	Gurugram	1996
Manav Rachna University	Faridabad	2004
OP Jindal Global University	Sonipat	2009
ITM University	Gurugram	2010
APJ Satya University	Gurugram	2010
AMITY University	Manesar, Gurugram	2010
Jagannath University	Bahadurgarh	2010
NIILM University	Kaithal	2011
MVN University	Palwal	2012
Baba Mastanath University	Rohtak	2012
Ansal University	Gurugram	2012
SRM University	Sonipat	2013
GD Goenka University	Gurugram	2013
Shree Guru Gobind Singh Tricentenary University	Gurugram	2013
KR Mangalam University	Gurugram	2013
Ashoka University	Sonipat	2014
BML Munjal University	Gurugram	2014
Starex University	Gurugram	2016
World Design University	Sonipat	2018
IILM University	Gurugram	2018
OM Sterling Global University	Hisar	2019
Rishihood University	Sonipat	2020
Geeta University	Panipat	2022

Other Vocational Institutions of Haryana

Vocational Institute	Location
Institute of Film and Television, Fashion and Design, Fine Arts and Professional Studies	Rohtak
Rajiv Gandhi Education City	Sonipat
Government Footwear Institute	Rewari

Prestigious Institutions in Haryana

National Dairy Research Institute

- It was established in the year 1955 in Karnal district of Haryana state. The institute was initially known as the Imperial Institute of Animal Husbandry and Dairying which first established in Bengaluru in the year 1923.In the year 1936, its name was changed to Imperial Dairy Institute. It was transferred to Karnal in the year 1955.
- In the year 1989, it was conferred with the status of deemed university.

The Indian Institute of Wheat and Barley Research

- It was established in Karnal in the year 1978. In the year 2004, this institute was recognised as Indian Wheat and Barley Research Institute.
- This institute ensures food security of India by improving the productivity of wheat and rice.

The National Institute of Animal Genetics

- Bureau of Animal Genetic Resources and National Animal Genetic Institute were established as twin entities in Bengaluru on 21st September, 1984 and were transferred to Karnal in 1985.
- Bureau of National Animal Genetic Resources was merged in the year 1995 to function as a single unit.
- This pioneering institute is dedicated to the task of identification, characterisation, conservation and sustainable use of livestock and poultry genetic wealth in the country as per its instruction.

Indian Institute of Management, (IIM) Rohtak

- Indian Institute of Management, Rohtak is a public vocational school. It was established in the year 2009 under the 11th Five Year Plan. Its motto is 'Gyanen Gunen Ch Prabandh'.
- It is the 8th Indian Institute of Management.

Major Schemes Related to Higher Education in Haryana

Scheme	Description
Rajiv Gandhi Education City	• It is a planned city of education in Sonipat district of Haryana. It was founded in June 2012. • Under this scheme, there is a plan to run 13 educational institutions in this city. • As of October, 2020, 10 educational institutions have been started in this operation. • India's first and only design university, the World University of Design, has been established in Rajiv Gandhi Education City, Sonipat in 2018.
Soft Skill Scheme	• This scheme was started in the year 2008 in 17 government colleges in Haryana. • The objective of the scheme is to enhance the ability of the students and provide them training for communication skills, interpersonal skills, BPO (Business Process Outsourcing) and ITES fields.
EDUSAT Project	• The then Prime Minister of India Dr. Manmohan Singh launched the EDUSAT Satellite based educational programmes in 2005. • This project was started by the Government of Haryana in the year 2007 in the government colleges of the state. The objective of this project is to provide education through satellite system. • Through EDUSAT (Education Satellite) education is being broadcasting in primary, secondary, college level and technical institutes. • The EDUSAT project has been started under the soft skill scheme. • The project was expanded to private colleges and government aided colleges in the year 2008-09. • In the year 2009-10, this project was implemented for the first year of B.A, B.SC and B.Com. In the same year, a state level competition was organised through this programme and speeches were given on topics related to music, film and drama.
English Labs	• English labs have been established in 25 government colleges of the state for students of higher education. • Its main objective is to impart education for English language and its application and to make students self-educated.
Women-Girl Empowerment Scheme	• Under this scheme, women's rooms have been established in all government colleges of the state. • The purpose of this scheme is to provide appropriate information to the students regarding the gender related topics. • From the year 2008-09, women's rooms were converted into centres of excellence.
Rajiv Gandhi National Fellowship Scheme	• Under this scheme, meritorious students of scheduled castes and tribes are provided scholarship by the Government of India for pursuing M. Phil and Ph.D in the field of higher education. • This scheme has been started by the Ministry of Tribal Affairs and Ministry of Social Justice and Empowerment.

Technical Education in Haryana

- At the time of Haryana's inception in 1966, there were only 6 polytechnic institutes, with 4 being government-run and 2 government-aided private institutes.
- The first engineering college was started in Kurukshetra, which is now known as the National Institute of Technology (NIT), Kurukshetra.
- The state now has several prominent technical universities and institutes offering a variety of engineering and technical education.

Major Technical Universities in Haryana

University/Institute	Description
National Institute of Technology (NIT)	• It is located in Kurukshetra district. • It was established in the year 1963 with its name Regional Engineering College, REC, through a joint venture between the Government of India and the Government of Punjab. • On 26th June, 2002, its name was changed to National Institute of Technology and was also given the status of deemed university. • It offers four years B.Tech course along with other programmes such as M. Tech, Ph.D, MBA and so on.
Deenbandhu Chhotu Ram University of Science and Technology	• This university was established in the year 1987 as an engineering college at Murthal (Sonipat). Initially, its name was Chhotu Ram Government College of Engineering. • This institution started with mechanical engineering and electronics and communications. It was the **first government engineering college** established in the state. • On 6th June, 2006 the Haryana Government converted it into a university in November, 2006 under Act-29 of the Legislature of the State of Haryana. • Its name was also changed to Deenbandhu Chhotu Ram University of Science and Technology. • This university was awarded the Improvement Programme for quality of technical education. • The **Central Institute of Plastics and Technology** was established in the year 2017 under this university.
JC Bose Institute of Science and Technology	• Initially JC (Jagdish Chandra) Bose Institute of Science and Technology was known as YMCA (Young Men Christian Association, YMCA) Institute of Technology. • It is located in the Faridabad district. It was established in the year 1969. • This institute is being fully operated by the Government of Haryana since the year 1996. It received the status of university in the year 2009. • The main objective of this institute is to develop science and technology through synthesised science.
Guru Jambheshwar University of Science and Technology	• This university was established on 20th October, 1995 in Hisar. • It provides high quality technical education in the state. In addition to technical education, courses in science, pharmacy and management are also available.
Indian Institute of Information Technology (IIIT)	• It is located at Sonipat. It is a joint venture of the Ministry of Education (Government of India), Government of Haryana, with industries in PPP model and has been declared as the institute of national importance. • The academic session of IIIT Sonipat started from its mentor institute NIT-Kurukshetra from year 2014.

Technical Institutions to be Established in Haryana

- The Central Government has announced the establishment of a National Electronic Education Institute in Kurukshetra.
- To expand technical education in the state, IIT Delhi is setting up an extension centre in Badsa village in Jhajjar district.
- A Science Park and Faculty Development Centre is also proposed to be built under this institute.
- There is also a plan to set-up a Development Centre and Bio-technology Research Park by the Delhi IIT in Jhajjar of the state.
- To promote technical education in Haryana, the following engineering colleges have been set-up in the state by the State Government
  - Chaudhary Charan Singh State Institute of Engineering and Technology (Jhajjar)
  - Rao Birendra Singh State Institute of Engineering and Technology (Rewari)
  - Engineering College Neelokheri (Karnal)

Principal Research Institutes of Haryana

Institute	Establishment Year
National Institute of Dairy Research, Karnal	1955
Central Institute of Soil Salinity Research, Karnal	1969
National Integrated Pest Management Research Institute, Faridabad	1981
National Institute of Animal Genetics, Karnal	1984
National Bureau of Animal Genetics Resources, Karnal	1985
Central Institute for Research on Buffaloes	1985
Directorate of Wheat Research, Karnal	1990
National Brain Research Institute, Gurugram	1997
Centre for Plant Biotechnology Hisar	2000

Polytechnic Educational Institutes in Haryana

- Two polytechnic institutions have been established in Faridabad (Neemka) and Kaithal (Shergarh).
- Additional polytechnic institutions have been set-up by the State Government in Nuh (Indri and Malab), Bhiwani (Chhapar), Fatehabad (Jamalpur Shekho) and Palwal (Mandakola).

> Several technical institutions have been established in Kaithal, Rewari, **Yamunanagar**, **Kurukshetra**, **Panipat**, **Fatehabad** and **Panchkula** districts, with financial assistance from the **Central Government**.

- In **Yamunanagar**, a polytechnic institute has been set-up by the Ministry of Minority Affairs of Central Government, under the **Multi-Sectoral** Development Programme.
- The **Ministry of Micro and Small Industries** of Central Government has also established a **technical centre** at the Polytechnic Institute in **Faridabad**.

Department of Skill Development and Industrial Training

- Industrial training was done by the Department of Industrial Training in the state, but in the year 2017, this department was also given the additional task of skill development campaign.
- After some time its name was changed to the Department of Skill Development and Industrial Training.
- All industrial training institutes in the state are directed by this institute.
- A total of 48 industrial training institutes were functioning in Haryana at the time of the establishment of the state.
- By the year 2019-20, the number of industrial training institutes in the state has increased to 418, out of which 172 are state industrial institutes and 246 private sector industrial institutes.
- Out of 172 State Industrial Institutes set-up in the state, 33% are reserved for women.
- To provide international level training to the youth of the state, the State Government is working closely with various institutions, which are as follow
  - The State Government is working on the Vocational Training Improvement Project with the help of World Bank.
  - Working under Public Private Partnership.
  - The State Government is also developing ITI as a center of excellence.
  - Currently, the skill development and industrial training department of the state is doing all the work digitally. For this reason, it is the **first paperless department of the state.**

National Cadet Corps (NCC)

- The National Cadet Corps has expanded widely in the state of Haryana. Its headquarters is located in Chandigarh.
- The Ambala and Rohtak group headquarters of NCC implement about 20 NCC battalions in the state.
- The NCC also has girl's battalion in Ambala, Rohtak and Hisar districts of the state.

Headquarters of NCC in Haryana

Group Headquarters	Ambala and Rohtak
Air Squadron	Hisar, Karnal
Navel Battalion	Faridabad
Girl's Battalion	Ambala, Rohtak and Hisar
NCC Battalion	Rohtak, Jind, Sonipat, Kurukshetra, Ambala, Karnal, Narnaul, Jagadhri, Rewari, Gurugram, Bhiwani, Hisar
R & D Squadron	Hisar
NCC Academy	Karnal

New Initiatives of the State Government

- A research institute has been established at **Maharishi Dayanand University** (MDU) to focus on research related to Dr. Mangalsen's personality.
- Previous research institutes dedicated to figures like Sir Chhotu Ram, Maharishi Valmiki, Maharishi Dayanand, and Pt. Lakhmichand have also been set-up at the university.
- Under the Integrated Skill Development Scheme, courses on textile spinning, weaving and handloom are being offered in 71 districts across the state.
- A modern **Nandghar Anganwadi centre** has been set-up in Hasanpur village, Sonipat district.
- The State Government plans to establish an **industrial training institute** in Gurugram, focusing on automobile, textile and information technology training.
- The state has transitioned from the semester system to an annual examination system for 10th and 12th classes.
- Daily Diary maintenance has been made mandatory for teachers to promote self-discipline.
- The State Government has included cleanliness campaigns in the school curriculum to highlight the importance of cleanliness.

Health Scenario in Haryana

- The State Government is dedicated to provide high-quality and affordable healthcare services to all citizens of Haryana.
- The health services in the state have been modernised, including the enforcement of the Registration of Birth-Death Rules, 2001.
- The **State Urban Health Mission** has been launched to offer comprehensive healthcare services in urban areas, with a focus on slum populations.
- Haryana is the first state in the country to implement such an ambitious scheme, with an Urban Health Centre for every 1 lakh people.
- New Blood Banks are planned for Jhajjar, Fatehabad and Mandi-Dabwali, as blood banks are already established in all other districts.

Healthcare Infrastructure

As per the Economic Survey 2024-25, the state has the following healthcare infrastructure

- 22 District Civil Hospitals
- 50 Sub-Divisional Hospitals
- 122 Community Health Centres
- 33 Civil Dispensaries
- 13 Poly Clinics
- 408 Primary Health Centres
- 107 Urban Primary Health Centres
- 2734 Sub-Health Centres

In addition to this, there is new construction work, which has been completed for

- 33 Hospitals
- 46 Community Health Centres
- 63 Primary Health Centres
- 73 Sub-Health Centres in the state

Institutes of Medical Science in Haryana

- When Haryana was formed, it had only one medical college in Rohtak, established in 1960.
- In 1994, the **Pt. Bhagwat Dayal Sharma Institute** in Rohtak received postgraduate status in Medicine.
- Currently, Haryana has 5 five government medical universities and 1 government-aided university.

Medical Science Institutes in Haryana

State Government Medical Institutes	Private Medical Sciences Institutes
Bhagwat Dayal Sharma Postgraduate Institute of Medical Sciences, Rohtak	Maharishi Markandeshwar Institute of Medical Sciences and Research, Mulana, Ambala
Bhagat Phool Singh Government Women Medical College, Khanpur Kala, Sonipat	Sri Guru Gobind Singh Tricentenary Medical College, Gurugram
Shaheed Hasan Khan Mewati Government Medical College, Nalhar, Nuh	NC Medical College and Hospital, Israna, Panipat
Kalpana Chawla Medical College, Karnal	World College of Medical Science and Research, Jhajjar
ESIC Medical College, Faridabad	Adesh Medical College and Hospital, Mohri, Kurukshetra
Maharaja Agrasen Medical College, Agroha (government-aided)	

Universities of Health Sciences in Haryana

The Universities of Health Sciences in the state are as follows

Pt. Bhagwat Dayal Sharma University of Health Sciences

- Established in 1960 as a guest institute, Pt. Bhagwat Dayal Sharma University of Health Sciences initially held its classes in Patiala. However, from 1963 onwards, the classes were shifted to the Medical College premises in Rohtak.
- In 1994, the university was upgraded to a postgraduate institute.
- On 2nd June, 2008, it was granted the status of a University of Health Sciences by the State Government. Currently, all medical institutions in the state are affiliated with this university.

Pt. Deendayal Upadhyay University of Health Sciences

- In 2012, the State Government decided to establish a medical college in Karnal with the aim of providing top-notch medical facilities to Northern Haryana. The hospital is named in honour of renowned astronaut Kalpana Chawla.
- Following this, the State Government established Pt. Deendayal Upadhyay University of Medical Sciences in Karnal in 2016.
- Currently, the Kalpana Chawla Medical College and Hospital, established in 2017, is operational in Karnal.
- Pt. Deendayal Upadhyay Medical University, located in Kutail, Karnal, began offering nursing and physiotherapy courses from the campus of Kalpana Chawla Government Medical College, while the construction of the university's main building is underway.

Medical Colleges of Haryana

- The State Government has set a goal of establishing a medical college in every district of Haryana to provide the best healthcare services to all citizens.
- Medical colleges are being established in the Bhiwani, Panchkula and Jind districts under this initiative.

According to the Economic Survey 2024-25, the state currently has 6 Government Medical Colleges, 1 Government Dental College, and 13 Government Nursing Colleges.

As part of this initiative, the State Government plans to establish the following hospitals

State Medical College

A new medical college is planned on a 24-acre plot in Haibatpur village, Jind district. This will be part of the state's campaign to have a government medical college in each district, with efforts to link it to the National Central Scheme.

Panchkula Medical College

A government medical college is planned at Bhainsa Tibba, Panchkula. The project details are currently being prepared by Rohtak University of Medical Sciences.

Medical College in Narnaul

A new medical college is being set-up on a 79-acre site in Koriyavas village, Mahendragarh district, near the proposed Integrated Multi-modal Logistics Hub near Basheerpur village.

Medical College in Gurugram

A medical college is under development on a 29-acre site in Kherki Majra village, Gurugram district, through collaboration between the Municipal Corporation of Gurugram, GMDA and Sheetla Mata Trust.

Kalpana Chawla Medical College

It was founded in Karnal in 2017, named after the late space scientist Kalpana Chawla. It is affiliated with Deendayal Upadhyay Medical College, Karnal and has received recognition from the Medical Council of India.

All India Institute of Medical Sciences

- The State Government has allocated 300 acres of land in Badsa village, Jhajjar district, for the establishment of an expansion centre for the All India Institute of Medical Sciences (AIIMS).
- The outpatient department at this centre has been operational since 2012.
- Additionally, a **National Cancer Institute** has been built within the facility, with its foundation stone laid by then PM Dr. Manmohan Singh on 3rd January, 2014. It is the largest cancer institute in the country.

Government Institute of Medical Sciences

- To establish a medical college in conjunction with the district hospitals in the state, the construction of a college in Prem Nagar village, Bhiwani has commenced.
- The Central Government will provide a 60% grant for the construction of this college, while the remaining financial responsibility will be covered by the State Government.

Institute of Health and Family Welfare, Haryana

- The State Institute of Health and Family Welfare, Haryana, was established in Panchkula in 1992 to provide technical training for individuals working in the state's health sector.
- In 2000, it was recognised as the National Institute of Health and Family Welfare.
- The institute also oversees all Health and Family Welfare Departments across the state.

Some Initiatives for Health and Family Welfare by the State Government

- **e-treatment system** in the state was started with the objective of proper management and digitisation of health services. Initially, the system was introduced in General Hospital Sector-6 Panchkula, CHC Raipur Rani, PHC Barwala and BPS Girls Medical College, Khanpur Kalan.
- Online medical facility is being provided from all 55 hospitals and PGI Rohtak of the state. Since 2016, the Prime Minister's Safe Motherhood Campaign has been conducted in the state with the help of the Central Government.
- There is a plan to establish Yoga and Ayurveda as a natural hospital in the state. Under this, Haryana State Government has opened **gymnasiums** in the state.

> On 21st June, **Yoga Day** is also celebrated in the state with complete preparation.

- The State Government plans to set-up a Naturopathy Service Centre in Panchkula district. An AYUSH training centre is being set-up at the Institute of Indian System of Medicine and Research located at Panchkula. This training centre is being developed as a centre of excellence for AYUSH.

Health Related Schemes in Haryana

Comprehensive Cashless Health Facility (CCHF) Scheme

- The CCHF Scheme was launched on 1st November, 2023, initially for the employees of the Horticulture and Fisheries departments.
- From 1st January, 2024, the scheme was extended to employees and dependents of All India Services.
- The plan is to extend the scheme to all employees, pensioners and their dependents across all departments.

Limited Cashless Medical Services Scheme

- This scheme was launched on 30th November, 2017, for government employees and pensioners.
- Currently, it covers only 6 critical conditions, with a provision of 15 lakh allocated for it.

Tuberculosis-Free Haryana Campaign

- The Tuberculosis-Free Haryana Campaign was launched by the Chief Minister of Haryana, Manohar Lal Khattar, on 20th November, 2015, in Gurugram.
- In the first phase, the State Government aims to eliminate tuberculosis from districts such as Rewari, Gurugram, Palwal, Mahendragarh, Jhajjar and others.
- The campaign is being implemented in the state through a Public-Private Partnership (PPP) model.

Birth-Death Registration

- In Haryana, it is mandatory to register births and deaths within 21 days of occurrence, as per the Haryana Birth and Death Registration Rules, 2002, enacted by the State Government.
- The Aadhaar-enabled online birth and death registration system was launched on 2nd May, 2015.
- This system allows for the online registration of children up to the age of 5 years.
- Additionally, the State Government is working on linking each child to the Aadhaar scheme from birth, making Haryana the first state in the country to implement such a process.

Chief Minister Free Treatment Scheme

- The Chief Minister Free Treatment Scheme was launched on 1st January, 2014, with the primary aim of providing quality medical care to all citizens of the state.
- This scheme offers seven types of services free of charge in government healthcare institutions, including surgery, check-ups, diagnosis, OPD, medicines, transport and more.

Janani Suraksha Yojana

- The Janani Suraksha Yojana was launched by the State Government in April 2008 to reduce maternal mortality.
- The main objective of the scheme is to encourage women from scheduled castes and tribes to deliver in healthcare centres.
- Under this scheme, women from scheduled castes and scheduled tribes receive an incentive of ₹ 1,500 after delivery in government and private healthcare institutions in Haryana.

Integrated Disease Surveillance Programme (IDSP)

- The Integrated Disease Surveillance Programme (IDSP) has been implemented by the Haryana State Government in collaboration with the World Bank since 2005.
- Its primary goal is to prevent the spread of epidemics and address them promptly.
- The project focuses on improving the monitoring system for epidemics and collecting data to track diseases, enabling quick response actions in case of an outbreak.
- The state also runs various programmes under this initiative, including the TB control programme, leprosy prevention programme, malaria control programme and the national tobacco control programme.
- The National Old Age Health Care Programme is being carried out in Nuh, Ambala, Kurukshetra and Yamunanagar districts of Haryana.

Swasthya Aapke Dwar Programme

- The Swasthya Aapke Dwar Programme has been running since 1st November, 2003, with the aim of improving health services in the state by delivering healthcare services at the doorsteps.

Haryana Mental Health Programme

- The Haryana Mental Health Programme was launched in 1999, starting in the Kurukshetra district. Hisar and Gurugram joined the campaign in 2006.
- **Key Components**
  - **District Mental Health Programme** This programme has been operational in Gurugram, Hisar and Kurukshetra since 2006, with Panchkula also included in 2015.
  - **State Institute of Mental Health, Rohtak** Established in 2011 at PGIMS Rohtak, this institute has been under the Department of Health and Family Welfare's management since 2015.
  - **Centre for Mental Health Excellence** Founded in 2009-10 under the Psychiatric Department of Postgraduate Institute of Medical Sciences, Rohtak, this centre focuses on training human resources for mental health programmes, especially psychiatrists and psychologists.

Deendayal Newborn Baby Safety Scheme

- Under the Deendayal Newborn Baby Safety Scheme, the state plans to provide baby care kits to all mothers and newborns in public healthcare institutions.

National Tuberculosis Programme

- A revised National Tuberculosis Programme has been implemented in five districts–Faridabad, Gurugram, Jind, Karnal and Sonipat–to control tuberculosis.
- The programme provides free medicines to those affected.

Mission Indradhanush

- Mission Indradhanush was launched by the Ministry of Health and Family Welfare, Government of India, on 25th December, 2014.
- It aims to provide 7 vaccines for 7 diseases included in the Universal Immunisation Programme: tuberculosis, polio, myelitis, hepatitis-B, diphtheria, pertussis (whooping cough), tetanus and measles.
- The Chief Minister of Haryana launched this mission on 7th April, 2015, across 13 districts: Nuh, Faridabad, Panipat, Karnal, Palwal, Gurugram, Jhajjar, Kurukshetra, Sonipat, Sirsa, Yamunanagar, Rewari and Rohtak.
- By 2024, five phases of the mission had been completed in the state.

National Health Insurance Scheme

- The scheme is run by the Employees State Insurance in Haryana, offering an annual insurance coverage of ₹ 30,000.

Family Welfare Programme

- The Family Welfare Programme in Haryana is implemented as a mass campaign, successfully reducing the state's birth rate. In 1971, the birth rate was 42.1, which decreased to 20.7 babies per thousand by 2018.
- Asha workers, who operate in hospitals, distribute contraceptive materials free of charge every Saturday. On Tuesdays, Copper-T procedures are carried out and sterilisation operations are performed on one day each week.

AIDS Control Programme

- The State Government established the State AIDS Control Committee to raise public awareness about AIDS and to provide treatment and care for AIDS patients in the state.
- The committee is setting-up AIDS control centres in every district and sub-division of Haryana.

Ayush Department

- The Indian System of Medicine is preserved in Haryana. The state's Ayurvedic Medicine Department operated under the Health Department until 1977, after which the State Government established a full-time directorate for the AYUSH Department.
- To promote traditional medical practices such as Naturopathy, Unani, Siddha and Homeopathy, these methods were brought under the Directorate of Ayurveda in 2006 as per the Government of India's directives.
- On 1st April, 2006, the Directorate of Ayurveda was renamed the **AYUSH Department of Haryana**, functioning under the Ministry of Health and AYUSH. Ayurvedic education is governed by the Indian Medical Council Act of 1970.
- To promote AYUSH medicine, the state has appointed a District Ayurvedic Officer in each district.
- Haryana is home to following Ayurvedic and homeopathic colleges
  - Srikrishna Government Ayurvedic College, Kurukshetra (run by the State Government).
  - MSM Institute of Ayurveda, Sonipat (established in 1973, currently a college under Bhagat Phool Singh Women's University).
  - Baba Khetanath Ayurvedic College, Narnaul (constructed by the State Government).
  - Government Unani Medical College and Hospital, Nuh.
  - National Ayurveda, Yoga and Naturopathy Centre, Panchkula.
  - A Central Yoga and Naturopathy Council and Research Institute are being set-up in Jhajjar.

Educational Institutions under the AYUSH Department in Haryana

- Shri Krishna Government Ayurvedic College, Kurukshetra
- MSM Institute of Ayurveda, Khanpur Kalan
- Baba Mastanath Ayurvedic College, Asthal Bohar, Rohtak
- Gaur Brahmin Ayurvedic College, Brahmanwas, Rohtak
- Murari Lal Rasiwasia Ayurvedic College, Charkhi-Dadri
- Chaudhary Devi Lal College of Ayurveda, Bhagwangarh Jagadhri
- Aayujyoti Ayurvedic College and Hospital, Sirsa
- Baba Khetanath Ayurvedic College, Pattikada, Narnaul
- Gangaputra Ayurvedic College, Kandela, Jind
- National Ayurvedic College, Barwala, Hisar
- Lal Bahadur Shastri Women's Ayurvedic College, Bilaspur
- J.R. Kisan Homoeopathic College, Asthal Bohar, Rohtak

AYUSH Medical Institute in Haryana

Medical Institute	Number
Unani Hospital	1
Unani Dispensary	16
Homeopathic Dispensary	24
Ayurvedic Dispensary	497
Ayurvedic Primary Health Centre	6
Ayurvedic Hospital	4

Source *Economic Survey 2024-25*

Council of Indian Medicine, Haryana

- The first Ayurvedic Board was established in Haryana on 26th November, 1968.
- This board was dissolved on 9th July, 1987 and replaced by a new board.
- The board consists of 7 members elected by the practitioners and 4 members are nominated by the Haryana Government.
- The Chairman of the board is elected by the Haryana Government.
- The board is responsible for registering Ayurvedic and Unani practitioners in India.
- To promote homeopathic medicine in Haryana, the Haryana Homeopathic Medical Council was formed on 31st March, 1970.
- The council has a total of 11 members, with three members elected by the Haryana Government and eight elected by registered homeopathic practitioners in the state.

CHECK CHAPTER KNOWLEDGE

1 What is the literacy rate of Haryana as per census 2011?

(a) 76.6% (b) 75.6%
(c) 74.6% (d) 71.8%

2 What is the rank of Haryana in the country in terms of literacy rate?

(a) 11th (b) 22nd (c) 25th (d) 30th

3 Which district of Haryana has the highest literacy rate as per census 2011? *HSSC 2020, Haryana Patwari 2016*

(a) Bhiwani (b) Panchkula
(c) Gurugram (d) Faridabad

4 Which district of Haryana has the lowest literacy rate? *Haryana Patwari 2016*

(a) Mahendragarh (b) Rewari
(c) Bhiwani (d) Mewat

5 The Directorate of Education, which administers and manages the primary and secondary education in Haryana is located in which district of the state? *HSSC 2023*

(a) Panchkula (b) Rewari
(c) Gurugram (d) Faridabad

6 In which year 'Beti Bachao, Beti Padhao' Programme was launched by the Hon'ble Prime Minister of India? *PGT 2016*

(a) 22nd January, 2015
(b) 2nd October, 2014
(c) 11th September, 2014
(d) 8th March, 2015

7 Which sportsperson has been made brand ambassador of the scheme 'Beti Bachao, Beti Padhao' in Haryana? *Haryana SSC Clerk 2016*

(a) Sakshi Malik (b) Vinesh Phogat
(c) Deepa Malik (d) Geeta Phogat

8 The scheme 'Aarohi Model School' was launched in which year by the Government of India?

(a) 2001-02 (b) 2004-05
(c) 2011-12 (d) 2013-14

9 Rashtriya Madhyamik Shiksha Abhiyan (RMSA) was implemented in which year in Haryana?

(a) 2000-02 (b) 2003-05
(c) 2005-07 (d) 2009-11

10 Sarva Shiksha Abhiyan was implemented in which year in Haryana?

(a) 2000 (b) 2002
(c) 2005 (d) 2010

11 Chief Minister School Beautification scheme was launched in which year in Haryana?

(a) 2000-01 (b) 2011-12
(c) 2004-05 (d) 2006-07

12 Free Text Books scheme was launched in which year in Haryana?

(a) 1990-91 (b) 2000-01
(c) 2005-06 (d) 2008-09

13 In which district of Haryana residential schools for physically challenged students have been opened? *HSSC 2022, 16*

(a) Sonipat (b) Hisar (c) Panipat (d) Karnal

14 In which year, Dr Ambedkar Medhavi Chhatar Sansodhit Yojana was started in Haryana? *PGT 2016*

(a) 2003-04 (b) 2004-05
(c) 2005-06 (d) 2008-09

15 Haryana Board of School Education was established in which year? *Haryana Anganwadi 2017*

(a) 1947 (b) 1969
(c) 1966 (d) 1970

16 Haryana Board of School Education was established in the year 1969 in Chandigarh and it was later transferred in *PGT 2016*

(a) Sonipat (b) Chandigarh
(c) Bhiwani (d) Rohtak

17 In which year 10 + 2 + 3 system was introduced by the State Government of Haryana? *PGT 2016*

(a) 1980-81 (b) 1976-77
(c) 1988-89 (d) 1985-86

18 The State Educational Research and Training Council was established in which year in Haryana? *HSSC 2024*

(a) 1960 (b) 1965
(c) 1970 (d) 1979

19 When was the first Sainik School in Haryana was established?

(a) 1968 (b) 1975
(c) 2002 (d) 1961

20 The first university of Haryana is located in which place of the state?
(a) Panipat (b) Rohtak
(c) Rewari (d) Hisar

21 Kurukshetra University was established in which year? *Haryana Anganbadi Paper 2017*
(a) 11th January, 1956 (b) 21st March, 1960
(c) 1st November, 1966 (d) 27th May, 1970

22 Kurukshetra University is a .... *PGT 2016*
(a) Central University (b) Private University
(c) State University (d) None of these

23 Which university was inaugurated by Dr Rajendra Prasad in Haryana? *Clerk 2016*
(a) Chandhary Charan Singh Agricultural University
(b) Kurukshetra University
(c) Chaudhary Devi Lal University
(d) YMCA University of Science and Technology

24 Who is credited to establish manuscript museum in Kurukshetra university? *Haryana Mandi Supervisor 2017*
(a) Pt. Sthanu Dutt Sharma
(b) Jayram Shashtri
(c) Shri Sitaram Shastri
(d) Kapil Dev Sharma

25 Chaudhary Charan Singh Agricultural university is established at *HSSC 2020, Anganbadi Paper 2017*
(a) Karnal (b) Rohtak
(c) Ambala (d) Hisar

26 Maharishi Dayanand University is established at which place in Haryana? *HSSC 2023, 15*
(a) Rohtak (b) Hisar
(c) Ambala (d) Kurukshetra

27 Chaudhary Devi Lal University is situated at which place in Haryana? *PGT 2016*
(a) Hisar (b) Sirsa
(c) Rohtak (d) Panchkula

28 The first women's state university of Haryana is named after which personality of the state? *PGT 2016*
(a) Kalpana Chawla
(b) Swami Shraddhanand
(c) Bhagat Phool Singh
(d) Swami Dayanand

29 Indira Gandhi University is located at which place of Haryana? *HSSC 2022, 16*
(a) Karnal (b) Hisar
(c) Rewari (d) Palwal

30 In which place Baba Khetanath College, is located in Haryana?
(a) Hisar (b) Rohtak
(c) Gurugram (d) Narnaul

31 The National Dairy Research Institute, Karnal was established in the year
(a) 1922 (b) 1955 (c) 1930 (d) 1926

32 National Dairy Research Institute is located in *HSSC 2020, 19*
(a) Hisar (b) Faridabad
(c) Karnal (d) Gurugram

33 The Indian Institute of Wheat and Barley Research is located at which place of Haryana?
(a) Rohtak (b) Karnal
(c) Jind (d) Rewari

34 Bureau of National Animal Genetic Resource is situated in *Haryana Forest Dept 2017*
(a) Kurukshetra (b) Sirsa
(c) Karnal (d) Faridabad

35 The Indian Institute of Management (IIM) is located at .... in Haryana.
(a) Rohtak (b) Karnal
(c) Jind (d) Rewari

36 Rajiv Gandhi Education city is located in which district of Haryana? *Mandi Supervisor 2017*
(a) Rohtak (b) Sonipat (c) Panipat (d) Hisar

37 EDUSAT Project was started through which project? *HSSC 2024, 17*
(a) Soft Skill project
(b) English lab
(c) Rajiv Gandhi education programme
(d) Direct to home

38 Deenbandhu Chhotu Ram university of Science and Technology is located at which place in Haryana? *PGT 2016*
(a) Sonipat (b) Hisar
(c) Jind (d) Rohtak

39 A research institute CIRB is located in Hisar in Haryana. What is the full form of CIRB? *HSSC 2022, 20*
(a) Council for Information and Research on Buffaloes
(b) Central Industrial Research Board
(c) Central Institute for Research on Buffaloes
(d) Council for Industrial Research on Buffaloes

40 National Brain Institute is located in which district of Haryana?
(a) Karnal (b) Gurugram
(c) Hisar (d) Rohtak

41 Urban health centres have been established by Haryana Government in the areas having population of approx *Mandi Supervisor 2017*
(a) 2 lakh (b) 5 lakh
(c) 50 thousand (d) 1 lakh

42 The first Medical College was established in which year in Haryana?
(a) 1960 (b) 1950 (c) 1947 (d) 1931

43 Maharishi Markandeshwar Institute of Medical Sciences and Research is located where in Haryana? *HSSC 2021*
(a) Ambala (b) Bhiwani (c) Hisar (d) Jind

44 In which year Pt. Bhagwat Dayal Sharma university of Health Sciences got the status of University of Health Sciences?
(a) 2000 (b) 2002 (c) 2005 (d) 2008

45 Medical university in Karnal is named after which personality? *HSSC 2024, 18*
(a) Chaudhary Devi Lal (b) Kalpana Chawla
(c) Karnal (d) APJ Abdul Kalam

46 Kalpana Chawla Government Medical College (KCGMC) established in 2017 is located at .... *HSSC 2021*
(a) Hisar (b) Rewari (c) Palwal (d) Karnal

47 Narnaul Medical college is located in which district of Haryana?
(a) Hisar (b) Rohtak
(c) Mahendragarh (d) Bhiwani

48 Cancer Institute was established in which place of Haryana?
(a) Jhajjar (b) Rewari (c) Hisar (d) Karnal

49 On which day, 'Yoga Day' is celebrated in Haryana?
(a) 1st August (b) 21st July
(c) 21st June (d) 1st September

50 From which place, Tuberculosis-free Haryana campaign was started in 2015?
(a) Hisar (b) Rohtak
(c) Bhiwani (d) Gurugram

51 Within how many days birth and death registration is mandatory in Haryana?
(a) 10 days (b) 21 days
(c) 25 days (d) 30 days

52 In which year Chief Minister Free Treatment Scheme was launched in Haryana?
(a) 2000 (b) 2004
(c) 2010 (d) 2014

53 'Swasthya Aapke Dwar Scheme' was launched in which year by the Government of Haryana?
(a) 1985 (b) 1992
(c) 2000 (d) 2003

54 The State Institute of Mental Health is located in which district of Haryana?
(a) Hisar (b) Rohtak
(c) Jind (d) Bhiwani

55 Mission Indradhanush is related to *HSSC 2023, 17*
(a) agriculture (b) revenue
(c) health service (d) higher education

56 To control the Tuberculosis, a 'Revised National Tuberculosis Control Programme' has been enforced in which district of Haryana?
(a) Faridabad (b) Gurugram
(c) Jind (d) All of these

57 As per the 2018 population estimation, the sex-ratio in Haryana was (females/1000 males). *Haryana Tehsildar 2019*
(a) 900 (b) 875
(c) 950 (d) 914

58 In which year Ayush Department was set-up in Haryana?
(a) 1970 (b) 1971
(c) 1977 (d) 1980

59 Mukhyamantri Muft Ilaaj Yojana, in Haryana includes the following services *HPSC HCS 2023*
1. Surgeries, laboratory, tests, diagnostics (X-Ray, ECG, Ultrasound)
2. OPD/IPD, medicines, referral transport, dental treatment
3. OPD/IPD, diagnostics, laboratory tests, surgeries
4. Dental treatment, referral transport, medicines, OPD/IPD, surgeries, laboratory tests, diagnostics (X-Ray, ECG, Ultrasound)

Which of the above statements is/are correct?
(a) Only 1 (b) Only 2
(c) Only 3 (d) Only 4

CORRECT ANSWERS

1. (b)	2. (b)	3. (c)	4. (d)	5. (a)	6. (a)	7. (a)	8. (c)	9. (d)	10. (b)
11. (b)	12. (d)	13. (c)	14. (c)	15. (b)	16. (c)	17. (d)	18. (d)	19. (d)	20. (b)
21. (a)	22. (c)	23. (b)	24. (a)	25. (d)	26. (a)	27. (b)	28. (c)	29. (c)	30. (d)
31. (b)	32. (c)	33. (b)	34. (c)	35. (a)	36. (b)	37. (a)	38. (a)	39. (c)	40. (b)
41. (d)	42. (a)	43. (a)	44. (d)	45. (b)	46. (d)	47. (c)	48. (a)	49. (c)	50. (d)
51. (b)	52. (d)	53. (d)	54. (b)	55. (c)	56. (d)	57. (d)	58. (c)	59. (d)	

KNOW YOUR STATE
HARYANA

CHAPTER 30

Sports and Awards in Haryana

- Sports activities play a vital role in human development, fostering healthy competition, relationships, recreation and physical fitness.
- Haryana's traditional rural sports include wrestling, kabaddi, pittu, gadda, ghori, chunia ghati, sulia-danda, fora jumping, khuliya, aankh-micholi, jhirka-jhanki, etc.

Famous Sports of Haryana

Some of the important sports of Haryana are as follows

Athletics

- Haryana has produced numerous athletes who have made the state proud by winning national and international medals.

> 'Haryana Athletics' is an association (founded in 1967) for the promotion of Athletes and Athletics in the state.

- Notable athletes include Deepa Malik and Narender Ranbir (Para athletes, Javelin Throw), Seema Punia Antil and Krishna Poonia (Discus Throw), Om Prakash Karhana (Shot Put), Chand Ram (Roadwalk), Manjit Singh, Geeta Zutshi (Middle distance running), etc.

Some famous athletes from Haryana are as follows

Bhim Singh

- Born — 13th April, 1945, in Dhanana village, Bhiwani
- Sport — Former high jumper
- International debut — 8th Commonwealth Games (Kingston, Jamaica in 1966)
- Achievements — Gold medal at the 1968 Asian Games with a record jump of 6.9 feet (2.05m)
- Awards — Arjuna Award (1967)

Bahadur Singh

- Born — 8th February, 1946
- Sport — Former shot putter
- Achievements — Gold medals at the 1978 (8th) and 1982 (9th) Asian Games. Gold medal at the 1975 Asian Athletics Championships.
- Awards — Arjuna Award, Padma Shri and Dronacharya Award

Chand Ram

- Born — 26th January, 1958
- Sport — Former athlete (20 km road walk)
- Achievements — Gold medal at the 1982 Asian Games (Delhi) with a world record. Gold medal at the 1983 Asian Track and Field Meet (Kuwait) with another world record.

Deepa Malik

Born — 30th September, 1970, in Bhainswal, Sonipat

Awards — Haryana Karambhoomi Award (2008), Arjuna Award (2012), Padma Shri (2017) and Major Dhyan Chand Khel Ratna Award (2019)

- She became first Indian woman to win a medal (Silver in Shot Put) in Paralympic games (Rio Paraolympic Games, 2016). She also won a gold medal in Javelin Throw at Para-Athletic Grand Prix, Dubai.

Seema Poonia Antil

- Born 27th July, 1983, in Khewda, Sonipat
- Sport Discus thrower
- Awards First woman to receive the Arjuna Award (2018) in Gymnastics. Bhim Award (2006) by the Haryana Government.
- First Indian woman to win gold at the 2000 World Junior Championship (Santiago, Chile). Gold at the 2014 Asian Games. Silver at the 2006, 2014 and 2018 Commonwealth Games. Bronze at the 2010 Commonwealth Games and 2018 Asian Games.

Manjit Singh

- Born 1st September, 1989, in Ujhana, Jind
- Sport Middle-distance runner (800m and 1500m)
- Achievements Gold in the 800m at the 2018 Asian Games (Jakarta)

Neeraj Chopra

- Born 24th December, 1997, in Khandra, Panipat
- Sport Indian Javelin Thrower
- Awards and honours Rajiv Gandhi Khel Ratna (2021), Padma Shri (2022) and Arjuna Award (2018) and Flag bearer at the 2018 Asian Games opening ceremony.
- He won Gold medals at the 2016 South Asian Games, 2017 Asian Championships, 2018 Commonwealth Games and 2018 Asian Games.
- He won Gold medal at the 2020 Tokyo Olympics (held in 2021), becoming India's first olympic gold medalist in athletics.
- He won Silver medal at the 2022 World Athletics Championships, India's first-ever in the event.
- He won Gold medal at the 2023 World Athletics Championships, becoming the first Indian to win it.
- He won Silver medal at the 2024 Paris Olympics.

> Neeraj Chopra is a National record holder with a throw of 89.94m.

Other Athletes from Haryana

Narendra Ranbir, Krishna Punia, Suresh Yadav, Chandra pal Rathi, Geeta Zutshi, Neelam J. Singh, Shri Chandra, Captain Hawa Singh, Captain Mohabbat Singh, Sabar Ali, Sundar Singh, Rajendra Kumar, Sant Kumar, Karan Singh, Punam Taneja, Anil Kumar, Sunita Sharma, Sandeep Kothia, Duti Chand, Swapna Barman etc.

Boxing

- Boxing is one of the main sports in Haryana. Bhiwani district is famous for Boxing. Bhiwani district is known as the power house of boxing.
- Haryana has a number of Boxing Training Centres and Boxing Clubs, which provide training to the national level boxers. Thus, it is known as **Mini Cuba of India**.

Some famous boxers from Haryana are as follows

Akhil Kumar

- Born 27th March, 1981, in Bhiwani
- Achievements Gold medal at the 2006 Commonwealth Games. Bronze medal at the 2007 Asian Championships
- Awards Arjuna Award (2005)

Vijender Singh Beniwal

- Born 29th October, 1985, in Kaluwas, Bhiwani
- Awards Arjuna Award (2006), Major Dhyan Chand Khel Ratna Award (2009)
- He won Bronze medal in Asian Games in 2006. He won a Bronze medal in 2008 Olympic Games in Beijing and became the first Indian boxer to win medal in Olympic Games.
- He is the first Indian professional boxer.
- He won Gold medal in 2010 Asian Games and Silver medal in 2014 Commonwealth Games.

Manoj Kumar

- Born 10th December, 1986, in Kaithal
- Awards Arjuna Award (2014)
- He won Bronze at the 2007 and 2013 Asian Boxing Championships, Gold at the 2010 Common- wealth Games and 2016 South Asian Games (64 kg category) and Bronze at the 2018 Commonwealth Games.

Jitender Kumar

- Born 18th July, 1988, in Bhiwani
- Achievements Bronze at the 2006 Commonwealth Games. Gold at the 33rd National Games (2008)

Vikas Krishna Yadav

- Born 10th February, 1992, in Hisar
- Awards Arjuna Award (2012)
- He won Gold at the 2010 Asian Games and 2018 Commonwealth Games, Bronze at the 2017 Asian Championships, 2011 World Amateur Boxing Championship and 2014 Incheon Asian Games.

Gaurav Solanki

- Born 21st January, 1997, in Faridabad
- Achievements Gold at the 2018 Commonwealth Games (youngest Indian boxer to win gold)

Sunil Kumar

- Born 5th May, 1990
- Achievements Won Istanbul (Turkey) under-17 World Championship in 2006

Other Boxers from Haryana

Saweety Boora (won Gold medal in 81 kg category), Nitu Ghanghas (won Gold medal in minimum weight category) in IBA women's world Boxing Championship 2023, Dinesh Kumar (honoured by Arjuna Award), Girwar Singh, Ajmer Singh, Amit Panghal, Manish Kaushik, Naman Tanwar, Sunil Kumar, Jitendra Kumar, Dinesh Kumar, Hawa Singh (won Asian gold medals), Jagdish Singh (awarded by Dronacharya Award), Jai Bhagwan, Mina Kumari, Jyotsna etc.

Cricket

- Haryana Cricket Association supervises the cricket sport in the state. The first Ranji Trophy match in the state was played in the year 1982. The first cricket stadium 'Nahar Singh' of the state is located in Faridabad. This stadium was built in the year 1981.
- The first Ranji match was played in this stadium.

Some famous cricketers from Haryana are as follows

Mansoor Ali Khan Pataudi

- Born 5th January, 1941, in Pataudi, Gurugram
- Famous as **Tiger Pataudi**, former Indian cricket captain. Recognised as one of India's greatest cricket captains and the best fielder of his time.
- Achievements Captain of the Indian cricket team in 1962
- Autobiography Tiger's Tale (1969)
- Awards Arjuna Award (1964), Padma Shri (1967)

Kapil Dev

- Born 6th January, 1959, in Chandigarh
- Nickname Haryana Hurricane
- Achievements Captain of the 1983 World Cup-winning Indian cricket team. Named Indian Cricketer of the Century by Wisden in 2002.
- Awards Arjuna Award, Padma Shri and Padma Bhushan

Virender Sehwag

- Born 20th October, 1978, Najafgarh, Delhi (His family hails from Haryana)
- Nickname Sultan of Multan
- Achievements Represented Delhi in cricket. First ODI in 1999 and first Test in 2001. Virender Sehwag is the first Indian Cricketer to score a triple century in Test Cricket. He is only the third Cricketer in the world who scored more than one triple centuries in Test Cricket, after Sir Donald Bradman and Brian Lara.
- Awards Arjuna Award (2002), Padma Shri (2010)
- Other Founded Sehwag International School and Sports Academy in Jhajjar

Joginder Sharma

- Born 23rd October, 1983, in Rohtak
- Role Right-handed batsman and right-arm medium-fast bowler, captain of Haryana
- Achievements Strong performance in the 2007 domestic season, earning national selection. Part of India's winning squad for the T20 World Cup 2007 in South Africa.

Yuzvendra Chahal

- Born — 23rd July, 1990, in Jind
- Role — Leg spinner for India (ODI and T20I) and Haryana (domestic).
- Achievements — ODI debut on 11th June, 2016 against Zimbabwe. Became the third Indian bowler to take 50 wickets in T20Is.

> **Other Cricketers** Ajay Ratra, Joginder Rao, etc.

Hockey

- Hockey sport has flourished well in the state. The 'Hockey Haryana', a recognised State Association, governs and conducts all activities for both men and women hockey in the state.
- It organises many events of Hockey Sports like, Hockey Indian Sub-Junior Women National Championship, Hockey State Sub-Junior Men National Championship, Hockey India Senior Women National Hockey Championship and so on.

Some famous hockey players from Haryana are as follows

Mamta Kharab

- Born — 26th January, 1982, in Rohtak
- Role — Former Captain of the Indian Women's Hockey Team
- Achievements — Gold in 2002 Commonwealth Games and 2004 Hockey Asia Cup. Silver in 2006 Commonwealth Games (Melbourne).
- Awards — Bhim Award (Haryana's highest sports honour), Arjuna Award (2003)
- Nickname — **Golden Girl** of the Indian Women's Hockey Team

Sandeep Singh

- Born — 27th February, 1986, in Shahabad, Kurukshetra
- Role — Former Captain of the Indian National Hockey Team, penalty corner specialist
- Achievements — International debut in January, 2004 at the Sultan Azlan Shah Cup. Captain of India in 2009, leading the team to Gold in the Sultan Azlan Shah Cup.
- Awards — Arjuna Award (2010)
- Other — Holds the rank of DSP in Haryana Police

Sardar Singh

- Born — 15th July, 1986, in Sant Nagar, Sirsa
- Role — Former Captain of the Indian National Hockey Team
- Achievements — Bronze in 2006 Sultan Azlan Shah Cup. Under his captaincy, India won Silver in 2010 and 2014 Commonwealth Games, Bronze in 2010 Asian Games and Gold in 2014 Incheon Asian Games.
- Awards — Arjuna Award (2012), Padma Shri (2015)

> **Other Hockey Players from Haryana**
>
> Bhupinder Kaur, Pritam Thakran, Kuldeep Siwach, Suman Bala, Surinder Kaur, Pritam Rani Siwach, Jasjit Kaur Handa, Sita Gosai, Sandeep Singh, Anil Nandal, Sanjay Dang, Kamla Dalal, Balvinder Kaur, Sunita Dalal, Rajvinder Kaur, Rani Rampal etc.

Kabaddi

- Kabaddi is a major sport in Haryana, known as its native sport.
- **Haryana Steelers** is a Sonipat-based professional Kabaddi team that plays in the Pro Kabaddi League (PKL), team in the league, debuting in 2017.

Some famous kabaddi players from Haryana are as follows

Pardeep Narwal

- Born — 16th February, 1997 in Sonipat
- Role — Currently plays for the 'Bengaluru Bulls' in the Pro Kabaddi League and also Indian national team.
- Achievements — Widely regarded as the greatest raider in Kabaddi history. He led the 'Patna Pirates' to three straight Pro Kabaddi League (PKL) titles.
- He holds a number of raiding records in PKL.

Surender Nada

- Born — 1st July, 1987 in Jhajjar
- Role — Captain and defender of Haryana Steelers (Pro Kabaddi League)
- Achievements — Represented India in the 2016 Kabaddi World Cup (Ahmedabad). Consistently ranked among the Top Ten Defenders in all seasons of Pro Kabaddi League.

Deepak Niwas Hooda

- Born — 10th June, 1994, in Chamaria, Rohtak
- Achievements — Part of the Indian team that won Gold in the 2016 Kabaddi World Cup, 2016 South Asian Games, 2017 Asian Kabaddi Championship and Kabaddi Masters. Part of the team that won Bronze in the 2018 Asian Games.

Other Kabaddi Players Rammehar, Ram Singh Thardak, Sher Singh, Brahma Prakash, etc.

Wrestling

- Wrestling is a traditional and famous sport in Haryana.
- **Lila Ram Sangwan from Charkhi-Dadri won the first Gold medal for India in 1958 Commonwealth Games.**

Some famous wrestlers from Haryana are as follows

Sajjan Singh

- Born — 24th April, 1932, in Mahendragarh
- Achievements — National Wrestling Champion (1959). Represented India at the 1960 Rome Olympics. Silver medal in wrestling at the Jakarta Asian Games.
- Given the title Rustam-e-Hind

Pahalwan Uday Chand

- Born — 25th June, 1935, in Hisar
- Achievements — Bronze medal in men's freestyle at the 1961 World Wrestling Championship in Yokohama, Japan.
- Awards — India's first Arjuna Award in wrestling (1962)

Master Chandgi Ram

- Born — 9th November, 1937, Hisar
- Achievements — Gold medal in wrestling at the 1970 Asian Games in Bangkok.
- Awards — Arjuna Award (1969) and Padma Shri (1971)
- Master Chandgi Ram created a record by winning the Bharat Kesari and Hind Kesari titles twice.

Yogeshwar Dutt

- Born — 2nd November, 1982, in Bhainswal Kalan, Sonipat
- Awards — Rajiv Gandhi Khel Ratna Award (2012) and Padma Shri (2013)

- Achievements
  - Gold medals in Commonwealth (2003, 2005, 2007) and Asian Championships (2008, 2012).
  - Gold medal in Asian Games (2014).
  - Bronze medals in 2012 Olympic Games and 2006 Asian Games.
  - He won Gold medal in 2010 and 2014 Commonwealth Games

Geetika Jakhar

- Born — 18th August, 1985, in Agroha, Hisar
- Awards — Became first female wrestler to win Arjuna Award, also honoured with Bhim Award and Kalpana Chawla Excellence Award (2009).
- She won Silver medal in Asian Games (2006), Gold medals in Commonwealth Wrestling Championship (2003, 2005), Bronze medal in 2013 Asian Wrestling Championship (Delhi) and Incheon Asian Games (2014) and Silver medal in Commonwealth Games (2014).

Gita Phogat

- Born — 15th December, 1988, in Balali, Bhiwani
- Awards — Arjuna Award, Bhim Award
- First Indian female wrestler to qualify for the Olympic Summer Games.
- She won Gold medal in Common wealth Games (2010), Bronze medal in World Championships (2012), Silver medal in Commonwealth Wrestling Championship (2013) and Gold medals in Commonwealth Wrestling Championships (2009, 2011).
- Dangal movie is based on her life.

Gita Phogat has been posted on DSP rank by Haryana Government.

Babita Phogat

- Born: 20th November, 1989, in Bhiwani
- Achievements: Gold medal in Commonwealth Games (2014). Silver medal in Commonwealth Games (2018). Bronze medal in World Wrestling Championship (2012).
- Award: Arjuna Award (2015) for her achievements.

Ravi Kumar Dahiya

- Born: 12th December, 1997 Nahri village, Sonipat
- Achievements: Silver medal in Tokyo 2020 Olympics and became 2nd Indian wrestler after Sushil Kumar to win an Olympic silver.

Sakshi Malik

- Born: 3rd September, 1992 in Mokhra village, Rohtak
- Awards: Major Dhyanchand Khel Ratna Award (2016) and Padma Shri (2017).
- She won Bronze medal in 2016 Rio Olympics (first Indian female wrestler to win an Olympic medal), Gold medal in 2017 Commonwealth Wrestling Championships, Bronze medal in 2018 Commonwealth Games and Gold medal in 2019 Senior Wrestling National Championship.

Sumit Malik

- Born: 9th January, 1993, Rohtak
- Awards: Won silver in Asian Championships, 2017 and Commonwealth Championships, 2017. He also won gold medal in Commonwealth Games, 2018.

Ravinder Khatri

- Born: 15th May, 1992
- Achievements: Won Bronze medal in 2016 at Asian Wrestling Olympic Qualification Tournament

Bajrang Punia

- Born: 26th February, 1994 in Khudan, Jhajjar
- Awards: Arjuna Award (2015), Padma Shri (2019) and Major Dhyanchand Khel Ratna Award (2019)
- He won Gold medal in 2016 and 2017 Commonwealth Championships, Gold medal in 2017 Asian Championship, Gold medal in 2018 Asian Games and 2018 Commonwealth Games.

> Bajrang Punia attained Number 1 ranking in the world (65 kg category) in November, 2018.

Vinesh Phogat

- Born: 25th August, 1994 in Balali village, Charkhi-Dadri
- Achievements: Gold medal in 2014 and 2018 Commonwealth Games. Gold medal in 2018 Asian Games.
- Awards: Arjuna Award (2016)
- **In Olympics 2024, Vinesh Phogat became the first Indian female wrestler to reach an Olympic final.** However, she was disqualified after exceeding the stipulated weight by 100 grams. After her disqualification, she announced her retirement. Now she is a Member of Legislative Assembly (MLA) from **Julana constituency.**

Other Wrestlers from Haryana

Sajjan Singh, Sushil Kumar, Priya Malik, Aman Sehrawat (won Bronze in Paris Olympics, 2024), Sagar Jaglan, Ramesh Kumar, Krishna Godara, Rohtash Singh Dahia, Omprakash Narwal, Tejbir Singh, Ashan Kumar Sangwan, Somvir, etc.

Bodybuilding

- Haryana conducts many bodybuilding events in the state like Haryana Bodybuilding Sirsa, Panipat Classic and Mr Haryana.
- Its sportspersons (Bodybuilders) also take part in the competitions of State level, National level and International level.
- **Haryana Bodybuilding Association** works for the development of this sport in the state.

Shooting

- Shooting is a popular sport in Haryana, with many youth pursuing careers in it. The state has made its mark globally in shooting.
- Numerous shooting academies have been established to promote the sport.

Some famous shooting players from Haryana are as follows

Gagan Narang

- Born 6th May, 1983 in Madras (Chennai), Gagan's family hail from the Simla Gujran village of Haryana's Panipat district.
- Achievements Won 4 Gold medals at the 2010 Commonwealth Games, won Bronze at the 2012 London Olympics
- Award Major Dhyanchand Khel Ratna Award (2011)

Ankur Mittal

- Born 30th March, 1992, Sonipat
- Achievements Silver medal in 2017 ISSF World Cup, Gold medal in World Championship and Bronze medal in 2019 Commonwealth Games
- Awards Arjuna Award and Bhim Award (The award is given by Haryana government).

Anish Bhanwala

- Born 26th September, 2002, Sonipat
- Achievements Gold medal in 2018 Commonwealth Games (25m rapid fire pistol) Youngest player to win a medal in the Commonwealth Games
- Awards President's Child Award

Manu Bhakar

- Born 18th February, 2002, Goria, Jhajjar
- Awards Padma Shri (2020), Arjuna Award (2018) and Major Dhyanchand Khel Ratna Award (2024)
- After winning two Bronze medals in different shooting events in Paris Olympics, 2024, she became the first Indian shooter to win 2 medals in the same edition.
- She won Gold medal in 2018 Commonwealth Games (10m air pistol). Gold medal in 2018 Youth Olympic Games and a youngest woman to win Gold in ISSF World Cup.

Football

- Football is a popular sport in Haryana, promoted by the Haryana Football Association to engage the youth.
- The association established a Football Academy in 2012 at **Maharishi Dayanand University, Rohtak,** in collaboration with Panasonic India Limited.
- The academy trains 30 players, fostering growth and interest in the sport.
- A football academy has been established in Gurugram, with additional training facilities in Ambala, Rohtak, Hisar and other areas, all under the Haryana Football Association to promote the sport across the state.

Other Sports Personalities of Haryana

Personality	Description
Karnam Malleswari 	• She was born on 1st June, 1975 in Andhra Pradesh. She was married in Haryana, so she represents Haryana in weightlifting sports. • She won a Silver medal in the Bangkok Asian Games in 1998 and a Bronze medal in the Sydney Olympics in 2000. She was awarded the Arjuna Award in 1994, the Rajiv Gandhi Khel Ratna in 1999 and the Padma Shri in 1999.
Ekta Bhyan	• She was born on 7th June, 1985 in Hisar. She won a Gold medal at the Women's Throw Games in the Asian Para Games 2018.
Abhinav Lohan	• He was born on 13th December, 1989. He is a golfer. He won the Silver medal (Golf Team) at the 2010 Guangzhou Asian Games.
Sania Nehwal 	• She was born on 17th March, 1990 in Hisar district. She is a badminton player. She won the Gold medal in the Commonwealth Games 2010 and also won Bronze medal in London Olympics 2012. • She also won Australian Open, China Open, and Indian Open in 2014. She is the only Indian player to win a silver medal in the 2015 World Championships. She won a gold medal in the Commonwealth Games 2018. • The Government of India honoured her with the Arjuna Award in 2009, Padma Shri and Rajiv Gandhi Khel Ratna Award in 2010 and Padma Bhushan in 2016.
Shivangi Pathak	• She is an Indian mountaineer. She was born on 10th July, 2001 in Hisar. She is the Indian woman to climb on the Mount Everest at an early age (on 16th May, 2018). • After this, she also mounted Mount Kilimanjaro on 24th July, 2018, the highest peak in Africa and Mount Elbrus on 2nd September, 2018.
Mahek Jyot Pannu	• She is an Indian mountaineer. She was born in Karnal district. She is the first Sikh girl to climb Mount Konet Peak of Argentina and Mount Kilimanjaro, the highest peak of Africa.

Other Famous Sportspersons in Different Sports of Haryana

Sports	Sportspersons
Volleyball	Ballu, Dalel Singh Ror, Balkar Chauhan, Ishwar Singh, Mehar Singh, Praveen Malhan, Balwant Singh Sagwal
Judo	Satish Kumar, Narendra
Gymnastic	Sunita Sharma, Sandhya, Nirmal Guliya, Seema Punia Antil, Rao Sultan Singh
Karate	Dinesh Kumar Kadyan
Golf	Diksha Dagar, Shubham Jaglan, PG Sethi
Basketball	Narender Kumar Grewal, Shiba Maggon, Ajmer Singh
Baseball	Sumit Khranger
Weightlifting	Kavita Devi, Deepak Lather
Mountaineering	Santosh Yadav, Anita Kuddu
Handball	Sandeep Kothia
Javelin Throw	Rohit Yadav
Shooting	Sanjiv Rajput, Deepak Kumar, Lakshya Shyoran, Saurabh Chaudhary

Famous Sports Organisation in Haryana

To promote sports talent, the following organisations have been established in the state

Haryana Chess Association

- Haryana Chess Association (HCA) is the official body for the game of chess in Haryana. It was formed in 1986, with the aims and objectives of spreading and promoting the game of chess among youths in Haryana.
- It is affiliated to the All India Chess Federation (AICF) and Haryana Olympic Association (HOA). It is registered under Societies Registration Act, 1860.

Bhiwani Boxing Club

- It was founded by the former coach and famous boxer of Sports Authority of India, **Jagadish Singh**, on 21st March, 2003. The co-founder of this club is Captain Hawa Singh who won the National Champion for 11 times and also clinched two gold medals in Asian Olympics.

> In Asian Games 2010 at Guangzhou (China), two Gold and one Silver medal are won by the boxers of Bhiwani Boxing Club. Important boxers of this club are Vijender Singh, Vikas Krishna Yadav, Jitendra Kumar, Akhil Kumar, Dinesh Kumar, Kavita Chahal and Dilbagh Singh.

- This boxing club is also known as a **Powerhouse of Indian Boxing**. In 2008, Summer Olympic Games, 5 boxers represented India out of those, 4 were from Bhiwani district of Haryana.

Hockey Haryana

- The Hockey Haryana was established on 24th June, year 2009. It is a recognised association of Haryana and is affiliated to **Haryana Olympic Association** (HOA) and **Hockey India** (HI).
- The HH has drawn out a development programme for an extended period with the help of HOA and department of Sports in Haryana.
- There are mainly 6 teams in the **Hockey Haryana** (HH) which are known as – Men Senior Team, Women Senior Team, Men Junior Team, Women Junior Team, Men Sub-Junior Team and lastly Women Sub Junior Team.

National Aero Sports Centre

- India's first aero sports centre was opened by the Aero Club of India, on 31st January, 2010. It is located on Bachhod airstrip near Narnaul town (Mahendragarh) in Haryana.
- It is named as **Rajiv Gandhi Aero Sports Centre.**

Haryana Olympic Association

- It was established in 1966 with headquarters at Panchkula.
- The Haryana Olympic Association is a body that works under the agency of the International Olympic Committee (IOC) and the Indian Olympic Association (IOA).
- It helps the State Government in making of sports policies in the state.

Haryana Cricket Association

- Haryana Cricket Association is the governing body of the Cricket activities in the Haryana and the Haryana Cricket team. It is affiliated to the Board of Control for Cricket in India (BCCI).
- The Haryana Cricket Association promotes and develops cricket by conducting various league tournaments, tournaments for the age group Under-13, Under-17, Under-19 and Under-25 categories besides organising and conducting national tournaments.

Haryana Sports Development Fund

- It was founded by the Chief Minister of the state, in order to provide a cash reward to sportspersons and athletes who won medals in National and International level competitions.
- It provides financial assistance to sports organisations, clubs and excellent sportspersons. It also provides financial assistance or pensions to outstanding sportspersons who belong to poor classes.

Kabaddi Association

- The state has two Kabaddi Associations as under
  - Haryana State Kabaddi Association (National Style)
  - Haryana State Kabaddi Association (Circle Kabaddi)
- These two Kabaddi Associations are associated with Haryana Olympic Association.

Haryana Sports Authority

- The State Government cleared the way for the creation of Sports Authority in the state for basic improvement in the field of sports under Sports Policy, 2015.
- The State Government had issued notification for the formation of Haryana Sports and Physical Fitness Authority in March, 2016.

> Haryana Sports Authority has been registered under the Haryana Registration and Regulation of Societies Act-2012.

- Haryana Sports Authority is headquartered in **Panchkula.**
- The Chairman of this Authority is the Chief Minister and Vice President of the State. Secretaries of State Industry and Commerce Department, Department of Urban Local Bodies, Youth and Sports Department and Public Works Department are the other members of this authority.
- The main goal of this authority is to increase sportsmanship and physical activity in the state.

Functions of Haryana Sports Authority

- To prepare the layout for development and modernisation in the field of sports.
- Provides permission for the construction of Anti-Doping Labs and Sports Lab in the state.
- Provides basic and modern infrastructure for various sports (adventure games, gymnastics).
- Provides support in the running of sports training centres, academies, etc. in the state.
- Provides financial facilities to government and private organisations related to sports.
- Develops sports training as necessary standards in the state.

Major Important Sports Stadiums in Haryana

Nahar Singh Stadium

- It was built in 1981. It is an International Cricket Stadium located in Faridabad, which was previously known as **Mayur Stadium.**
- The first match in this stadium was played in 1982 for Ranji Trophy between Haryana and Services Cricket Teams. As on 11th September, 2018, the stadium has hosted around 8 One Day International Cricket Matches.
- The first One Day International (ODI) match was played between India and West Indies in this stadium. More than 50 Ranji Trophy matches have been organised in this stadium.
- The stadium has a seating capacity of 25000 audiences. The stadium is managed by the Haryana Cricket Association.

Nehru Stadium

- It was established in 1987 in Gurugram. It is designed for football, cricket and athletics. It is a home ground for Haryana Cricket Team and also known as **Dronacharya Stadium.**

Chaudhary Bansilal Cricket Stadium

- It was established in 2006 in Rohtak district. The stadium came to prominence when Sachin Tendulkar played his last Ranji Trophy match here in October 2013. Haryana Cricket Association maintains and operates this stadium.

Other Major Stadiums and Academies in Haryana

Location	Stadium
Panchkula	Tau Devi Lal Stadium, Lawn Tennis and Badminton Academy, Hooda Complex
Yamunanagar	Tejli Sports Complex, Bilt Football Stadium
Karnal	Karna Stadium
Kurukshetra	Women's Hockey Stadium
Gurugram	Football Academy, Devi Lal Stadium
Faridabad	Shooting Academy, Aravalli Golf Ground, Haryana State Sports Complex
Panipat	Shivaji Stadium
Sonipat	Wrestling Academy, Motilal Nehru Sports School, Office of Sports Authority of India
Bhiwani	Boxing Club, Bhim Singh Stadium
Hisar	Mahavir Stadium
Sirsa	Shahid Bhagat Singh Stadium, Shah Satnam Ji Stadium
Jind	Arjun Stadium, Kabaddi Academy
Kaithal	Indoor Stadium
Mewat	Classic Golf Resort
Mahendragarh	Bhawacheli Ramdas Stadium

State Level Sports Complex in Haryana

District level sports complexes have been constructed in about 21 districts of the state. One sports complex is being constructed by HUDA in Panchkula and Gurugram.

Apart from this, two state level sports complex are also located in the state, which are as follows

Rajiv Gandhi Sports Complex

- It is located in Rohtak district and established in 2012.
- This multi-purpose stadium offers facilities for cricket, football, hockey, etc.
- It also facilitates indoor sports like basketball, badminton, gymnastics, handball, volleyball, lawn tennis, table tennis, kabaddi, etc.

Haryana State Level Complex

- This is the second sports complex in the state, located in Faridabad.
- Training of sports like gymnastics, boxing, badminton, athletics, etc. is given in this sports complex.

Motilal Nehru Sports School

- It is located in Rai village of Sonipat district, Haryana. It is the only sports school in the state. This school was established by Haryana Government on 1st July, 1973 for world class training in sports. The school is spread over an area of 300 acres.
- The Government of Haryana is endeavoring to promote this sports school to a sports university. This school offers world class training in sports like tennis, basketball, volleyball, athletics, swimming, gymnastics and squash.

Centre of Training and Excellence in Haryana

- The Sports Authority of India (SAI) has established training centres, centres of excellence and academies in Haryana which provide international level training to the players of the state.
- This authority has set up a sports training centre at HAU University, Hisar.

Training Centres in Haryana

SAI Training Centre and Centre of Excellence, Sonipat

- This training center is also known as Chaudhary Devi Lal North Regional Centre.
- It is located in Bahalgarh area of Sonipat district of Haryana. It is also the Northern Training Centre of Sports Authority of India. Training of kabaddi, football, judo, hockey, basketball, wrestling, swimming, etc. is given under this centre.

SAI Training and Excellence Centre, Hisar

- It is the major centre of boxing training in the country.
- Along with boxing, training in athletics, handball, hockey and wrestling is also given in this training centre.

SAI Training Centre, Kurukshetra

- This training centre is located in Kurukshetra. This training centre works under Chaudhary Devi Lal North Regional Office, Sonipat.
- Under this, training in judo, cycling, weightlifting, hockey and athletics is given.

SAI Training Centre, Bhiwani

- This training centre is located in Bhiwani. This training centre is under the Chaudhary Devi Lal North Regional Centre (Sonipat).

SAI National Boxing Academy, Rohtak

- SAI National Boxing Academy is located in the Rajiv Gandhi State Sports Complex in Rohtak district. It was founded in January, 2017. It is the country's first National Boxing Academy.
- The academy trains Boxers for the upcoming Olympic Games. Sports Authority of India has linked up with Guru Gobind Singh University (Delhi) to prepare the details of trainees in this academy.
- There is a complete arrangement for the stay of 120 trainees (60 male and 60 female) in this academy.

Haryana Adventure Sports Academy

- The Haryana Government issued the notification of formation of Haryana Adventure Sports Academy on 4th January, 2016.
- Its main **objective** was to create awareness about adventure sports in the state. The registration of this academy was done by the State Government under the Haryana Institution Registration and Regulation Act, 2012. The headquarters of this institution is in Panchkula district.

- Chief patron of Haryana Adventure Sports Academy is the Chief Minister of the State and the Chairman is the State Sports and Youth Minister. The Secretary of State's Sports and Youth Affairs is its Vice-Chairman and the Additional Director Secretary of this Department.

Objectives of Haryana Adventure Sports Academy

- To provide training related to ground-sports, aero sports, water sports to the sportspersons of the state so that the players of the state can take interest in these sports.
- To establish satellite centres and base camps and training centres for adventure sports in the state and to establish cooperation with the institutes working in this field.
- To generate interest in adventure sports through skill development and vocational training programmes in the players of the state.
- To provide physical facilities and a strong infrastructure to trainers for adventure sports in the state.
- To provide employment to experienced sportspersons of the state as coaches and consultants.

State Physical Fitness Programme

- In the year 2015, the State Government implemented physical fitness programmes in the state in collaboration with NSS, NCC, Nehru Youth Centers and Bharat Scouts and Guides.
- The main goal of this programme was to connect citizens of different age groups with sports and physical activities.

Activities done under State Physical Fitness Programmes

- Special fitness campaigns were launched in schools
- Community sports training programmes were organised
- State-level sports competitions were held
- Sports became an 'entry-level activity' in community development programmes

Arena Competitions of Haryana

- Haryana hosts arena competitions yearly to uphold its wrestling traditions.
- The government organises District Kumar and District Kesari at the district level and State Kumar and State Kesari at the state level.

As per the Sports Policy 2015, players who win will receive cash prizes which are as follows

Competition	First Prize (₹)	Second Prize (₹)	Third Prize (₹)
State Level Arena Wrestling	5,100	3,100	2,100
Haryana Kumar Dangal	51,000	31,000	21,000
Haryana Kesari Dangal	1,51,000	1,00,000	51,000

Haryana State Sports Policy, 2015

- The Government of Haryana implemented the Sports Policy, 2015 to promote sports and develop infrastructure.
- Haryana has made significant contributions to sports, with its players bringing global recognition.
- **Wrestling is the state's traditional sport** and the youth are highly interested in sports.

Objectives of the Sports Policy

- To provide equal opportunities to all citizens of the state to participate in sports. To promote collective participation and excellence in sports.
- Development of high quality sports infrastructure.
- To encourage, train and support players to participate in national and international competitions.
- To emphasis on development and other facilities in educational institutions including universities.
- To build an excellent sports culture by teaching moral and ideological values.
- To attract young energy and minds towards sports, identify talent in sports sector and reward players who have excelled in sports.
- To identify special needs of disabled players and facilitating their participation in sports, promote adventure sports in the state.
- On 4th May, 2015, the Haryana Government included the Deaflympics (Olympic for the deaf) sport in its sports policy.

Haryana State Sports Associations (Registration and Regulation) Act, 2024

- To regulate the sports related activities in the state, Haryana Assembly passed 'Haryana State Sports Associations (Registration and Regulation) Act, 2024. Following are the key provision of this Act
  - Mandatory registration of all sports bodies and regulation of their activities with Haryana Sports Registration Council.
  - Any violation of law is punishable with imprisonment of three to six months or fine which shall not be less than ₹ 50,000 but may extend to ₹ 1,00,000 or with both.
  - Government shall establish Regional Sports Registration Council in each region.

Cash Prize for Various Sports Competitions

The Cash prize to be given to the winning players under the New Sports Policy is as follows

Event	Gold Medal	Silver Medal	Bronze Medal	Participation
Olympics and Para Olympics	₹ 6 crore	₹ 4 crore	₹ 2.5 crore	₹ 15 lakh
Asian and Para Asian Games	₹ 3 crore	₹ 1.5 crore	₹ 75 lakh	₹ 7.5 lakh
Commonwealth Games	₹ 1.5 crore	₹ 75 lakh	₹ 50 lakh	₹ 7.5 lakh
World Cup	₹ 25 lakh	₹ 20 lakh	₹ 15 lakh	₹ 7.5 lakh
Youth Olympics	₹ 10 lakh	₹ 7.5 lakh	₹ 5 lakh	–
National Competition	₹ 3 lakh	₹ 2 lakh	₹ 1 lakh	–
National Kesari Dangal	₹ 31,000	₹ 21,000	₹ 11,000	–

Haryana at the International Level

London Olympics 2012

- India has won 6 medals in the competition.
- **Haryana's Performance**
  - **Sushil Kumar** won Silver medal in Wrestling.
  - **Gagan Narang** won Bronze medal in shooting.
  - **Saina Nehwal** won Bronze medal in Badminton.
  - **Yogeshwar Dutt** won Bronze in westling.
- On 6th August, 2013, the Cabinet, chaired by CM Bhupinder Singh Hooda, decided that Olympic Gold medalists would be appointed to 'Group A' posts.

20th Commonwealth Games 2014

- India won 64 medals in the 2014 Commonwealth Games in Glasgow, including 15 Gold, 30 Silver and 10 Bronze.
- **Haryana's Performance**
  - Haryana contributed 21 medals, including 5 Gold, 13 Silver and 3 Bronze.
  - Yogeshwar Dutt and Sushil Kumar Babita Kumari, Amit Kumar and Vinesh Phogat won Gold medals.
  - **Lila Ram** of Haryana won the **first Gold medal** in freestyle wrestling in 1958.

Rio Olympics 2016

- In the 2016 Rio Olympics, India won 2 medals.
- **Haryana's Contribution**
  - Sakshi Malik won Bronze Medal in Wrestling. She is from Rohtak, Haryana.
  - Out of 119 Indian participants, 22 were from Haryana. Ashok Bhanwala served as a referee at the event.

21st Commonwealth Games 2018

- In the 2018 Commonwealth Games at Gold Coast, India won 66 medals, including 26 Gold, 20 Silver and 20 Bronze.
- **Haryana's Contribution**
  - Haryana players won 22 medals: 9 Gold, 6 Silver and 7 Bronze.
  - Notable winners include Vikas Krishan Yadav (Boxing, Gold), Manu Bhaker (Shooting, Gold), Saina Nehwal (Badminton, Gold), Vinesh Phogat (Wrestling, Gold) and Seema Antil (Athletics, Silver).

18th Asian Games 2018

- At the 2018 Asian Games in Jakarta and Palembang, India won 69 medals, including 15 Gold, 24 Silver and 30 Bronze.
- **Haryana's Contribution**
  - Haryana players won 18 medals: 6 Gold, 5 Silver and 7 Bronze.
  - **Vinesh Phogat** became the first Indian woman wrestler to win Gold at both the Asian and Commonwealth Games.
  - **Rani Rampal**, from Kurukshetra, was the flag bearer of India at the closing ceremony.

South Asian Games 2019

- India won 312 medals at the 2019 South Asian Games in Nepal, including 174 Gold, 93 Silver and 45 Bronze.
- **Haryana's Contribution**
  - Notable Gold medalists include Sakshi Malik (wrestling), Gori Siron and Kajal Saini (shooting) from Haryana.
  - Deepak Hooda (Haryana), captain of the Indian Kabaddi team, secured his fourth consecutive Gold at the Asian Games.

Tokyo Olympics 2020

- The Tokyo 2020 Olympics, held from 23rd July to 8th August, 2021.
- **Haryana's Contribution**
  - 32 players from Haryana took part in Tokyo 2020 Olympics.
  - **Neeraj Chopra** won Gold in Javelin, **Ravi Dahiya** secured Silver in wrestling and **Bajrang Punia** earned Bronze.
  - **Sumit Kumar** and **Surendar Kumar** were part of the Indian men's hockey team, which won Bronze.

Commonwealth Games 2022

- At the 2022 Commonwealth Games in Birmingham (28th July-8th August), India won 61 medals.
- **Haryana's Contribution**
  - Haryana contributing 20, including 9 Gold, 2 Silver (individual), 2 Silver (team), 6 Bronze (individual) and 1 Bronze (team).
  - Gold medalists from Haryana include Bajrang Punia, Sakshi Malik, Deepak Punia, Vinesh Phogat, Ravi Dahiya, Naveen Kumar (Wrestling), Sudhir (Para Powerlifting), Neetu Ghanghas and Amit Panghal (Boxing).

Paris Olympics 2024

- The Paris Olympics held from 26th July to 11th August, 2024.
- In these games, India won a total of 6 medals (1 Silver and 5 Bronze).
- **Haryana's Contribution**
  - Out of 6 medals, players from Haryana won 4 medals.
  - Medal winners from state are as follows
    - Neeraj Chopra — Javelin Throw (silver)
    - Manu Bhaker — Shooting (Bronze)
    - Manu Bhaker/ Sarabjit Singh — Shooting (Bronze)
    - Aman Sehrawat — Wrestling (Bronze)

Paris Para Olympics 2024

- India achieved a historic milestone at the Paris 2024 Paralympics, securing a total of 29 medals: 7 Gold, 9 Silver and 13 Bronze.
- **Haryana's Contribution**
  - Haryana made a significant contribution to this success, with its athletes winning 8 medals: 5 Gold and 3 Silver.
  - Sumit Antil (Gold in Men's Javelin Throw), Harvinder Singh (Gold in Men's Individual Recurve Open Archery), Pooja (Gold in Women's Individual Recurve Open Archery), Rinku Hooda (Gold in Men's Javelin Throw F46) and Navdeep (Gold in Men's Javelin Throw F41).

Awards of Haryana

The awards are presented by the Government of Haryana in various parts which are as follows

Khel Ratna Awards

Bhim Award

- The Bhim Award is Haryana's **highest sports honour**, established in 2001, recognising outstanding athletes based on four years of achievements.
- It is considered equivalent to the **Arjuna Award**, it includes ₹ 5 lakh cash, a citation, a Bhim statue, a blazer and a lifetime free travel facility on Haryana State Transport buses.

> The award is presented annually by the Haryana Ministry of Youth Affairs and Sports. The first recipient was **Geeta Zutshi**.

Maharana Pratap Award

- This award is given annually to the players who have promoted sports throughout their life.
- A cash prize of ₹ 2 lakh has been determined under this award.

Dr. Radhakrishna Award

- This award is given to the PTI/ DPI teacher of the state. This award is being given every year from the year 2015.
- Under this award, a cash prize of ₹ 1 lakh, a scroll, blazer, tie and scarf are given to the awardees.

Best Sports Association Award

- This award is given to the Sports Association for its outstanding work in the field of sports.
- This award has also been given every year since the year 2015. Under this award, ₹ 5 lakh are given as awards to the Sports Association.

Other Sports Awards in Haryana

Award Name	Description	Cash Prize
Eklavya Award	Given to five junior players every year for their sporting achievements	₹ 1 lakh (each)
Guru Vashistha Award	Awarded to sports coaches for their contribution to the field	₹ 2 lakh
Rani Laxmibai Award	Given to women for their lifelong contribution to sports	₹ 2 lakh
Vikramaditya Award	Given to referees, judges and umpires associated with the game for their service	₹ 2 lakh

Gallantry Awardees from Haryana

The Government of India provides gallantry awards to the military personnel of the state in different categories.

The winners from Haryana in different awards are as follows

Param Vir Chakra Awardees

- It is India's highest gallantry award. **Major Hoshiar Singh** (later also became the Brigadier) was awarded Param Vir Chakra in 1972 by the Government of India for his bravery and exceptional leadership.
- He was born in the year 1936 in Sisana village of Sonipat district.
- He is the only Param Vir Chakra awardee of Haryana.

Vir Chakra Awardees

- This is the third highest gallantry award in the country.
- The people of Haryana who received this award are **Roop Chand** (Sonipat district, Kharkhoda village) in 1948, **Subedar Shivochand Ram** (Hisar district, Kuleri village) in the year 1945 and **Havildar Lakhmi Chand** (Bhiwani district, Dhanana village) posthumously, in 1967.

Prize Money for the Gallantry Awardees by State Government

Gallantry Awards at the Time of War	Award Money
Param Vir Chakra	₹ 2 crore
Maha Vir Chakra	₹ 1 crore
Vir Chakra	₹ 50 lakh
Army/Navy/Air Force Medal (Gallantry)	₹ 21 lakh
Mention in Dispatch (Gallantry)	₹ 10 lakh
Ashoka Chakra	₹ 1 crore
Kirti Chakra	₹ 51 lakh
Shaurya Chakra	₹ 31 lakh
Army/Navy/Air Force Medal (Gallantry)	₹ 10 lakh
Mention in Dispatch (Gallantry)	₹ 7.5 lakh

Apart from this, the State Government gives gallantry prize money every year to the gallantry award winners before 5th October, 2007.

Annual Prize Money to the Gallantry Awardees by the State Government

Gallantry Awards	Award Money
Param Vir Chakra	₹ 3 lakh
Ashoka Chakra	₹ 2.5 lakh
Maha Vir Chakra	₹ 2.25 lakh
Kirti Chakra	₹ 1.75 lakh
Vir Chakra	₹ 1.25 lakh
Shaurya Chakra	₹ 1 lakh
Army/Navy/Air Force Medal (Gallantry)	₹ 50,000
Mention in Dispatch (Gallantry)	₹ 30,000

Source *Sainik and Ardh Sainik Welfare Department, Haryana*

Grants/Pension given to Gallantry Awardees and their Families Before Independence of India

Gallantry Awards	Grants/Pension Amount
Victoria Cross (Britain's highest soldiers honour)	₹ 15,000
Military Cross	₹ 10,000
Military Medal	₹ 5,000
Indian Order of Merit	₹ 3,000
Indian Exceptional Service Medal	₹ 2,000
Mention in Dispatch (Pre-Independence Gallantry Awards only)	₹ 2,000

Source *Sainik and Ardh Sainik Welfare Department, Haryana*

Prize Money to be given by the State Government to the Winners of the War Service Medal or Extraordinary Service Award

Award	Lump Sum
Sarvottam Yudh Seva Medal	₹ 7 lakh
Param Vishisht Seva Medal	₹ 6.5 lakh
Uttam Yudh Seva Medal	₹ 4 lakh
Ati- Vishisht Seva Medal	₹ 3.25 lakh
Yudh Seva Medal	₹ 2 lakh
Vishisht Seva Medal	₹ 1.25 lakh

Padma Awardees from Haryana

- **Narinder Nath Vohra** was awarded Padma Vibhushan for his contributions to the field civil service in the year 2007.

Padma Bhushan Awardees

List of Padma Bhushan Award Recipients of Haryana

Name	Field	Year
Tarlochan Singh	Public Affairs	2021
Darshan Lal Jain	Social Work	2019
Saina Nehwal	Sports	2016
Krishen Khanna	Arts	2011
Rajendra Singh Pawar	Trade & Industry	2011
S. K. Misra	Civil Service	2009
T. K. Oommen	Literature & Education	2008
Tarun Das	Trade & Industry	2006
Kamleshwar	Literature & Education	2006
Jasjit Singh	Others	2006
Sardar Anjum	Literature & Education	2005
Shri Krishna Joshi	Science & Engineering	2003
Harbans Singh Wasir	Medicine	2000
Umrao Singh	Civil Service	1983
Lala Hansraj Gupta	Public Affairs	1970

Padma Shri Awardees

- In the year 1963, K.C. Johorey received Padma Shri Award in the field of Civil Services.

List of Padma Shri Award Recipients of Haryana (2000-25)

Name	Field	Year
Jagan Nath Kaul	Social Work	2000
Jai Bhagwan Chaudhary	Science & Engineering	2003
Surinder Kaur	Arts	2006
Sudhir Kumar Sopory	Science & Engineering	2007
Syamal Bhushan Ghosh Dastidar	Civil Service	2009
Ajeet Bajaj	Sports	2012
Sachchidanand Sahai	Literature & Education	2012
Lokesh Kumar Singhal	Science & Engineering	2012

Name	Field	Year
Yogeshwar Dutt	Sports	2013
Sunil Dabas	Sports	2014
Brahm Dutt	Social Work	2014
Pawan Raj Goyal	Medicine	2014
Amod Gupta	Medicine	2014
Narendra Kumar Pandey	Medicine	2014
Yuvraj Singh	Sports	2014
Mamta Sodha	Sports	2014
Sardara Singh	Sports	2015
Deepa Malik	Sports	2017
Sakshi Malik	Sports	2017
T. K. Viswanathan	Civil Service	2017
Kanwal Singh Chauhan	Others	2019
Bajrang Punia	Sports	2019
Narendra Singh	Others	2019
Sultan Singh	Others	2019
Rani Rampal	Sports	2020
Jaibhagwan Goyal	Literature and Education	2021
Virender Singh	Sports	2021
Sumit Antil	Sports	2022
Neeraj Chopra	Sports	2022
Om Prakash Gandhi	Social Work	2022
Moti Lal Madan	Science and Engineering	2022
Raghuvendra Tanwar	Literature and Education	2022
Sukama Acharya	Others - Spiritualism	2023
Bakshi Ram	Science & Engineering	2023
Mahabir Singh Guddu	Art	2024
Hari Om	Science & Engineering	2024
Ram Chander Sihag	Science & Engineering	2024
Gurvinder Singh	Social Work	2024
Harvinder Singh	Sports	2025
Sant Ram Deswal	Literature and Education	2025

**Padma Shri recipients from 1964 to 1999 are not covered in this list.*

Educational Award

- Every year on the occasion of Teachers' Day (5th September), the Government of Haryana confers the **State Teacher Award** to the outstanding teachers in the field of education.
- This award is given in two categories - **Primary Teacher** and **Secondary Teacher.**
- Teachers awarded with this honour are given a cash amount of ₹ 1 lakh and a citation. Also, a provision has been made to increase the duration of his government job by two years.

Science Awards

The following awards are given annually by the Haryana Government to scientists who have done exceptional work in the field of science

- ***Haryana Youth Science Ratna Awards*** The award is given by the State Government on 28th February every year on the occasion of National Science Day to the young scientists of the state for doing excellent work in the field of technology and science. A cash amount of ₹ 1 lakh is given under this award.
- ***Haryana Vigyan Ratna Award*** This award is also conferred by the Government of Haryana on the occasion of National Science Day on 28th February every year. A cash amount of ₹ 5 lakh is awarded under this award.

Chaudhary Devi Lal Award

- The award is sponsored by ICAR (Indian Council of Agricultural Research) with objective to recognise excellent performance of AICRP (All India Coordinated Research Project).
- It consists of ₹ 3 lakh in cash, a citation and a plaque for contribution to agricultural productivity.

National Gopal Ratna Award

- The award is conferred by Department of Fisheries, Animal Husbandry and Dairying.
- The award is given in the field of livestock and dairy sector.
- **Smt. Renu** from Jhajjar got this award under the category 'Best Dairy Farmer Rearing Indigenous Cattle/ Buffalo Breeds' for 2024.

State Level Award for Women

Three State level awards for women have been announced by the Haryana Government on 8th March, 2010, to celebrate the 100th International Women's Day, with the aim of encouraging women of the state.

These awards are as follows

Award	Description
Indira Gandhi Mahila Shakti Puraskar	• On 8th March, 2010 this award was instituted by the State Government of Haryana. • This award is given to those women of the state who have done outstanding work for society and for the rehabilitation and welfare of women and children. • The awardees get a cash prize of ₹ 1.5 lakh and a citation in this award.
Kalpana Chawla Shaurya Award	• 'Kalpana Chawla Shaurya' award was instituted in the honour of Kalpana Chawla, India's first female astronaut in the year 2010. • This honour is given to those women who have shown exemplary courage by taking risks in their lives and done meritorious services for the society and nation. • The awardees get a cash prize of ₹ 1 lakh and citation under this award.
Bahin Shanno Devi Panchayati Raj Award	• The award was instituted in the year 2010 in the name of Bahin Shanno Devi, the first Woman Speaker of the Haryana Legislative Assembly. • This award will be given to those women panchayat heads who have done extraordinary work for women empowerment, female literacy, health and nutrition, environmental protection and universalisation of education etc. • An amount of ₹ 1 lakh is provided by the Government of Haryana under this award.

CHECK CHAPTER KNOWLEDGE

1 Haryana Athletics was founded in which year in Haryana?
(a) 1962 (b) 1965
(c) 1963 (d) 1967

2 Bahadur Singh, who won Gold medal in 1978 and 1982 Asian Games is an Indian
(a) Shot putter (b) Runner
(c) Wrestler (d) Boxer

3 First Indian woman to win a medal in Paralympic Games is
(a) Pooja Rani (b) Sakshi Malik
(c) Deepa Malik (d) Karamjyoti Dalal

4 Vijender Singh: Boxing :: Geeta Zutshi: .... *Bus Conductor 2017*
(a) Tennis (b) Badminton
(c) Athletics (d) Gymnastic

5 In which of the following sports did Hawa Singh won the Asian Games gold medal in successive editions in the year 1960 and 1970? *HSSC CET 2024*
(a) Weightlifting (b) Boxing
(c) Shooting (d) Badminton

6 Which district of Haryana is known as 'Power House of Boxing'?
(a) Sonipat (b) Rohtak
(c) Sirsa (d) Bhiwani

7 Vijender Singh Beniwal of Haryana is a national *Haryana Clerk 2016*
(a) boxer (b) wrestler (c) athlete (d) cricketer

8 Who won the first Olympic medal for India in Boxing sport? *PGT 2018*
(a) Vikas Yadav (b) Vijender Singh Beniwal
(c) Gagan Narang (d) Jagdish Singh

9 Who won a Bronze medal in boxing in Beijing Olympic Games, 2008? *Haryana Patwari 2016*
(a) Vijender Singh Beniwal
(b) Dinesh Kumar
(c) Gagan Narang
(d) Pinki Jangra

10 Sunil Kumar of Haryana is associated with which sports? *HSSC 2023*
(a) Boxing (b) Kabaddi
(c) Shooting (d) Athletics

11 Vikas Krishan Yadav, who won a gold medal in 2018 Commonwealth Games is associated with *Haryana Police Constable 2018*
(a) boxing (b) shot put
(c) shooting (d) wrestling

12 In which year the first Ranji Trophy match was played in Haryana?
(a) 1980 (b) 1982 (c) 1989 (d) 1990

13 The famous Nawab Mansoor Ali Khan Pataudi was associated to which field? *HSSC 2022, 16*
(a) Literature (Poetry) (b) Drama
(c) Sports (Cricket) (d) Politics

14 Who among the following is associated with Haryana? *PGT 2016*
(a) Kapil Dev (b) Sunil Gavaskar
(c) Sachin Tendulkar (d) Azharuddin

15 Who is the fastest Indian bowler to take 50 wickets in T-20 series held in Bangladesh 2019?
(a) Rishabh Pant (b) Jasprit Bumrah
(c) Bhuvneshwar Kumar (d) Yuzvendra Chahal

16 In which year the Indian Cricket Team won World Cup under Captaincy of Kapil Dev? *HSSC 2020, PGT 2016*
(a) 1981 (b) 1983 (c) 1982 (d) 1984

17 Which woman hockey player is known as 'Golden Girl' in Haryana?
(a) Sunita Dalal (b) Sita Gosai
(c) Suman Bala (d) Mamta Kharab

18 Sandeep Singh is associated with which sports? *Agriculture 2017, PGT 2016*
(a) Volleyball (b) Hockey
(c) Wrestling (d) Cricket

19 Which of the following pair is correct? *PGT 2016*
(a) Vikas Krishna-Wrestling
(b) Suman Bala- Hockey
(c) Santosh Yadav-Volleyball
(d) Sandeep Singh-Boxing

20 Surendra Nada is associated with which sports of Haryana? *HSSC 2024*
(a) Wrestling (b) Hockey
(c) Kabaddi (d) Athletics

21 Prominent kabaddi player, Deepak Niwas Hooda belongs from which village of Rohtak district?
(a) Bhainswal Kalan (b) Mokra
(c) Balali (d) Chamaria

22 The State Sport of Haryana is *TET 2010*
(a) shooting (b) wrestling
(c) cricket (d) football

23 Lila Ram from Haryana is very famous because he *HSSC 2022, 15*
(a) won first gold medal in Commonwealth Games
(b) won first silver medal in Commonwealth Games
(c) won first bronze medal in Commonwealth Games
(d) None of the above

24 Yogeshwar Dutt is associated with *Haryana Police 2016*
(a) Road Walk (b) Hockey
(c) Wrestling (d) Kabaddi

25 In London Olympics, Yogeshwar Dutt won *PGT 2016*
(a) Gold medal (b) Bronze medal
(c) Silver medal (d) None of these

26 Gita Phogat is associated with which sports?
(a) Wrestling (b) Boxing
(c) Paul Volt (d) Shot put

27 Which female wrestler won Gold medal in the Commonwealth Game for the first time? *HSSC 2023, 20*
(a) Babita Phogat (b) Gita Phogat
(c) Sakshi Malik (d) None of these

28 Who was the first Indian female wrestler who qualified for the Olympic Summer Games?
(a) Gita Phogat (b) Babita Phogat
(c) Geetika Jakhar (d) Sakshi Malik

29 Which of the following famous personalities belongs to Mokhra village of Rohtak? *Haryana Clerk 2016*
(a) Kalpana Chawla (b) Sakshi Malik
(c) Baba Ramdev (d) None of these

30 Which wrestler won gold medal in the Senior Wrestling National Championship held in November 2019?
(a) Sakshi Malik (b) Anju Kumari
(c) Nitu Sarkar (d) Kavita Devi

31 Olympic medal winner, Haryana's Pride, Sakshi Malik is connected to which sport?
(a) Badminton (b) Swimming
(c) Wrestling (d) Boxing

32 Which player is not related to wrestling?
(a) Yogeshwar Dutt
(b) Vinesh Phogat
(c) Sakshi Malik
(d) Chand Ram

33 Satish Kumar of Haryana is a player of
(a) Handball (b) Hockey
(c) Cricket (d) Judo

34 Who received the Padma Shri Award in the field of sports in Haryana for the year 2019? *HSSC 2021, 20*
(a) Yuvraj Singh (b) Bajrang Punia
(c) Sakshi Malik (d) Deepa Malik

35 Which woman wrestler from Haryana won Gold medal in Asian Games, 2018?
(a) Sakshi Malik (b) Vinesh Phogat
(c) Gita Phogat (d) Babita Phogat

36 .... was the first wrestler who won three medals in World Wrestling Championship. *Haryana Lab Attendant 2018*
(a) Vinay Phogat (b) Bajrang Punia
(c) Sakshi Malik (d) Sushil Kumar

37 Arjun Awardee Vinesh Phogat is related to
(a) Kabbadi (b) Boxing
(c) Wrestling (d) Hockey

38 Sania Nehwal is associated with which sports? *PGT 2016*
(a) Badminton (b) Wrestling
(c) Hockey (d) Shooting

39 Rani Rampal of Haryana is associated with which game? *Haryana Accountant 2018*
(a) Hockey (b) Cricket
(b) Wrestling (d) Kabbadi

40 Santosh Yadav and Anita Kundu is related to *HSSC 2022, 15*
(a) Boxing (b) Judo
(c) Handball (d) Mountaineering

41 Shivangi Pathak of Hisar district is a player *HSSC 2016*
(a) Skiping (b) Wrestling
(c) Mountaineering (d) Boxing

42 Who is the founder of Bhiwani Boxing Club? *HSSC Civil 2015*
(a) Jagadish Singh (b) Sushil Kumar
(c) Kapil Dev (d) Vijender Singh

43 Manu Bhaker is associated with which sports of Haryana? *Haryana Group D 2018*
(a) Athletics (b) Wrestling
(c) Badminton (d) Shooting

44 Karnam Malleshwari is associated with which sports of Haryana? *PGT 2016*
(a) Hockey (b) Weightlifting
(c) Cricket (d) Basketball

45 Which place of Haryana is known as 'Powerhouse of Indian Boxing'? *Ayush Department 2017*
(a) Sonipat (b) Sirsa
(c) Rohtak (d) Bhiwani

46 Nahar Singh Stadium is located in which district of Haryana? *HSSC 2023, 20*
(a) Faridabad (b) Ambala
(c) Kurukshetra (d) Yamunanagar

47 In which year Motilal Nehru Sports School was established in Haryana? *HSSC 2024*
(a) 1973 (b) 1975
(c) 1974 (d) 1977

48 What is the provision of cash reward to Olympic Gold medalists in Haryana? *HSSC 2018*
(a) ₹ 4 crore (b) ₹ 3 crore
(c) ₹ 5 crore (d) ₹ 6 crore

49 What are Government Schemes to promote sports in Haryana? *HSSC 2012, 19*
(a) To give training
(b) To construct sports stadiums
(c) Provide grants to sports institutions
(d) All of the above

50 Highest award of Haryana Government in the field of sports *HSSC 2021*
(a) Eklavya Award
(b) Maharana Pratap Award
(c) Rani Laxmi Bai Award
(d) Bhim Award

CORRECT ANSWERS

1. (d)	2. (a)	3. (c)	4. (c)	5. (b)	6. (d)	7. (a)	8. (b)	9. (a)	10. (a)
11. (a)	12. (b)	13. (c)	14. (a)	15. (d)	16. (b)	17. (d)	18. (b)	19. (b)	20. (c)
21. (d)	22. (b)	23. (a)	24. (c)	25. (b)	26. (a)	27. (b)	28. (a)	29. (b)	30. (a)
31. (c)	32. (d)	33. (d)	34. (b)	35. (b)	36. (b)	37. (c)	38. (a)	39. (a)	40. (d)
41. (c)	42. (a)	43. (d)	44. (b)	45. (d)	46. (a)	47. (a)	48. (d)	49. (d)	50. (d)

CHAPTER 31

Social Welfare Schemes in Haryana

Several welfare schemes have been initiated by the State and Central Government to provide social equality and justice to the socially, economically and educationally backward people in Haryana.

Major Women and Child Development Schemes

Following are the major schemes related to women and child development

Matrushakti Udaymita Scheme

- Launch date: 8th March, 2022 (International Women's Day)
- Target beneficiaries: Women Entrepreneurs in Haryana
- Eligibility: Women with Family annual income less than ₹ 5 lakh (verified by Parivar Pehchan Patra)
- Loan amount: Soft loans up to ₹ 3 lakh
- Interest subsidy: 7% subvention for 3 years
- Implementing agency: Haryana Women Development Corporation

Mahila Evam Kishori Samman

- Launch date: 5th August, 2020
- Target beneficiaries: Women aged 10 to 45 years in Haryana
- Provision: 6 sanitary napkins provided free of cost
- Distribution method: Through Anganwadi centres and schools
- Implementing agency: Department of Women and Child Development, Haryana

Mukhyamantri Doodh Uphar Yojana

- Launch date: 5th August, 2020
- Target beneficiaries: Children, pregnant women and lactati'ng mothers in Haryana
- Objective: Improving nutrition levels in children, pregnant women and lactating mothers
- Provision: 200 ml of fortified milk will be provided to each beneficiary
- Distribution method: At Anganwadi centres
- Implementing agency: Department of Women and Child Development, Haryana

Haryana Mahila Samridhi Yojana

- Launch date: July, 2020
- Target beneficiaries: Women from the scheduled caste category in Haryana
- Objective: Provide employment opportunities to scheduled caste women.
- Loan provision: Loan of ₹ 60,000 at an annual interest rate of 5%
- Purpose: For setting-up self-employment
- Implementing Agency: Haryana Scheduled Castes Finance and Development Corporation (HSFDC)

Poshan Abhiyan

- Launch date — 8th March, 2018
- Objective — To lay emphasis on nutritional status of adolescent girls, pregnant women, lactating mothers and children from 0-6 years age
- Implemented in — All districts of Haryana

Sakhi (One Stop Centre)

- Launch date — 1st April, 2015
- Objective — To provide justice and support to women suffering from violence in a phased manner
- Services provided — Medical facilities, mental and social counselling, police assistance, legal aid
- Implementation — Centres set-up in several districts, i.e. Karnal, Gurugram, Faridabad, Hisar, Rewari, Bhiwani, Narnaul Nuch, etc. The first centre was in Karnal.
- Implementing agency — Ministry of Women and Child Development, Haryana

Swadhar Greh Yojana

- Launch date — 1st January, 2016
- Objective — Prepare a supportive institutional plan for women facing difficult circumstances
- Provision — Provides social and economic security to women
- Implementing agency — Ministry of Women and Child Development

Mukhyamantri Vivah Shagun Yojana

- Launch date — July, 2015
- Beneficiaries — Women with annual income below ₹ 1 lakh. Women players are not included in this scheme.
- Eligibility — – One spouse must be a permanent resident of Haryana.
  – Bride and groom must be 18 and 21 years old respectively.
- Financial Assistance — ₹ 11,000 to ₹ 51,000 as Shagun (gift) for marriage
- Objective — To provide financial assistance for the marriage of girls from economically weaker sections.

> Mukhyamantri Vivah Shagun Yojana is the latest form of 'Indira Gandhi Priyadarshini Vivah Shagun Scheme', which was started in the year 2005.

Aapki Beti-Hamari Beti Yojana

- Launch date — 24th August, 2015
- Objective — Eliminate sex-selective abortion, increase child sex-ratio, promote education for girls
- Implementing agency — Department of Women and Child Development, Haryana
- Under this scheme, a cheque of ₹ 21,000 will be given to the first girl child, who belongs to the families of Scheduled Castes and Below Poverty Line (BPL) and has born on or after 22nd January, 2015.
- This cash amount can be used by the girl in her education or marriage. In the same way, all second girl child born on or after 22nd January, 2015 of all families will get ₹ 21,000.

> Under 'Aapki Beti Hamari Beti' this scheme, a girl child can withdraw an amount of ₹ 1 lakh after 18 years of age.

Haryana Kanya Kosh

- Launch on — 8th March, 2015
- Purpose — Support development and empowerment of girls and women in Haryana.
- Implementation — Women and Child Development Department (WCD)
- It is expected to increase the amount of this Kosh to ₹ 100 crore.

Beti Bachao-Beti Padhao Campaign

- Launch date — 22nd January, 2015
- Launch by — Prime Minister **Narendra Modi** in Panipat district, Haryana
- It aims to address the issue of the declining child sex-ratio. It also focus on education and empowerment of the girl child.
- The Nodal agency of this scheme is Department of Women and Child Development.

- **Sakshi Malik** is the Brand Ambassador for Beti Bachao Beti Padhao Campaign.

Sukanya Samriddhi Yojana

- Launch year: 2015 as a part of Beti Bachao Beti Padhao Scheme
- Objective: Address gender imbalance in society and encourage positive discrimination in favour of girl child
- This scheme is to encourage parents of girl child to invest on her name. The account can be opened from birth of a girl child till she attains the age of 10 years. The minimum deposit amount is ₹ 250 (per month) and maximum is ₹ 1.5 lakh (per annum). The deposited amount would get 7.6% interest rate.
- A girl child, who attained the age of 10 years, one year prior to notification will also be eligible for this account scheme. Parents can deposit the amount for a period of 15 years only.

> The depositor can withdraw 50% of the immatured amount for marriage of a girl of 18 years age or for her higher studies.

SABLA Scheme (Rajiv Gandhi Scheme For Empowerment of Adolescent Girls)

- Launch date: 1st April, 2011
- Launch by: Haryana Government in 6 districts (Hisar, Ambala, Rohtak, Rewari, Yamunanagar and Kaithal)
- The main aim of the scheme is to make adolescent girls strong physically and mentally and enable them for self-development.
- It covers adolescent girls of the age group 11-18 years.
- Under this scheme, adolescent girls are given training to improve their nutrition and health status, to promote awareness about Adolescent Reproductive and Sexual Health (ARSH) and family and child care, to upgrade their home-based skills and vocational skills and to access education/learning.

Ladli Social Security Allowance Scheme

- Launch date: 1st January, 2006
- Launch by: Government of Haryana
- Target group: Families with only girl child/children and one of the parents must be aged 45 years or older.
- An amount of ₹ 3,000 per month is provided to any of the parents who attained the age of 45 years till their 60th birthday. After 60 years, parents will be eligible for Old Age Samman Allowance Scheme.

Ladli Scheme

- Launch date: 20th August, 2005
- Launch by: Department of Women and Child Development
- Objective is to stop the female foeticide and raise the sex-ratio in the state.
- This scheme is especially for those parents who have two girl child.
- The scheme has since been subsumed under the 'Aapki Beti Hamari Beti' scheme.

> Under Ladli scheme, an incentive of ₹ 5,000 per year is provided to those parents for 5 years whose second girl child is born on or after 20th August, 2005.

Nutrition Programme for Adolescent Girls

- Launch by: Government of India on a pilot basis for 2005-06
- Two districts of Haryana, namely, Ambala and Yamunanagar were selected for this project.
- Under this programme, all the adolescent girls of age group 11-19 years got 6 kg wheat for 3 consecutive months under Public Distribution System (PDS).

Devi Rupak Yojana

- Launch date: 25th September, 2002
- Launch by: Ministry of Health and Family Welfare, Haryana
- The main aim of this scheme is to control population growth, eliminate discrimination between boys and girls and to check the declining trend in the male and female sex-ratio of the state.

Swayam Sidha Scheme

- Launch year: 2001, dedicated to women's empowerment
- Programme type: Self Help Group (SHG)-based initiative
- Target districts: 6 districts of Haryana, covering 16 blocks
- In collaboration with: Indian and State Governments
- It was specifically introduced for couples adopting terminal methods of family planning to help stabilise the state's population.

Apni Beti, Apna Dhan Yojana

- Launch date: 1994-98
- Launch by: State Government

- Objective — To improve the health status of women and children in the state
- This scheme was implemented for the poor girls of Haryana.

Major Social Justice and Empowerment Schemes

The Ministry of Social Justice and Empowerment, Government of Haryana has launched several schemes, which are outlined as follows

Teerth Darshan Scheme

- Launch date — 1st April, 2017
- Launch by — Tourism Department of Haryana
- Target group — Senior citizens above 60 years with Haryana domicile
- The objective is to provide free travel opportunities to senior citizens across India at government expense.
- Under this scheme, the State Government bears 70% of the cost but the government bears the entire cost of the journey of senior citizens who belong from BPL families. More than 400 destinations can be visited under this scheme.

Vidhur Pension Yojana

- Launch year — 2017-18
- Target group — Widowers who have lost their wives for any reason
- Objective — To provide financial support to widowers
- Pension amount — ₹ 1,600 per month

> By implementing Vidhur Pension Yojana, Haryana has become the first state in India to launch such type of scheme for men.

Old Age Samman Allowance Scheme

- Launched by — Department of Social Justice and Empowerment, Haryana
- Target group — People aged 60 years or above
- Under this scheme, families whose annual income is less than ₹ 2,00,000 have been included, under which the old age people of 60 years or more are included.
- Haryana is the first state, where all the widows, old age people and destitutes get pension on a regular basis on every 7th day of each month.

> On 1st November, 2017, the monthly pension has been increased from ₹ 1,600 to ₹ 1800 which again increased to ₹ 2,000 from November, 2018. It has been increased to ₹ 3,000 with effect from 1st January, 2024.

Widow Pension Scheme

- Launch year — 1980-81
- Launch by — Department of social justice and empowerment
- Target group — Widows and destitute women aged 18 years or above
- Objective — Provide regular financial support to widows and destitute women.
- Under this scheme, ₹ 3,000 per month is given to these women, (w.e.f. 1st January, 2024)
- This pension is given to those women who have no other financial support and her own income from all sources is below ₹ 3 lakh.

Pension to Differently Abled Persons

- Launch by — Department of Social Justice and Empowerment, Haryana
- Target group — Differently abled individuals with 60% disability (previously 70%), aged 18 years or older
- Objective — To make differently abled persons self-dependent by providing regular pension support
- Pension amount — ₹ 3,000 per month is provided as pension (w.e.f. 1st January, 2024)

'Thari Pension-Thare Pass' Pension Scheme

- Launch date — 4th August, 2015
- Launch by — CM Manohar Lal Khattar in Chandigarh
- Type of scheme — A social security initiative
- Objective — To provide direct pension payments to beneficiaries
- Pension is directly transferred to the beneficiary's bank account, eliminating any **mediation.**

State Samman Pension for Freedom Fighters

- It provides pension to the freedom fighters and their widows.

- The amount of this scheme is increased from ₹ 25,000 to ₹ 40,000 (w.e.f. 1st July, 2024)
- It also includes a fixed medical allowance at the rate of ₹ 1,000 per month.

Financial Assistance Scheme for Destitute Children

- Launch date 1st March, 2009
- Launch by State Government of Haryana
- Children whose parents have died or are imprisoned for life in prison or physically disabled by 100% are included in this scheme.
- At present, financial assistance of ₹ 2,100 is given to destitute children (w.e.f. January, 2024).

Financial Assistance Scheme for Children with Disabilities

- Launch date 2008-09
- Launch by State Government of Haryana
- Under this scheme, those mentally retarded children are covered, whose intellectual capacity is less than 50 or the minimum disability is more than 60% or their mother's monthly income is less than the minimum monthly wages.
- Financial assistance of ₹ 2,400 per month is being given by the State Government from January 2024.

Kinnar Bhatta Yojana

- Launch date 1st June, 2006
- Launch by State Government of Haryana
- Under this scheme, those have been included who are over 18 years of age and have a certificate of being eunuchs issued by the civil surgeon.
- Under the scheme, Haryana Government is providing ₹ 2,750 per month.

Major Health Schemes

Following are the health related schemes of the Government of Haryana

Nirogi Haryana

- Launch date 29th November, 2022
- It is one of the flagship schemes of Government of Haryana, which endeavours to provide comprehensive health check-up alongwith mandatory laboratory investigations to Antyodaya population, once in two years.
- For smooth conduct of health cheekup, Antyodaya beneficiaries are divided into six age categories
  0-6 months, 6-59 months
  5-18 years, 18-40 years
  40-60 years, over 60 years

Sanjeevani Pariyojana

- Launch Date 24th May, 2021
- Its aim was to help people get quick access to healthcare at home for mild to moderate symptoms of COVID-19.

Limited Cashless Medical Services Scheme

- Launch year 2017
- Objective Provide cashless medical services to government employees and pensioners
- This scheme is implemented for a person suffering from heart attack, accident, third and fourth stage cancer, coma, cerebral hemorrhage and electrocution.

> Limited Cashless Medical Services Scheme is implemented in all government medical colleges, government-aided medical colleges, all district hospitals, all private hospitals, which are affiliated under the Haryana Government.

Mission Indradhanush

- Launch date 25th December, 2014
- Launched by Ministry of Health and Family Welfare
- Objective Keep children healthy and disease-free in Haryana
- Under this scheme, children are given seven vaccines related to Diphtheria, Tetanus, Polio, Tuberculosis, Measles, Hepatitis-B, Jaundice and Tuberculosis (TB).

Mukhyamantri Muft Ilaaj Yojana

- Launch date 1st January, 2014
- Objective To provide free treatment to all residents of the state in government health institutions, including major components of health care.
- It is one of the flagship initiatives of Haryana, which provides 7 types of services free of cost to patients, such as surgery, laboratory tests, diagnostics (X-ray, ECG and ultrasound services), OPD/indoor services/essential medicines, referral transport and dental treatment.

- Additionally, non-free laboratory tests, wherever available in the hospital, are also provided free of cost to BPL patients, Schedule Caste people, urabn dwellers, disabled patients and certain other categories of patients.

e-Upchaar Yojana

- Launch by — State Health System Resource Centre, Haryana
- The objective of this Yojana is to bring administrative efficiency through ICT enabled Hospital information system and to improve patient care as well as service delivery.

> e-Upchaar is being implemented in 56 health care facilities in Haryana. It has been successfully integrated with "Mera Aspataal" application of Government of India for all the implemented sites.

Jeevan Rekha Yojana

- Launch year — 2013
- Objective — Scheme was started for the patients suffering from Hepatitis-C (black jaundice)
- Initially, free medicines were provided to only Scheduled Castes and Scheduled Tribes under this scheme, but from the year 2017, free medicines are being provided to all categories of people.

> Under Jeevan Rekha Yojana, the State Government is providing facility for Hepatitis-C virus screening and treatment in 21 district hospitals of the state.

Nehru Drishti Yojana

- Launch date — 26th January, 2010
- Launch by — Haryana Government
- The main objective of this scheme is to encourage eye donation in the state and make the cornea available to the people suffering from blindness.

Indira Bal Swasthya Yojana

- Launch year — 2010
- Under this scheme, health check-up of children up to 18 years of age is done in the school itself.
- Also, children's health cards are made and they are treated free of cost in government hospitals.

Major Insurance Schemes

The Haryana State Government has introduced several insurance-related schemes, which are as follows

Chief Minister Traders Collective Private Accident Insurance Scheme

- Launch year — 2019
- Launch by — Haryana Government
- Under this scheme, the government will provide insurance cover of ₹ 5 lakh to registered small and medium traders.
- It is an accident insurance scheme for merchants, retailers, small shopkeepers, shop owners and self-employed people.
- Benefit of Insurance is acceptable in case of death in accident, permanent disability and damage to two body parts or eyes or one body part or one eye.

Chief Minister Traders Compensation Insurance Scheme

- Launch year — 2019
- Launch by — Haryana Government
- Under this scheme, the State Government offers a package of ₹ 5 lakh to ₹ 25 lakh to business retailers, small shopkeepers and self-employed persons depending on their turnover.
- This scheme gives compensation for the loss of their stock, furniture and other goods due to fire, earthquake, flood, theft.

Rajiv Gandhi Parivar Bima Yojana

- Launch date — 1st April, 2006
- Launch by — Haryana Government
- Objective — Provide social security to the people of Haryana
- Under this scheme, the State Government provides ₹ 1 lakh to all the age group of 18-60 years who have faced accidental death or permanent disability.
- A person gets ₹ 50,000 when loses his/her two limbs, two eyes, one limb and one eye (any of the two parts of body). If a person loses any one part of his/her body i.e. one eye or one limb, he gets ₹ 25,000.

Devi Rakshak Yojana

- Launch date — 2nd October, 2003
- Launch by — Haryana Government
- It is also known as 'Devilal Jansuraksha Bima Yojana'.
- Under this scheme, a compensation of ₹ 1 lakh is given to the affected families after the death or permanent disablement of their sole earner, ₹ 50,000 when loses his/her any of two body parts and ₹ 25,000 when loses his/her any one body part.

Surakshit Bhavishya Yojana

- This scheme is for the welfare of anganwadi workers and helpers. An amount of ₹ 100 is invested to LIC every month for an anganwadi worker.
- An amount ₹ 50,000 is given to the family of the anganwadi worker after his/her sudden death.

Employment-related Schemes

The State Government has implemented the following employment-related schemes

Saksham Yuva Scheme

- Launch date — 1st November, 2016, during Haryana's Swarna Jayanti Year
- Purpose — Provides monthly financial assistance to unemployed post-graduates.
- The unemployed post-graduate youth get ₹ 6,000 for honorary assignment for work of 100 hours in different departments, boards, corporations and registered committees of the state.
- They also get ₹ 3,000 as unemployment allowance. This scheme also included unemployed graduates who get ₹ 1,500 as unemployment allowance.

Model Career Centre

- Launch year — 2015
- Founded by — Central Government
- Location — Model Career Centre, Hisar
- It is aimed at empowering the youth so that they can develop their skills and achieve their professional goals.

Unemployment Allowance Scheme

- Launch date — 1st November, 2005
- Launch by — State Government
- Target — Educated unemployed individuals in Haryana
- Under this scheme, the Government of Haryana is providing ₹ 300 per month for unemployed who have passed 12th or equivalent class and ₹ 500 per month for unemployment allowance to graduates or diploma holders.

> Since 1st April, 2009, under Unemployment Allowance scheme, 12th class women are given ₹ 900 and graduate pass women are given ₹ 1,500 per month.

- Apart from this, ₹ 750 is given to boys who have passed 12th class from science stream and ₹ 1,000 per month to graduate male students who have science stream.

Saksham Sarthi/Saksham Rakshak

- The State Government has partnered with various private institutions to provide employment to unemployed youths.
- Under the Saksham Haryana Campaign, 57185 youths have been provided employment under MoU with Ola, Uber, Zomato and Swiggy as drivers and security guards.

Major Schemes Related to Scheduled Castes

The State Government is implementing the following key schemes for Scheduled Castes

Anusuchit Jati Chhatra Shiksha Protsahan Yojana

- Launch date — 18th August, 2009
- Launch by — Haryana Government
- After 10+2, students studying in science, commerce or vocational courses are given class-wise annual scholarship up to ₹ 5,000 to 14,000 under this scheme.
- The purpose of this scheme is to motivate parents of scheduled caste girls and prevent girls from dropping out of education after passing the 10+2 exam.

> The benefit of this scheme will be given to those students whose parental income is less than ₹ 2.40 lakh.

Legal Aid to Scheduled Castes and Vimukta Jatis Scheme

- Launch on — 13th February, 1961
- Launch by — Department of Welfare Scheduled Castes and Backward Classes
- Objective — To provide legal aid to member of Scheduled Castes for defending his/her case relating to land, rent, etc pending in the court

Dr. B.R. Ambedkar Awas Navinikaran Yojana

Under Dr. B.R. Ambedkar Awas Navinikaran Yojana, SC, nomadic and roadside persons living below the poverty line will be provided with a grant amount of ₹ 80,000 to repair their houses.

Inter-Caste Marriage Incentive Scheme

- The State Government has launched the Inter-caste Marriage Incentive Scheme to eliminate caste discrimination and encourage mutual harmony in the society.
- To get the benefit of this scheme, one person from the couple must be from the scheduled caste and the other from the non-scheduled caste.
- The couple should also be permanent residents of Haryana.
- Under this scheme, a grant of ₹ 50,000 was given by the State Government for scheduled caste boy and girl to marry a non-scheduled caste girl and boy. At present, this amount has been increased from ₹ 50,000 to 2.5 lakh.

Farmers Welfare Schemes

The following schemes related to farmer welfare are being implemented in the state

Chaara-Bijaee Yojana

- Launch date: 10th May, 2022
- Objective: Provide financial assistance to farmers cultivating and supplying fodder to Gaushalas (Cowsheds)
- Assistance amount: ₹ 10,000 per acre for up to 10 acres of land
- The scheme aims to address the State's fodder shortage and rising stray cattle. The Subsidy will be directly credited to the farmers account under Direct Benefit Transfer (DBT).

Mukhyamantri Bagwani Bima Yojana

- Launch date: December, 2020
- Through this scheme, the government gives compensation will compensate the farmers growing horticulture crops who have lost their crops due to natural calamities or adverse weather.
- The scheme covers 23 vegetables, 21 fruits and 2 spice crops.
- Farmers have to pay a minimal fee of ₹ 750 for vegetable and spice crops and ₹ 1,000 for fruit crops in such amount and the farmers get the insurance of ₹ 30,000 for vegetable and spice crops and ₹ 40,000 for fruit crops.

National Agricultural Market (e-NAM)

- Launch year: 2017 in Haryana
- Launch by: Haryana State Agricultural Marketing Board
- The scheme was launched by linking 54 mandis to the e-NAM platform.
- e-NAM is an online platform that provides training facility to farmers, traders and buyers.

eNAM

Uttam Fasal Uttam Enaam

e-Procurement Scheme

- Launch year: 2016
- Launch by: Haryana State Agricultural Marketing Board and Food and Supplies Department jointly
- Initial Implementation: Started in Karnal district, Haryana
- The objective of this scheme is to bring transparency in the procurement process of foodgrains at all levels.

Scholarship Scheme for Children of Cooperative Milk Producers

- Launch date: 1st March, 2015
- Launch by: Department of Dairy Development, Government of Haryana
- Under this scheme, children of co-operative milk producers are included who have secured more than 80% marks in the 10th and 12th examinations. Scholarship of ₹ 2,100 is offered to the students of class 10th and ₹ 5,100 to the students of class 12th.

Insurance Scheme for Cooperative Milk Producers

- This is an accident insurance scheme implemented by the Department of Dairy Development in the state.
- Under this scheme, accident insurance of ₹ 10 lakh is provided to the families of milk producers of cooperative societies.

Other Major Schemes of the Central and State Government in Haryana

Scheme	Implementation	Important Features
Parivar Pehchan Patras Scheme	4th August, 2020	The aim of the scheme is to monitor each family (around 54 lakh) living across Haryana. Under the scheme, each family is considered as a single unit and allotted an 8 digit unique identification number. This enables seamless delivery of State Government services.
Samadhan Se Vikas Scheme	2021	The scheme is applicable in respect of full amount outstanding on account of the EDC and on interest and penalty interest. Many colonisers and builders mostly in Gurugram and Faridabad failed to pay the State Government over ₹ 10,000 crore as EDC.
Mukhyamantri Parivar Samman Nidhi Yojana (MMPSY)	26th January, 2020	This scheme is for farmers of the state. The MMPSY has four options for the beneficiary families of the first category of honour fund. In which the beneficiary family can get cash of ₹ 6,000 per year, which will be deposited in the bank account of the family head in three similar installments of ₹ 2,000.
Pradhan Mantri Shram Yogi Maan-Dhan Yojana	February, 2019	This Yojana aims to ensure old age security of unorganised workers whose monthly income is less than ₹ 15,800 pension of ₹ 3,000 per month will be given. If member holder dies, his spouse will get entire amounts. The subscriber's contribution is through auto debit facility from his/her savings account/Jan Dhan account, ranging from ₹ 50 to ₹ 500 per month.
Haryana Parivartan Yojana	21st February, 2018	The State Government has started this scheme in 46 developing blocks to address 10 issues of the state including cleanliness and pollution.
Antyodaya Aahar Yojana	17th February, 2018	This scheme provides meals to poor people at ₹ 10 and a healthy breakfast at ₹ 5.
Sant Guru Ravidas Scheme	4th February, 2018	Under this scheme, loans up to ₹ 25,000 are provided to the small artisans without interest and hostels are opened in 11 districts of the state in the name of Baba Sahib.
Star Village Scheme	26th January, 2018	Under this scheme, the State Government provides assistance to Gram Panchayats according to the rate.
Jay Jawan-Jay Awas Yojana	3rd June, 2016	This scheme was started from Matanhail village of Jhajjar district. The aim of this scheme is to provide affordable housing to serving and retired army officers. The project is being operated by Army Welfare Housing Organisation.
Gramuday se Bharatuday Abhiyan	14th to 24th April, 2016	The scheme was started in Hisar, on the occasion of 125th birth anniversary of Dr. Bhimrao Ambedkar. The goal of this campaign is to strengthen the Panchayati Raj System in all the villages of India by making efforts for social development, rural development, development of farmers and progress at the national level for the livelihood of poor people.
Salamati Scheme Project	28th March, 2016	The aim of this project is to maintain healthy gap between the births of children by using injectable contraceptive. Haryana has become the first state in India to implement the use of injectable contraceptive as a family planning measure. This project was started by Ministry of Haryana with the assistance of Bill and Melinda Gates foundation.
Anukul Greh Yojana	27th March, 2016	This scheme was started by the Department of Social Justice and Empowerment, Haryana, for the disabled people. Under this scheme, the government provides six months advance pension to disabled people to renovate their home according to their special needs. This amount is given within 42 months period.
Mhara Gaon, Jagmag Gaon Scheme	1st July, 2015	This scheme aims to provide 24 hours uninterrupted power supply to rural areas and improve electricity bill collections in order to reduce huge accumulated loss of power utilities.
Operation Muskan	1st July, 2015	This programme was launched by Haryana Police and Department of Women and Child Development to trace and rescue missing children in the state.
Pradhan Mantri Bhartiya Janaushadhi Pariyojna	2015	This scheme aims to provide affordable medicines keeping in mind the poor and middle class families. Earlier, it was named as Pradhan Mantri Jan Aushadhi Yojana.
Pradhan Mantri Jan-Dhan Yojana	28th August, 2014	This scheme aims to provide universal access to banking facilities including basic savings bank accounts, remittance, credit and pension services.
Priyadarshini Awas Yojana	8th June, 2013	The aim of this scheme is to provide housing in rural areas to the needy people. Under this scheme, ₹ 91,000 would be given to the beneficiaries to built a home.
Beej Yojana	8th June, 2011	This scheme encourages farmers to cultivate alternative crops and reduce wheat and paddy crops in Haryana.

CHECK CHAPTER KNOWLEDGE

1 In which year Mahila evam Kishori Samman Yojana was launched in Haryana?
(a) 2018 (b) 2019
(c) 2020 (d) None of these

2 Women/Girls of which age group are included in Mahila evam Kishori Samman Yojana?
(a) 10-45 years
(b) 16-45 years
(c) 14-60 years
(d) 20-45 years

3 To set-up self-employment, how much amount is given to women under Haryana Mahila Samridhi Yojana?
(a) ₹ 25,000 (b) ₹ 40,000
(c) ₹ 60,000 (d) ₹ 1,00,000

4 The Sakhi Scheme was started by the Department of Women and Child Development, Haryana for which purpose? *PGT 2016*
(a) Child welfare
(b)Women victims
(c) Women and child security
(d)Employment for women

5 Haryana's first One Stop Centre for women 'Sakhi' was opened in *HSSC 2023*
(a) Karnal (b) Panipat
(c) Hisar (d) Rohtak

6 Under which scheme, funds ranging from ₹ 11,000 to ₹ 51,000 are given as Shagun (gift) for the marriage of girls?
(a) Swadhar Grih Yojana
(b) Mukhyamantri Vivah Shagun Yojana
(c) Mahila and Bal Suraksha Yojana
(d) Sakhi Yojana

7 Aapki Beti-Hamari Beti Scheme was launched in which year?
(a) 2000 (b) 2005
(c) 2010 (d) 2015

8 'Aapki Beti-Hamari Beti' scheme was launched with an aim to *HSSC 2024*
(a) eliminate sex-selective abortions
(b) provide vocational education to girls
(c) Provide gender based reservation
(d) Eliminate pay disparities between men and women

9 'Haryana Kanya Kosh' will be used under the name of which scheme?
(a) Sukanya Samriddhi Yojana
(b) Ladli Yojana
(c) 'Aapki Beti-Hamari Beti'
(d) None of the above

10 In which year the campaign 'Beti Bachao-Beti Padhao' was started? *PGT 2016*
(a) 22nd January, 2015 (b) 2nd October, 2014
(c) 11th September, 2014 (d) 8th March, 2015

11 From which place the Prime Minister of India started Beti Bachao-Beti Padhao campaign? *Bus Conductor 2017*
(a) Rohtak (b) Ambala
(c) Hisar (d) Panipat

12 'Beti Bachao-Beti Padhao' campaign started to prevent *HSSC 2022, 20*
(a) Child-marriage
(b) Gender biased sex-selective abortion
(c) Child education
(d) Child labour

13 Which of the following is the nodal agency of the campaign 'Beti Bachao-Beti Padhao'? *PGT 2016*
(a) Women and Child Development
(b) Health and Family Welfare
(c) Ministry of Human Resource
(d) Ministry of Information and Broadcasting

14 'Beti Bachao-Beti Padhao' campaign is related to which department? *Food and Supply 2017*
(a)Women and Child Development
(b) Cultural Works Department
(c) Panchayat and Development
(d)Family and Health Development

15 SABLA Scheme was launched in which district of Haryana?
(a) Ambala (b) Rohtak
(c) Rewari (d) All of these

16 Ladli Social Security Allowance Scheme was launched on *HSSC 2020, 16*
(a) 1st January, 2006
(b) 1st March, 2006
(c) 1st March, 2005
(d) 1st January, 2005

17 Ladli Scheme was started on *Bus Conductor 2006*
(a) 1st January, 2006 (b) 26th January, 2005
(c) 2nd October, 2005 (d) None of these

18 Which scheme was launched by Haryana Government not only to control population growth, but also to check the declining trend in the male and female sex-ratio in the state? *PGT 2016*
(a) Devi Rupak Yojana (b) Indira Saheli Yojana
(c) Farlo Yojana (d) Bhagyodaya Yojana

19 Which scheme was launched to improve the health status of women and child in the society?
(a) Apni Beti-Apna Dhan Yojana *HSSC 2020, 15*
(b) Apni Beti-Paraya Dhan
(c) Paraya Dhan Parayi Beti
(d) Indira Saheli Project

20 Which scheme is implemented for the poor girls of Haryana? *TGT 2016*
(a) Apni Beti-Apna Dhan
(b) Apni Beti-Paraya Dhan
(c) Paraya Dhan Parayi Beti
(d) Indira Saheli Yojana

21 The pension given to widows under Widow Pension Yojana is *HSSC 2024*
(a) ₹ 1,600 (b) ₹ 1,800
(c) ₹ 3,000 (d) ₹ 2,200

22 Which scheme was launched by the Chief Minister of Haryana, Manohar Lal Khattar on 4th August, 2015? *Auction Recorder 2016, HSSC 2016*
(a) Thari Pension-Thare Pass
(b) Aapki Beti-Hamari Beti
(c) Beti Bachao-Beti Padhao
(d) Biomass Project

23 'Thari Pension-Thare Pass' scheme was launched in the year, 2015 to ensure...... . *HSSC 2022, 18*
(a) transparency in pension
(b) transparency in government result
(c) transparency in LPG
(d) transparency in social security pension

24 How much pension is given to freedom fighters under the scheme of State Samman Pension for Freedom Fighters?
(a) ₹ 10,000 (b) ₹ 15,000
(c) ₹ 40,000 (d) ₹ 50,000

25 Mission Indradhanush was launched on
(a) 25th December, 2014
(b) 13th April, 2010
(c) 2nd October, 2005
(d) 1st December, 2001

26 Which scheme was started for the health check-ups of children upto 18 years of age in Haryana? *PGT 2018, 16*
(a) Indira Bal Swasthya Yojana
(b) Nehru Bal Swasthya Yojana
(c) Devilal Bal Swasthya Yojana
(d) Amrit Kaur Bal Swasthya Yojana

27 How much insurance cover is given to registered small and medium traders under Chief Minister Traders Collective Private Accident Insurance Scheme? *HSSC 2023*
(a) ₹ 2.5 lakh (b) ₹ 4 lakh
(c) ₹ 5 lakh (d) ₹ 6 lakh

28 Rajiv Gandhi Parivar Bima Yojana was started in which year in Haryana?
(a) 2003 (b) 2004 (c) 2005 (d) 2006

29 Devi Rakshak Scheme was started in which year? *PGT 2016*
(a) 25th September, 2002
(b) 2nd October, 2003
(c) 2nd October, 2005
(d) 15th August, 2004

30 Which scheme was launched on 1st November, 2016 on the occasion of Haryana Swarna Jayanti Varsha?
(a) Unemployment Allowance Scheme
(b) Saksham Yuva Scheme
(c) Mukhya Mantri Vivah Shagun Yojana
(d) Manohar Jyoti Scheme

31 'Saksham Yuva Scheme' launched in 2016 provides unemployment allowance to
(a) doctorate holders
(b) intermediate passed unemployed youths
(c) illiterate youths
(d) graduate and post graduate unemployed youths

32 Model Career Centre is located in which district of Haryana?
(a) Rohtak (b) Hisar
(c) Jind (d) Kurukshetra

33 Anusuchit Jati Chhatra Shiksha Protsahan Yojana was started in
(a) 2009 (b) 2010
(c) 2011 (d) 2012

34 Under Dr. BR Ambedkar Awas Navinikarn Yojana, how much grant is provided to SC, nomadic and roadside persons living below poverty line to repair their house?
(a) ₹ 10,000 (b) ₹ 20,000
(c) ₹ 30,000 (d) ₹ 80,000

35 Which condition is required under Inter-Caste Marriage Incentive Scheme?

(a) One person from the couple must be from the SC
(b) The couple should be permanent residents of Haryana
(c) Both (a) and (b)
(d) None of the above

36 Which of the following is/are not true regarding the Pradhan Mantri Shram Yogi Maan-Dhan Yojana (PM-SYM) to ensure old age protection for unorganised workers?

1. Each subscriber shall receive minimum assured pension of ₹ 2000 per month after attaining the age of 55 years.
2. Each subscriber shall receive minimum assured pension of ₹ 3000 per month after attaining the age of 60 years.
3. During the receipt of pension, if the subscriber dies, the dependent members of the beneficiary shall be entitled to receive 50 percent of the pension received by beneficiary, as family pension.
4. The subscriber's contribution to PM-SYM is through auto-debit facility from his/her saving bank account/Jan Dhan Account and it ranges from ₹ 50 to 500 per month depending upon the entry age of the subscriber.

Which of the options given above is/are not correct? *HPCS (Prelims) 2023*

(a) 1, 2 and 3 (b) 2, 3 and 4
(c) 1, 3 and 4 (d) 1 and 3

37 The e-Nam Scheme was launched in which year in Haryana?

(a) 2011 (b) 2013
(c) 2015 (d) 2017

38 Pradhan Mantri Jan Aushadhi Yojana (PMJAY) has been renamed as

1. Pradhan Mantri Aushadhi Pariyojana
2. Pradhan Mantri Janaushadhi Vikas Yojana
3. Pradhan Mantri Bhartiya Janaushadhi Pariyojana
4. Pradhan Mantri Bhartiya Aushadhi Vikas Yojana

Which of the options given above is correct? *HPCS (Prelims) 2023*

(a) Only 1 (b) Only 2
(c) Only 3 (d) Only 4

39 e-Procurement Scheme was started in which district of Haryana?

(a) Hisar (b) Karnal
(c) Jind (d) Panipat

40 Which Department has launched the "Legal Aid to Scheduled castes and Vimukta Jatis scheme" in Haryana?

(a) Department of Women and Child Development
(b) Department of Welfare of Scheduled Castes and Backward Classes
(c) Department of Social Welfare
(d) National Commission for Scheduled Castes

41 Due to which scheme/project, Haryana has become the first state in India to implement the use of injectable contraceptives as a family planning measure?

(a) Salamati Scheme
(b) Operation Muskan
(c) Antyodaya Aahar Yojana
(d) Gramodaya Se Bharatodaya Abhiyan

42 'Mhara Gaon-Jagmag Gaon' scheme was started in which year in Haryana state? *PGT 2016*

(a) 1st July, 2015 (b) 15th August, 2015
(c) 20th October, 2015 (d) 15th December, 2015

43 In which year 'Priyadarshini Awas Yojana' was started? *PGT 2016*

(a) 8th June, 2013 (b) 25th June, 2002
(c) 14th August, 2004 (d) 12th March, 2004

44 Beej Yojana was started in which year in Haryana? *HSSC 2020, 19*

(a) 2005 (b) 2009 (c) 2011 (d) 2007

45 In which year Mukhya Mantri Parivar Samman Nidhi Yojana was started? *HSSC 2021*

(a) 27th February, 2018
(b) 26th February, 2019
(c) 28th February, 2018
(d) 25th February, 2019

CORRECT ANSWERS

1. (c)	2. (a)	3. (c)	4. (b)	5. (a)	6. (b)	7. (d)	8. (a)	9. (c)	10. (a)
11. (d)	12. (b)	13. (a)	14. (a)	15. (d)	16. (a)	17. (a)	18. (a)	19. (a)	20. (a)
21. (c)	22. (a)	23. (a)	24. (c)	25. (a)	26. (a)	27. (c)	28. (d)	29. (b)	30. (b)
31. (d)	32. (b)	33. (a)	34. (d)	35. (c)	36. (c)	37. (d)	38. (c)	39. (b)	40. (b)
41. (a)	42. (a)	43. (a)	44. (c)	45. (b)					

CHAPTER 32

Famous Personalities of Haryana

Haryana state remained the land of many extraordinary people from the historical period to present era. Haryana has produced numerous notable personalities who belonged to various fields like history, politics, literature, arts, sports, etc. Some of the important personalities of Haryana are discussed below

Historical Personalities

Harshavardhana

- Born — 590 AD, Thanesar (Haryana), ancient power centre
- Father — Prabhakara Vardhana, founder of **Pushyabhuti** dynasty
- Ruler of — Thanesar (Pushyabhuti dynasty), 606-647 AD
- Died — 647 AD, leaving a legacy as a ruler and patron
- He is considered the last Hindu ruler of the Northern India.
- Harshavardhana was defeated by Pulakeshin II of the Chalukya dynasty on the bank of Narmada river.
- The famous Chinese traveller Hiuen Tsang travelled to India during the reign of Harshavardhana.
- He was the patron of many famous scholars and writers. Banabhatta was his Court Poet, who composed **Harshacharita** (an account of harsha's life and deeds) and **Kadambari.**
- Harshavardhana was a famous scholar and writer. He wrote three sanskrit plays i.e. **Nagananda, Ratnavali** and **Priyadarshika.**

Anangpal II

- Ruler of — Tomar dynasty
- Territory — Haryana to Delhi (Capital was Delhi)
- He played a significant role in strengthening the Tomar region. He established **Lal Kot,** the very first fort of Delhi.
- In 1052 AD Anangpal II established the **Iron Pillar** in Delhi and built the **Anangtal Sarovar** near this pillar. He constructed **Surajkund** and also built 27 palaces and temples.

Mahipal

- Ruler of — Delhi and its neighbouring regions
- Belongs to — Tomar dynasty
- In 1043 AD, he established his reign over a large territory including Hansi and Thanesar after the death of Masood, successor of Mahmud Ghaznavi. He founded **Mahipalpur** town in Delhi.

Prithviraj Chauhan

- Born — 1166 AD
- Ruler — Kshatriya ruler of Chahamana (Chauhan) dynasty
- Ruled over — Ajmer and Delhi (Northern Indian Territory)
- Reign — 1178 to 1192 AD
- Other names — Rai Pithora, Prithvi Raj III, Hindu Samrat and Sapadalaksheshwar
- He defeated Muhammad of Ghor in the first Battle of Tarain (Karnal) in 1191 AD, but was defeated and killed by Muhammad of Ghor in the second Battle of Tarain in 1192 AD.
- His love story and war stories have been described in the epic called **Prithviraj Raso**, composed by Chand Bardai.

Jatwan

- Role — Commander of Hansi and Hisar
- Conquest — Captured Hansi fort after second Battle of Tarain (1192 AD)
- He was defeated by Qutub-ud-Din Aibak, the commander of Muhammad of Ghor in a battle on the Western Bagar region and was killed.

Hasan Khan Mewati

- He was the ruler of Mewat which was under the possession of Lodhi rulers.
- He became an independent ruler of Mewat after the defeat of **Ibrahim Lodhi** in the first Battle of Panipat in 1526 AD.
- In 1527 AD, he was defeated by **Babur** at the Battle of Khanwa where he was killed in 1527 AD and his son Nahar Khan was imprisoned by Babur.

Suraj Mal

- Birth place — Bharatpur (1707 AD)
- Ruler of — Bharatpur
- Successor to — Badan Singh (his father)
- After the death of Aurangzeb in 1707 AD, several powerful states emerged in North India; Bharatpur was one of these states.
- In 1755 AD, Suraj Mal made Bharatpur his capital (formerly Dig was the Capital). Dig was founded by Suraj Mal in 1743 AD.

> Maharaja Suraj Mal was a wise, brave warrior and a successful General. Due to his wisdom, he was given the name of **Aflatoon of Jats** or **Plato of Jats**.

- Bharatpur Princely State included many areas of Haryana such as Gohana, Bhiwani, Kalanaur, Rohtak, Dadri, Gurugram, Ballabhgarh, Nuh and Palwal.
- Jawahar Singh, son of Suraj Mal, also conquered many areas of Haryana.
- He led the Jats from 1756-63 AD.
- He was killed in an ambush by the Rohilla troops on the night of 25th December, 1763 near the Hindon river, Sahadra, Delhi.

Banda Bairagi

- Born — 27th October, 1670
- Belonged to — Rajput family of a village called Rajouri in Poonch district of Jammu and Kashmir
- Real name — **Lakshman Dev**
- After becoming a disciple of the famous Saint Ramdas of Lahore, he was called **Madhodas Bairagi**.
- In September 1708, the 10th Sikh Guru Gobind Singh named him Gurubaksh Singh. Later on he was known as **Banda Singh Bahadur**.
- He met Guru Gobind Singh in Nanded (South India). After being inspired by Guru Ji, he came to North India and made Sehri Khanda village his headquarters in the present Sonipat district.
- After that he took control of Sonipat, Kaithal and Shahabad and defeated Wazir Khan, Military Commander of Kunjpura. After this Banda Bahadur made Sirhind his headquarters.

> Mewati Sardar Feroz Khan defeated Banda Bahadur in a battle on 26th October, 1770, therefore, when the situation in Sirhind was not under control, Banda Bahadur made Lohgarh as his hideout in Yamunanagar district.

- He was forced to leave Lohgarh in October, 1713 due to the invasion of the Mughal army. Later, he was captured by the Mughal army and was killed.

Kaku Rana Mewati

- Ruler of — Mewat in the 13th century
- Fought against — Ghiyasuddin Balban (1266)
- Headquarters — Mewat's base was **Gadhdhamina** (Mehrauli)

Hemu (Hemchandra)

- He was a simple tradesman of Rewari, who was appointed as the Prime Minister of Adil Shah the successor of Sher Shah Suri.
- In 1556 AD, after taking control of Delhi and Agra, he assumed the title of **Vikramaditya** and became the ruler of these regions. But he was defeated by Akbar in the second Battle of Panipat in 1556 AD and was killed by Bairam Khan, the regent of Akbar.
- He was the last Hindu ruler of Delhi and last **Vikramaditya**.

Gopal Singh

- Origin Sihi village
- Founder of **Jat principality** in Ballabhgarh
- Died 1711
- After many invasions, the Mughal Faujdar of Faridabad accepted him as the ruler and Chaudhary of Ballabhgarh in the year 1710.

Political Personalities

Sir Shadi Lal

- Birth place Rewari, in a well-off family.
- Career Began as a lawyer in 1900
- He received the title of **Rai Bahadur** in 1909 by the British Government.
- He became the member of **Punjab Legislative Assembly** in 1910.
- He became the first Indian to be appointed as the first Chief Justice of Punjab High Court in 1913. He became a member of **Privy Council**, London for 5 years.

Gulzarilal Nanda

- Born 4th July, 1898
- Birth place Sialkot (Pakistan)
- Died 15th January, 1998
- He became the Union Home Minister on 21st September, 1963 and the **first Acting Prime Minister of India** after the death of Jawaharlal Nehru on 27th May, 1964.
- After the death of PM Lal Bahadur Shastri on 11th January, 1966, he again became the **interim Prime Minister** of India.
- He was elected from Kaithal Lok Sabha Constituency in the year 1967. He founded the **Kurukshetra Development Board** in the year 1968 for the promotion, preservation and development of pilgrimage centers of Kurukshetra.
- He became the **Union Railway Minister** on 18th February, 1970.

> The Government of India honoured Gulzarilal Nanda with the **Bharat Ratna** in 1997 for his matchless service.

Sucheta Kripalani

- Born 25th June, 1908
- Birth place Ambala, Haryana
- Died 1st December, 1974
- She was elected a member of the Constituent Assembly in the year 1946.
- From 1948 to 1960 she was the General Secretary of the Indian National Congress.
- She was also a member of the Lok Sabha twice. In the year 1963, she also became the **Chief Minister of Uttar Pradesh.**
- She was **India's first female Chief Minister.**

Kishan Das

- Born 1926
- Birth place Rohtak
- He was elected as the President of Municipality of Rohtak twice (1961-63 and 1964-67).
- He has also been the financier of Haryana Vikas Party. He was elected as an MLA in the year 1972.

> Kishan Das was awarded the **Padma Shri** by the President of India in the year 1976. He became MLA for the second time in 1982 and Cabinet Minister in 1986.

Bansi Lal

- Born 26th August, 1927
- Birth place Golagarh village, Punjab, British India, Haryana
- Also known as Iron man of Haryana, Architect of Modern Haryana
- Died 28th March, 2006
- He is an Indian Freedom Fighter, Senior Congress leader, former Chief Minister of Haryana and the Architect of Modern Haryana.
- He was elected as a member of the Haryana Legislative Assembly seven times (1967, 1968, 1972, 1986, 1991, 1996 and 2000).
- Bansi Lal was also served as the country's Defense Minister (21-12-1975 to 21-05-1977).
- He had also held the Railway Ministry in December, 1984 and Transport Ministry in June, 1986.
- Haryana Vikas Party was formed in the year 1996 by Bansi Lal.

> Bansi Lal served as the Chief Minister of Haryana four times from **1968, 1972, 1986** and **1996**. He was the third Chief Minister of Haryana after Bhagwat Dayal Sharma and Rao Virendra Singh.

Chandravati Sheoran

- Born 3rd September, 1928
- Birth place Charkhi-Dadri
- Died 15th November, 2020
- She was the first woman in Northern India to study Law education.
- She became the Legislator from Dadri in the PEPSU Assembly elections in 1954.
- She was the Deputy Minister of Food and Supplies Department till the year 1964-66.
- She was re-elected in the 1972 Haryana Legislative Assembly elections and was the State Minister between the years 1972-74.
- She became the Member of Parliament from Bhiwani Lok Sabha Constituency in the year 1977.
- She has the honour of being the **first woman Lieutenant Governor** of India and the first-ever woman Member of Parliament from Haryana.
- She was also the **Lieutenant Governor** of Puducherry from February 1990 to December 1991.

Sushma Swaraj

- Born 14th February, 1952
- Birth place Ambala Cantt, Haryana
- Died 6th August, 2019 (New Delhi)
- Sushma Swaraj has been a seven-time Member of Parliament and 3 times Member of Legislative Assembly.
- She also has the honour of being the **youngest Cabinet Minister** (Labour and Employment Minister) **in Haryana.**
- She became the President of Haryana unit of Janata Party at the age of 27 in 1979.
- She also has the honour of being the **first woman Chief Minister of Delhi** in the year 1998.
- In 1996, she became the Information and Broadcasting Minister in Atal Bihari Vajpayee's 13-day government for the first time.
- In March 1998, she again became the **Union Minister for Information and Broadcasting.**
- She again became Cabinet Minister of Information and Broadcasting for the third time in September, 2000.
- In the year 2003-04, she served as the Union Minister of Health and in the year 2009 as the leader of the opposition in the Lok Sabha.
- She had served as the Indian **Minister of External Affairs** under the Government of PM Narendra Modi from May, 2014 to May, 2019.

Arvind Kejriwal

- Born 1968
- Birth place Siwani town, Bhiwani district
- Founder of Aam Aadmi Party (26th November, 2012)
- He received the degree of Mechanical Engineering in the year 1989 from IIT Kharagpur.
- He passed the UPSC CSE competitive exam in the year 1992 and was appointed to the post of Assistant Commissioner. He laid the foundation of a social organisation called **Parivartan.**
- He along with Anna Hazare and Aruna Rai fought for the **Right to Information Act.**

- He started his political career in the year 2012.
- He served as 7th Chief Minister of Delhi from 2013-14 and from 2015-24.

Social Activists

Seth Chaudhary Chhaju Ram

- Born 1861
- Birth place Alakhpura village, Bawani Kheda tehsil, Bhiwani district
- Founder of Jat School in Hisar (1924)
- Died 7th April, 1943
- In 1926, he was elected as Member of the Punjab Legislative Council.
- He was conferred the title of **Sir** in the year 1931 by the British Government due to his services provided during the severe famine of 1928-29.
- He had good business of jute, people used to call him as **Jute King**. He was popular for doing charity, due to which he is also called **Bhamashah**, the donor of Jats.
- Due to his donations, many hostels, libraries and Dharamshalas were constructed in the state.

Uday Singh Mann

- Born 14th January, 1911
- Birth place Village of Sidhipur Lowa Kalan, Jhajjar district
- Died 8th July, 2016
- He was the head of Jat educational institutions of Rohtak till 1958-61. His era is considered the **Golden Age of Jat Educational Institutions.**
- In 1957, he participated in Hindi Raksha Andolan and went to jail.

Ramakrishna Gupta

- Born 1918
- Birth place Barnala, Punjab
- In 1955, he formed a union of labourers working in Dalmia Cement Factor and became its chief. He was elected to the Lok Sabha in the year 1957.
- In 1960, he established **Gandhi Memorial Education Society** in Dadri.
- He changed the name of Dadri from Dalmia Dadri and got it renamed as 'Charkhi-Dadri'.

Baba Ramdev

- Born 25th December, 1965
- Birth place Said Alipur (Nangal Chaudhary town), Mahendragarh district
- Childhood name Ramkishan
- Father Ramnivas
- Mother Gulab Devi
- He joined a Gurukul in Khanpur village for yoga and Sanskrit education. He was introduced to the word 'sannyas' during the course of yoga education, after which he named his name Ramdev.
- In 1995, Baba Ramdev founded the **Divya Yog Mandir Trust** with Shankar Devi Ji Maharaj.
- His Guru's name was **Acharya Baldev**. He has started a wonderful revolution in the field of yoga by presenting simple methods of Yogasana and Pranayama to the people of the country and abroad.
- He has taught yoga to crores of people within country and abroad.

> Baba Ramdev started the **Patanjali Yoga Peeth Trust** in Dayanand village on 6th August, 2006.

Defence Personnel

Chhelu Ram

- Born 1905
- Birth place Village of Dinod, Bhiwani district
- Chhelu Ram was a soldier of the 4th Battalion of the Rajputana Rifles of the British Indian Army, who died on the night of 19-20 April, 1943 while fighting in Tunisia during World War II.
- Havildar Major Chhelu Ram was posthumously awarded the **Victoria Cross Medal.**

Umrao Singh

- Born year 1920
- Birth place Palra village, Jhajjar
- Retirement 1965
- He was awarded the Victoria Cross Medal during World War II, becoming the only 'Non-Commissioned Officer' to receive the medal.

Brigadier Hoshiar Singh Dahiya

- Born 5th May, 1937
- Birth place Sisana village, Sonipat district
- Retirement 1996 as Brigadier
- Died 6th December, 1998
- He participated in the wars of 1965 and 1971.
- He was awarded the **Param Vir Chakra** after the war for demonstrating unparalleled valour in the Indo-Pak war of 1971.
- He is the **only Param Vir Chakra awardee** of the state.

General Deepak Kapoor

- Born 1948
- Military service Served as Chief of Indian Army
- Service period From 30th September, 2007 to 31st March, 2010.

General Vijay Kumar Singh

- Born 10th May, 1951
- Place Bapora village, Bhiwani
- After receiving commission in the Indian Service in the year 1970, he became the **24th Chief of the Indian Army.**

> General Vijay Kumar Singh was the Chief of the Indian Army from 1st April, 2010 to 31st March, 2012. He became the Minister of State for External Affairs of India in May, 2014.

Admiral Sunil Lanba

- Born 17th July, 1957
- Birth place Palwal district
- Military service Commissioned in the Indian Navy in 1978
- He served as the **23rd Chief of the Naval Staff** of the Indian Navy. He assumed the office on 31st May, 2016 and demitted office on 31st May, 2019.
- During this time, he also served as Chairman of the Chiefs of Staff Committee and Honorary Aide-de-Camp to the President of India.

General Dalbir Singh Suhag

- Born 28th December, 1954
- Place Visan village, Jhajjar district
- Military service Commissioned into Indian Army in June, 1974.
- He was the **26th Chief of the Army Staff** (COAS) of the Indian Army from 31st July, 2014 to 31st December, 2016.

Miscellaneous Personalities

Pandit Bastiram

- Born 1842
- Birth place Kheri Sultan village, Jhajjar district
- Died 1959
- He was known as the preacher of the famous Arya Samaj.
- After meeting Swami Dayanand in 1880, he started propagating the Arya Samaj by going from village to village.
- His special areas were Haryana, Uttar Pradesh (Western) and Rajasthan.

Hardev Sahai Lal

- Born 26th November, 1892 (in Vaishya family)
- Birth place Satrod village near Hisar
- Died 30th September, 1962
- He was a freedom fighter as well as a philanthropist. He established a school in Satrod in 1912.
- He founded Vidya Pracharini Sabha in 1923 in association with Pandit Nekiram Sharma and Pandit Thakurdas Bhargava.

Karna Singh

- Born 18th September, 1921
- Birth place Kurar Ibrahimpur village, Sonipat district
- Died 19th November, 1969
- He established a 'stud farm' in Tohana and become the first person to own a stud farm as a Veterinarian.

> Karna Singh was awarded the Defence Medal (1965), the Summer Service Star (1965) and the Independence Day Silver Jubilee Medal (1972).

Balaram Ludesar

- Born 19th August, 1924
- Birth place Ludesar village, Sirsa
- He joined the **Azad Hind Fauj** in Singapore.
- He also participated in the war of Burma. After this, he started social service. He has also been the Head (Sarpanch) of the village.
- He has been awarded **Copper plate** and pension by the Government of India and Government of Haryana.

Daryao Singh Malik

- Born 11th July, 1938
- Birth place Ugrakheri village, Panipat
- Also known as Khunda
- He joined the Public Relations Department in the year 1961. He played the comic role of Khunda in the first Haryanvi film **Chandrawal.**

Jagdish Prasad Chaudhary

- Born 7th March, 1949
- Birth place Morkheri village, Rohtak district
- He was a linguist of German language.
- In the year 2005-06, the Government of India honoured him with the **National Tourism Award.**

Magician Samrat Shankar

- Born 6th September, 1950
- Birth place Ellenabad, Sirsa district
- Original name Shiv Kumar Modi
- From 1974, he started doing his magic show. People of the state call him Magician Samrat.

Kalpana Chawla

- Born 17th March, 1962
- Birth place Karnal

- In 1994, she was selected in the **US Space Mission Organisation** (NASA). Her training for space travel started in the year 1995.
- On 19th November, 1997, she became the first woman of Indian origin to travel to the spacecraft from the Colombia spacecraft.
- She left for the second space trip from Cape Kennedy Space Centre to Colombia spacecraft on 16th January, 2003, but died on 1st February, 2003, due to the crash of the vehicle just 16 minutes before reaching the Earth.

Santosh Yadav

- Born 10th October, 1969
- Birth place Rewari
- She is the Deputy Superintendent of the Indo-Tibetan Border Police and the only woman from India to have twice conquered the 8848 m high Mount Everest (May, 1992 and May, 1993, respectively).

> Santosh Yadav has been awarded the **Padma Shri Award** in the year 2000 by the Government of India and Tenzing Norgay National Adventure Award in 1994.

Shekhar Gupta

- Born 26th August, 1957
- Birth place Palwal
- He is the Chief Editor of famous Indian newspaper 'The Indian Express'. He anchored in the programme **Walk the Talk** to be broadcasted on NDTV.
- In 2009, the Government of India honoured him with the **Padma Bhushan** Award in the field of journalism.

Manushi Chhillar

- Born 14th May, 1997
- Birth place Rohtak
- She is an Indian model. She won the title of **Femina Miss India** in the year 2017.
- She won the title of **Miss World 2017** in the Miss World 2017 competition held in Arena City, China in the year 2017. It is the title won by an Indian after 2001 (Priyanka Chopra).

CHECK CHAPTER KNOWLEDGE

1 Who is known as the last Hindu ruler of the Northern India?
(a) Harshavardhana (b) Mahipal
(c) Anangpal II (d) Prithviraj Chauhan

2 Pulakeshin II who defeated Harshavardhana, was a descendant of .... Dynasty. *HSSC 2017*
(a) Kadamb (b) Pallavas
(c) Pushyabhuti (d) Chalukya

3 Hiuen Tsang travelled to India during the reign of *HSSC 2019*
(a) Samudragupta (b) Harshavardhana
(c) Shahjahan (d) Chandragupta II

4 Banabhatta was .... in the court of king Harshavardhana. *HSSC 2020*
(a) Asthanakavi (b) Minister
(c) Senapati (d) Royal Preceptor

5 Who was the court poet in the reign of king Hashavardhana? *HSSC 2022, 20*
(a) Panini (b) Uday Bhanu Hans
(c) Banabhatta (d) Chauranginath

6 Who wrote Harshacharita? *Haryana Conductor 2017*
(a) Mahatma Gandhi
(b) Rajendra Prasad
(c) Ravindra Nath Tagore
(d) Banabhatta

7 In which book did the poet Banabhatta write the life events of King Harsha? *HSSC 2017*
(a) Ratnavali (b) Nagananda
(c) Kadambari (d) Harshacharita

8 Banabhatta was a court poet of which ruler? *Forest Department 2017*
(a) Harshavardhana (b) Rajyavardhana
(c) Prabhakarvardhana (d) Chandragupta

9 King Harshavardhana wrote the famous Sanskrit play *HSSC 2021, 19*
(a) Bharatanjali (b) Narayaniyan
(c) Nagananda (d) None of these

10 Who built Anangtal sarovar?
(a) Mahipal (b) Hemchandra
(c) Anangpal II (d) Hasan Khan Mewati

11 The town founded by Tomar ruler 'Mahipal' in Delhi is
(a) Mahipalpur (b) Hauz Khas
(c) Meharuli (d) Dhaula Kuan

12 Who was known as 'Rai Pithora'? *HSSC 2015*
(a) Mahipal (b) Prithviraj Chauhan
(c) Anangpal II (d) Jatwan

13 The first Battle of Tarain took place in which year?
(a) 1191 AD (b) 1194 AD
(c) 1291 AD (d) 1299 AD

14 The second Battle of Tarain between Prithviraj Chauhan and Muhammad of Ghor, took place in which year?
(a) 1191 AD (b) 1192 AD
(c) 1199 AD (d) 1205 AD

15 Who is the author of 'Prithviraj Raso'? *HSSC 2018*
(a) Surdas (b) Banabhatta
(c) Prithviraj Chauhan (d) Chandbardai

16 Who documented the life of Prithviraj Chauhan through poetry? *HSSC 2020*
(a) Shri Uday Bhanu Hans
(b) Shri Balmukund Gupt
(c) Shri Lakhmi Chand Sangi
(d) Shri Chandbardai

17 Whch of the following was written by Shri Chandbardai? *HSSC 2023, 20*
(a) Shyan Sat Sai (b) Tiriya Ke Masmoom
(c) Prithvi Raj Raso (d) Sur Sagar

18 Who was the Commander of Muhammad of Ghor who defeated 'Jatwan', Commander of Hansi and Hisar?
(a) Ghiyathod-Din Muhammad
(b) Bahaal-Din Sam
(c) Qutub-ud-Din Aibak
(d) Balban

19 Who was defeated by Babur at the Battle of Khanwa?
(a) Jatwan
(b) Hasan Khan Mewati
(c) Harshavardhana
(d) Gopal Singh

20 Who established Bharatpur town?
(a) Rana Sanga (b) Raja Jai Singh
(c) Suraj Mal (d) Harshavardhana

21 What was the real name of Banda Bairagi?
(a) Ramdev (b) Ramdas
(c) Lakshman Dev (d) Lakshman Das

22 The famous king, Hemu Vikramaditya who had ruled in Haryana was earlier a *HSSC 2020*
(a) Trainer (b) Peasent
(c) Tradesman (d) Administrator

23 Who was the last 'Vikramaditya'? *HSSC 2024, 16*
(a) Gopal Singh (b) Hemu
(c) Mahipal (d) Sir Shadi Lal

24 Founder of Jat principality in Ballabhgarh was
(a) Pandit Deen Dayal Sharma
(b) Gopal Singh
(c) Gulab Singh
(d) Mohan Singh

25 Who became the first Indian to be appointed as the first Chief Justice of Punjab High Court in 1913?
(a) Gopal Singh (b) Sir Shadi Lal
(c) Dr. Sarup Singh (d) Chaudhary Bansi Lal

26 Who received the title of 'Rai Bahadur' in 1909 AD by the British Government?
(a) Sir Shadi Lal
(b) Pandit Deen Dayal Sharma
(c) Harshavardhana
(d) Mahipal

27 Who was the first Acting Prime Minister of India?
(a) Sucheta Kripalani
(b) Gulzarilal Nanda
(c) Madan Mohan Malviya
(d) Sushma Swaraj

28 Which freedom fighter later become the Chief Minister of Haryana? *PGT 2020*
(a) Shri Rao Birender Singh
(b) Chaudhary Bansi Lal
(c) Chaudhary Devilal
(d) Shri Manohar Lal Khattar

29 Who is known as the 'Architect of Modern Haryana'? *HSSC 2020, PGT 2015*
(a) Dr Sarup Singh (b) Chaudhary Bansi Lal
(c) Om Prakash Jindal (d) Bhajan Lal

30 Chaudhary Bansi Lal is best known as *HSSC 2023, 20*
(a) Favourite Chief Minister of Haryana
(b) Iron Man of Haryana
(c) Father of Haryana
(d) Haryana Kesari

31 Who became the first woman Lieutenant Governor of India?
(a) Chandravati (b) Sucheta Kripalani
(c) Sarojini Naidu (d) Sushma Swaraj

32 The first woman politician of Haryana, who served as the Governor of a state is .... *Haryana Police Constable 2018*
(a) Shanno Devi (b) Chandravati
(c) Chandrakala (d) Renuka Vishnoi

33 Indian Minister of External Affairs, Sushma Swaraj belongs to *HSSC 2017*
(a) Karnal (b) Rohtak
(c) Ambala (d) Faridabad

34 Who is the second woman to be India's External Affairs Minister?
(a) Indira Gandhi (b) Sushma Swaraj
(c) Manushi Chhillar (d) Geeta Phogat

35 Arvind Kejriwal, Chief Minister of Delhi , was born at
(a) Sirsa (b) Jind
(c) Nuh (d) Bhiwani

36 Who among the following was conferred the title 'Sir' by the British Government?
(a) Pt. Shriram Sharma (b) Ch. Chhaju Ram
(c) Uday Bhanu Singh (d) Ramkrishna Gupta

37 Which famous yoga guru was born in the Mahendragarh district of Haryana? *HSSC 2019, Agriculture 2007*
(a) Swami Chitranand Saraswati
(b) Swami Kuvlaynanda
(c) V.K.S. Ayangar
(d) Baba Ramdev

38 'Divya Yog Mandir' trust, founded by Baba Ramdev in the year
(a) 1992 (b) 2000
(c) 1995 (d) 2001

39 In which year Baba Ramdev started the Patanjali Yoga Peeth Trust?
(a) 2000 (b) 2002
(c) 2003 (d) 2006

40 Who among the following posthumously awarded the Victoria Cross Medal? *HSSC 2022*
(a) Bholuram (b) Chhoturam
(c) Chhelu Ram (d) Chhaju Ram

41 Umrao Singh was born in which district of Haryana?
(a) Karnal (b) Jind
(c) Jhajjar (d) Ambala

42 Who is the only Param Vir Chakra Awardee of Haryana?
(a) Lt. Colonel Umrao Singh
(b) Cap. Abhimanyu
(c) Br. Lahna Singh
(d) Br. Hoshiar Singh Dahiya

43 Admiral Sunil Lanba belongs to which district of Haryana? *HSSC 2021*

(a) Rohtak (b) Bhiwani
(c) Palwal (d) Jind

44 Noted Arya Samaj preacher Pandit Bastiram was born in which place of Haryana? *HSSC 2020*

(a) Sisana
(b) Kheri Sultan
(c) Hudani
(d) Bapora

45 .... was the first person to own a stud farm as a veterinarian.

(a) Pt. Bastiram
(b) Karna Singh
(c) Jagdish Prasad Chaudhary
(d) Raj Indra Singh

46 Where is the birth place of Magician Samrat Shankar? *HSSC 2022, 17*

(a) Ellenabad (b) Kaithal
(c) Hansi (d) Hisar

47 Kalpana Chawla belongs to which district of Haryana? *HSSC 2017, Patwari 2015*

(a) Sonipat (b) Karnal
(c) Panipat (d) Charkhi-Dadri

48 Name the Indian born space scientist who died in the year 2003 during a US space shuttle disaster? *HSSC 2020*

(a) Saina Nehwal (b) Arunima Sinha
(c) Kalpana Chawla (d) Sunita Williams

49 Kalpana Chawla was died on a space mission in

(a) 1985 (b) 1995
(c) 2000 (d) 2003

CORRECT ANSWERS

1. (a)	2. (d)	3. (b)	4. (a)	5. (c)	6. (d)	7. (d)	8. (a)	9. (c)	10. (c)
11. (a)	12. (b)	13. (a)	14. (b)	15. (d)	16. (d)	17. (c)	18. (c)	19. (b)	20. (c)
21. (c)	22. (c)	23. (b)	24. (b)	25. (b)	26. (a)	27. (b)	28. (b)	29. (b)	30. (b)
31. (a)	32. (b)	33. (c)	34. (b)	35. (d)	36. (b)	37. (d)	38. (c)	39. (d)	40. (c)
41. (c)	42. (d)	43. (c)	44. (b)	45. (b)	46. (a)	47. (b)	48. (c)	49. (d)	

Haryana

Current Affairs

Haryana launches Sports Equipment Provision Scheme

- On 4th February, 2026 the Haryana government has launched the **Haryana Sports Equipment** Provision Scheme to promote sports culture among youth in rural areas and urban local bodies. The main aim of the scheme is to encourage young people to participate in sports and stay away from substance abuse/drugs.
- Under this initiative, sports equipment will be provided to Gram Panchayats and Municipal Bodies as per prescribed standards. The equipment will cover multiple sports such as volleyball, football, basketball, handball, boxing, wrestling, judo, cricket, yoga, and weightlifting.
- The scheme is expected to strengthen sports infrastructure at the grassroots level, ensuring that children and youth get access to basic sports facilities in their own villages and localities.

Pro Wrestling League 2026: Haryana Thunders Win Championship Title

- In Wrestling, Haryana Thunders were crowned champions of the Pro Wrestling League 2026 after a gripping, back-and-forth final against Delhi Dangal Warriors at the Noida Indoor Stadium on 1st February, 2027.
- **Neha Sangwan** (Haryana Thunders) won the Player of the Match for keeping the final alive till the last bout, while **Ronak** (Delhi Dangal Warriors) won Fighter of the Match for his impressive performance in the men's 125 kg category. Impact player of the match was claimed by **Akshay Dhere** (Haryana Thunders) for his strong performance in the 57 kg men's category.
- **Turan Bayramov** of Delhi Dangal Warriors received the Player of the Tournament award for his 7 out of 7 bout wins in the 57 kg men's category, accumulating a total of 59 points in PWL 2026, while **Chandermohan** from Punjab Royals was the highest point scorer of the tournament.

Union Budget 2026: New Momentum for Haryana's Development

- Finance Minister **Nirmala Sitharaman** presented the Union Budget 2026-27 in Parliament. This budget has opened new doors of development for Haryana.
- The total budget size is ₹ 53.5 lakh crore, in which capital expenditure has been increased to ₹ 12.2 lakh crore. This is about 9% higher than last year.
- This increased investment will be a major benefit for fast-developing states like Haryana, as it will:
  - speed up development in areas near NCR,
  - strengthen industrial growth, and
  - accelerate agriculture-based development in the state.

NEP Implementation Excellence Award 2025

- J.C. Bose University of Science and Technology, YMCA, Faridabad, received the NEP Implementation Excellence Award 2025 in the Gold Category.
- The Haryana State Higher Education Council presented this award, which was given by Haryana Education Minister Shri Mahipal Dhanda on 29th December, 2025.
- The university was recognised for its commitment to implementing the National Education Policy (NEP) 2020 through innovative practices in education, skill development, and research.
- **Prof. Ashutosh Dixit** and **Dr. Ravi Kumar** accepted the award for the university.
- Amity University Gurugram and The NorthCap University also received Gold Category awards at the event.

23rd District of Haryana : Hansi

- On 16th December, 2025, the Haryana government announced Hansi as the **23rd district of the state.** It is carved out from the existing Hisar district. This move aims to improve administrative efficiency and local governance.

- The district includes two main subdivisions: Hansi and Narnaund.
- Following the separation, the Hisar district will now consist of the **Hisar** and **Barwala** subdivisions.
- The new district will feature three tehsils (Hansi, Narnaund, Bass), one sub-tehsil (Kheri Jalab), and three blocks (Hansi 1, Hansi 2, Narnaund).

7th Khelo India Youth Games

- At the 7th Khelo India Youth Games (KIYG) held in Bihar from 4th May to 15th May, 2025, Haryana secured the second position in the overall medal tally. The state achieved a total of 117 medals, comprising 39 gold, 27 silver and 51 bronze medals.
- Haryana's athletes delivered notable performances across various disciplines. In fencing, the state clinched 7 gold, 2 silver and 3 bronze medals. Additionally, Haryana's girls' 4 × 400m relay team set a meet record, contributing to the state's strong showing in athletics.

'Pandit Lakhmi Chand Kalakar Samajik Samman Yojana' Launched

- The Haryana government has introduced the Pandit Lakhmi Chand Kalakar Samajik Samman Yojana on 5th May, 2025.
- It is a significant welfare initiative aimed at supporting **senior artists** and **cultural contributors** across the state.
- This scheme, named after the legendary Haryanvi poet and folk artist **Lakhmi Chand**, aims to provide financial stability to senior artists who have made substantial contributions to the cultural and artistic heritage of the region.
- Under the scheme, eligible senior artists will receive a monthly honorarium of ₹ 10,000.

Haryana Declares Two Harappan Sites as Protected Archaeological Monuments

- The Haryana Government officially declared two Harappan civilisation sites, **Mitathal** and **Tigrahana**, located in the **Bhiwani district**, as protected archaeological sites and monuments in **April, 2025**.
- These sites are approximately **4,400 years old** and hold significant historical and cultural importance. They provide glimpses into the development of early agricultural societies, urban planning, craft industries and trade during the **Harappan and Post-Harappan periods**.

Maharaja Agrasen's Statue Unveiled

- Union Home Minister Amit Shah, on 31st March, 2025, unveiled the grand statue (20-foot-tall and 800-kg) of Maharaja Agrasen in a programme organised at **Maharaja Agrasen Medical College**, Agroha, Hisar.
- The statue, made of **fibreglass** and **mild steel**, was constructed at an estimated cost of around ₹ 2 crore.
- It stands on a **10-foot-high platform**, enhancing its grandeur and visual impact. The unveiling of this statue will establish a new historical identity in the region.
- On this occasion, he also inaugurated the newly constructed ICU block and laid the foundation stone for the PG hostel.

Haryana in Khelo India Para Games 2025

- The 2nd edition of the Khelo India Para Games was organised in Delhi between 20th March to 27th March, 2025.
- Haryana secured the **top position**, winning the team championship with a total of 104 medals, including **34 gold, 39 silver and 31 bronze.** This marked their second consecutive victory in the Khelo India Para Games.
- Tamil Nadu and Uttar Pradesh finished in second and third place, respectively, with 74 and 64 medals.

Health Helpline 104 Launched in Haryana

- The Haryana Health Department has taken a major step towards providing online citizen services for the residents of the state.
- Through this initiative, a **toll-free number – 104** has been introduced, allowing people to book appointments with doctors at hospitals across Haryana.

- The Health and Medical Education Minister of Haryana, **Aarti Singh Rao**, inaugurated this portal on 21st March, 2025, from **Panchkula**.
- Common citizens of the state can also register their health-related complaints on this portal. After filing a complaint, the complainant will receive a callback within 5 days.
- Information about medicines can also be accessed on this portal.

Vikas Dhamu among the World's Top 30 Young Scientists

- Vikas Dhamu, from the village of Siswal in Hisar district, has been included in the list of the world's top 30 young scientists. He was honoured at a special event held in Paris, France, with the **Inflection Award** 2025. He was recognised for his scientific excellence, vision and impactful research.
- This award is presented by **Marble** with the support of the **Breakthrough Energy Fellows**, established by Microsoft's founder **Bill Gates** and the **Wanderer Climate Foundation.**

Haryana Aatmanirbhar Textile Policy 2022-25

- Haryana Cabinet, on 25th March, 2025, has decided to extend the operative period of the Haryana Aatmanirbhar Textile Policy 2022-25 along with its subsequent schemes by one year till 18th December, 2026.
- The Haryana Aatmanirbhar Textile Policy 2022-25 was notified with a targeted investment of ₹ 4,000 crore and targeted employment generation of 20,000 persons for a period of three years.

BJP Appointed 27 District Presidents for 22 Districts

- Haryana has 22 districts, but the BJP has appointed 27 district presidents, keeping in mind the future delimitation. The new districts include **Hansi, Gohana, Dabwali, Ballabgarh** and **Gurugram Metropolitan.** The BJP appointed the district presidents on 17th March, 2025.
- A **Cabinet Sub-committee** formed by the Haryana government is considering the demand for the creation of above mentioned **five new districts** in Haryana.
- The process of creating new districts, sub-divisions and tehsils in Haryana is expected to be completed by 30th June, 2025.

38th National Games and Haryana

- The 38th National Games were held between 28th January to 14th February, 2025 in **Uttarakhand.**
- The mascot of the games was **Mouli**, inspired by Uttarakhand's state bird, the **Monal.**
- Haryana's athletes secured **48 gold, 47 silver** and **58 bronze medals**, showcasing their dominance.
- The list of medal winners from Haryana is as follows
  - **Anmol Kharab** won gold medal in badminton.
  - Haryana's women's kabaddi team won the gold medal.
  - Haryana's women team won gold medal in 4,000 m velodrome cycling.
  - **Hena Phogat** won gold medal in pentathlon.
  - Haryana's women football team won gold medal.
  - Haryana's men and women, both teams won gold medal in netball.

▲ Shubhankar Mouli

38th Surajkund International Crafts Mela

- The 38th Surajkund International Crafts Mela was held between 7th to 23rd February, 2025 at **Surajkund, Faridabad.** This annual event, one of the largest crafts fairs in the world, showcases Indian and international handicrafts, handlooms, cultural performances and cuisines.

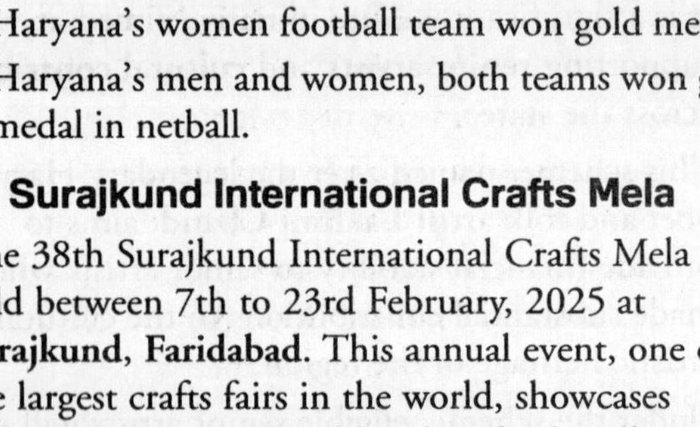

- The Mela is organised by the **Surajkund Mela Authority and Haryana Tourism** in collaboration with Union Ministries of Tourism, Ministry of Textiles, Ministry of Culture and Ministry of External Affairs.
- The theme states for the 38th Surajkund International Crafts Mela in 2025 were **Odisha and Madhya Pradesh**. These two states shows their rich heritage through traditional arts, crafts and performances.

Rakhigarhi Mahotsav 2024 Organised

- The Haryana government's department of heritage and tourism has organised the first ever Rakhigarhi Mahotsav from 20th to 22nd December, 2024 to shed light on the recent discoveries at the Rakhigarhi archaeological site in Hisar.
- This **three-day festival** featured various attraction centers showcasing **traditional folk-themed objects** and **materials**.
- The exhibition highlighted nearly **200-year-old ancient artifacts.**
- The festival also provided simple explanations about the process of discovering and excavating archaeological sites, making it easily understandable for visitors.

Haryana Ranked 14th in Fiscal Health Index

- Haryana has been ranked 14th in NITI Aayog's Fiscal Health Index (FHI) 2025 report, placing it among the bottom five of 18 major states.
- The ranking is based on five parameters - quality of expenditure, revenue mobilisation, fiscal prudence, debt index and debt sustainability.
- Punjab, Andhra Pradesh, West Bengal, Kerala and Haryana are at the bottom of the Niti Aayog's list on fiscal health.

Haryana Cabinet Approved Clean Air Project

- The Haryana cabinet, on 23rd January, 2025, approved the Haryana Clean Air Project for Sustainable Development (HCAPSD) from 2024-25 to 2029-30 financial year.
- The HCAPSD is a Haryana government initiative supported by the World Bank and the ₹ 3,647 crore project aims at improving air quality and reducing emissions across the Indo-Gangetic plain.
- It aims to implement **air pollution control technologies** and coordinate efforts with other states to reduce **cross-border emissions.**
- The project will also work on enhancing the **ease of living** for citizens through cleaner air.
- The project will be led by the **Haryana Department of Environment, Forests and Climate Change,** in collaboration with several other departments, including agriculture, transport and industries.

Most Powerful Hydrogen Train Engine's Trial in Haryana

- The Union Railway Minister, **Ashwini Vaishnav** announced in January 2025 that India has achieved a significant milestone in **green energy** leadership by developing the world's most powerfu hydrogen-powered train engine.
- Haryana government announced that the hydrogen-powered train engine will undergo its **first trial run** on the **Jind-Sonipat route** in Haryana.
- The train, designed to carry 2,638 passengers, is powered by a 1,200 horsepower hydrogen engine.

Key features of India's hydrogen train engine are given below

- **Power Output** 1,200 horsepower, surpassing global counterparts.
- **Technology** Fully developed using indigenous expertise.
- **Green Milestone** Marks a significant step in India's transition to hydrogen-powered transportation.

Renu Sangwan Received National Gopal Ratna Award 2024

- Renu Sangwan, a cattle farmer from **Farmaan village in Jhajjar**, Haryana, received National Gopal Ratna Award on 11th January, 2025.

- This award was given in New Delhi on 26th November, 2024 in collaboration with NITI Aayog and Indian Agricultural Research Institute (ICAR), Pusa.
- Union Agriculture Minister **Lallan Yadav** and Home Minister **Amit Shah** honoured Renu Sangwan with this award. Renu Sangwan has also been selected for the Millennium Farmer of India Award.

Bhagavad Gita to be Included up to Class 8 curriculum in Haryana

- Haryana Chief Minister Nayab Singh Saini, on 16th January, 2025, announced that the **Bhagavad Gita** should be included in the curriculum upto Class 8 to instil **moral values.**
- The CM also announced that the comprehensive plan should be prepared by rationalising the arrangement of teachers in the schools to address the shortage of the teaching faculty, if any.
- He emphasized that there is **no shortage of teachers in Haryana, but rather the allocation of teachers should be adjusted according to the number of students.**

Har Ghar-Har Grihini Yojana Launched

- Haryana Chief Minister Nayab Singh Saini introduced the Har Ghar-Har Grihini Yojana during Hariyali Teej celebrations in Jind on Aug. 12, 2024.
- This new initiative will provide domestic gas cylinders at a subsidised rate of ₹ 500 to around 50 lakh Antyodaya families.
- The scheme is expected to offer an annual benefit of ₹ 1500 crore to women, who can receive up to 12 cylinders per year.
- The Haryana government will cover the additional cost of the cylinders, and the subsidy will be refunded to consumers' accounts.

'IT Saksham Yuva Scheme' of Haryana Launched

- **The Haryana Cabinet on July 13, 2024 approved the IT Saksham Yuva Scheme, 2024, aiming to employ 5000 youths in its initial phase.**
- **Aligned with the 'Mission 60000' initiative from the 2024-25 budget, the scheme targets young individuals from economically disadvantaged backgrounds.**
- **Graduates or postgraduates in IT fields will undergo specialised short-term training courses lasting a minimum of three months.**

Haryana Council of Ministers

Name	Departments
Nayab Singh Saini (Chief Minister)	Home, Finance, Institutional Finance and Credit Control Planning, Excise and Taxation, Town and Country Planning and Urban Estates, Information, Public Relations, Language and Culture, Administration of Justice, General Administration, Housing For All, Criminal Investigation (C.I.D), Personnel and Training, Law and Legislative, Any other department not allotted to any other Minister
Anil Vij (Minister)	Energy, Transport, Labour
Krishan Lal Panwar (Minister)	Development and Panchayat, Mines and Geology
Rao Narbir Singh (Minister)	Industry and Commerce, Environment, Forest and Wild Life, Foreign Cooperation, Sainik and Ardh Sainik Welfare
Mahipal Dhanda (Minister)	School Education, Higher Education, Archives, Parliamentary Affairs
Vipul Goel (Minister)	Revenue and Disaster Management, Urban Local Bodies, Civil Aviation
Arvind Kumar Sharma (Minister)	Co-operation, Jails, Elections, Heritage and Tourism
Shyam Singh Rana (Minister)	Agriculture and Farmers Welfare, Animal Husbandry and Dairying, Fisheries
Ranbir Gangwa (Minister)	Public Health Engineering, Public Work (Building and Roads)
Krishan Kumar Bedi (Minister)	Social Justice, Empowerment , SCs and BCs Welfare and Antyodaya (SEWA) Hospitality and Architecture
Smt. Shruti Choudhry (Minister)	Women and Child Development, Irrigation and Water Resources
Ms. Arti Singh Rao (Minister)	Health, Medical Education and Research, Ayush
Rajesh Nagar (Minister of State)	Food, Civil Supplies and Consumer Affairs (Independent Charge), Printing and Stationery (Independent Charge)
Gaurav Gautam (Minister of State)	Youth Empowerment and Entrepreneurship (Independent Charge), Sports (Independent Charge), Law and Legislative (Attached)

**As on January 2026*

Some Important Officials

Officials	Name
Governor	Ashim Kumar Ghosh
Chief Justice	Justice Sheel Nagu
Speaker of Legislative Assembly	Harvinder Kalyan
Chairman, State Public Service Commission	Alok Verma
Director General of Police	Ajay Singhal
Chief Secretary	Anurg Rastogi
Advocate General	Pravindra Singh Chauhan
Lokayukta	Justice Hari Pal Verma
Chief Electoral Officer	Shri A. Sreenivas
Haryana State Commission for Women	Renu Bhatia

**As on January 2026*